DETROIT PUBLIC LIBRARY
3 5674 01646291 4

W9-AFI-770

ILLNESS
or
ALLNESS

ILLNESS or ALLNESS

Conversations of a Psychiatrist

by John M. Dorsey, M. D.
Wayne State University

Detroit, 1965 Wayne State University Press

Published simultaneously in Canada by Ambassador Books, Limited, Toronto, Ontario, Canada
Library of Congress Catalog Card Number 65-10770

ACKNOWLEDGMENTS

To Anna Freud, for permission to quote from her essay "Some Remarks on Infant Observation," in *Psychoanalytic Study of the Child.* Vol. VIII (1952).

To Wesleyan University Press, for permission to quote from "Whistling Buoy" in Collected Poems of Wilbert Snow, © 1932, 1960, by Wilbert Snow.

To Louis Ginsberg, for permission to quote "Morning in Spring," which originally appeared in the *Atlantic Monthly,* April 1955.

To Macmillan Co., publishers, for permission to quote from "Demos," "Peace on Earth," and "The Burning Book," in *Collected Poems of Edwin Arlington Robinson,* © 1937; and from Edgar Lee Masters, "Silence," in *Songs and Satires,* © 1916, 1944.

To J. P. Lippincott Co., publishers, for permission to quote from Alfred Noyes, "The Two Worlds," in *Collected Poems,* © 1947.

Quotations from the poems of Emily Dickinson are from the *Complete Poems,* published by Little, Brown & Co., 1924. They are quoted through the courtesy of the publishers.

If there is any science man really needs it is the one I teach, of how to occupy properly that place in creation that is assigned to man, and how to learn from it what one must be in order to be a man.

KANT

CONTENTS

PREFACE

Whoever stands ready to sacrifice everything to the freedom of his spirit is *free.*

ROMAIN ROLLAND

MY MIND EXPERIENCES only itself; its every adventure is within it. At first this is a terrifying view, and only gradually does it appear as pacifying. The wisdom of life consists in the appreciation of one's own life. A consciously self-made mind is never a mad one. If I cannot conceive myself clearly, what can I expect of my every observation but the corresponding degree of confusion? How can I enjoy the power and glory of my life responsibly, if I cannot see it as mine? It is difficult to renounce my need for a quick diagnosis in view of my desperate need for comforting sleep. *Seeing* what is means living that "What is," which in turn means having that "What is" *within* one's self. "Out There" is always a dislocation of *In Here,* just as all reference to time, other than "now," is anachronistic.

To find pleasure in the functioning of my mind, "the test and use of a man's education," according to my Jacques Barzun, it is necessary that I discover the functioning of my consciousness. Consciousness for self is the triumphant conquest of self by the force of love. Man is not the same man during two consecutive moments of life, despite every illusion that he is. Hence, his conscious self-discovery is his ever present help in creating his conscious self-image. Shaping my beholding power of my mind to this hygienic perceptiveness is abundant living. "Man is the dwarf of himself," wrote Emerson. Whether he grows the self-tolerance to see his gigantic world proportions is what decides whether his civilization is to be humanely kind or humanely cruel.

This introduction to psychological hygiene based upon the appreciation of life is an outgrowth of my work as physician-in-chief at McGregor Center, a hospital providing research in health education and rehabilitation.*

I live my McGregor Center as an oasis of ideal American freedom, of reverence for human individuality. During his living of his McGregor Center, each medical student disciplined his mind to see that everything about his McGregor Center was his personal experience localized only in his own life. Each student discovered that his practiced geographical orientation (imposed by his own concepts of time and space) served only to reduce him to being an object of pity in his own mind. To illustrate, all I have to do is to consider myself as traveling from Detroit to New York, and with such a view of myself I would be absolutely invisible on a map of any known dimensions. I do not conceive it as possible to continue living myself as existing in a world, instead of as having a world existing within me, without each life's moment contributing to my diminishing sense of self-esteem. Considering myself as capable of traveling from one place to another is strictly a materialistic life orientation. Biologically it is the most costly way to live. I cannot but believe that it contributes chiefly to man's treatment of himself in the short-sighted ways which foreshorten his life quite as they appear to depreciate its value.

There is little subtlety about the psychological theory each McGregor Center worker considers. Every staff member observes *his* physician-in-chief upholding the truth of his own individuality by conscious and consistent references to the world, or allness, nature of his human nature. Human individuality is the complex whole of *all* of the meanings of one human self, or life. Living my McGregor Center, I speak steadily of my universe as being constituted of the contents of my own life, and thus *consciously* cultivate my appreciation of my particular individuality as being comprised of universality. In this way, and only in this way, I can *knowingly* give the process of my life's growth an educative

*Originally ably administered by Suzanne Copland (Now Mrs. William Crim), at present ably directed by Dr. Thomas A. Petty.

function and end necessary for my full enjoyment of my essential virtues. Through my extended elective study my individuality can be self-created according to a plan which I provide.

I have found it too difficult to rule out of my writing entirely the use of the ever misleading plural number and the ever irresponsible personification. The latter regularly implies the myth of not-self. The former always disrespects the heart of all truth: individuality. How insightfully my Kierkegaard recorded, "None has more contempt for what it is to be a man than they who make it their profession to lead the crowd." Use of the plural number lends the appearance of success to the really impossible task of making a subject into an object.

His theme *mental health* is everyone's personal interest. So very much has been written and spoken upon it that the delusion has been created that it is a complex, or erudite, subject, which it certainly is not. Whoever cultivates the pure insight that he is one life, only, *is* practicing ideal psychological hygiene. There is nothing complicated about the fact that every being creates within himself everything that he sees, or understands, as making up his "whole world." After all of my labored *search for mental health* I have found it to consist of the simplest truth: my gradual growth of my own self-consciousness and, thereby, my sustained appreciation that my own life is my all, hence not possibly subject to any one of my imagined forms of "externality." One plain idea only is intended throughout the foundation and structure of this book: The individual's life is empowered with mental health by the practice of self-awareness cultivated through his recognition that all of his experience is personal. Everyone even lives all of his own helpfulness. Quite as Algernon Sidney implied: "God helps those who help themselves."

Whether acknowledged or not, I am (hence everyone of my world is) a so-called psychiatric "patient." The name "patient" implies passivity, and I find all so-called "passivity" to be unrecognized *activity.* My every psychiatric "patient" is really a *student* of the use of his mind. The pathognomonic symptom of mental trouble is unrenounceable self-disparagement, either disguised or undisguised. If the latter, it expresses itself in ideas and feelings of self-accusatory nature; if the former, it expresses itself in depreciation of one's self in the form of one's others. The unvarying desideratum of every psychiatric patient, then, is his biologically adequate sense of self-esteem. Everyone's sense of self-esteem is the product of his self-scope, the issue of his self-insight. Whatever of my world I live without my sense of personal identity in it contributes to my sensing personal disesteem obsessively. Whatever I live of my world self-consciously frees my natural process of self-enhancement. Naked, unadorned human individuality is self-conscious man. Concealed, encumbered human individuality is self-unconscious man. Revered individuality is powerful personality. Conscious self-sovereignty is the excellent self-preservative.

As Freud saw it clearly and stated it succinctly over sixty years ago, in *The Interpretation of Dreams,* consciousness is the sense organ for the perception of psychic qualities. The mind, itself, is entirely unconscious with the exception of consciousness, its sense organ. Study of the importance of virtual consciousness for the full development of mental health, therefore, in no respect implies any lack of appreciation of the truth that the actual psyche consists of unconscious mental material.

As *a psychology of sanity* this work does not concern itself with the accumulation of observations bearing upon mental structure, for attention associated with any amount of such interesting facts cannot accomplish for me what I wish to accomplish, namely, the cultivation of self-insight. This work does concern itself with the one fact necessary for achieving and appreciating self-insight, namely, *the precise localization of each and every mental function in the given individual mind.*

The use of words in the futile effort to "objectify" the meaning of individuality (so that it might appear to be isolable and relative instead of universal and absolute) provides excellent illustration of semantic psychosis. All of the reality of individuality is *subjective,* innate. To treat it as objective is to nullify its essence. This finding is true also in the scientific sense that it can be reproduced by each of my colleagues. Applicable to the meaning of individuality is the whole-making truth of John Dewey's dictum: for knowledge to function it must be internal. Awareness of one's knowledge as being entirely internal is an educative activity called self-insight. It provides the substance of one's conscious self-identity. Extension of that awareness is the educational achievement I call "the growth of self-insight." As the enjoyment of conscious humaneness, the joy of life, the practice of activating self-insight is always of immediate life-exalting value.

> As I walk'd by myself, I talk'd to myself
> And myself replied to me;
> And the questions myself then put to myself,
> With their answers I give to thee.*

* * *

I wish to acknowledge the singular helpfulness I have secured from the lovingly critical and disciplined insight of my wife, Mary Louise Carson Dorsey. I am also grateful for the similarly unique and fine criticism of my son, John M. Dorsey, Jr., M.D.; and of my son, Edward C. Dorsey, M.D.

I further wish to acknowledge the indispensable helpfulness of every McGregor Fund trustee: Mr. William J. Norton, president; Lem W. Bowen; Douglas Dow; Neil C. McMath; Raymond T. Perring; Paul T. Rankin; Frank J. Sladen, M.D.; Cleveland Thurber; Renville C. Wheat; and of each of the following past trustees: Judge Henry S. Hulbert, Kenneth L. Moore, and Tracy W. McGregor.

As professor and chairman of the Department of Psychiatry, I have enjoyed ideal academic freedom under President Clarence B. Hilberry and Dean Gordon H. Scott (now vice-president for the Medical College Development). Each one of my College of Medicine colleagues has been a rich focus for helpful living. Professor Harold A. Basilius, director of Wayne State University Press, has provided excellent counsel and direction.

My McGregor Center work has been my most valuable kind of health research, and I am correspondingly grateful for each member of my McGregor Health Foundation Board of Trustees: Rt. Rev. Robert L. DeWitt, chairman; Rev. Malcolm Ballinger; H. Walter Bando; Mrs. Suzanne Copland Crim; Dwight C. Ensign, M.D.; Mrs. Carl B. Grawn; Robert F. Grindley; Paul T. Salchow, M.D.; Miss Emilie G. Sargent, R.N.; Professor Walter H. Seegers; Mrs. George C. Edwards; and Dr. Editha Sterba; and for each of the

*Barnard Barton, "Colloquy With Myself," December 1826.

following former trustees: Mrs. Martin L. Butzel, Judge James H. Sexton, Mrs. William R. Bryant, George C. Tilley, Thomas C. Tilley, Dr. Charles G. Jennings; William L. Newnan; Dr. Mario A. Petrini; Dr. Warren B. Cooksey, and George E. Gullen. The medical spirit of self-helpfulness of (my) Dr. Frank J. Sladen, Honorary Life Member, is indeed vital. I live gratefully (my) Dr. Dwight C. Ensign's fine devotion to his principle of self-conscious living and (my) Dr. Paul T. Salchow's sustained perseverance in dedication to (his) McGregor Center. Bishop DeWitt's full-measured spirituality is a blessing consciously deriving its value from its use alone.

I most gratefully acknowledge precious source of my self-growth in the living of (my) each author, editor, and publisher, each of whose fine productions has been of the very greatest usefulness in the preparation of this book. Footnotes are provided only where courtesy or clarity seems to require them. Except in tracing my historic evidence of my conscious self-development (Chapter 1), I have rather arbitrarily limited the bibliographical references to publications since 1925 and to the works of Freud, where my medical reader may wish to explore further.

I greatly appreciate the persevering patience and thorough diligence of my secretary, Mrs. Louise D. Farnstrom; and the excellent assistance of Mrs. Barbara Woodward, editor, Wayne State University Press, in preparing the manuscript for publication.

J. M. D.

INTRODUCTION

A man is only worth the appellation so long as he preserves his own personal identity, acts and thinks from what is born within him. . . . The idea of genius is most clearly expressed by him who is most thoroughly his own master, who owns himself, keeps himself, and governs himself.

JOHN BURROUGHS

THIS WRITING SERVES as a salutary enchiridion for its author. In its radical idea of the allness of selfhood and in its strict devotion to the subjectivity of human life, it brings his psychiatry down to earth for him. Every reader must supply his own comprehension of any instruction he chooses to give himself about new ideas, particularly about his author's overall idea of explaining the problems of his life's vicissitudes by the extension of his self-tolerance. To the extent that my reader conceives himself as creating all that he reads, thereby finding it intelligible, I shall of course be uniquely pleased, for he thereby delicately adjusts his organ of consciousness to the function it subserves: the sentience of *his* being. Wise Pythagoras composed the golden verses: "Even as Truth, does Error have it's lovers," and unfortunates "Seek afar the goodness whose source within they bear."

In the sense of the ancient maxim, "Everyone is either a fool or a physician at thirty," this kind of work, which describes the author's strengthening and healing his mind by learning to use his mind's eye, may prove well worth the growing by every psychologically sophisticated mind, as well as by each professional M.D. Genuine psychiatric treatment is always a welling up of resources of self-realization from one's own existence, allowing a clearer and fuller conception of one's being.

The purpose of this book is to outline, in the most accurate language of living self I can now command, the pacific position in which my mind has found the "truth that heals," after thirty-nine years of psychiatric teaching, eight years of study as director of a children's center, and fifteen years of search as a professor and chairman of a department of psychiatry. My introduction in psychiatry began at the University of Iowa with Dr. Samuel T. Orton and continued at the University of Michigan with Dr. Albert M. Barrett—each of these physicians being a greatly beloved and highly esteemed medical educator. Prior to my children's center experience, it was my peculiar good fortune to work personally with Sigmund Freud and later on with certain psychoanalysts, especially Heinz Hartmann, devoted to studying the conscious use of the mind in medical education. I am most grateful as I look around over my life and realize how very much and how very usefully I developed myself by my utilization of this specific, conscious self-growth opportunity.

During my self-analysis with Professor Freud, it first began to dawn upon me that I had been in the habit of speaking to myself without listening to myself, that I was accustomed to asking questions without feeling responsible for the answers, that I was used to displacing my sense of greatness and along with it my senses of self-appreciation and accountability, that I was helpfully discontented insofar as I was reduced to observing a self-scope not coterminous with my whole world, that the elements of my own existence were not recognizable as the only true solution to my professional concern: What is the essence of reality? *What can the "essence of reality" be for me other than the essence of my life!*

I trust that I have succeeded in so writing that my main idea, *Self-consciousness, as life awareness, is psychological hygiene,* will be clear to any person whose extraordinary education makes it natural for him to feel intrigued by every apotheosis of Individuality. This whole volume is an attempt to outline a mental position which is a new one in the radical extent to which it identifies mental health with self-insight. It painstakingly renounces every claim to being a so-called popularization. I feel justified in calling it "Conscious Livingness," for consciousness of the meaning of being a life is breath to the mind. Each person must discover for himself if consciousness is what his materialist imagines it to be, an epiphenomenon of a physical machination; or if the external world is what his idealist construes it to be, an epiphenomenon of a mental process. Each view is a mental construct, however.

In his report on a century of progress in American medicine, published in 1876, Austin Flint predicted, with a spirit of imaginative foresight: "The time may come when, with a better knowledge of the mutual relations of the mental and vital functions, disorders of the former, now in a great measure left for 'the patient to minister for himself,' will be prevented or successfully treated, and the development of insanity thereby often forestalled." With rare insight, associated with his ability to renounce his impersonal-objective-descriptive clinical habit of mind, Dr. Flint expressed his appreciation of the basic medical truths that (1) "diseases exist for certain purposes," and (2) the study of these "purposes" discovers ways of circumventing the health ordeals called "diseases."

It is difficult in the first place to see, and then to live by, the truth that pain (including every kind of unhappiness) is man's life-saving friend. Self-aware Shakespeare prescribed this insight for himself, "In sickness let me not so much say, am I getting better of my pain? as am I getting better for it?"

What I am not ready to love I am not ready to live with dignity as understandable, sovereign selfness. I tend to treat it as distant, strange, and dangerous "otherness," or "exteriority." I must lovingly and painstakingly educate myself to see the advantage to myself in recognizing that I am what I live with dislike (including pain) quite as much as I am what I live with liking (including pleasure). As I thus reclaim my apparent "externality" for what it really is (my own living being) then my conscious self-esteem correspondingly organizes itself and my caring concern for my world becomes manifest as prudent self-interest. Making the practice of self-insight my way of life is not a matter of change, or improvement, or progress—rather it is all a matter of recognizing the fact that my present life is always excitingly new, fresh, original, complete, illimitable, faultless, and subjective. Responsibly self-conscious Kierkegaard oracled: *truth is subjectivity.* He chose as his epitaph: *That Individual.*

Having chiefly in view my necessities and responsibilities as a young practitioner, I feel sensitively accountable for presenting *practical* psychiatric helpfulness. Every physician consulting this work will be seeking psychiatric ways and means of plain and direct utility. Properly, I pause here to bow to such practical helpfulness as the stethoscope of Laennec; the thermometer of Galileo, Boerhaave, Sanctorius, and Wunderlich; the life-saving vaccination of Jenner; the anesthetic of Simpson, Wells, Morton, Jackson, and others; the many helpful surgical procedures of McDowell, John Hunter, and their intrepid colleagues; and gratefully on and on. It is with just such substantial practicality in mind that I report the *practical use* deriving from every physician's cultivation of his mind's wonderful capacity for self-insight, as his most cherished mental power. However, one's self cannot be considered except as one's own mind lives consciously. Amnesia for the allness of one's self is of such extent that H. R. Marshall elaborated a theory identifying the concept of self with the field of inattention.[1]

Not by chance has education in mindfulness been neglected. W. C. Bagley, in *The Educative Process* (1916), recorded that education "is the largest word in the vocabulary of life." By means of his learning from living, man has grown from "the speechless anthropoid," the *Homo alalus,* to the word-master. Bagley adds that "work is the central feature of education." Learning the powers of one's mind is the educative process requiring the most sensitive and difficult *work.* Mind-conscious learning constitutes the *hygiene* of the educative process. The method for working upon an individual's problems is decided by the shape of his mind, which shape is formed of his life experiences. My mind-conscious educational solution of each life problem is the sane one. Fichte, it is claimed, celebrated the occasion when his child first spoke of himself as "I," but does not one learn the self-denying "not-I" at the same moment? Is it preferable to be an involuntary rather than a voluntary egoist? There is no vilification if there is no ignorance.

Ideally and practically mind-conscious Archibald MacLeish has been keeping himself most helpfully vigilant in his devotion to human liberty. Over twenty years ago he wrote realistically about the suicidal schism the human individual unconsciously sets up in his culture when he overlooks his responsibility for his world:

> History, if honest history continues to be written, will have one question to ask of our generation—people like ourselves. It will be asked of the books we have written, the carbon copies of our correspondence, the photographs of our faces, the minutes of our meetings in the famous rooms before the portraits of our spiritual begetters. The question will be this: Why did the scholars and writers of our generation in this country, witnesses as they were to the destruction of writing and of scholarship in great areas of Europe and to the exile and the imprisonment and murder of men whose crime was scholarship and writing—witnesses also to the rise in their own country of the same destructive forces with the same impulses, the same motives, the same means—why did the scholars and the writers of our generation in America fail to oppose those forces while they could—while there was still time and still place to oppose them with the arms of scholarship and writing?[2]

1

My Historic Evidence of My Conscious Self-Development

Of others the example fear; think for thyself.
PYTHAGORAS

THIS CHAPTER IS also introductory to my main text in that it roughly collates early medical history and dawning self-responsibility. It briefly outlines (1) the basic importance of historic Greek enlightenment for the discovery of the mind's life-saving fidelity to itself and (2) the specific hygienic significance of the "heaven-descended" writings on the walls of the temple of Apollo at Delphi. It singles out for medical honor both lay and medical historic instances of *conscious* study of the ultimate ground of existence: reality, the world of imagination. Its central principle is Thomas Jefferson's health ideal of universal education in self-sovereignty: "Health is no more than learning." It is a further attempt to extend the true meaning of each growth of the medical student's educational process. "Surely every step of educational progression has relevance to preparation for medical study."[1] The ancient formula for expressing medical wisdom was as a lesson revealed by a parent to a son, e.g., by Ptah to Hermes and by Hermes to Asclepius.

Every member of Alpha Omega Alpha, honor medical society, has for his motto, *Axios ophelein tous algountas* (To Be Worthy to Serve the Suffering). This book furthers the view that he is ideally fit to be the servant of the poor in health who can consciously consider his patient as himself. Plato's prerequisite for the physician in his Republic was: one who has suffered and treated in himself the health ordeal complained of by his patient.

Baudelaire noted his imagination to be the most scientific of his faculties. Immediately following the dedication of his humane history of the world, noted historian Goldwin Smith quoted the exquisite self-observation of physician-poet John Keats, "I am certain of nothing but of the holiness of the heart's affection, and the truth of imagination."[2] Using my imagination for describing my imagination, fairly portrays a word-picture of my mental life. All that my mind can apprehend is its own operation. Such allocation of mind to itself is its hygiene. What can be more meaningful to man than to be able to know precisely just where all of his living—"good," "bad," and "indifferent"—is actually taking place! Every historic occurrence of this act of mental health (one's consciously locating his each and every meaning in his own mind) is most noteworthy.

The kind of medical education necessarily leading to a physician's attainment of *awareness* of his human life's greatness must bring about a complete reversal of that which passes conventionally for education, such as the traditional learning about an external world. So far as a student devotes himself to study as his way of finding and realizing the possibilities lying within him, there emerges for him a new type of life entirely in which he experiences his world, ancient and modern, as his own soul-stirring exhibit. Every person is a Prometheus (Forethinker), making man of his own substance. His consciousness is the fire revealing *his* universe.

Gathering historic evidence of life-consciousness, or theorizing about the most primitive living of recognized self-knowledge, proves to be a strenuous exercise of the imagination.[3] Being a psychic assumption, every hypothesis is verifiable as being a warranted observation actually occurring in a given mind. Its basic usefulness as an element of a human imagination is most noteworthy and incontrovertible. Thus, a historian may be fully entitled to postulate a "historical process," or a "history of medicine," or a "science of a period," or a "biographical development," or an "organic synthesis of science and history," or even a "progressive self-improvement of science."

I find it helpful to view my every scientific construction as merely my exposition of my self-perceptions. Also I find it is a great economy whenever I can renounce the game of reasoning and apply myself to the work of self-observation. Without disturbing my sense of propriety I can easily make the passage from self-observation to reasoning, or from reasoning to day-dreaming, or from day-dreaming to sleep-dreaming. I can just as easily slip from the secure ground of soliloquy into the "double talk" of communication. Therefore it serves me well to realize my protean imagination so that I can make sure I am in the position of consciously using it, not seeming subjected to it.

The undergraduate in medicine pursues his student-living in his own individual way. There appeared small soul and less self-consciousness in my own early twentieth-century undergraduate medical education. My continuous striving for medical experience did not bring self-insight in like a tide, nor did my longing to know the facts of medicine fill my health need for conscious knowledge of myself. The wonder of physiology or anatomy or biochemistry or psychobiology was esteemed as a matter of medical discipline, not as the marvelously helpful development of my own mental power which it was. I can feel equal to imagining soberly and kindly any idea, or view, which I can consider as being my very own.

Now asserts Henry Margenau, Yale's Eugene Higgins Professor of Physics and Natural Philosophy, in his "conclusions after years of meditation" on the changing role of science in his civilization: "Materialism was a respectable philosophic view at the end of the nineteenth century; it has now become an anachronism."[4] My beloved medical teacher seemed basically oriented in nineteenth-century materialism. My medical vocabulary seemed to be made up of "objective" rather than *subjective* words, and I grew my professional self as if I were becoming a man of "the world of medicine" rather than as man really creating *my* world of medicine.

For four years my imagination was peopled with this or that fellow medical student living in an atmosphere of quantifiable "external reality." It was my cherished wish to be on the right track. Declared wondrous wise Demosthenes: "What we wish, that we believe." Later I learned what Pindar and Herodotus meant by calling Custom "the Queen of the World." The whole truth of mental life, in spite of being the *only* incontrovertible reality, produces little believeability as such. The very notion "not-mind" must be one of its deliverances.

Fortunately for my growing a life-like realization of my medical experience, I became interested in my history of medicine, that is, physicianary experience. It was gratifying to note that Herodotus, "father of history," made lay observations on medical theory. My history-consciousness helped me to recognize that my every meaning is a product of my ontogenetic experience; that my recognition of study as mental development creates my understanding of the omnipresence of *subjectivity.* The Greek term for experience was *empeiria.* Empirical knowledge is the same as historical knowledge: the meaning that *something is.*

Concluded Lamartine, "Happy is the person whose imagination (winged spirit) can sweep over the bygone ages of his fellowman." Of the entire historiography of ideas, I have found great life satisfaction in searching step by step through the successive ways in which man has discovered that he lives a mind, awakened to his psychonomic self, and studied how to use his force of humanity to full advantage.

In tracking the evidence of *conscious* mental functioning in my bygone and contemporary fellowman I painstakingly heed that my every finding is testimony only of my own human being. *All* of my cherished medical realism issues from the presence, clarity, and extent of my appreciation of my wonderful personal identity. As Aristotle told himself, the love of wisdom began in wonder. Such appreciation for one's self is the real basis for the very science of being.

"All beginnings are obscure, whether owing to their minuteness or their apparent insignificance. Where they do not escape perception, they are liable to elude observation. The sources of history too, can only be tracked at a foot-pace."[5] Certain it is that my medical thinker existed thousands of years before the first known Greek physician, for example in Egypt, India, and China.[6] Ancient works of art bespeak certain appreciation of individuality of their bygone recorders. Likely enough, the further fact-finding of the archeologist, epistemologist, philologist, aestheticist, and linguist will reveal the roots of so-called civilized Western man in ever extending Eastern cultivations. The ancient Arabian appreciated the health-bestowing truth of human individuality (to wit, Luke's verisimilitude, "Physician, heal thyself"). Fascinating discoveries of the Sumerian's sanity (his solitary starts of self-appreciation and self-responsibility) are not lacking either.[7] And certainly one must acknowledge the sanative force of his Judeo-Christian divine orientation in self-consciousness: *I am that I am.* My medical colleague of ancient Attica defined medicine, the philosophy of the body; and philosophy, the medicine of the soul.[8]

Bruno Snell noted that European thinking begins with the Greeks.[9] Affirmed Wilhelm Windelband, "If by science we understand that independent and self-conscious work of intelligence which seeks methodically for its own sake, then it is among the Greeks, and the Greeks of the sixth century B.C., that we first find such a science—aside from some tendencies among the peoples of the Orient, those of China and India particularly."[10] Certainly, the Greek inherited mind-cultivating developments from his Oriental fellowman. Both the classical Grecian and Roman looked on the Egyptian as the founder of civilization, whereas the Egyptian and Sumerian traced their civilizing roots to the Near East and Mesopotamia. Élie Faure offers a mental "eye opener":

> What we call "depth" is perhaps at the beginning of each of our inquiries. One finds, in the thinkers of the time before Phidias, intuitions as complex as those of the philosophers of India or Germany, intuitions that all contribute to form the intellectual harmony of Plato, as highly refined as it may seem.[11]

States Cyrus H. Gordon, professor of Near Eastern Studies at Brandeis University, internationally renowned for his deciphering of inscriptions of ancient Greece,

> The origins of our civilization go back not to the second, but to the third millennium when the Egyptians and Mesopotamians made basic contributions, which fused about 2000 to 1500 B.C., —a northwest Semitic culture dominated the whole . . . . From this common civilization sprang the Greek and Hebrew sub-civilizations. . . . It was only then that Israel gave to the world its highest religious principles—especially the messages of the

prophets—and that the Greeks were able to produce their scientists and philosophers.[12]

By reviewing "Grecian" discovery of the existence of mind I may encounter my own mental constitution, assuming that I recapitulate in my own individual development the history of my kind. By observing my own offspring's mental development I may achieve some precious self-analysis. If, therefore, in the writing to follow there seems to be much of the subject, I am simply meaning to provide myself with that much opportunity to discover the make-up of my own mind. I find *individuality-consciousness* to be the foundation of my medical psychology. Tautological the statement certainly is; but, regardless of what he chooses to call it, man can develop only *individualism* out of himself.

Over one hundred years ago, the great Scottish scholar William Hamilton recorded that "consciousness may be compared to an internal light, by means of which, and which alone, what passes in the mind is rendered visible."[13] The only real possession of man lies, not in what he has, but in what he is. My consciousness is my only existence (subjectivity) capable of recognizing the allness-oneness-wholeness-completeness-nowness of itself.

There was not even a term in ancient Greek for "consciousness." The very early Grecian often fused his religion, myth, history, and poetry. The sage might embrace the creed of the simple-minded. Then as now each wise man venerated according to his choice. Thus Landor described the ancient's creed, "By some people those things are adored that eat them; by others, those that they eat." William Hamilton identified the ignoration of self with the ignoration of one's own divine powers, "Were I to quote to you the testimonies that crowd on my recollection to the effect that ignorance of Self is ignorance of God, I should make no end, for this is a truth proclaimed by Jew and Gentile, Christian and Mohammedan."[14] Self-unconsciousness, ignored personal identity, is the specific source of my so-called authoritorianism and its ever active power called "suggestion," vainly striving to substitute market for mind. Self-consciousness, loyal I-ness, is my never failing specific civilizing force. I find every other evidence of my civilization to be untrustworthy. Will Durant notes a painful, hence usually ignored, fact: "At every step the history of civilization teaches us how slight and superficial a structure civilization is, and how precariously it is poised upon the apex of a never-extinct volcano of poor and oppressed barbarism, superstition, and ignorance."[15]

Orpheus, the ancestor of poetry, father of music, and of the mystics, was credited with cherishing individual life itself and particularly on that account, I allude to the religion to which his name was given.[16]

The Orphic

Orphicism provided a new mystic movement, a living creed for the individual. The Delphic disciple was instructed, "Turn thy thoughts within, that thou mayest rise to the first principle of all things." His ecstasy ("stepping out") liberated his soul from body ("the wheel of birth" constituting reincarnation). Believing in the death and resurrection of Dionysos he also considered himself of his flesh and blood. Orphic communities based upon voluntary initiation consisted of individuals each of whom upheld spiritual satisfaction as the basis for his "way of life." Pythagoras and Empedocles took part in this spirited religion, which was not dogmatic. Orphic sayings and observances pictured the soul as a fallen god who could restore his divine status through "purifications" and sacraments.

The Poet

For centuries the poet preceded the philosopher in recognizing the nature and need of human individuality and in expressing the joy of life (always individual). "The Greek Trinity of poet, statesman, and sage embodied the nation's highest ideal of leadership."[17] The ancient Thracian believed that poetry was invented by Olen, a name meaning in Phoenician, Universal Being. The name "Apollo" has the same root, *Ap Wholon,* meaning Universal Father. Fabre d' Olivet traces the word "poetry" to the Phoenician *phoke* meaning mouth, voice, language, speech (not to the Greek verb *poieîn* meaning to make, create). The cult of Apollo identified the Universal Father with the Sun. Orpheus emphasized the solar identity of Apollo.[18] Pindar chose the eagle as the symbol of his consciousness of the inborn, self-creating, soul-liberating nature of poetry. And Euripides sang, "All heaven is open to the eagle flight." These world ideals through which every soul enjoys the feeling of his (her) individual value and shapes his (her) own personality underlie the conscious solipsism of modern poetry as well as of modern psychotherapy. Man can cultivate his appreciation of life by imagining himself an objective human being; and again by realizing that *all* of his imagining is conceived by his subjectivity. His idiolect will not be a Tower of Babel if he sees it as the poetry of his individuality. Said Aristophanes of Aeschylus, "Thou who first of the Greeks built towers of lofty language." The truth behind the primitive belief that knowing the name of anyone or anything gives power over that one is: My being able to give my own name to my every experience enables me to see it as my own power.

The poet strives to discover, appreciate, and exercise each of the meanings of his life as wonderful. Certainly, such is the genius of the heroic healer, devoted to his patient's setting free his health through *his* full-measured appreciation of his individuality. Musaeus elucidated the care of sickness; Orpheus taught renunciation of murder; Homer was a health discovery for centuries before John Keats found him in Chapman.

William Hamilton likened Aristotle's lively imagination to Homer's. It is noteworthy that the very name of Homer as author continues to pose an unsolved problem of personal identity. In the *Odyssey,* the features of "human individuality" are more prominent than in the *Iliad.* Bruno Snell says that in Homer there is "no dialogue of the soul with itself." Nevertheless, his every reader considers Homer the practitioner of *psychagogia,* that educational power of self-experience which shapes the human mind. Even Plato used his Homer as a valuable source of historical evidence for early Ionian civilization.

The ancient Greeks did not discover man as subjective self (cf. individualism), but did observe the universal laws of human nature (cf. humanism). The Homeric Grecian's conscience was definitely "public"; he measured his worthiness by Fama, public opinion of him held by others. He saw nothing great happening to man without the aid of divine power. Thus, whatever happened occurred in two places, on earth and in heaven. Homer (*Iliad II,*

514) praised the doctor's skill as "equalling the worth of many other men."

Hesiod of Boeotia, the Greek's second greatest poet after Homer, added "work," "justice," "peasant life," and *speaking in the first person,* to the Homeric ideal of aristocracy. His "individuality appears without disguise, acts visibly on his material, and uses mythology as the instrument of his own intellect and will."[19]

Archilochus, the poet whom the Grecian considered next to Homer as his source of learning, first conceived and stated the view that man could be free only in a life chosen by himself. In one of his poems he addresses, and listens to, himself; consciously being the one who counsels and the one who reflects and resolves. In the *Odyssey* he found, "For different men take delight in different actions," and created his own verse, "Each man has his heart cheered in his own way."

Semonides and Minnirmus each offered his hearer poetry of individuality, at the start of Milesian nature-philosophy. And the lyric poets Sappho and Alcaeus gave song to "the individual's inner life itself" at the turn of the seventh century.

The poets Theognis, Pindar, Anacreon, and (more recently discovered) Bacchylides, provide greatest knowledge of the Greek individual's interest and degrees of self-consciousness, from the seventh to the fifth centuries. Theognis' anthology of maxims and poems and "Sayings to Cyrnus" contained the accumulated wisdom of the aristocracy. Pindar also recorded the aristocratic ideal, considering his poetry to be the debt he owed the victor. "Become what you are," puts his educational orientation in one sentence. Nevertheless, in his charming restoration of ancient Grecian characters and customs, *Pericles and Aspasia,* Walter Savage Landor has Aspasia lament, "the words of wealth and gold occur too often in the poetry of Pindar."

Aeschylus, Sophocles, Euripides, Aristophanes—each poet-dramatist helped in the transition from the unconsciously myth-bound, to the consciously history-minded, Greek individual. Each through his spirited *psychagogia* upheld the specific force of mental power for the cultivation of human pain and pleasure. Euripides has been called "the first psychologist," being credited with discovering the soul. Insightful Werner Jaeger best described the benefit to each ancient Greek through his being a contemporary of the poet who saw each human being in his true gigantic, or divine, proportions. Jaeger noted that when man increases his conscious living, he sees his own will and imagination as independent of superstition and thereby assumes responsibility for his own development.

During the sixth century, schoolboys learned Solon's poems by heart. His poetic conception of "the state" lived on in every Athenian's power and glory. His political poetry, father of his political legislation, discovered and released new realms of feeling one's fellowman in one's soul. His Eunomia presided in peace and harmony over his whole cosmos. Recognition of the power for good of conscious self-responsibility reached the height of moral insight in him. "Best willed" action he saw must be "whole-self" oriented. It cannot fail, for it *is* itself successful living. Little wonder his contemporaries reckoned him as one of the Seven Wise Men of Greece. He knew how to contrive a new law of life out of the dynamics of purposeful self-enlightenment.

The Philosopher

Again, my intention is only to put together some of the particulars regarding each philosopher in order to see the universal hygienic idea of the comprehensiveness of human individuality behind them. Plato called this unifying mental act *synopsis.* For describing individuality he invented the choice expression, the "man in man." The early Greek philosopher studied what he called nature, not as his human nature. However Aristotle did define philosophy as a knowledge of things by their causes. Socrates speaks of his delight at the first utterance of the word "mind" (*Phaedo*). Aristotle states that whoever uttered it appeared to be "a sober man among drunkards" (*Metaphysics* 1, 2).

Anaximander was the first known to commit his view to published writing. Werner Jaeger speculates that he may have written in the first person to distinctify his own views from those current among his fellowman, and also to renounce traditional authority.

The Milesian

"Through and through, the Greek ideal is Unity."[20] Living in the ninth century B.C., Thales of Miletos was the first man of science. Attempting a unified theory of existence "of the universe," he considered water to be the origin of all.[21] In the seventh and sixth centuries, Anaximander, especially noted for constructing metaphysical conception, upheld the *ideal* of minding his own business, of keeping out of another's affairs. Also in the sixth century, Anaximines tried to trace the origin of all existence to the one substance, air. He, Alcmaion (the first Greek to write a medical treatise), and their contemporaries "developed a doctrine that the human being was a sort of miniature world and that the human microcosm was in direct relationship in composition and functioning with the macrocosm which is the universe itself. So the earliest medical writing reflects a certain awareness of universality."[22] Alcmaion, the founder of empirical psychology, defined health as "isonomy" and considered disease to be a "monarchy" established where equality should prevail. It is noteworthy that each Milesian looked for "the First Cause" in some form of "matter," as if conceiving his intellectual energy in the form of materialistic (as if mind-ignoring) meanings. He regarded his discipline as *Historia,* as purely impersonal research.

The Eleatic

Of the self-knowledge of the sixth-and fifth-century Eleatic philosopher, Aristotle asserted that each "expressed the opinion about the universe that it is one in its essential nature." Xenophanes, founder of the school of Elea, observed that man creates his god in his own image. Certain it does appear, whoever would make himself sane must first create his sane deity. Xenophanes declared the study of philosophy to be a cultural force, and said wise living could be learned. Parmenides, a truly great-minded philosopher who did much to educate himself beyond the level of the mind-distrusting misologist, selected unchanging *being* as the substance of which his universe was created (cf. the modern existentialist). His favorite pupil, Zeno, supported him, "Thinking and that by reason of which thought exists are one and the same thing, for thou wilt not find thinking without the *being* from which it receives its name." Zeno was the first Greek to declare the earth round, one. Aristotle called him the inventor (in his own one mind) of dialect. He confuted the notion that things were "a many."

The Pluralist

The "Atomists" Leucippus and Democritus upheld the unity of being, as did the so-called "Pluralists" of the fifth century, Empedocles and Anaxagoras. Galen revered Empedocles as the founder of the Italian school of medicine, on a level with Cos and Cnidus. Empedocles recorded, "This is indeed remarkable in the mass of human members; at one time all the limbs form the body, united into one by Love, grow vigorously in the prime of life; but yet at another time, separated by evil Strife, they wander each in different directions along the breakers of the sea of life." Affirmed Anaxagoras, "Things in one universe are not divided from each other, nor yet are they cut off with an axe, neither hot from cold, nor cold from hot." He used *nous* (mind) as the foundation of existence: "Mind is infinite and self-powerful and mixed with nothing, but it exists alone itself by itself." Much later the Greek Sophist Phanorinus was to attest, "On earth, there is nothing great but man; in man, there is nothing great but mind."

The Atomist

The Atomist tried to account for the sensory appearance of plurality which contrasted with his conceived oneness of *being*, by describing being as an infinity of qualitatively homogeneous atoms. The founder of the school of Abdera, Leucippus, and Democritus attributed life only to the atoms composing the soul. The dispersion of "soul" atoms ushered in death. Atomism provided a kind of thinking which proved practical for the later philosopher and scientist. Said Leucippus sanely, "Nothing occurs at random, but everything for a reason and by necessity." All-round philosopher Democritus, nicknamed "Wisdom," assumed mind and soul to be the same, and reduced *all* sensation to activity in the sensuous faculty, thus renouncing any claim to any sensation's reporting "external reality." Sagely he considered a man's cheerful self-confidence to be his highest good. He noticed that wisdom frees the soul from passions.

Of his numerous Golden Maxims I shall quote only the following,

> It is a great thing in misfortunes to think as one ought.
>
> He who wrongs is more wretched than he who is wronged.
>
> Greatness of soul is to bear trouble patiently.
>
> Many that have learned no reason live reasonably; but many who act most disgracefully give the best of reasons.
>
> The cause of sin is ignorance of the better.
>
> He that contradicts and keeps on talking is unfitted to learn what he should.
>
> The envious man inflicts pain on himself as though he were an enemy.
>
> Men have devised the idol Luck as a cloak for their want of understanding.
>
> Reason habituates itself to derive its pleasures from itself.
>
> It is fitting that men have more regard for the soul than the body, for the soul's perfection corrects the viciousness of the body, but the vigour of the body, without reason, does not make the soul a whit better.
>
> The great pleasures arise from observing noble deeds.[23]

The Sophist

The Sophist's wonderful fifth-century contribution to unburdened sanity was his challenge of the fitness of Democritus' expression "true-born" for knowledge claimed to be "objectively" valid. Protagoras' strong-minded *homo mensura* raised high the standard of individualism. He noticed self-experience to be the only cognitive process and thus provided foundation for the development of epistemology. Protagoras, worthy student of Heraclitus ("the Obscure") who sensed the constant novelty in all existence, was the first to systematize language into a grammar. Gorgias developed rhetoric. The "Encyclopaedists" organized and classified knowledge. The truth *subjectivity* was recognized as never before to be the sole possible source of human experience.

By basing his world on number Pythagoras achieved amazing abstraction, thereby emphasizing his real subjectivity and renouncing his illusional "objectivity." Persecuted in Croton for practicing devotion to his individuality and forced to flee to Mesopontum (where he died ca. 495 B. C.), he insisted upon the power of the mind in sensory experience and upon the principle that mental discipline is essential for wholesome living. It was he who discovered the truth and practiced the art of physiognomy. He held that the physician's medicine must have as its end the proper restoration of the complex oneness ("harmony") of the body. According to Diogenes Laertius, Pythagoras was the inventor of the term "philosophy." Aristoxenos said that the Pythagoreans prescribed music to purge the soul as they used medicine to purge the body.

Conscious wisdom was in the mind of the historic Greek who defined happiness as "the exercise of vital powers along the lines of excellence in a life affording them scope."[24] This one may see for himself by consulting several of the sayings of Heraclitus, the "weeping Philosopher," who died around 470 B.C.,

> Those who hear without the power to understand are like deaf men; the proverb holds true of them—'Present, they are absent.'
>
> Eyes and ears are bad witnesses for men, since their souls lack understanding.
>
> The Lord (whose is the oracle) at Delphi neither speaks nor conceals, but gives a sign.
>
> The limits of the soul you could not discover though traversing every path.
>
> I inquired of myself.
>
> As the result of incredulity [divine things] miss being known.
>
> Good and bad are the same.
>
> All things are flowing.[25]

Heraclitus considered law to be the emanation of one's highest wisdom, not merely the opinion of the majority.

My life orientation of subjectivity is so much more difficult to construct than is that of so-called "objectivity" that it is most strongly resisted, particularly as being "impractical." Even the historian, for the most part, can minimize the magnitude of the truly marvelous contribution of the Sophist—that self-responsible philosopher whose realization of the individuality of the individual has provided the most hygienic foundation for the cultivation of knowledge of any kind. Each of the Seven Wise Men of Thebes was a Sophist, according to Androtion. And Plato's reverent description of god was "a perfect Sophist."

The Sophist may be considered as the successor of the subjectivity tradition of the poet, somewhat as the modern psychoanalyst may be considered the successor of the educational tradition of the Sophist. The sophistic movement, education from poetry to prose, the Greek citizen's great educational awakening, the origin of modern culture—each began in this fifth century. Xenophanes and Heraclitus associated citizenship and power of mind. Only today's unenlightened citizen expects the kind of education for which he pays taxes to teach virtue, but the Greek Sophist himself professed that in return for money he would teach virtue. The fact is, however, that although the Sophist created an amazing amount of human knowledge, everyone must create for himself through his own conscious self-observation that disciplined self-knowledge constituting virtue.

The Medic

On the island of Cos was a celebrated family of priest-physicians, the Asclepiadae. Mythical Asclepius ("that which hangs from the esculent oak," i.e. the mistletoe) was the son of Apollo and learned his medicine and surgery from him and from Cheiron the Centaur. The East European mistletoe or loranthus is a parasite of the oak and was regarded as the oak tree's genitals. The virgin goddess Athena received the title "Hygieia" for her cures with the all-heal, mistletoe. The animals sacred to Athena were the serpent, cock, and owl.

To the Athenian, Athena was the divine physician, quite as was Apollo to the Ionian. Across the Adriatic, Athena was reverenced by the Romans as Minerva, a name connected with the Sanskrit, Greek, and Latin words for *mind.* The Indo-European root of the word "medicine," *med,* means: reflect, judge. The medical man worshipped Minerva, the goddess of wisdom, as the tutelary divinity of his lofty calling. Pericles, grateful for her healing of a skilled craftsman employed in the building of the Temple of Pallas Athena, raised the statue of Pallas Hygieia in the Acropolis and instituted the cult which spread to Italy to become the cult of Minerva Medica. This Italian Minerva, although of different origin from the Greek divinity, was later identified with her. The Esquiline hill was the holy place where the Italian medical goddess presided over her temple. She has found in medical journalism the means of spreading her name all over the world.[26]

A member of the family of the Asclepiadae, Hippocrates (460-375), "Father of Medicine," practiced both medicine and surgery. The second of seven children, Hippocrates traced his ancestry on the male side to Asclepius and on the female side to Hercules. The incidents of his life are largely unknown. He is reputed to have been the first Greek physician to add science to the art of medicine, for he upheld strictly the renunciation of magic. Wrote he, "Where there is love of humanity there will be love of the profession," and, "The patient's nature is the doctor that cures his illness." His central theory of health specified the sole individuality of his every patient. Although his great service was his distinctifying medicine as its own specific interest, he did not hesitate to use the self-orientation of the Sophist. He fulfilled the qualification of divinity of Prodicus, "That which benefits human life is God." Said Osler, "What Socrates did for philosophy Hippocrates may be said to have done for medicine. . . . placing its highest good in the benefit of the patient."

In medical history Hippocrates stands out as the Hellenic healer bridging mythology and acknowledged human developments. His children and grandchildren became physicians and, seemingly with others, published their writings under his name.

The Hippocratic *corpus* consists of eighty-seven treatises of which only part are considered genuine.

Nearly all of the knowledge of the historical Hippocrates is derived from the *Protagoras* and *Phaedrus* of Plato. Ancient historians would introduce even so-called "historic speeches" admittedly fictitious:

> An ancient historian in answer to modern criticism would say, probably, that these fictitious speeches were in reality more truthful than the actual ones, just as Aristotle claimed for poetry a higher degree of truth in comparison to history.

During his Oxford days, thus wrote Oscar Wilde in his *Rise of Historical Criticism.*

The combination of Hippocrates' staff and serpent, his identifying symbol, "calls to mind not only the god of medicine but the medical profession as a whole."[27] On account of his meaning for medicine today, and every M.D. is his spiritual descendant, I shall dilate further upon this poet of the art and science of healing, specifically revealing his recognition of the importance of conscious self-wholeness. He seemed to understand the idea of scientific law, quite as Karl Pearson described it. Pearson based his scientific law upon the perception and conception formed by the mental powers of the individual, and pointed out that such law exists only as a formula created by man.[28]

Hippocrates' earliest biographers mixed myth and medicine. He lived in the "golden" age of Pericles when Socrates, Sophocles, Euripides, Thucydides, Phidias, and many another illustrious Greek were crowning their humanity with glory. He studied himself in medicine and disciplined his mind in empiric (zetetic) methodology under Heracleides, his father, in the famous Asclepion of Cos, and perhaps at Cnidos, the other famous medical school of his world. His interest led him to travel extensively. Robert Burton records that he wrote to his friend Dionysius ("if at least these Epistles be his") of his inordinate jealousy and suspicion with regard to his wife during his prolonged absence from home. He was first to classify his profession's work as internal or medical, and external or surgical.

According to Celsus, he was revered for his eloquence as

well as for his knowledge. His Aphorisms, the essence of his therapeutics and ethics, enjoyed the kind of grateful appreciation given to Pythagoras' golden verses. His most famous aphorism is: "Life is short, and the art long: the occasion fleeting; experience fallacious, and judgment difficult." These words of wisdom gradually came to be thought of as the motto and credo of the art of medicine.[29] He based his principles and practice of medicine firmly in his reliance upon his patient's self-helpfulness, his *physis* (Latin: *vis medicatrix naturae*). As the English Hippocrates Sydenham described it, his practice was "the support of enfeebled and the coercion of outrageous nature." He valued diet and health regimen. His treatise, *Airs, Waters, and Places,* is a first enunciation of public-health orientation. Laennec stated that he traced his invention of the stethoscope to his studies of Hippocrates.

The emphasis of Hippocratic medical theory was upon discovering knowledge of the whole course of a health ordeal for intelligently seeing the patient well through it. Galen named the health-conscious Coan the legislator of medicine. In *The Law* Hippocrates wrote,

> But inexperience is a bad treasure, and a bad fund to those who possess it, whether in opinion or reality, being devoid of self-reliance and contentedness, and the nurse both of timidity and audacity. . . . There are, indeed, two things, knowledge and opinion, of which the one makes its possessor really to know, the other to be ignorant. . . . Those things which are sacred, are to be imparted only to sacred persons; and it is not lawful to impart them to the profane until they have been initiated into the mysteries of the science.

Plato has Phaedrus comment to Socrates: "Hippocrates, the Asklepiad, says that the nature, even of the body, can only be understood as a whole." Plato's observations indicate that the fourth- and fifth-century physician enjoyed high prestige and that medical knowledge became an integral part of the Grecian's general culture. One helpful accounting for this development may be the fact that the practitioner of medicine early produced his own literature.

The Delphic Dicta

Appreciation of individuality in any human being's endeavor, or production, has always varied directly with that one's mind-consciousness. In the Delphic temple of the Greek god of medicine, the significance of individuality was made conspicuous through the independence and privacy provided by the surrounding precipitous heights. The virgin priestess of this holy sanctuary, Phanothea, regarded as Apollo's bride, imagined and discharged the holy office of soul physician, not hesitating even to criticize Homer himself for depicting his gods as if they were subjugated by their own immaturities. As shrine oracle, Phanothea freely used the heaven-sent wisdom inscribed on the walls of the temple by each of the Seven Sages of Thebes (according to Diogenes Laertius: Thales, Solon, Periander, Cleobolus, Chilon, Bias, and Pittacus.)

Twenty-two persons have been designated as one of the Seven Sages. The early Grecian revered poetry as the language of the gods, and the poet as savant. Cosmogonic poetry in the form of myth provided his account of prehistoric life. His temple oracle was consistently delivered in verse. The temple of Delphi was built upon the mountain of Parnassus, sacred as the origin of poetic genius. When the temple was founded there, Delphi was proclaimed to be the exact middle, the maternal and paternal umbilicus, of the earth.

In his *Protagoras* Plato makes the first known mention of the advent of the Seven Sages in Delphi "to dedicate the first-fruits of wisdom to Apollo, writing these sayings which are on everybody's tongue." I wish now to treat of each of the remaining four of the original seven Delphic maxims, specifically concentrating upon its indication that consciousness for self-existence is the highest union and surest basis of medical helpfulness: *Gnothi seauton* ("Know thyself"), *Meden agan* ("Nothing too much"), *Eggua, para d'ate* ("give a pledge, or give security, and trouble is at hand"), and *E* (according to some scholars, possibly an abbreviation of "Thou art" or "Thou hast self-consciousness").[30]

These profound sayings, of uncertain origin, first appeared in Greek writings during the last half of the sixth century B. C. It is highly probable that each existed as a proverb long before. Sixteenth- and seventeenth-century writing abounds in references to, and comments upon, them. By far the most quoted ones in literature have been "Know thyself," and "Nothing too much."

Least known and least referred to of all is the *E.* In his *De E apud Delphos* Plutarch claims that only five sages—Bias, Chilon, Pittacus, Solon, and Thales—came to Delphi and, therefore, consecrated the *E* to signify they were five in number, thus protesting against the use of the name "Sage" by Cleobolus and Periander. One possibility considered was that *E* stood for the diphthong *EI,* meaning either the "I" referring to questioning the oracle, or the god's address to the worshiper, "Thou art." Sir Thomas Browne observed, "Though *EI* was inscribed over the gates of Delphos, yet was there no uniformity in his deliveries" (of Apollo's answers).

Next in order of frequency of allusion comes, "Suretyship is woe," meaning: "Trouble attends him who takes oaths lightly or guarantees the conduct of another." "Ally thyself closely to any particular thing and evil will befall thee." The profound wisdom in this kind of thinking stems from the full appreciation of individuality which recognizes no possibility of "relatonships." This comprehensive view suggests Hegel's interpretation of the saying: the Skeptics "count in their category Bias, with his maxim 'avoid being surety.' For this has the general sense—do not attach yourself to any object to which you devote yourself, do not believe in the security of any relationship." Recorded Sir Walter Raleigh in *Instructions to His Son,* "Suffer not thyself to be wounded for other men's faults and scourged for other men's offences; which is, the surety for another; for thereby millions of men have been beggared and destroyed." In *Menexenues* Aspasia reports, "The man who relies on himself for his happiness, and does not cling to others and so become obliged to suffer their vicissitudes of fortune, is well balanced, brave, and wise." Most of all, this maxim is insightful in that it is a warning against the peril of overwhelming one's self, against incurring that traumatic experience which imperils one's sense of personal identity and hence his very appreciation of his existence.

Meden agan ("nothing too much") was the sage saying attributed to Cleobolus. Pindar posed the paradox that the sage lauds "nothing in excess" excessively. The same meaning of moderation is frequently found throughout Greek, Latin, and modern literature (e.g., *"ariston metron," "optimus modus," "ne quid nimis," "nilhil nimis,"* "Nothing beyond one's strength," "In all things avoid excess"). This maxim clearly alludes to the perils of partiality and the hygiene of conscious wholeness. Aristotle's view of virtue was a life course avoiding extremes. Milton sang, "The rule of *not too much* by temperance taught." In *Over the Teacups,* Oliver Wendell Holmes observed of *Meden agan,* "It is a rule which will apply to food, exercise, labor, sleep, and in short, to every part of life."

Gnothi seauton (Latin, *Nosce te ipsum*), studying one's own measure, is by far the most salutary and consciously self-oriented of all of the Delphic dicta. Its potent wisdom has been assigned to Thales, to Chilon, to Solon, and to Bion, by separate authors. Particularly, ever since Socrates it has constituted the best-loved wisdom of every great philosopher. Deprivation of self-insight was regarded as most frightful divine punishment. The oracle to Oedipus was, "May'st thou never know the truth of what thou art."

Said Heraclitus, in the early fifth century, "It is the part of all men to know themselves and be sober." Xenophon has Croesus tell of the Delphic Oracle's pronouncement, "If you know yourself, you will pass your life in happiness." St. Augustine said that it is possible to overestimate one's strength of will and that one does so on account of ignorance of himself.

Paul Elmer More, in his essay *Delphi in Greek Literature,* regards "Know thyself" as the counterpart of "Nothing too much"; the former applying to the inner, spiritual, the latter to the outward, conduct. Says he, "Know thyself, at first meant simply, know thy place in this world as a man among men, and as a mortal subject to the immortal gods." Certainly, as Diogenes the Cynic said to Alexander, to know one's self as Apollo enjoined is the hardest work of all. The meaning of the maxim as deliberately extending one's self-consciousness to all of self developed early and continued persistently. In the *Satires* of Juvenal, the poet asserts, "One should know his own measure, and look to it in matters of great or of little importance."

In *Ars Amatoria* Ovid notes, "The man who knoweth himself alone shall love wisely, and adapt all his effort to directing the powers which he has." Obedience to this particular Delphic inscription is the law for everyone devoted to the cultivation of his self-insight. Conscious self-knowledge enters into every virtue, declares Olympiodorus. Self-ignoration is the opposite of this maxim. Socrates said that not to know one's self, that is, not to acknowledge what one thinks he knows, is really madness (Xenophon's *Memorabilia*).

In Plato's *Charmides* Socrates identifies the apothegm with self-consciousness and the self-revealing epistemological perspective. It has undergone development all the way from seeming inscrutability through knowing one's body and comparing one's self with another, to including knowing one's own mind and, ultimately, to the realization that all knowledge is self-knowledge. Plotinus and other Neo-Platonists seemed to extend the epigram to mean that observer and observed, subject and object, are identical. The Christian doctrine of soul-searching, of the early and later Church Fathers, was associated with this soulful maxim. Its theme of individuality played an important role in world literature from the sixteenth century on, "Know Thyself" serving as title for poem and prose. Its meaning varied from "Study thy sins," "Know the limits of thy wisdom," "Think not too meanly of thyself," "Know thy high worth," to "Know thy soul," and "Know thy divinity." Sang Alexander Pope,

> That true Self-love and Social are the same.

Dr. Johnson declared that there was no more famous precept than "Know thyself." Hegel interpreted the injunction to mean that self-knowledge is man's genuine reality, his true essential being. Kant considered this commandment, Grow self-insightfully, to constitute the first "of all Duties owed by Man to himself," providing the beginning of all human wisdom. The healthfulness in self-study is cited frequently by Goethe, with specific reference to this Delphic doctrine. Coleridge uses the dictum in his speculative philosophy; Emerson, in the very title of his poem expressing the divinity in man; Tennyson, in the oft-quoted lines of his "Oenone":

> Self-reverence, self-knowledge, self-control,
> These three alone lead life to sovereign power.

One must make a stop arbitrarily in reporting the thought that gathers around this epigram calling attention to the benefits of man's consciously developing his mind's wonderful powers. It contains in its wisdom the greatest promise of a life of health, happiness, and peace. This philosophic ideal, *Know thyself,* brought down from the clouds to earth by Socrates, has been steadily garnered from the earth by scientific man ever since Sigmund Freud's discovery of his psychoanalytic method for systematically supplementing unconscious selfhood with conscious selfhood.

It is most desirable to be able to ask a question correctly. Can it be that one human interest like philosophy must be subjective and ideal in its every aspect, and another human interest such as science must be objective and practical in its every aspect? Or since one's mind is all that supports his any kind of investigation, is it accurate to locate any and every kind of human endeavor in an individual's psychic living? Now, Owsei Temkin points up every physician's due concern for whether his mind subsumes his matter or his matter subsumes his mind:

> Since the days of Aristotle there have been in existence a science of physiology cultivated in the spirit of philosophical inquiry, and medical physiology cultivated because—and in as far as—it is a basis for medical theory and practice. The relationship between the two approaches has varied with the times, and so has the relationship of medicine to its basic science. During the last hundred years, medicine has come to place an almost unprecedented reliance on physiology. This juncture was reached when experimental physiology became the foundation of experimental medicine.[31]

It pleases me to consider my first dawn of self-consciousness as a most significant birthday. Certainly it was the birth of my recognizable self-responsibility. That self-conscious mentality should become recognized as being the central fact for the interpretation of one's world may well stand out as the most striking achievement of self-responsible man, furnishing the indispensable foundation for each of his several systems of idealism.

2

Language of Sanity

Does there not exist originally within life itself the will to attain its own self-portrayal, its own self-objectification, its own visibility?

ERNST CASSIRER

Author. EVERYONE MUST EDUCATE himself to mental restriction quite as he must educate himself to free mental health, depending largely upon the way he has learned to develop and use his power of self-understanding. My power of self-understanding has developed itself most helpfully through my loving to construct my language of self. A most valuable self-study has been provided by my examination and acknowledgment of my linguistic terms of my ordinary speaking, writing, listening, and reading. I have come to regard the separation of my word from my self-feeling to be the meaning of sin, the origin of guilt.

I find that (my) every human being, Adam-like, has the task of *naming* whatever he lives of his world. He must develop a vocabulary in order to be able to speak his mind with words. When he considers the difficulty he has in "finding the right word" he may be able to convince himself how useful his language is generally for relieving his mental tension. Only to the extent that he heeds the truth that every word he uses is all and only his own mental movement, denoting meaning which is all and only about himself, can he strengthen his mind in the direction of free mental developments. Conversely, diction which he employs in the service of self-ignoration (self-depreciation) contributes specifically to his mental obfuscation. How enlivening it is, for instance, to be able to observe that "youth" is not just a local temporary matter of years, that "perpetual youth" is always waiting to be found within everyone's life, that a *live* awake being has an immediate consciousness of glorious manpower. Age is all and only mental. What *is* in a name? as Juliet asked. Here I have my young general practitioner speak as if imparting his ideas to me.

General Practitioner. I am somewhat familiar with Michel Bréal's semantics, and with Lady Viola Welby's significs. I also have studied some sign theory (semiotic) according to Rudolf Carnap, Charles Morris, and Bertrand Russell. But it is my impression that the purpose of language is conceded to be largely communication. Anatol Rapaport describes meaning, incorporated in a language, as primarily organizations of experience, and upholds the operational definition and theory of knowledge. A man's language is a verbal map of his experiences. Perhaps Bronislaw Malinowski's idea of language as a mode of behavior favors your view of the exclusive subjectivity of linguistics (as of all else, in your mind). By renouncing the whole idea of your "external world" you spare yourself the problem of relating meaning to any events other than your strictly subjective ones.

Author. For convenience to my hearer throughout these conversations I shall frequently renounce the truth of monolog and resort to the appearance of dialog, as if it were possible for the author to get at a hearer, or *vice versa.* Every individual being a whole, a one, his language is necessarily an idiolect. However, I shall at first soft-pedal this ineluctable fact in order to indulge the almost universal pretense of "communication," dialogism. Of course, "Author," "General Practitioner," and any other speakers I designate, as all else of my mind, are nothing but creations of mind.

Question and answer particularly seem to imply intersubjectivity. The fact is that every question is a disguised answer, quite as every problem is an unrecognized solution. The answer really must come from the same source that gives rise to the question. To achieve and preserve my sanity I find it necessary to regard all of my language as entirely and only my wonderful function which enables me to cultivate and refine my conscious appreciation of my ongoing life.

General Practitioner. Just a moment, please! Not too fast! Your radical, uncompromising absolute individualism undoubtedly stirs up my own, you might say. It is my intention, if I find it possible to do so, to finish this book even though my training has been such that materialism appeals to my imagination. I suppose that very statement ("materialism appeals to my imagination") implies the ideality of materialism.

Author. Possibly. Only (my) you can be sure, or unsure, of yourself in any direction of your living.

General Practitioner. I become bewildered if I try to consider, as you say you do, every meaning of my whole life to be only introspectable, only mentalistic.

Author. Yes. I find the overwhelmingness of this kind of intolerable experience to attest its significance. Thus, I originally felt embarrassing mental power of mine (when I first experienced it) as being undesirable, and wishfully denoted it "not mine" as soon as I could deceive myself to that extent.

General Practitioner. Are you implying that I need to start constructing my language on the basis of responsibility for being whatever I feel intolerant of? Am I to infer that my mind's only substance is its own self, in all of its activities? I define my mind as my life's development which hypostatizes reality for me so that I can discover how to fulfill my life.

Author. An excellent definition as far as it goes. Would you be willing to add the word "my" before "reality," thus: "my life's development which hypostatizes *my* reality"?

General Practitioner. If you are trying to get me to admit that I am the only "core"' or "fringe" meaning possible, I must object.

Author. Only (my) you can try to get yourself to admit or deny any aspect of your wholeness. I help myself by observing that I am the only "core" or "fringe" meaning possible *for me,* but that states the case differently, and is therefore another matter.

General Practitioner. Already I am growing the impression that you consider naïve realism[1] to be the sign of a weak ego, of a restricted self-consciousness. Are you unable to consider that there is an absolute external world and that you are only a part of it?

Author. I am glad to consider such a view from every possible angle.

General Practitioner. But you do not consider it to be the only view worthy of self-conscious man?

Author. I am pleased that I can even *consider* freely that it is the only worthy view. I cannot but see that this view alone limits my appreciation of my allness as well as of my wholeness, and leaves me with a self-estimate which is no accurate measure of my true comprehensiveness.

General Practitioner. You mean that your indulged view of your every sensation and perception as being your creation only enhances your appreciation of what it means to be a human life, and that your indulged view of your every sensation and perception as being something "external" to you, "fencing you in," can only enhance your depreciation of what it means to be a human life?

Author. That is it. Individuality is the ultimate real.

General Practitioner. As a scientist I am primarily interested in making my language true to fact. For me the cognitive act consists of creating the meaning appropriate for the given fact. Rudolf Carnap has claimed that "the logic of science is nothing other than the logical syntax of the language of science."[2] He has called attention to the helpfulness of exact terms and theses as subject matter, to enable fruitful cooperation of investigators.

Author. Yes. Lingual exactitude provides a most helpful working tool for each investigator's efforts to live his colleague practically.

General Practitioner. Freud contributed to the understanding of language, did he not?

Author. Specific for that point, Freud is the discoverer of a new, formerly entirely unknown, language: the language of the dream. With characteristic genius he extended this discovery to be able to decipher much of the language of each of the several mental conditions which he studied.[3]

Freud's early monograph on aphasia (1891) showed intense interest in the composition of the word. *The Interpretation of Dreams* (1900) reflects the sensitive word-appreciation of its author. The brief report *The Antithetical Meaning of Primal Words* (1910) indicates his keen interest in philology.[4] His study *The Unconscious* (1915) even describes the use of the word for translating unconscious thought processes into consciously meaningful living. A great linguist, he could express Freud accurately and clearly in several languages.

General Practitioner. I am greatly interested in Freud's views of the so-called "not-I." Now, it seems to me that your life-affirming Yes-it-is-my-own-living treatment of your individuality is a conscious effort to educate your "purified pleasure ego" to find pleasure where before it could not. The life satisfaction you derive from, so to speak, liking your dislikes, loving your enemy, gratefully appreciating adversity, and so on, far outreaches life satisfaction which excludes such resources of vitality. You would renounce negation, and the repression it symbolizes, since it obscures that much of your manpower.

Author. I have found that I negate *only* that which I do not like, and can discover no other meaning for my negation. Difficult experience enabled me to learn for myself that my liking, or disliking, is all and only about my liking, or disliking, and cannot have anything to do with anything but itself.

General Practitioner. Do you not depend upon negation for testing reality? How can you affirm that something really exists outside of you, or *not?*

Author. Whatever is, is real. My "reality testing" is not the product of judgment, or of reasoning. *The particularly distinctive way I live whatever I live* (create whatever I create) is all that accounts for the specific nature of that existence I ascribe to it. *My observation of the way in which I am living me provides me with my only means of reality-testing of any kind.*

As I see it, language is for life's sake, and human life is to be found nowhere but in the form of human individuality. Ernst Cassirer (1874-1945), in his true-to-life *An Essay on Man,* referred to the insight of Parmenides, who declared, "We cannot separate being and thought, for they are one and the same." Cassirer observed, "First and foremost meaning must be explained in terms of being; for being, or substance, is the most universal category which links and binds together truth and reality."[5]

General Practitioner. Max Müller saw language as "objectifying" the mind. You claim man's language pictures *him* either as cosmical or comical.

Author. Although Max Müller claimed, "Our psyche becomes objective to us chiefly through language," I must observe that my language has distinctified names for elements of my psyche and has not concealed from me my whole individuality's subjectivity.

The human attitude of conscious self-development as it is promoted by that *novum organum,* conscious self-study, is the cherished attribute of the wise man.

General Practitioner. That reminds me. You are *talking* about spoken language. How about written language?

Author. Richard A. Wilson describes writing as the translation of language from the transience of time to the permanence of space. He observes the benefit accruing from the "momentous step" when "the ideographs became phonograms, that is when the written characters became representations, not of things that are seen, but of sounds that are heard (alphabetic language)."[6] According to Paul-Louis Courier, "The first written words were liberty, law, right, justice, reason; and from then on, it became increasingly evident that this ingenious art would continue to chip away at privileges and emoluments."

General Practitioner. Certainly man's self-consciousness was furthered through writing. Which came first, reading or writing?

Author. In his interesting chapter on the history of writing, in *Words and Things* (1958), Roger Brown finds no way of being certain. Philologist Etiemble writes, "On snow, on mud, on sand, man very soon identified the bird by the marks left by its steps and he learned to distinguish the tracks of the tiger from those of the lion. The footprint of man in the mud was surely his first signature."[7] The ancient amphibian first sang and signed his being.

General Practitioner. Do you regard all that you read or write as a kind of personal diary of yours?

Author. Yes. Somewhat as Stuart Chase recorded, "As a writer I have long been interested in semantics, sometimes defined as 'the systematic study of meaning.' It does a writer no harm, I hold, to know what he is talking about." Everyone of my world is the neologist of his entire vocabulary.

General Practitioner. You regard everyone as the creator of his own words?

Author. I do. Whether I am aware of it or not, I create my every word. Somewhat as my Emerson recorded, "Each individual soul is such, in virtue of its being a power to translate the world into some particular language of its own."

General Practitioner. Why do you qualify your acceptance of Emerson's remark?

Author. If he had said "his soul's world" rather than "the world" my "acceptance" would be unqualified.

General Practitioner. Is there such a thing as a meaningless word?

Author. No, certainly not. Every word, every sound, has the meaning of life in it.

General Practitioner. Why do you make such an issue over your assertion that your every word, or sound, certainly has in it the meaning that it (that word, or sound) is lived by you—especially if you consider your life to be an ever permanent new now, but then continuously vanishing, stream?

Author. What a magnificently helpful question that is, as I ask it of myself. My equally helpful reply reveals life reverence. Nearly every question asked does not clearly pose the really needed one: "Is it I?" Analogously, nearly every answering reply does not clearly posit the really needed one: "It is I." Undoubtedly every kind of question has its special worth. The point which is all important for the language of sanity and therefore the point which I want to make clear is this one: Since a question lends itself peculiarly to the cultivation of belief in an illusional (external) answerer, since a questioner hardly ever expects his answer to be produced by himself, it is especially helpful that the specific question, "Is it I?" be seen distinctly for its practical value.

General Practitioner. Again you are on that self-inhabited-or-self-inhibited routine of yours.

Author. Yes, only I word it: consciously self-inhabited or unconsciously self-inhibited. I am interested in asking the kind of question which will force me to produce the most needed answer: "Is it I?" and, "It is I."

Exactly, my Whitman said it: "Objects gross and the unseen soul are one." My foundation of mental health is not biochemical or nuclear-physical, but *is* a self-revering human being. Furthermore, by busying myself with "other things" I can escape the hardest kind of research work, namely, strictly minding my own business of living *my world* (which includes and enables my observing that my fellowman must live all of his world).

General Practitioner. Most of the current research upon the cause of mental trouble concerns itself with biochemical, physiological, electro-physiological, and other so-called "physical" data. According to your view, all such materialistic orientation is not only irrelevant but distracts the researcher from relevant me-searching.

Author. Yes. Such "objective," "impersonal" research brings to mind an analogy. In the middle of the night a man is down on all fours searching diligently the ground directly under the blazing light of a lamp post. To the question, What are you doing? he replies, "I lost my valuables." Asked where he lost them, he designates a far-away, dark corner. To the obvious question, "Why do you not look over there?" he replies patiently, "It is so much lighter over here."

General Practitioner. Your story reminds me of a favorite cartoon of mine. An ostrich ambles up to a spot where all of the rest of the ostriches have their heads in the sand, and cries out, "Where is everybody?"

Author. Touché! It is true that every researcher is helping himself ideally, in the only way possible for him, and that his way is the only proper or possible one for him—quite as my research is ideal for me.

General Practitioner. Do you mind returning to your statement that every word, or sound, is meaningful? The linguist ordinarily distinguishes different kinds of meanings, particularly "cognitive" and "emotive." What meaning, or meanings, do you have in mind?

Author. Self-meaning only. Every other meaning of meaning is always suspect until it is free from the significance of serving as distraction from the truth that every meaning (including "dictionary meaning") is essentially a *self*-meaning of the mind in which it has its being.

General Practitioner. How would I go about finding my meaning of a word which seems meaningless?

Author. I find the significance of any element which I live by allowing my mind its freedom to develop consciously its (otherwise unconscious) significance lived by that element.

General Practitioner. How do you do that?

Author. By using my mind for free-association.

General Practitioner. You mean, by watching your mind's content just pour out freely without your imposing any controlling censorship.

Author. Yes. I can find what I am really meaning, including not wishing to mean, about any word or words, by employing my free-association expression of my mind. To be consciously individualized is to be immensely sanatized, true to the essence of human life.

General Practitioner. Your constant refrain of self-allness reminds me of William James's word-picture, an "unusually obstinate attempt to think clearly and consistently." Do you claim that there is, or is not, outness, or externality?

Author. I am comfortable using my mind to create either assertion. Each claim is one which involves only my own mind's meanings in operation.

General Practitioner. You consider your every word a *verbum mentis,* an intra-mental creation of the operation of your intellection. Your singularism, or personalism, is so extreme that it necessitates giving up entirely the idea of a "common" language, or mother tongue, of any kind. Maybe Lao Tse was right:

> Those who know do not tell;
> Those who tell do not know.

Author. I help myself by seeing my language as entirely an expression of my mental equilibrium. My figures of speech are so many balancing acts with which I keep my way of life.[8] My words are devices by which I can distinctify and bear witness to the meanings of my mind that go to make up what I call my world. My every word, being a name, has only the meaning of name. A mind consists of its meanings. Meaning is the concrete substance of the mind and words are inventions for naming mental events. With this viewpoint it becomes evident that one may find the secret of the character of mental health by studying the way language itself develops. Quite as Hobbes recorded, words are wise men's counters, they but reckon by them; words are the money only of fools.

General Practitioner. Schelling made a similar observation:

"What we call Nature is a poem which lies locked up in wonderful, secret script. Yet the riddle could be solved, if we would but learn to recognize the spirit's Odyssey as, wondrously deceptive, it seeks itself in continual flight from itself." Novalis also sanely observed, "Linguistics is the dynamism of the realm of the spirit."

Author. Yes. The problem of mental trouble is situated at the place of its source, for instance, at every word which is lived as if its total meaning were not the naming of the mental property of the worder.

The ideal of democracy, *conscious* self-government, exists only in the mind of the citizen who creates such a meaning and names it with such a word ("democracy"). The concept called "conscious self-government" (democracy) derives its meaningfulness from mindfulness, not from its name, and is found only in the given individual citizen. In the apt phrase of Edward Carpenter it is "the Demos in every man," "the rule of the mass-man in each unit-man." As Carpenter observed in *Civilization, Its Cause and Cure* (1902): "No true life can rely upon an external support." And with his insane (self-unconscious) efforts to secure "external" help, man "soon loses the knowledge that he is a man at all, his true self slumbers in a deep and agelong swoon." Edwin Arlington Robinson's eternally manworthy poem about Demos words the needed warning:

> All you that are enamored of my name
> And least intent on what most I require,
> Beware; for my design and your desire,
> Deplorably, are not as yet the same.

The ideal of conscious self-government is most powerful of all human meanings and is appreciated by the individual citizen to the extent that he has been able to devote himself to his appreciation of it. The need is clear that this development be guarded by the individual from the very beginning of his living of his world, until, like Robinson's contented metaphysician;

> He has come to the end of his words
> And alone he rejoices
> In the choiring that silence affords
> Of ineffable voices.

To a realm that his words may not reach
He may lead none to find him;
An adept, and with nothing to teach
He leaves nothing behind him.[9]

Everyone's family living has profound significance for his growing true appreciation of the allness of his individuality. The growing infant (and child) who creates within himself a mother and a father, each of whom is devoted to the appreciation of conscious self-government—that growing individual is fortunate indeed. However, everyone's family living is a test of the strength of his mind. Everyone's home events have at times an overwhelming force, and by "overwhelming" I mean specifically the degree of mental tension which necessitates the individual's "forgetting himself," suspending his "presence of mind," upsetting his mental equilibrium so that his sense of personal identity is obscured. Every person is familiar with this kind of incident in the living of his home events and does all that he can do to prepare himself to avoid such mental trauma.

When I am not aware that my living is all self-contained, then I am not "in my right mind," and my language no longer describes me so that I can recognize myself. Thus I begin to use words as if they apply to "somebody else," or "something else." With this development I am no longer capable of conscious self-government but have unwittingly resorted to authoritarianism. By "authoritarianism" I mean specifically: living as if someone else can be the author of some part of my living.

Only the word which I am conscious of creating can I see as all and only a name for a meaning of my mind. Disciplining my mind with attention to this fact not only helps me to clear up the mystery of myself but entirely resolves the phantom of "somebody else." Out of my own mind I make up my everything. What other possibility do I have? Yes, indeed, I have the possibility of denying that truth. However, when I have my colleague ask himself whether or not it is true that all he can do is live himself, he comes up with the affirmative answer. When I address the same question to my own view of myself, I can find no other answer. It is only when I conceive of myself literally as being all that I live, and thus imaginatively identify myself with my all, that I find it possible to live my fellowman, also, as a universe of his own making.

General Practitioner. Are there not certain aspects of your world you prefer to disown, consider bad or evil or sinful?

Author. Whatever I live in this way (by disowning it) illustrates a weak spot in my mind. I have learned to see my whole orientation of sin as a sign of my unreadiness to recognize salvation in that disguise. A fall from grace can be only a fall to unrecognized grace. Every such judgment as bad, vicious, wicked, and so on, stands for an area of self-unconsciousness and its corresponding want of self-control. Every pejorative word describes a force of repression (the activity of forgetting).

And now I come to a key concept of psychotherapy. I have found that a human being's sense of his personal identity is of paramount life importance to him. *It is so important that his fear of loss of his own ability to identify himself (as being himself) tends to control his conduct.* He is rarely aware that his realization of being himself is obscured by his (unrecognized) illusion of "externality" (e.g. elseness, otherness, not-self, etc.). Yet he grows increasingly indulgent of his cultivating experience which he cannot classify as his own self-experience. As his quantity of his repudiated selfness grows, his appreciation of just who he is becomes more shaky, and his compensating need to feel sure of his joyous use of self-power becomes thoroughly aroused. He leans upon his ignored idealism ("materialism") for spiritual support, for moral power. Thus, he becomes most "logical" and "matter-of-fact." He "forgets" that it is his mind which really sees, or hears. *He tries to limit his imagination's work to the one assignment of assuring himself that he lives in an external world* (concealing the truth, that his external world exists only in and of himself).

The gap between his conscious self and his use of words widens. This person becomes increasingly "resistive to change" and "hangs on for dear life" to "keep everything just as it is," for new self-orientation necessitates his loss of that customary view of himself which at least favors his recognizing somewhat of himself in his living. As his "external world" delusional system is extended (by his continuing reliance upon self-unconsciousness) the likelihood of his choosing a conscious psychological approach for a psychological analysis of his problem gradually vanishes. Only a conscious self-analysis can reveal to him the binding limitations and costly commitments of the way he chooses for treating his mind. Nevertheless, he is wise in treating his mind so that he can cling to some remaining life orientation. Otherwise he would lose his conscious hold upon preserving his life. If *I* cannot see that my life is mine, *I* can secure no pleasure or benefit of any kind from living it. Without my sense of personal identity, whether *I* live, or die, is a matter which *I* cannot even consider. A great contribution to my sense of personal identity is my discovery that *I* am the creator of my every word. Herder observed a profound truth of human nature, "If it is incomprehensible to others how a human mind could invent language, it is incomprehensible to me how a human mind could be what it is without discovering language for itself."

General Practitioner. Your emphasis upon everyone's doing everything for himself is certainly consistent.

Author. May I point out that my intended emphasis is upon the benefit I derive from *being aware* that I do everything for myself; that the appearance of (my) another's doing something for me is an illusion which, in every instance, costs me life-saving self-appreciation.

General Practitioner. What does then constitute mastery of the art and science of speech, of your iatrology? When did it begin? How do you reduce your world problem to a word problem? What proficiency in talking must I achieve to avoid "talk" trouble? Berkeley proposed confining his thinking to his own ideation *divested of words* as a method of avoiding mistake. Is my conventional habit of speech little more than a matrix of misconception, a tool for my appearing to "agree" with the psychotic majority (free to come and go as "sane") of my world and "disagree" with the psychotic minority (hospitalized as "insane") of my world? Am I depending upon a speech habit for intelligibility? Your arithmetization of the incidence of human life into a single integer may be the culmination of your mathematical experience, but not of mine. How can I learn to be a word artist?

Author. Interest in language for its own sake as a self-power is seemingly as old as recorded history. However, Richard A.

Wilson mentions 1772, when Johann Gottfried Herder's prize essay on the origin of language was published, as the year when the scientific investigation of language began. Conscious view of the power of language, although it may be the hardest to create, is the surest preventive of the use of words for the purpose of developing and maintaining mental trouble. At the very start, it is well to make peace with the observations that human life is a tremendously magnificent and wonderful existent and that every person is wholly and solely responsible for driving himself either sane (self-consciously oriented) or insane (self-unconsciously oriented) through the conduct of his life.

General Practitioner. Is man the only being who uses language to help him fulfill his life?

Author. As I see it, everyone and everything speaks for itself. Once his illusion of communication is renounced, I feel sure that my fellowman will be much readier, as a rule, to attribute the power of language at least to each individual of his animal world. Each one human individual being an all one, the only "missing link" must consist of repudiated selfness. In *Faust,* Goethe provided a word picture of his necessity to live in the consciousness of his individuality (individual-allness):

> The God that dwells within my soul
> Can stir to life my inmost deeps.
> Full sway o'er all my powers he keeps,
> But naught external can he e'er control.

I know of no single exception to the truth that anyone's deep and thorough research upon his use of his words is in every instance mind-strengthening mental exercise in self-understanding, which is most worthy of attention at every peace table. Furthermore, talking without listening, speaking "lip-wisdom," "mouth homage"—and all such self-dumb and self-deaf uses of language, contribute to one's conscious sense of self-disesteem by inducing one's self-unconciousness. Mental trouble may be defined even as language trouble, as an instance of a person's misleading himself by the way he learned to express himself linguistically. No doubt, linguistic disorder is universal on account of the innumerable snares which one's language can set. Each of these disorders, however, is nothing more or less than trouble associated with a localized loss of personal identity, without the consciousness that this conscious self-unity (homogeneity) is the loss suffered.

Psychotherapy may be defined as the patient's cultivation of his ability to learn to talk a conscious idiolect, in the true sense of his learning to talk and listen to, about, and for himself.[10] For conscious self-orientation I must rely upon an epistemology by definition subjective, rather than a psychology by definition "objective." Appreciation of human health, recognition of desirable humaneness, is a matter of clearly perceiving the wholeness of human individuality. My every meaning not observable as my mental process provides magnitude, force, and direction for my mental anarchy. It is such wayward ideal material which expresses itself by giving life to my cancer, or to some neoplastic growth, for it certainly does not vitalize my appreciation of being governed entirely by my own cherishable autonomy. Wilhelm von Humboldt (1767-1835) developed the theory that each separate language is the product of the characteristic mental life of the people who made it.[11] My experience demonstrates to my complete satisfaction that my personal language has grown out of, reflects, and safeguards the nature and needs of my own individuality—and that *that* is all there is to it.

My language is potentially the most helpful action system I have for finding out what there is to know about myself. I find that the person who has the ability to think of himself consciously can be capable of thinking *for* himself. This kind of insight is the educator's most needed specific. However, it is too rare a self-property to be practical for teacher screening. A teacher who indulges his delusion that he can help his pupil, thereby lives *his* pupil as hiding from himself the fact that only he can help himself. As might be expected, Osler made this point: "The higher education so much needed today is not given in the school, is not to be bought in the market place, but it has to be wrought out in each one of us for himself."

The educator with no insight that all help is self-help is insensible to his own personal identity in all of his own living. This teacher has no recourse other than to operate on the delusional level of "communication" with his pupil. Forfeiting his sense of personal identity (in any of his living), he signalizes this loss in the form of experiencing painful feelings of "inequality," "injustice," "wrongdoing," "boredom," and similiar signs that he is living an oppressed type of existence. Each of these obstacles in his educational living is itself his own cry for help, which he is unable to recognize and hence heed. Until he succeeds in living some experience with which he can rescue himself from his plight of self-ignoration, he has no recourse other than to go on pursuing his life of ignored personal identity. There is always a possibility that he may live the specific kind of teacher in-service educational experience with which he can help himself to find himself just where he lost himself.

There appear to be innumerable problems in the field of education, but *they are all variations of the only one possible problem, namely, self-ignoration.* Everyone (of my world) who discovers this truth in himself finds it extremely helpful. Research upon the way in which my language works is the hardest kind of work. I would avoid it entirely were it not for the fact that, seeing the importance of it, I am afraid to do so.

I duly acknowledge that I account for mental health and strength in a way quite contrary to established customs of thinking on the subject. Specifically, I refer to my declaration that the development of the free mind is the direct sequence of its sustained devotion to self-consciousness. The advancement of this discipline appears to oppose the ways of thinking of the majority of my world's public educators. Thus, even my young, growing American citizen finds it necessary to teach himself to avoid the use of the first person singular and to avoid the application of honorifics to himself. Sanative self-esteem can hardly find its way into ordinary spoken language, due to the fact that the "auditor" suffers from limited ability to find his own identity in his living of his "speaker," quite as the "speaker" is rarely conscious of his own identity in his living of his "auditor."

Undoubtedly, any conscious living of myself must appear objectionable to the extent that my asserted self-extent seems to exclude anyone or anything of my world. The truth of the matter is that no human being (of my world) can be exclusive. Furthermore, he cannot speak of himself at all except focally. The words

"I speak of myself" are most misleading. It is clarifying to keep noticing that the "I" can stand for only a minute fraction of myself as subject, and the word "myself" can stand only for a minute locus of my subjectivity as "object."

In every instance the successful treatment of mental trouble consists of the patient's discovery that he has always been talking about himself only, as well as hearing about himself only. Semiotic (the general theory of signs) is a "must" discipline for one who wishes to know whereof he speaks. A person's every word, heard or spoken, is all and only a sign of his life. Every kind of mental trouble is traceable to the way in which each individual has had to use his language for the purpose of becoming unconscious of the fact that his life is all and only about himself. Semantics, the study of meaning, aptly describes psychotherapy, provided that the study of words is undertaken as the study of the expression of one's own self-meanings. "Quantity" introduces plurality (delusion); "quality" observes oneness (reality).

The enormous part played by self-ignoration in language suffices to obscure the truth of the individuality of the linguist. Obscured individuality is always the specific source of mental trouble. Von Humboldt conceived his language to be life activity, not a product. Fortunate is the linguist who sees the advantage to himself in realizing that he is the originator of his every moving word, and that it behooves him to know the *how* and *what* of the usage of his every word act.

A person may speak his mind as if he is exceedingly verbalized and yet suffer from the most serious kind of mental trouble. His vocabulary is correlated positively with his mental health, only to the extent that each word is observable by him as being a sign of his own self-possession. *Words are used to hide behind when they are not used as self-manifestations.* Despite superficial appearances to the contrary, there is no way in which a human being can use words except in a personal and private way. To be "impersonal" is simply to ignore the presence of the personal.

General Practitioner. This view of the absolute allness of oneness is reminiscent of the living-orientation of Meister Eckhart (1260?-1327), the father of German mysticism: "Man, yes, I stood with God before time and the world were created;

yes, I was included in the eternal Godhead even before it became God. Together with me God has created and is still and always creating. Only through me He became God."

Author. Only insofar as I can see my every word as a name for a self-meaning (of my own) am I capable of verbal insight. It is insight upon myself which constitutes any and all insight I have. My words, such as "language," "human speech," "reality," "humanity," and so on—words (names) which I use without sensing my denoting selfness by them, are empty of sanity, full of self-deception.[12] My every word is a symbol of certain selfness of mine, and it is essential for my proper sense of self-measure that I heed this truth.

Whatever I regard as "alien to me" detracts from my sense of my individuality, obscures the spirit of humanity, and belongs wholly to the useful realm of symptomatology. The entire nomenclature of symptomatology is the naming of warning signs that my conscious self-government is in abeyance, that I am working the parenchyma of my life heedlessly in some extreme effort to help myself. It is life-saving for me to grow the strength of mind that enables me to pass from unconscious helpfulness to conscious helpfulness, particularly with regard to my wording myself.

General Practitioner. You believe that no single word can ever mean the same for any two persons?

Author. Every word is the name for a meaning in the person (all) who uses it. "Any two persons" is always a term denoting a meaning in the one person's mind using the term. Each moment of living has its own unique wholeness so that, strictly speaking, every element of an individual's language is never the same for "any two moments" of the one individual's life. I am the only possible subject suitable to my activity as an author and as a reader.

General Practitioner. Please explain again why it *seems* as if one (all) can communicate with another (all).

Author. Everyone must explain everything to his own satisfaction. To me it is only evident and natural that my very own necessary personal experiencing of my (repudiated) personal identity in what I call "external world" must necessarily support and enhance my illusion of being "in communication" with it.

My craving to indulge my illusion of communication is understandable as an expression of my need to exercise my capacity for appreciating my sense of personal identity without appearing (to my conscious self) to do so.

General Practitioner. You mean that my spirited defense of the use of language as a means of communication is based upon the fact that I have grown to depend upon illusional communication as a disguised way of indulging my narcissism?

Author. I can only "mean" anything about myself. I see clearly that every word I write or read, speak or hear, is a sign of my life (my all) only.

I have found only one mental health prerequisite, namely, that I identify myself, *momentarily* to be sure, to myself. All there is, or can be, for every existent is its selfness. Its self-consciousness is its supreme truth. It is the highest distinction of Freud to have discovered a scientific method for extending his self-consciousness, for consciously appropriating the depth and height of his human soul.

Alfred Korzybski made valiant effort to point out the extent to which a person seems to be used by his words rather than to be the conscious creator and manipulator of his words. He made the important point that applying the methods of general semantics to education at all levels, and to the professions, usually produces beneficial results which cannot be expected if the methods are merely talked about. He demonstrated the therapeutic value of semantics, which provides a person with an appreciation of his uniquely human potentialities. Who is there who realizes that he creates the pleasures he enjoys and the tribulation he employs?

It appears evident to me that no one (of my world) has learned how to talk sanely, that is consistently verbalize his creating his life's evolution. What one calls his life seems to be a vaguely conceived, largely impersonal kind of existence, rather than a glad growth of his magnificence. Indeed, it is exceedingly rare for anyone (of my world) even to question himself in regard to his use of language. Almost invariably he "takes for granted" that he already knows how to utter words in a way that demonstrates beyond doubt that he can "talk sense" both fluently and eloquently. However, *to be capable of saying anything adequately is to be able to see clearly that the observation is a self-grown self-observation.* The great scientist Kepler is famous for the passionately personal way in which he self-consciously observed and recorded his data. Emerson noted: "It makes a great difference in the force of a sentence whether a man be behind it or no." Walter H. Seegers, renowned physiologist, records his scientific living self-consciously.[13] *Conscious living of a man is noticeable as being instinct with the life of him.*

General Practitioner. The biological survival value of man's ability to "project" his self-experience, that is, to displace it in his imagined "externality," is evident. This protective rind preserves his equanimity and safeguards his sense of self-control. It seems only natural for me to be able to sort out and localize my life experiences in this helpful way. My vocabulary of foreignness is life-saving. I do see the value in *consciously* suppressing and renouncing immediate living which I cannot assume as my own controllable self's. I am reminded of Ernst Cassirer's linguistic orientation,

> Word and mythic image, which once confronted the human mind as hard realistic powers, have now cast off all reality and effectuality; they have become a light, bright ether in which the spirit can move without let or hindrance. This liberation is achieved not because the mind throws aside the sensuous forms of word and image, but in that it uses them both as *organs* of its own, and thereby recognizes them for what they really are: forms of its own self-revelation.[14]

As Cassirer noted, language is only what the life-giving moment makes of it.

Author. Of Cassirer himself, Professor James Gutmann of Columbia University wrote, that he raised the standard of self-knowledge, reaffirmed the doctrine that the unexamined life is no life for man, that the proper study of mankind is man, and asserted that man is best known and studied in his creative life. Than that, what more or less, can a philosopher wish to say of himself?

"Objectification" is always a subjective construction, always a given mind's process. Subjectivity is the only possible source of reality. My wish to be "objective" is traceable to my need to put my subjectivity to sleep. For living my sensory experience I depend entirely upon my mind's power to *create* sensory experience. I *imagine* my sensation quite as I imagine my perception, conception, and every other imagination (mental activity). *If I wish to find out what any sensory experience means, I free-associate upon it exactly as I would free-associate upon a dream element.*

The *Cratylus* offers a marvelous treatment of etymology. Plato's method of having Socrates use his imaginative insight to investigate the meaning of words is strikingly similar to the method of free-association. To illustrate,

> Socrates: Joy is the very expression of the fluency and diffusion of the soul.
>
> Hermogenes (speaking of the etymological method of Socrates): Indeed Socrates you make surprising progress.
>
> Socrates: I am run away with. . . . By the dog of Egypt I have not a bad notion which came into my head only this moment.

Socrates defines a word as a name, and a name as an instrument for the name-giver's denoting whatever is named. He also calls attention to Homer's serious concern about the origin and fitting use of names. Socrates considers the word "name" to be a compressed sentence signifying: being for which there is a search. He stated that "the name is not the same with the thing named," and that things "must be studied and investigated in themselves."

My "phenomenal world" is *my* named world of my own mind's creation. "Phenomenon" is *noumenon* unrecognized, since it is experienced as sensory activity which is unrecognized (or undiscovered) mental activity. However, mind itself is a second nature in that life is first.

General Practitioner. Does that last statement involve you in a repression of your psychologism?

Author. As I ask this question, my reply is, "That last statement only appears to belie my contention that life itself expresses its meaning through the mind it creates." I help myself by using my mind (imagination) to conceive a view of life as being prerequisite to a view of mind.

With increasing self-ignoration supported by an illusional language of not-self appears increasing demand for the prop of rejected selfness: "others." With self-realization goes the inspiration characteristic of life's freedom. Liberty is the name of conscious self-helpfulness. As long as my selfishness is narrow (undeveloped, restricted to shortsighted views of myself), just so long will I find my world blind, uncaring, "sick." All of my knowledge is a burden except my conscious self-knowledge. My "worldly" wisdom is my *asylum ignorantiae* which keeps my verbalized conscious selfishness primitive, infantile, unenlightened, wild. Consciousness of my self-powers is my methodological ideal, the exercise of which enlarges my verbalized selfishness so that I can see that a help or hurt to *my* fellowman is a help or hurt to me.

General Practitioner. Are you not speaking of the need to be open-minded for new impressions?

Author. Possibly, in a way. Open-mindedness can be a misleading way to describe self-tolerance or self-devotion, unless by it is meant "open for the business of living self-consciously." The free spirit of tolerance derives from conscious self-tolerance. In plain words, and my mind needs an evident language of itself, I cannot tolerate my fellowman. Only he can tolerate himself. At most my tolerance must depend upon my love of my personal experiences, upon my extension of my self-love. It helps to say it: No one else of my world can have any experience with my point of view. I cannot make up my fellowman's mind for him. I can do more than that, however: I can see that *my* fellowman can make up his own mind and that only he can do it. A sure way for me to show myself that I do not believe in the validity of my own viewpoint would be my impelling need to have (my) somebody else believe it for me.

My words are so much machinery which I use for help in imagining my steering my life. My every word is itself my living, and is not just about my life. Without my realizing it, I can have my words usurp the functions they are intended to serve. This diversion of my manpower is so very great that I need to recover my conscious use of my words. On account of these verbal griefs I cannot enjoy freely my use of my own linguistic powers. Thus, I forget that my all resides within me. A most enlightening exercise is provided by studying the built-in solecism of accepted and promulgated rhetoric. However, I wish to detail another kind of literary madness which everyone may, if he will, observe in and for himself. I refer to the ubiquitous reference displacement found specifically in the literary bull.

My reading of my educational literature discovers it to be compounded of one literary bull or analogous irrelevance after another, each implying the possibility that one person, or thing, can have something to do with another. Simply by noticing such lingual incongruities, the two uses of language become obvious as being self-concealment and self-insight. To illustrate:

"A beginning must be made in the tenderest age to establish the child's feeling for nature." Only a given child can establish his feeling for nature, and that must be for his own human nature.

"Insight is sympathetic wisdom." I cannot shed my identity in any way, shape, or form. All "sympathy" is (self-grown, self-directed, self-contained) self-discontent or self-content.

"The great secret of educating the child lies hidden in the maxim, 'Do not educate.'" Regardless of counterfeit appearances, there is no education except that which an individual actively constructs (grows) for himself.

"It is good to face the fact that we are absolutely alone." The illusion of plurality ("we") obscures the truth of all oneness, aloneness. Pythagoras was right, I live in a world of number—the number *one* which includes my individuality's all.

"It is only out of his own heart that I should care to convince the skeptic." Only the individual can convince himself. The only possible "understanding of human life" is self-understanding.

"You can be sure of external reality when you can see it, feel it, weigh it, measure it." Each use of the word "it" begs a question. A self-conscious scientist must become a specific kind of specialized linguist.

"He is incapable of forming his own opinion and must have it done for him." Every person creates all of his own mental life. I cannot "arrive at a true picture" of anyone or anything which is not my own self's scene.

"The mind's objects are representations of the real objects in external reality." Every thing is its own self and cannot represent anything else. My mind's reality does not consist of "images" but of its own *reals.*

"I am asking you a question and I want an answer." One cannot address anyone but himself for he is all that he has in his world. The appearance of speaking to "another" is pure illusion.

"Idealism may be held as a notion or a doubt, but never again as a well-grounded scientific conviction." Every word of this sentence is a mental construct, and nothing but that.

"Mind cannot be made the subject of scientific study." One's own mind, regardless of its disguise as "impersonal science," is all that it is possible to study.

"My external world is adventitious to me and does not constitute an integrant part of my individuality." No meaning that I live can be foreign to me. I do not grow facsimiles of "externality"; I grow facts of my internality.

"I cannot understand you." There can be only self-understanding. My living is a going on which requires ever corresponding fresh self-estimate. My river of life is always and never the same.

"I am the history of myself." Only my *now* has any life in it. The only possible "historian" is the conscious *now*-liver. What is not *presently* lived is non-existent. Plato to the contrary, love is not the desire for an abstract immortality, but is the desire to live a concrete now. Every human now is a new life synthesis. One is ever putting on "the new man."

"Please explain to me what you mean. I get a glimpse now and then but cannot make it stick." One can have *meaning* only for himself. Self-order is the only "concordance with the fact." As Goethe observed, the clearest vision sees all factual truth as being one's theoretical living.

"I go about in a half-trance, as though partially hypnotized, hardly being conscious of myself at any time or place; so please show me how to become self-conscious." All demonstration implies the illusion of betweenness. "Time" is a useful myth which supports repression (ignoration) of *now,* quite as "space" is a useful myth which supports repression (ignoration) of *here.* The "philosophic" problem (of Time, or Space, or Evil, and so on) resolves itself only when it is seen clearly as a self-problem created by *self*-ignoration. "Historical consciousness" is a succedaneum for self-consciousness.

"Man cannot find himself, he cannot become aware of his individuality, except through the medium of social life." Every man's medium of social life is the issue of his own productive spontaneity.

The literary bull is regularly found in pseudo-scientific claims:

"The phenomena of the physical world are based upon an entirely hypothetical idea, 'the conception of matter.'" This sentence, the produce of a mind, takes for granted nothing less than "the physical world." "Physical" observation, measurement, classification, matter, extension, motion, control, and experiment, are all and only mental events. Denial of this orientation is, likewise, a mental event.

"We should not permit ourselves to take a psychical action for granted without any physical bases. A few mental provinces have been so far inaccessible to the physiologic-psychological method." This sentence attempts to use the mind for the purpose of rejecting the mind.

"I do not use self-consciousness in scientific work, and I am a renowned scientist." "Renown" is illusional, a succedaneum for self-respect.

"I enlarge my self-confidence in and through other scientists." The craving for fame grows in increasing degrees, the more one accomplishes without self-consciousness. *Self*-appreciation can be only a private growth.

"The consciousness of man's worth comes into conflict with external circumstances." Whoever sees that he has no choice other than to create his own external circumstances, *that* one, by sensing his own identity in the so-called "external circumstances," experiences no conflict.

"The famous French physician, Cabanis, conceived the celebrated phrase that the brain produces the 'secretion of thoughts.'" Again a mind shows its reach of power by exercising its ability to cancel itself (illusionally).

"Of course, every individual accepts the facts of his personal identity, even though he does not work at it the way you do." Only the given individual, such as myself, can have any idea whatsoever about his self-consciousness.

"I have nothing but contempt for unscientific views on life." Contempt is all and only about and for contempt. Galileo's contemporary refused to look through the telescope to convince himself of undesired astronomical findings. Insofar as my science is based upon impersonal objectivity, it is a true myth from beginning to end.

"According to Poincaré, all that the scientist contributes to objective fact is the language in which it is enunciated." This sentence unassumingly assumes "objective fact" as well as that "it" can be enunciated.

"Leibnitz defined Space as the order of all possible togetherness and Time as the order of all possible successiveness." The meanings "togetherness" and "successiveness" are taken for granted as indicating possibles other than illusions.

"Racine said, 'I copied my personages from the greatest painter of antiquity—I mean Tacitus.' " All of my Racine's Tacitus was his own original living.

"Hermann Grimm said, 'The air which Goethe breathed was filled with Rousseau's spirit.' " Goethe's Rousseau was entirely his own novel creation.

"We are continually arriving at that old Hindu dialectic that ended in teaching that the creative world of things was all illusory, and that only the supreme creative Spirit or Self is real." I am my own "we," "dialectic," "Hindu," "creative world of things," "Spirit," "Self," and "real."

So-called "animal language" is recognized as remaining entirely subjective. However my pseudoscientific craving for the possibility of "communication," which necessarily follows upon my mind's dissociating itself into recognized selfness and unrecognized selfness ("otherness"), prompts me to try to scientize the magic of intersubjectivity as being an unquestioned function of my language. Thus, objectification (the systematic concealment and denial of subjectivity) becomes my respectable craze.

Seeking the origin of language, tracing the word derivative to its etymon, does appear to lead to a *lingua Adamica* of sorts, insofar as it may discover language to express originally the meaningful phonetics of the linguist's self-activities. Thus, William von Humboldt exercised his self-activity as a consciously original linguist when he described language as an individual's continuous discharge of mental energy producing the utilization of articulated sounds to express meaning.

General Practitioner. From these statements I assume that you consider "communication" to be a myth of man quite as his every word is. Cassirer stated, "Language and myth are near of kin. . . two different shoots from one and the same root." You see the myth "communication" as a device an individual uses to compensate for his helping himself necessarily at times by disowning his own life's creations.

Author. Yes. The only way to "unite men" is through individual man's uniting himself. He can learn to tolerate denoting his soul (or mind) as his own and his all as his soul (or mind).

General Practitioner. Accurate knowledge of the true nature of human speech is necessary for the development of insight about the human mind, is it not?

Author. Every psychologist and educator of my world would advance that truth.[15] However, it is not everyone who is ready to see his every word as being nothing but a meaningful naming of one of his mind's meanings. When one does find out that his language is necessarily a language of self, an idiolect, he enjoys a tremendous access of conscious freedom. *Whenever I discover a use of my very own where before I could only feel used by that power, I enjoy a conscious appreciation of my wonderfulness.* The insatiable hunger for answers of the inquisitive child is traceable to his more or less frantic efforts to recover his sense of wholeness by learning (living) names which can in part compensate him for not recognizing all of his mental growths as being his own. My insightless exploration of "the objective world," extending to "the stars," is a necessary compensation for my ignoration of my subjective world.

General Practitioner. As Caliban said to Miranda: "You taught me language; and my profit on't Is, I know how to curse." I have learned to think in one language (of objectivity), and now you require me to think in the language of subjectivity. You must realize how extremely difficult it is to learn to think in another language.

Author. Yes. Fortunately, only you can require yourself to think in any way at all. I am only describing how I have had to learn how to use my mind's linguistic powers. Denominating my every meaning as a self-meaning has been, and is, an extremely difficult voyage of self-discovery in what appears to be a foreign world. On the other hand, my former everyday naming of my life's experiences was making me more and more confused, more and more a foreigner to myself.

General Practitioner. You mean that experiences, which you could not give your name to, just kept accumulating as power which you could not use purposefully but as power which you seemed to be constantly threatened to be *used by*?

Author. Exactly.

General Practitioner. In the sense that Socrates defined idleness as including any work if a person might be better employed, do you feel that this learning to see one's self in all of his living is the ultimate in diligence?

Author. Everyone of my world must decide that matter and every other matter for himself. (My) Aristotle found that "to be learning something is the greatest of pleasure not only to the philosopher but also to the rest of mankind." For instance, the only sure safeguard I know of for the preservation of the health and happiness of the person who is no longer able to gratify himself with a job's occupational satisfaction, is his learning as soon and as much as possible the pleasures of study. *A studious person, one who has learned the self-gratification he creates for himself by learning, is never a retirement casualty.* This devotion to living as learning is a life-fulfilling self-realization which is not limited to the formal education resources. It can be exercised by any sense remaining to man and it invariably yields functional triumph of the most life-satisfying order.

General Practitioner. Getting back to language, I have read that the Greeks for a long time showed deep distrust for the written word. For centuries they employed writing, not as an instrument of thought, but almost wholly for memorial purposes. They cherished an inaptitude for reading and writing, referring to the alphabet as "Phoenician symbols." Unlike the Egyptian, the Greek did not go through a pictographic stage of writing. Long after writing was known in Greece, *unwritten law* was all of the law. Written codes were likened to unvarying medical prescriptions, to being doctored by formulae.

Author. Yes. The Greek sensed life as innovation. Socrates stated a profound truth beautifully in describing the written as the mere phantom of the spoken word (*Phaedrus*). He observed that self-knowledge is the product of painful effort and self-questioning, not conveyed by formal doctrine. Said Plato, "It is for this reason that I have never myself written anything upon these subjects. There neither is nor ever shall be a treatise of Plato's. What goes by his name are the words of Socrates."

General Practitioner. The literary dissatisfaction rampant today over dictionary changes favoring the truth of mobility of language is an effort to enliven writing. Much of your writing lacks vividness. A man should write as he speaks, vitalize the dead letter.

Author. The reader's life is all that can enliven any of his reading.

General Practitioner. The greater the literary ability of the writer, the livelier his writing. Milton said, "A good book is the precious life-blood of a master-spirit embalmed and treasured up on purpose to a life beyond life."

Author. Yes. Whitman stated, "I wrote things down: I saw them better in my handwriting than in my mind's eye—could tell better whether they suited me or not."

General Practitioner. Some kind of standard of mental health is practical. Please try to define what *is* meant by *normal mental health.*

Author. Ideal mental health, in my view, is the presence of conscious mindfulness which permits me to see every kind of mental life as healthful. What is conventionally called "mental weakness" or "mental illness" I see as perfect mental health for each given individual. Any other view would have to represent perfect fault-finding, as I see it.

General Practitioner. You mean no person is healthier-minded or stronger-minded than another?

Author. Exactly. In addition I would add that no person (of my world) has any "other" than whom to be stronger-, or healthier-, minded.

General Practitioner. No wonder this way of thinking cannot be "popular." Again, your radical individualism is such that it is fortunate for yourself that you, as you aver, must keep it to yourself. Can you refer me to some other source for the kind of down-to-earth, useful definition of mental health I seek?

Author. Almost every textbook of psychiatry, psychology, or psychoanalysis contains its own definitions. The latest helpful account of this kind which I have read is that of E. E. Krapf, of Geneva.[16]

General Practitioner. There is a technical word which refers to a person's attitude towards any meaning of his life which he refuses to accept as being his own.

Author. Yes. That word is "transference." I am "in transference" to any part of my world which I cannot consciously claim as my own.

General Practitioner. What does that mean?

Author. It has the most profound meaning. I cannot take a fresh look at any part of my life which I live in transference. Instead, I must live that particular selfness rigidly according to the pattern which I worked out for disposing of it originally as "not-mine."

General Practitioner. You mean that you cannot live sanely to the extent that you live in transference the persons and things of your world?

Author. It amounts to that.

General Practitioner. Please illustrate how your being in transference to one of your fellowmen shows itself.

Author. It shows itself by my living with personal intensity whatever I repudiate as being my own living. Thus, I constantly create the predicament of appearing to claim that I can have something to do with the life of my fellowman, or that I can have him have something to do with a life other than his own.

General Practitioner. I see. You mean transference-living embroils you in such phantom problems as "getting mad at somebody else," "having somebody else please (or displease) you," "being jealous, or envious, of your friend," etc. Please formulate a list of questions and answers bearing upon transference-living.

Author. Is all so-called successful "learning," including curing, merely one's recalling or recognizing his original personal wholeness while living (self-experiencing)? Yes.

Does your singularity consist entirely of original subjectivity, which is your soul, and which is, of course, incommunicable? Yes.

Do you mean by "soul" what Socrates meant: the seat and site of all of your individuality, your Orphic psyche, a name identical with your self? Yes.

Is your possible business in life, conscious or unconscious, that of tending your soul? Yes.

Is your conscious self-knowledge your only source of assured insight, as of conscious moral excellence? Yes.

Is your every confession of wrongdoing an acknowledgement of its being an expression of limited self-consciousness, rather than a manifestation of self-ignoration? Yes.

General Practitioner. All mental turmoil then is traceable to transference-living, as you see it?

Author. Yes.

General Practitioner. Must one live with conscious responsibility for that living, in order to cultivate his (her) interest in living?

Author. Yes.

General Practitioner. Is all moral consciousness purely self-consciousness which extends itself to subsume its ideal altruistic (so-called "unselfish") interests quite as it does its egoistic (so-called "selfish") interests?

Author. Yes.

General Practitioner. Does such carefully developed moral self-consciousness which maintains its every altruistic interest as it does its every egoistic interest, for its own independent sake, entail a most comprehensive conception of the capacity for peacemaking love in human nature?

Author. Yes.

General Practitioner. Is it true that common speech has no words to express this full-scoped development of the individual's self-love which consciously encompasses its "otherness" within its sense of personal identity?

Author. Yes.

General Practitioner. May my personal-identity ignoring vocabulary account largely for my not seeing clearly that my moral law is no more than the *natural* law of my life (soul, mind, being)?

Author. Yes.

General Practitioner. If, as you claim, all love is self-love, why is so much emphasis placed upon the illusion that one person can love, and be loved by, another? Indeed, why is self-love generally disliked, except in the very young?

Author. The feeling of love is essential for life. Love must be lived, whether responsibility for it is shouldered or shirked. However, I cannot acknowledge loving myself unless my conduct is such as to require my loving myself. On the other hand, I can behave irresponsibly, if I can delude myself that someone else can love me or that I can love someone else. The responsibility for conscious self-love is so heavy that it is honored more in the denial than in the observance.

General Practitioner. Does language imprison man? Or does he impose his ready-made language upon his life? Why do you resort to your language idiosyncrasies?

Author. My life provides my language with whatever meaning it may have, but I am not necessarily conscious about that. Therefore, I may use my language unconsciously for self-concealment. I help myself by seeing that I am solely and wholly responsible for my words. (My) Joshua Whatmough writes:

> Language is an emergent conceptual pattern that, if unfettered by a dread tradition, solves its own problems; modern attempts at intelligibility and coherence, amid new problems, are like what people have been doing with language all along through recorded history. . . . Man need not bend to linguistic circumstance, but may easily bend language to his needs.[17]

General Practitioner. Terms name conceptions. Nathaniel Holmes, in his *Realistic Idealism* (1886), used the term "isity" as a synonym for "the being of being." He claimed "there is no true Philosophy but Idealism—not a mystical 'pure idealism' of our subjective imagination, but that realistic idealism of the universe itself which is the unity and identity of the Real and the Ideal in the one absolute Whole."

Author. Yes, my Holmes held fast to *his* terms for *his* metaphysical conceptions. The only language which can be meaningful for me is my idiolect. Besides his famous treatise on the circulation of the blood, William Harvey published one other little book, *Exercitationes de Generatione,* wherein he records, "Those who, reading the words of authors, do not form sensible images of the things referred to, obtain no true ideas, but conceive false imaginations and inane phantasms."

Disciplining my language, my choice instrument of my thought and conservator of human effort of my heritage, delivers me from many a mare's nest. Hard work it is, but any human excellence exists only through excellent work.

General Practitioner. Even your demand for mental accuracy based upon linguistics, as I live it, confronts me with a necessity for thorough and entire personal reconstruction. (My) your views introduce me to *practical* difficulty, that is certain. My friends, "the people," will never undertake the discipline you call "systematic growth of self-insight." About "the people," I grant Kipling's wisdom, "Lord! what *do they* understand?" As R. M. Wenley observed of his "people,"

> Be it observed, nature has made them parents, political fortune has induced them to foot the bills, and psychological hallucination has led them to prophesy as authorities on matters educational. Ladies and gentlemen, it's our psychology that besets us with dangers, the more subtle that they are neither touched nor tasted.[18]

Nevertheless your *novum organum,* self-consciousness, would change the traditional humanistic ideal radically, so that it would be rarely recognizable. Do you consider that the study of a so-called "foreign language" tends to effect that kind of modification of mind which you associate with the growth of self-insight, with the cultivation of humanization, with practical value in the ordering of affairs?

Author. My study of every "foreign" language has been most rewarding for my understanding of my use of my own mind. My early persistence in Latin, late picking at Greek, and interim painstaking study and practice of my mind in French and German—each of these linguistic disciplines has contributed specifically to my appreciating all of my meaningful living as being mental. By forcing myself to use my mind in unaccustomed ways (required by the learning of a new language), I could observe even my sensory living as being all mental. Commented Victor C. Vaughan, M.D.,

> No one can become a student of anything until he learns how to study, and he does this only under the whip of application. No knowledge, save that of the most superficial character, is easily acquired. Like gold, true knowledge lies beneath the surface and he who would possess it must dig for it, and systematic education should begin in learning how to use the senses—the pick and shovel, as it were, of the mind.[19]

His life helpfulness depends upon the individual's having become conscious of his own mind by loving it—not upon his mastery of any subject of schooling, but upon his seeing his own mental activity and appreciating his independence and originality. As Levi L. Barbour observed over fifty years ago, everyone may well be aware of the humanistic studies as making life worth living. My education forms, not informs, my mind. As the reviews of the literature show, each mind-worker must define and locate uniquely ("differently") the essence of psychic substance. The stream of my world of my senses reminds me of the Heraclitean philosophy of flux, except that my flux is entirely of me—I am its only truth, or reality.

General Practitioner. Please try to reconcile that selfism with your scientific view of sensation.

Author. Bacon recorded, "What in operation is most useful, that in knowledge is most true." Certainly, the use of language as an ideal way of operating my own mind is a self-evident truth. Destutt de Tracy (1754-1836) insightfully unified thinking, feeling, and sensation (including consciousness itself) by attributing to sensation the general signification of generic mental activity. He consolidated this integration in his renowned aphorism: *penser c'est sentir.* His appreciation of the allness of individuality was outstanding.[20]

General Practitioner. Plato said knowledge was not possible through "external" activity of any kind, and claimed that the senses, at best, make knowledge conscious *which was already the self's unconscious possession.* He held all knowledge to be inborn, and considered so-called "education" to be only the learner's illustrating his self-knowledge in a specific instance limited to a particular event. He described love as the soul's desire to live good appreciated as beautiful, as the soul's self-attraction. How do you differ from all of that in your views?

Author. In a very important way. I like to say: As I live it, *I* am *my* Plato achieving and wording (my) his every insight. By acknowledging all of my experience, thus, as being my self-experience, I avoid impoverishing my realization of my personal identity, so that it tends towards conscious oneness with my truth of *my* allness.

General Practitioner. Your morality, "looking after number one," ignores number two, three, four, and so on. Everybody wants everything you know, so what solution have you for that practical fact?

Author. Yes, "everybody" blindly wants everything cruelly if he does not realize that he already has (is) it. Greed is a longing for stretches of the ostracized homeland of one's own rejected selfhood. The experience of satiety is entirely that of self-satisfaction. It is practical for me to be able to see the extent to which I can seem to rob myself of immense areas of my own mind, by the simple device of consciously disowning my living which is unpleasant. With characteristic brevity my William J. Norton, life-minded social worker and self-insightful humanitarian, has described the socialization of the individual as the person's extension of his kindly self-tolerance. Choice of so-called "evil" living is a matter of lack of this self-insight. He is most moral who can acknowledge the greatest extent of himself.

It does appear that man (woman) has succeeded considerably in sensing personal identity in his (her) opposite-sex living. Some primitive tribes have a characteristic language for males and another characteristic language for females. J. G. Frazer propounded the theory that masculine and feminine names of things go back to a time when language was modified according to the sex of the speaker.

General Practitioner. I suppose I ought to learn to question obvious "popularity" of every description. Certainly, obvious "popularity" seems to be enjoyed by each morality based upon its discreet antithetical principles: "good" and "bad." My own habit of mind has been to help myself by thinking in terms of "right" and "wrong," of "true" and "false." I have seemed to base my "yes" and my "no" largely upon this kind of dichotomy.

Your view, *all is perfect,* clearly includes that the only progress possible is the perfect progress of perfection. For my living, I have depended heavily upon such distinctions as good, better, best, and bad, worse, worst. Now I am able to understand your designation of the word "bad" as being a pejorative term. I can see that the meaning "bad" expresses a resistance to the recognition of perfection in whatever is being named "bad." In fact, I can almost feel myself resisting whatever kind of living I am designating as being "bad." I can understand your idea: Whatever is lived as undesirable living, is already unconscious selfness. Please speak your mind about the unquestionable popularity of the "good *vs.* bad" system of values.

Author. My reader's insight just indicated in his treatment of the "good-bad" strategy for screening his life experiences is noteworthy. I find my "good *vs.* bad" duality to rest upon a plan of "external" reward and forfeit for steering my life's course. Thus, I can uphold a program of receiving and meting out reward and punishment, respectively, for "good" and "bad" done. Often it may be impossible for me to notice the too grievous limitations in such a formula.

My naming anything "bad" is in the category of using punishment to secure my desired results. Unquestionably, punishment *seems* to work like magic in appearing to rid me of what I dislike. The fact is: punishment, including depreciation in the valuation "bad," functions as a repressing force which always creates emphasis and inequality through prohibition. It is the height of sanity for me to work patiently and long-sufferingly with the appreciation that any living in question is all ideal and, therefore, to be lived carefully and caringly (indulged or renounced at conscious will).

General Practitioner. I understand clearly now the claim that virtue is its own reward; that the system of "external" reward and forfeit obscures the incentive of self-interest, introduces the illusion of authoritarianism, and undermines the valuable development of personal responsibility. I can also see that any program based upon "good" and "bad" induces the necessity for pharisaical "better than thou" and "better than I was" views of my living. I can also realize that my morality founded upon "good" and "bad" has always helped me ideally, but at the expense of my growing innumerable obsessive life dissatisfactions. My resulting lack of self-esteem created the goad of ambition associated with the delusion of progress. My true, full self-estimate always makes me satisfied to live just as I am, exactly as I may be. This full self-estimate frees my ambition to apply itself upon my interest in staying alive and upon my steering myself accordingly.

Author. It is a tremendous access of sanity to awaken enough to see how every term implying denial or negation is all and only my conscious mind's effort to avoid exerting itself beyond its present limits of self-conscious observation. I achieved release of enormous mental power, once I could understand that my every unpleasant word, such as "bad," "evil," "wrong," "vicious," "false," "inaccurate," "untrue," "injurious," "indecent," "unkind," "unhealthy," "unhappy," "unholy," merely expresses my making unconscious whatever of my personal power I feel unequal to imagining with love (with self-consciousness). To illustrate, when I say to myself, "It is wrong for me to consider myself as divine," or, "It is false of me to consider the localization of my external world as entirely within my own mind"—then I simply mean that I must live my "divinity" or "externality" unconsciously, that is, as if it were not of my lovable self. As I strengthen my mind (by cultivating my conscious self-love and thus extending my conscious self-tolerance) I can freely imagine (feel equal to) my "divinity," "externality," or whatever.

I recognize a truth of the greatest significance for establishing my conscious mental balance: No matter whether I say that I am greater (better, holier, smarter, etc.) than my neighbor, or that my neighbor is greater (better, holier, smarter, etc.) than I am—by each comparison I imply the same degree of mental imbalance, for each is life orientation based upon *my* insightless "otherness" living.

General Practitioner. Why won't every educator drop all else he is doing and concentrate upon the development of his language of sanity?

Author. Every question I ask helps me to pay attention to

mental limits I have set for myself. Each educator has always done all he could do. William T. Harris observed, "Imitation is self-activity." Johann K. F. Rosenkranz wrote in his *Philosophy of Education,* "The Latin tongue is crowded with expressions which paint presence of mind, the effort at reflection, a critical attitude of mind, the importance of self-control." Leibnitz, in his *Monadology,* stated that the human soul creates for itself the world it perceives.

General Practitioner. As I now understand the language of sanity:

1. It refers only to the individual mind creating it.
2. It only provides names for self-meanings.
3. It helps to preserve a sense of personal identity by appearing to condense past and present.
4. It provides a means for exercising mental power, thus preventing its atrophy.
5. It contributes to conscious thinking, the knowing of the self by the self.
6. It can create and dispel the illusions of memory and prophecy.
7. It helps to establish and organize conscious self-knowledge.
8. It provides signs of self-activities.
9. It can help to manifest an individual's self-consciousness.
10. It signifies universal and particular to be essential phases of the same mental action.
11. It provides the paradigm for the study of whatever of one's world.
12. It enables a record, for furthering the accuracy of self-orientation.
13. It appears to enable the mind, which is entirely subjective, to express itself as if it could be objective.
14. It facilitates free-association.

15. It furthers the introduction of the individual to his learning power, to his capacity for conscious self-development.
16. It helps to clear one's view of the workings of his mind, particularly by way of grammar.
17. It upholds the mental operation of conscious introspection, particularly by way of the study of language itself.
18. It indicates the unity of the self by way of the unity of the vocabulary.
19. It allows the individual to help himself
    (a) by growing his fellowman verbalizing wisdom.
    (b) by having his fellowman grow his fellowman verbalizing wisdom.
20. It distinguishes the substance of subjectivity from the shadow of appearance, in distinguishing substance from name of substance.
21. It reifies "materiality" as being an illusion of solid *ideality.*
22. It can help man to identify himself as god. "Creation is here and now," as Thoreau expressed himself.
23. It protects me from my self-consciousness whenever that would seem unbearable for my prevailing sense of personal identity.

Author. "One must be a creator to read well," said Emerson in *The American Scholar.* All creativity is an outgrowth of the creator. It is reported that long, long ago a Russian student was exiled to Siberia for having in his possession a copy of Emerson's *Self-Reliance.*

General Practitioner. Your language now is not quite so difficult to understand. Maybe I see some possible application to it of Wordsworth's renowned reminder to Lady Beaumont (in a letter of 1807), "Never forget what, I believe, was observed to you by Coleridge, that every great and original writer, in proportion as he is great or original, must himself create the taste by which he is to be relished; he must teach the art by which he is to be seen."

3

Preeminently Practical Self-Consciousness

Were there a single man to be found with a firmness sufficient to efface from his mind the theories and notions vulgarly received, and to apply his intellect free and without prevention the best hopes might be entertained of his success.

BACON

Author. THE ANCIENT PHILOSOPHERS found it practical to refuse to admit slaves to their instruction. Modern aptitude tests eliminate the uninterested and protect the educator considerably. The physician tries to extend his helpfulness with (his) *everyone* who needs to help himself medically. The author may exert himself in favor of a choice reader. To the extent that such prerogative is mine, my conversation is created with my fellowman who is practical enough to *intend* to extend himself to comprehend himself. It advances the practice of conscious living as being the most concrete and the most *practical* of all human pursuits.

"Science in general" justly vaunts its goal and method as being: work based upon *experience.* "Scientific idealism" epitomizes this scientific technique.[1] Only a given human mind *can* breed experience. Every kind of personification (such as "society," "laboratory," "common sense") contributes a "throwing of one's weight around," and is best undertaken with due acknowledgment of one's very own authorship of, and responsibility for, that personification.

General Practitioner. I have grown my self-seeking, self-helping author painstakingly thus far. It appears that he wants me to live him as being a patient of mine, studying his account of how he has gotten himself into his present mental condition. Am I right?

Author. I could ask for no more accurate description of my purpose in all of this talk.

General Practitioner. To start my case study of my author most usefully, I would like to have him attempt a clear accounting for some of the key expressions he uses. Shakespeare said it in *King Lear,* "Mind your speech a little, lest it mar your fortune." Each of your key terms is highly individualized by you, is it not? Certainly, your writing does not remind me of any "neutral world of observed objects" or "objective world of scientific data." You realize that the objective scientist finds the meaning of consciousness to be a hindrance rather than a help and indeed has tried to repudiate it, or at least, to limit its importance to that of an epiphenomenon or even a superfluous verbalism. Thomas Hardy described as "ghastly" the sensation of one's soul seeming to shrink as his conception of "outerspace" widens.

Author. Just so! My style is as radically stylized as I am thus far able to make it, in the one direction of vigilant attention to my primary subject matter of my science of my psychology: my mind-forming, mind-healing, and mind-strengthening force of my self-consciousness. I aim to make myself *feel* my value.

General Practitioner. Trying to put my request in my author's way, I would like to live my examination of my patient-author by having him enounce a kind of glossary of his main hypotheses.

Author. Every conversationalist who has advanced himself thus far has, in my opinion, earned some right to consider himself hardy and able to finish. It pleases me to have him have his request fulfilled. "Genius," said Buffon, "is only a protracted patience." As might now be expected, I shall proceed with more description of self-consciousness, that is, reality-consciousness.

From most primitive sentience to most experienced self-awareness, consciousness demarcates and observes *now*-living of the given individual and thereby provides his only possibility of life appreciation, his self-significance or creaturehood meaning.

General Practitioner. You use the word "observes" often. Please define it, for it seems to me that you may be hiding behind it.

Author. Excellent. It is my intention to see myself, rather than hide, behind it. By "observe" I mean nothing but focus attention for, or restrict consciousness about. By "observation" I mean nothing but a conscious self-datum, a consciously lived self-experience. All of my observation is contained in my observing, itself. The observing *is* the observation.

General Practitioner. Well, the least I can notice is that you appear to have studied your subject. Please go on with your definitions. By the way, I want you first to distinguish a perception, hallucination, imagining, and memory, from one another. Will you please attempt that?

Author. Gladly. *I distinguish whatever I live simply by the way in which I live it.* The term "imagination" subsumes the activation of any of my mental power. I imagine each mental event in a way peculiar to it.

General Practitioner. Every mental distinction is made only on the basis of the way you live it, then? Your "awareness" for a datum means that datum consists only of your awareness?

Author. Yes. My supreme mental development, uniquely my own, is my marvelous imagination of *self-consciousness.* The way in which I use and care for this insight-providing "mind's eye" of mine decides the degrees of conscious freedom of my mental health. My "awareness" for my present living necessitates a new limit of my self-consciousness, an observed boundary providing no longer a conscious self-limit. *Self-conscious living entails the extension of self-conscious living, and is a prerequisite to the growth of self-insight.*[2] Self-unconscious living is always helpful, of course; but it is of life-saving importance to be able to have as much as possible unconscious mental content accessible for conscious living, should the occasion for its volitional use arise. Aversion to extending my power of self-consciousness began in my earliest mind-forming years, as a means of "forgetting" my painful personal living; then it hardened into a habit. As my unconscious living of myself augmented, conscious meaning for my life decreased. Only self-conscious living can round out the potentially marvelous meaning of every human life. Restriction of the zone of my life which I can call my own to cherish as such (be self-conscious about) accounts for *all* of my self-disesteem. Mental discomfort, even "embarrassment," cannot be traced to self-consciousness. As shall be repeated, if I am "embarrassed before an audience," it is on account of my inability to live my "audience" as my own (self-consciously). The purpose and content of the science of psychological medicine may be simply stated: the study and practice of acknowledged self-consciousness. Similarly, the purpose and content of psychopathology may be simply stated: the study and practice of (illusional) self-disregard.

General Practitioner. What, please, do you mean by your "mind"?

Author. My *mind* is the organization of my life force which is (all that is) active when I develop the *meaning* for my wonderful human being. That the mind *is* the man was a favored view of Aristotle. I find, at any rate, that it is my mind which I use in order to be able to take notice of my personal identity, to heed that which I term my "life." I define, or describe, my "mind" as my human agency comprised of all of my life activities (all of my personal experiences) which consist of *meaning.* Any psychological experience which I have consists of nothing but a modification of my mind. Healthy appreciation of my wonderful human being requires that I heed (notice, make conscious, keenly observe) the constant use of my mind in its operations. To illustrate: every sensation (or perception) which I can heed as being all and only a modification of my mind contributes to my mental strength and health.

General Practitioner. Please, what is your working definition of "meaning"?

Author. "Meaning" is the unit of mental life and, as such, merits special attention. Aristotle wisely stated, "The nature of everything is best seen in its smallest portions." Anything and everything which I live, having meaning, is mental. A working definition of "meaning" is: unified mental worth, usefulness of any mental experience. Meaning may be viewed as function itself. Meaning is the basic element, the unique essence, of the mind. Only meaning counts as mind, is an amount of mentality. The momentous significance, point and purpose, of any mental action, is its *meaning.* The thread of mental life consists of successive meanings. The meaning of any mental event is all there is to it.

General Practitioner. How do you describe "health"?

Author. I define *health* as the quality of being consciously whole (hale). It now becomes evident that by the words "mental health" I comprehend *the meaningful living of appreciated individuality.* My mental health is not a boon conferred upon me; it must be earned by my hard and steady work on understanding myself. "Meaningful living" produces successful self-development which is readily *esteemed* (consciously realized and valued for whose it is). "Successful living," to me, means living devotedly in the way that enables me to observe and revere the wonderfulness of human life. Emerson knew it: "Health is always private and original."

General Practitioner. What is your description of "adjustment"?

Author. I define *adjustment* to be a process of extending my hardihood, of compliantly fitting my conscious self-tolerance to whatever it is that I must live. My living consists entirely of my *growing* myself. By my "mental development" I mean the way in which I experience the ever new issues of my meaningful existence. My "adjusting" to my evolving mental life is my realizing my continuous personal existence as being in no sense adventitious. My ability to adjust my conscious measure of myself to fit my constant growth of myself, may be spoken of as my "power of adaptability." The "success" of my life adjustment favors my staying alive and growing self-consciously. My I is a growing I.

General Practitioner. What is "idealism"?

Author. All of my mental life is constituted of ideality.

General Practitioner. What is "materialism"?

Author. Repressed idealism—my necessary, but consciously disowned, ideality.

General Practitioner. What is "reality" besides: Whatever is, is *its own* meaning?

Author. Whatever is of an individual is real. His illusion is as real as is his any other existent or individuation. My reality is my mental content only. I have no reality or meaning which is not based upon the identity of my individuality.

General Practitioner. What is "psychotherapy"?

Author. Whatever is mental is psychotherapy. By *conscious psychotherapy* I mean the individual's treatment of his mental life by its own creating, healing, and strengthening power: self-consciousness.

General Practitioner. What does "growing mature" mean?

Author. My *growing mature* means: my being aware for the growth of me, my consciously *completing* myself in every personal development, my consciously realizing my potential. I define my mature mental health to be: my ability to call my mind my own and to see my mind's identity in all of my living of any *meaning.*

General Practitioner. As a scientist who quantifies, I would like to know your unit of mental health.

Author. My unit of mental health is: self-insight. "Self-insight" may be defined as: *conscious* self-knowledge. Loss of insight is loss of the wholesome use of my mind. Loss of my mind would result in my dead body, "The lifeless Lump uncoupled from the mind" (Dryden).

General Practitioner. Please try to bring your notions of "individual" together. Individuality is your stated only area of interest, and my discussion of your work must limit itself to what you state your work area to be.

Author. In his unfinished work, *Selina,* self-conscious Jean Paul Friedrich Richter observed:

> Our measurements of the rich territory of the Me are far too small or narrow when we omit the immense volume of the *unconscious,* this real interior Africa in every sense. . . . In the case of certain men we immediately survey the whole cultivated soul, even to the borderland marked by emptiness and sterility; but the kingdom of the *unconscious*, at once a kingdom of the unfathomable and the immeasurable, which possesses and rules every human mind, makes the barren rich and pushes back their boundaries into the invisible. . . . Is it not a consolatory thought, this concealed wealth in our soul?

Being an *individual,* I consist of nothing but of individuality. Therefore I *see* nothing else for me to write or read or talk about but this truth. This true self-look enables me to see myself as an end only to myself, hence, to see *my* fellow creature as an end only to himself. Thus, I can renounce my every temptation to live myself as a tool, as a means. Thus, I can renounce my every temptation to have my fellow-creature live himself as if he could be a tool of an (illusional) exploiter.

"Insight," pointedly acknowledging that I can only be looking in the direction of myself, is a specific function for my discriminating the several elements of my *individuality.* "Individuality" is a word which alludes to the fact that I have but *one* life to live, and that *all* that I experience can be nothing but a development of that one life. Without insight I cannot *see* that I, an individual, am doing all of *my* living. Insight is the one and only solvent of all "psychopathological" structures (delusions, illusions, hallucinations)—since *seeing* that a delusion is a delusion, or seeing that an illusion is an illusion, and so on, is the one requirement for dispelling (renouncing) it. Once any of my mental deviation is *seen* for what it is (namely, my own effort at self-help) it can no longer bother me as if it were an involuntary power over me. Instead, it becomes a harmonious element in my mind, humanely contributing to my full appreciation of myself.

Self-insight is a synonym for self-consciousness (appreciation of my identity), the mental modification which enlightens an area of my mind so that it can see itself for what it is, quickens an area of my mind so that it can feel itself for what it is, and frees an area of my mind so that it can act for what it is. I can create a mental view of myself acknowledging that I am a whole self; but as far as living self-consciously otherwise is concerned, I can do that only in a limited, piecemeal way. All of my self-consciousness is nothing but a mental modification occurring only at the surface of my mind. Nevertheless, it is my specific force in forming, healing (freeing), and strengthening all of my mind.

General Practitioner. What is the individual stuff of human consciousness? Is it self-sentience?

Author. Something like that. It is the irreducible stuff of all of my mental experience, or knowledge; the thrusting forth of life which produces meaning.

General Practitioner. Is self-consciousness just a specialized variety of consciousness?

Author. In the sense that it means an appreciation of being an individual—all, yes. However, in the broad sense, all consciousness can be nothing but its self-activity.

General Practitioner. How can I, as an objective scientist, discover something about the individual if it has no objective existence?

Author. The idea of an operation of an "objective" scientist which might discover subjectivity involves a contradiction. To illustrate, as an objective scientist you would distinguish a person's private from his public life. Your idea of making his private life public without modifying its privateness might be somewhat analogous to your trying "objectively" to investigate another's subjectivity.

General Practitioner. There is a system of psychology which works the principle that only observations made upon another are psychologically acceptable.

Author. I am sure that everyone of my fellowmen is the only one who can know what works best for him.

General Practitioner. You are educating your reader upon how to live healthfully, wholly, and happily, are you not?

Author. Not at all. I certainly cannot, and do not attempt to, recommend my way of life to my reader or to anyone else of my world. Indeed I must observe the contrary about my teaching: *You cannot do as I do or say.* My way of self-help is specific for me and it cannot apply to you. Even to try to apply *my* life-orientation to yourself must be an instance of your trying to hypnotize yourself, as I see it. Only your present way of life, your current self-education, *can be* the foundation for your further self-education. If, from your living of *your* author's describing his self-orientation, you wish to try any living of that kind of helpfulness on your own as an individual—that conscious self-activity can be wholesome educational living.

General Practitioner. What is your definition of "life"?

Author. Whenever I attempt to describe my *life* (the only life about which I can make any observation at all) I suffer the shortcomings of the part vainly striving to describe another part. My *whole* life is never observing. All of my "observed" living is made up of my observing, itself. The "I," or living subject, *observing,* can only be a minute part of the whole "I"; and the "me," or living self, *observed,* can only be a minute part of the observing "I." My ability to describe the meaning of life is limited by my ignorance of the meaning of death, of not-life. That my life is far more than I can appreciate, I can readily allow.

My words enable me to undertake a scientific study of my individuality, to develop a science of my mental life. By a process of naming my mind's elements, I enable my mind's eye to visualize, and place, its mental functioning exactly where it is taking place, *in itself.* The dictionary is the "accepted" word (or definition) authority, and it is well to be consciously mindful that its "accepted" authority is no more reliably honest than usage. For instance, no word-user has ever enforced the "law of parsimony" to the extent of wording all of his individuality as his own. Yet the range of each and every scientist's mind is the range of his verifiable.

General Practitioner. How do you conceive the most efficient working of the mind?

Author. That mind enjoys the healthiest running order which notices all of its activity as being its own, and, hence, allocates its every element (sensation, perception, idea, meaning, or whatever it might be) to its own *self*-order. The mental athlete devotes himself to this scientific, accurate kind of life accounting. In honor there is health. An honored self is a healthy self. Carefully heeded self-growth honors personal experience and glorifies the meaning of life in a life of wonderful meaning.

General Practitioner. Is there a natural aversion to the mental health ideal: Consciously Know Thyself? Otherwise, how can I reconcile the truth of its helpfulness with the rarity with which it is either practiced or "prescribed"?

Author. This line of questioning discloses the fact that everyone learns to speak his mind, put his mind to words, with a degree of self-consciousness which he finds acceptable *for the living of his loved, or loving, ones.* One who is working at understanding his life from the illusional end, "objectivity," and whose self-acceptance is contingent upon his belief that he is accepted by his colleagues, can hardly understand the orientation of subjectivity.

General Practitioner. Is that why you never argue, namely, on account of your realization that *your* worthy discussant is approaching his understanding of himself "from the other end" (that of objective research)?

Author. Exactly. Everyone is doctoring his mind in one way which he finds works for him. I have found that my longing for "agreement" is always traceable to my inability to live with conviction whatever I wish agreement upon. My every need for "followers" is likewise traceable to my limitations in being my own disciple. When my auditor questions or criticizes or protests, I approve of each of his individualistic expressions as being an instance of the principle I uphold (conscious self-orientation) and am too pleased about his illustrating his independence to feel like arguing with him about it.

General Practitioner. This explanation of yours seems to be of greatest value in accounting for your peaceful living of your fellowman, even while he may be denouncing (his) you. Why have you not stated it before?

Author. Like every question, I find this one an excellent one as I pose it to myself. The reply which comes to me is that this explanation is implicit in every statement of my individuality position. However, I am pleased that my speaking it out is particularly practical.

General Practitioner. Can you prove very active in a symposium if you just sit and voice no opposition?

Author. Each member of my symposium is an individual treating his mind in the only way he presently can, and that is as much as I can lay claim to as my position.

My Freud focused attention upon the grievous error prevalent in psychological and philosophical work, namely, that an unappreciated (self-unconscious) mind is capable of immediate intuitive realization that its own modifications account for all of its activity, for its every meaning. As a self-help, he demonstrated the necessity for, and efficacy of, his mental discipline: the systematic study and practice of conscious individual living, of personal identity. Haste to classify living experiences as other than personal events annihilates the evidence of the lovable truth of individuality.

Even without such formalized training, every human being attains his own preferred range of acknowledged self-tolerance, capacious enough to permit his "getting along in life without going to too much trouble." Human conduct is the operation of self-knowledge which may be either conscious or unconscious. However, every limitation upon the conscious cultivation of self-tolerance imposes a corresponding zone of restricted appreciation of personal living. Repugnance to assuming the unpleasant living required by any effort to increase self-tolerance is so distressing that one tends to settle for a short measure of his *acknowledged* personal identity. This limited view of his life cannot excite his true and proper sense of (full) self-value.

There is but one "sin" and but one "sickness"—each a misnomer for a holy and a healthy effort to help oneself. I refer specifically to the "sin," or "sickness," inherent in the illusion of "separation." My helpful feeling of sin, or sickness, is my reminder that I am denying (separating my sense of personal identity from) my whole divinity. My unhappiness is my pained love.

General Practitioner. B. Brinton records: "The expression in the Algonkin tongue for a person of the same name is *nind owiawina,* 'He is another myself.' "[3] Cassirer suggested the possibility that without a name primitive man tends to lose consciousness of his distinctiveness as a personality.

Author. The extent to which my language decides my thinking is so great that it would seem to do my thinking for me, if I would allow it.

General Practitioner. Carlyle wrote Emerson, "A pen is a pen, and expresses something; though it expresses about as much of a *man's* meaning perhaps as the stamping of a hoof will express of a horse's meaning; a very poor expression indeed!" Please egotize on that with your undoctrinaire spirit of self-examination. Obviously your science of psychology is based only upon introspection. You would extol your devotion to insight as sane piety. Your reduction of all life trouble to unhappiness, "pained love" I think you call it, reminds me of Robert Burton's similar reduction over three hundred years ago. I refer to his *Anatomy of Melancholy.*

Author. Yes. I shall try to practice greater self-consciousness in this paragraph, using my meanings as recognized organs of my own which reveal my self-power. The specific sign that I am denying my possession of some part of my own living is: unhappiness. To illustrate, the unhappy feeling of guilt marks the spot where I am unable to support the feeling of personal responsibility about the function of any substantiality of my human being. Hence,

I must conduct a guilt-ridden existence to the extent that I disown my personal responsibility for any of my own (individual) life. "Tribulation" derives from the Latin *tribulum,* a threshing sledge used to eliminate pure grain from impurities. My living myself as if I could be a compound of self and not-self introduces tribulation as my appeal to myself to attend to the wholeness of my life. I am always tempted to try to triumph over my depression rather than to study the lesson of wholeness of life which it teaches. Therefore, I may succeed in distracting my attention from my depression to indulge only my feeling of elation, deluding myself that I have "cured myself" of my depression. I can distract my awareness from my painful feeling of guilt (from my sensing myself as a wrong-doer in that I view any living of my life as not mine), but I thereby lose track of the precious sign (unhappiness) that I am restricting my ability to own up to the truth of my wholeness. I cannot exercise humane care about any of my life which I cannot recognize as mine, that is, live with the appreciation of its thorough subjectivity. Then I practice the therapy of grief. For me, genius is but a large consciousness of one's manpower.

Wherever there is painful living, there the presence of consciousness is fearful, for consciousness discloses pain, quite as disregard conceals it. A child fears having his tooth examined, for the examination reveals the pain which properly signalizes the need for care.

For the practical purpose of health (appreciation of my allness) it is essential that I grow the mental endurance permitting me to acknowledge, weather, and use my life's experiences, however trying they may be, rather than to resort to amnesia for them.

As every student of his mind knows, each "relative," *subject* or *object,* designates a most important traditional mental distinction. Since each constitutes most fundamental philosophical and psychological language, it is a major scientific requirement that each term be used accurately. To illustrate, disregard for the fact that the terms "object" and "objective" are nothing but subjective meanings of a given mind, can account for all of the phantom problems (of "not-self", of "externality") of that mind.[4] Whenever I do not take notice of the fact that my mind is my one and only author of my every mental experience, right then and there I make mental trouble for myself. *Only consciousness noticed as self-possession can accurately observe the sphere of selfhood.* Therefore, with minimal distraction, I now attempt to focus upon the health and happiness benefits of life-consciousness. Nothing can be of greater practicality than mental freedom. Nothing can bring greater life enjoyment than free mental life consciously cultivated.

General Practitioner. But how is free mental life cultivated for enjoyment?

Author. Each one must ask and answer this question for himself. I found that I had to begin to conceive myself as a poet or as a parrot. I. A. Richards keenly observed, "The full exercise of an activity is commonly its own 'satisfaction.'" Habit of disuse creates inhibition of function. He wisely noted, "The poet makes unconsciously a selection which outwits the force of habit; the impulses he awakens are freed through the very means by which they are aroused, from the inhibitions that ordinary circumstances encourage."[5]

My systematic practice of self-insight is required to free me from viewing myself as a tool developed for the sake of something "outside of myself." Devotion to the work of extending my consciousness for my life is necessary to affirm my realization of my life as being an end unto myself. Than either of these personal perfections there can be no greater, except the all-meaningful success of being alive itself. Insight, mental vision, is not the same as believing. Rather, only insight can reveal each belief as a convincing kind of self-acceptance.

Mental health is the product of *acknowledged* self-perception and self-observation—not a product of logic or judgment. My task is not that of "making my life my own," only that of seeing that it is my own. Emerson wrote Carlyle of *Sartor Resartus,* "I am glad that one living scholar is self-centered, and will be true to himself though no one ever were before; who, as Montaigne says, 'puts his ear close by himself, and holds his breath and listens.'" *Once I begin to conceive any of my living as not-mine I introduce the necessity to posit some kind of material besides my own acknowledged self-content.* Thus I give birth to my illusion of "materialism," including "objectivity," and develop a correspondingly weak affirmation of my wonderful wholeness.

(My) A. G. Keller remarked, "One of the warning signs for the student of human society is: 'Beware Of Logic.' " David Hume described reasoning as being "the slave of the passions." Judgment and logic are processes of thinking, of creating affirmations, recognized (positive) and unrecognized (negative). The whole process of thorough awakening from the deepest sleep, however, is entirely a succession of graduating adjustments of one's self-scope: of continuously extending one's self-comprehension and, thereby, tolerantly enlarging one's self-appreciation until it embraces all of one's world. Fully free mental health would be the cherished attainment of the person who had thus *worked* at discovering how all-inclusive he is. My mind's active freedom (imaginative power) is in direct proportion to its tolerance (insight).

General Practitioner. Possibly I may tend to be complaining about my Author. Or, do you mind my complaining?

Author. Freedom to complain is a helpful power which is rarely acknowledged as such. Indeed it is, itself, most complained about. It is as natural, proper, healthful to complain (including cry) when self-endurance is stretched too far, as it is to smile when happy. Voicing a protest against over-exertion is a safeguard against having to express the same complaint by means of a headache, high blood pressure, or some other even more painful cry for help. Free ability to complain about my life dissatisfactions is a wonderful health protector. Indeed, in my world everyone lives himself more or less desperately, and to that extent he frequently needs to complain. Through my allowing myself to complain I finally realized that I was not listening to myself complain and, hence, did nothing to relieve or spare my complaints. What a day when a man first learns (1) that he can talk only to himself and (2) that only he can hear, or listen to, himself! May complaint be undisguised and unrestrained so that it can function most wholesomely!

Sincerity is a unifying force. In all sincerity, "complaining" is a natural (necessary) experience on the road to increasing self-endurance. Therefore, it is but truthfully practical to complain. Once this protest is clearly recognizable for all that it *can* be, namely, a reporting of distress of one's self to one's self then, it can be lived with wholesome dignity and contribute to consciously self-helpful (morale-based) peace of mind.

Jefferson stated prudently, "Nature has constituted *utility* to man the standard and test of virtue." I find it practical to observe this complaint: In all of my experience I have never been able to cultivate my sense of self-reliance by any kind, or quantity, of "communicated" teaching. Rather, all such "education" based upon the illusion of "communication" (in every instance of my living it), has proved itself to be a demoralizing way of my helping myself. The term "inculcation" is especially disregardful of learning as being self-revelation, since it means literally "grind in with the heel."

To (my) Thomas Carlyle is accorded the distinction of creating a term of greatest usefulness: *self-help.* The law of mental health requires a person's helping himself to adjust his view of his selfhood (his "self-concept") so that it applies accurately to the extent to which he is actually growing himself. *Everyone's self-growth is a silent process which must escape notice to the extent that it is not carefully heeded.* Only the person who helps himself by carefully and caringly exercising his consciousness of his living can achieve the deep, calm life satisfaction healthfully attributable to life.

General Practitioner. Do you object to efforts to correct injustice, to criticize deplorable conditions?

Author. Helpfulness takes protean forms, even these you describe. I have learned the truth that self-deception and dishonesty to one person can be utmost sincerity and honesty to another.

General Practitioner. I do not care to quibble with words. Please unify the meanings of science and mental health again.

Author. All of my meaning for "mental health" is produced only by my self-conscious knowledge, that is, by knowledge recognized as consisting entirely of my very own experience (life). The purest culture of science in its most elemental form may be defined as conscious self-observation. In the sense that science is "organized knowledge," it is bred of personal experience, and is most helpfully viewed as consciously self-possessed organized knowledge. May it now become apparent that the scientific knowledge which is of the most practical worth is: *conscious* self-knowledge.

General Practitioner. Supposing it is true that mental health can be founded only upon consciously recognized self-knowledge, how can I start seeing all of my knowledge as my own living of it? How can I give up my dependence upon "authorities" and their fearsome superiority? How can I learn to see that all of my conversation is my mind's dialog with itself? How can I learn how to change my view of my mind to correspond with the ever new growth which it actually is? How can I restore to my often seeming monotonous existence its true meaning of creative power? How can I develop a habit of mind which makes it natural for me to live my experience of *my* home, school, hospital, or "environment" of every kind, as entirely my own personal living?

Author. How fitting it is for the conscious development of self-possession and self-reliance that one cannot answer another's questions! How insightful Goethe's Egmont, "If I were a somnambulist and walked on a ridge pole, would it be friendly to call me by name to warn me, and thus to awaken and kill me? Let each man go his own way and take care of himself." I feel *inside of me* whatever meaning I create when I have my fellow-man speak (to his self).

General Practitioner. Well, just go ahead talking of yourself to yourself and how you try to grow insight. I am realizing that you get a thrill out of sensing your selfness where you never did before. I see one cannot realize another's nature.

Author. Insight begins in despairing of insightless living. I have found that there is much wisdom in the old adage: Where there is a will there is a way. What I live as spirit grows recognizable spirituality. I have discovered that my strong wish to accomplish a task is essential for my applying myself to that task. Furthermore, my experiencing the keen desire and strong intention to live myself in a given way—*that* already counts as beginning to live myself that way. As (my) Lowell noticed his reality,

The thing we long for; that we are
For one transcendent moment.

General Practitioner. Walter Kaufmann described Rilke's reality somewhat as you do yours, maybe, "For Rilke reality is a call to perceive—but to perceive as has never been perceived before—and to transform, to create our own world, which is essentially new." Kaufmann adds that "otherworldliness slights the power of man."[6] I seem to see truth in other people's greatness, but how do I learn to see that *my* "other one" is mine? By keeping on trying?

Author. That is what I do. Another rich discovery of mine has revealed: greatest goals and highest attainments are achieved by a succession of even the littlest individual efforts. For instance, every time I am able to say to myself sincerely (of any event of my life), "It is I," I am employing the only means for my developing my due sense of self-possession. *I know of no sorrier human plight than a man's lacking the power to find his meanings in himself.*

Integrated by my unifying feeling of sincerity and supported by my right sense of self-possession, I enable myself to see that even my views of my "heredity" and of my "environment" are made up of my own mental materials. Quite as free mental health enables me to see how wonderful I am, so my seeing my true wonderfulness in all of my living contributes to my free mental health.

From all of this concentration upon mental health as being the fruit of *recognized* self-greatness, the produce of fitting devotion to life, may it become clear that human individuality is the one and only mental health workship. Reverence for the dignity of human individuality is duly recognized in the religious ideal ("sacred integrity of the soul"), in the basis of medical practice ("respect for the individual variant"), and in every American's governmental principle ("rights of man").

Continuous self-consciousness (ongoing self-identity) is the specific kind of health education to which the least self-conscious person is the most averse. For instance, my sociologist finds that the most primitive man is the most conservative when it comes to cultivating his capacity for self-consciousness. The neglected child craves attention and, without helping himself to see that such "attention" is a succedaneum for self-consciousness, grows into a man who craves "distinction." Insofar as I require praise I lack conscious self-respect. Desiderated self-consciousness is the most widespread and most troublesome of all so-called "deficiency diseases." A prophet cannot be without honor save in his own mind. The greater the self-insight, the greater the life of health and the greater the urge to keep the peace. However, as my supremely self-conscious Shakespeare recorded (*Love's Labour's Lost,* I, i):

> Small have continual plodders ever won
> Save base authority from others' books.

As my most trustworthy means for measuring how much self-knowledge my fellowman has *consciously* cultivated, I observe how much his language (speaking, writing, listening, and reading) appears to be devoted consistently to self-insight. Can he see that his every word is a memorandum of a mental modification? *Conscious* self-knowledge evacuates every pretense of knowledge of "somebody else" (or "something else"). In all of my experience I have never found a more *practical* life view.

General Practitioner. In your devotion to your epistemological idealism you encounter the problem called the "ego-centric predicament" (Ralph Barton Perry). You cannot get outside of your own experience. How about that?

Author. As I have already indicated, I create a problem for myself when I live *as if* I can get outside of my own experience.

General Practitioner. Are you not aware that solipsism is a point of view which has not been held by any school of philosophers or by any outstanding philosopher? Solipsism is generally conceded to be the *reductio ad absurdum* of subjectivism.

Author. Solipsism, by definition, *cannot* be a point of view of any "school of philosophers," or of any "outstanding" philosopher. Understanding of the solipsistic orientation of mind would preclude the expectation that it could be the philosophy of anyone but the radical individualist whose every "school of philosophers" and "outstanding philosopher" are nothing but creations of his own imagination. However, I do not deem even such wishful expectations to be "absurd," for they do defend the individual against overwhelming himself with the view of his allness, until he can see its usefulness. My being conscious that I am conscious (self-consciousness) is a power which, more than any other, distinctifies the nature of my existence for me as I develop from potentiality to actuality. Research on the *allness* nature of individual man deserves first priority in my world, for its findings are prerequisites for human survival.

General Practitioner. Please discuss "consciousness" again.

Author. Most important of all, "consciousness" is only a word. It is all and only about itself. As a term, it denotes the power of observation described as "inward beholding" of one's being. It supports the sensing of one's existence and is essential for the recognition of the allness meaning of one's individuality. I find that I either live self-consciously, that is, with the appreciation that I am living my life, or that I live without bethinking myself of my omnipresence. In the latter way of living, my mind is overwhelmed, embarrassed with my life experience which I cannot recognize by means of my available sense of personal identity. I regain my mental equilibrium, renounce the pose of "not-I" for the poise of "I," as soon as I can feel equal to comprehending myself as the creator of whatever I live.

General Practitioner. How can you be so sure about consciousness meaning the selfness of selfness, about awareness meaning your sensing your existence, about wakefulness meaning your noticing your creaturehood, about self-observation meaning your experiencing your acknowledged living of your individuality? You are aware are you not, that Jean-Paul Sartre attributed a negative character to consciousness, that he claimed consciousness involves self-awareness, yet denies being that immediate awareness? As may Sartre, so may I, escape from solipsism simply by positing *the* "other" and avoiding positing *my* "other." I can objectify "the other" simply by denying *I* am positing it.

Author. Yes, I have studied the ways my Sartre has described the workings of his own being. What can his writings be but his verbal account of the operations of his own mind? For me, the exercise of self-consciousness provides an indispensable practical advantage of nourishing and healing my mind. It is always difficult to apply when I need it, but whenever I can apply it, it works wonders in elucidation and relief from tension. On organic action of my individuality all of my life's meanings depend. My every mental process is my expedient for conducting my life process. My health is more than just my power to resist overwhelming ways of living; it includes my power of freedom to live whatever I do live with insightful appreciation of my wholeness.[7]

General Practitioner. Nearly every philosophy textbook I read treats the topic of solipsism both briefly and with rejection, and then goes on to use the self-allness orientation as if unaware of the inconsistency. I suppose such uniformity of repression speaks in its favor, does it not? For example, Bertrand Russell in one place writes critically of one "shut up in a solipsistic world, and ignorant of everything except his own mental states and their relations," and in another offers the profound insight, seemingly based upon the appreciation of the allness of individuality, "Any event, and any group of events, is logically capable of standing alone, and therefore no group of events affords *demonstrative* proof of the existence of other events."[8]

Even a dictionary may omit the term "solipsism," or deprecate its "one-sidedness," or describe it as "an over-emphasis of mind," or as "unvarnished egoism." Sometimes references are made to the possibility that solipsism is of the nature of insanity. For example, did not Eduard von Hartmann, admirer of Max Stirner, and Max Stirner himself, the classic solipsist, each commit suicide? Did not Nietzsche, another Stirner supporter, go insane? And so on.

Author. Yes. Everyone who puts forth the effort to extend his conscious self-tolerance (to include his mental content which he once helpfully disowned as being unsafe, undesirable, too disturbing, and the like) may cope with the feeling that he is "losing his mind" while he is finding it. The expression "going to pieces" may accurately describe my "picking up the pieces" which I must reclaim if I would restore myself to appreciation of my full allness, wholeness, and unity.

The key to the solipsistic life orientation is the recognition of the necessity to love all of one's living, and that recognition is achieved by seeing that every feeling which seems to be other than love is really a modification of love. I am reminded of Anna Hempstead Branch's unifying lines,

> Once I thought to find on earth
> Love, perfect and complete.
> Now I know it carries wounds
> In its hands and feet.

I now see that I must acknowledge my solipsistic living, once I renounce my illusion of separation.

I can see also that my efforts to make conscious my unconscious mind must confront me with the strangeness, fearfulness, guilt, and all of the other experiences I have always associated with "insanity." My self-unifying work is to see my sanity in my so-called "insanity," to see the usefulness of all of my living which formerly I could only overwhelm and demoralize myself with.

Unifying myself with my consciousness is my daily, hourly, momentary source of upkeep for my sense of personal identity. In *The Art of Creation* (1904), Edward Carpenter soliloquized,

> This form of Consciousness is the only true knowledge—it is the only true existence. And it is a matter of experience; it has been testified to in all parts of the world and in all stages of history. There is a consciousness in which the subject and object are felt, are *known*, to be united and one—in which the Self is felt to *be* the object perceived ("I *am* the hounded slave") or at least in which the subject and the object are felt to be parts of the same being, of the same including Self of all. And it is the only true knowledge.

General Practitioner. Josef Goldbrunner writes plainly, "The person is the beginning and end of all the expressions of life," and "The 'core of the person' is as it were the interior of the self." He adds,

> As a personal being man is confronted with a task. It is his task to realize his existence. To do this it is necessary that he should wake up to his real nature, be wrenched out of the security and solidity of his everyday routine and attain to his own reality.[9]

4

Medical Studies

The true and lawful goal of the sciences is none other than this: that human life be endowed with new discoveries and powers.
FRANCIS BACON, *Novum Organum*

Author. SELF-CONSCIOUS STUDY is the one and only way for the student to put his soul into his living of his medical discipline. Living is the one and only possible "action," the diversity in its unity consisting of many directions of being. Greatest practicality lies in recognizing this one and only humane basis for one's profession of medicine in its earliest beginnings, in basic medical sciences. Observing the learning of anatomy or physiology or biochemistry as a specific instance of self-development not only occasions a deepening of each student's speculative insight but also presents his life lesson in its most useful form.

Oliver Wendell Holmes stated that medicine learned "from a Jesuit how to cure agues, from a friar how to cut for the stone, from a soldier how to treat gout, from a sailor how to keep off scurvy, from a postmaster how to sound the Eustachian tube, from a dairymaid how to prevent smallpox, and from an old market-woman how to catch the itch-insect." By "medicine" he meant everyone's medical living.

Medical Student. You seem to reduce all words to "I" and all numbers to "one." Your idea of radical individualism wakes just about all of my feelings of mental pain, which you have claimed gradually accomplished denial of the existence of the thought associated with the unpleasant feeling.

Author. My attempt to secure an accurate comprehension of individuality is necessarily radical, but peaceful. I certainly do not intend it as a revolt against the established idea of individuality. The established conception of individual man is wonderful as far as it goes. My mental constitution provides for appreciation of that too.

New England transcendentalist Cyrus A. Bartol recorded,

> When Schiller complains that a lecturer had shown Nature not in her unity, but in specimens and bits, Goethe eagerly expounds to him that unity in the metamorphosis of plants, each portion as a transformed leaf. Schiller replies, that this is not an observation but an idea. Goethe rejoins, that he is glad to have eyes to behold such ideas in nature. He says, "When I look, I see all there is." So he saw the topmost vertebra expanding into the skull, and the seven colors as mixtures of light and shade. Schiller did not consider that we can see, with eyes, only what the frame of nature tends to.

My mental process extends *itself* in each sensory organ, and may begin in it. What I do not make myself ready (by means of making up my mind to it) to sense or perceive I simply cannot sense or perceive. Every psychological process is one which involves the whole mind.

Medical Student. I am discovering that reaching my proper understanding of the shape my mind is in due to the experiences it has lived (in other words, my understanding of my psychology) would be my most valuable medical and pre-medical educational accomplishment. I am now appreciating some of this conscious-individuality business.

Author. Insightful Socrates claimed that the best flavoring for drink is thirst. Stephen Paget forcefully records his views upon the importance of psychological medicine in his *Confessio Medici* (1908):

> I believe that many students, by a loose and off-hand notion of Psychology, do themselves more harm than good, and go into practice believing what is not true. Illogical talk drifts, like a mist, through Hospital life, all tending to deny that the word Psyche means anything. I hate that sort of talk.

That any medical student possesses the power of growing insight is the healthiest appreciation of his psychology that he can possibly grow. I find it, though, to be the rule that a freshman medical student already looks upon his capacity for self-consciousness as a fixed quantity incapable of increase. His introducing himself to the realization that conscious self-knowledge is his most precious health possession, first leads him to considering the possibility that he might augment it. The unrelenting principle of inviolable individuality, with which he first tends to overwhelm himself (to the extent that he is unable to live its full meaning with self-composure), later on in his freshman year of life proves to be a needed kind of medicine with which he can mobilize his self-interests and summon his most useful directive force.

My own most satisfying medical school living as a "teacher" consisted of the gratifying personal experience of having my medical student discover his capacity for self-help in this all-important matter of his animating his insight (self-consciousness). It now seems that any and every appreciation of my success as a "teacher" of medicine was traceable to my living my medical student during his cultivating his conscious devotion to extending the limits of his acknowledged self-tolerance.

Medical Student. How would you go about "screening" the applicant to a medical school?

Author. I would use most of the devices now in force but would make sure of one of greatest meaning: insightful, expert, painstaking effort to estimate each applicant's (1) possession of self-insight and (2) capacity for development of insight. I regard each of these qualifications as *essential.* Only the applicant who would be clearly appreciative of the importance of his sincere devotion to this truth, that his learning is his living, would qualify in this regard. Throughout his undergraduate medical living I would have every student, as a requirement of his continuing qualification for medical study, examine his steadfastness to his ideal of self-conscious living.

Medical Student. In a most general sense what should a medical student learn or, in your terms, become, after four years of medical study?

Author. His chief growth of self-knowledge might be designated: his lesson of his *life,* his discovery of the wonderfulness and allness of his own living. Ancillary to that growth of self-insight, he must cultivate technical skills which enable him to avoid and recover from the numerous health ordeals he may expect to work with in his medical experience. His medical education falls short of its ideal meaning unless it includes in each discipline and at each unit of study his active realization that it is all and only his own growing of himself, his own carefully planned, elected, and studied self-origination.

The fact that every medical student needs to help himself to recognize his medical study as being nothing but a cultivation of the powers of his personality, a generation of his inner life, has been the one essential fact underlying my teaching of psychological medicine. The alternative to my student's finding out that the whole wonderful curriculum of his medical work is wholly and solely a system of ideas lived by himself has been and remains very painful to consider. In brief, it means my medical student's growing his medical living as if it were possible for it (him) to be "out of his mind." Distressing as it might appear to be for my freshman medical student to make himself conscious of the fact that his living of his cadaver is entirely a matter of his own living, his passing from unconsciousness to consciousness concerning that truth is nothing but a strengthening and healing exercise of his mind and an activation of the mental process by which he grows himself a profound, rather than a shallow, mentality.[1]

Whether or not my medical student conceals his conceit in his rejected selfness (which he feels he may then flamboyantly reveal in the disguise of "the great medical authority" or "the great college of medicine") is not safely disposable as being impractical speculation. It is indeed a matter of the greatest health significance that he habituate himself to a life of sincere self-esteem.

Medical Educator. Please discuss this "force of habit of mind" as it relates to a medical student's efforts to give up his lifelong illusion of externality, an illusion shared by his beloved parents.

Author. Renunciation of this habit of mind necessitating restricted self-esteem is associated with withdrawal symptoms, quite as is the renunciation of any other addiction. It is hardly expectable therefore that my beginning medical student will take to the stretching of his self-consciousness, the extension of his self-insight, as a "duck to water." He will naturally attempt to spare himself such growing pains by resort to various kinds of arguments, and to this end will parade his own resistance in the name of every kind of philosophical system in his effort to maintain the *status quo* of his self-insight. When hard pressed to live his medical psychology as a mental discipline requiring his producing additional self-insight, one of his first defenses is to try to shelve it as a "doctrine of creative evolution," "philosophy of solipsism," "theory of personalism," "theory of existentialism," "psychologizing of subjective monism," and so on and on. However, it is beneficial for my medical student to reject the whole idea of the health significance of self-insight rather than never to have considered it at all. Rejection itself is a degree of knowing, and a regular beginning of a new acceptance.

Medical Student. I have always considered that the physician's work consisted chiefly of discovering new remedies and of applying them from without. Maybe that idea is based on the assumption that, at least during health trouble, the patient cannot be expected to try to use his mind in new hygienic ways involving the cultivation of his self-consciousness.

Author. I grow in the direction, and to the level, of my devotion. What I concentrate my mind upon—that I grow, or become. My exertion to modify my consciousness for myself will make the greatest sense to me when pain or sorrow naturally makes me concentrate consciously upon my own life. Medical treatment, to be truly scientific, must utilize self-resources hitherto slumbering, for vitality can only be invigorated by and within each patient. A patient's devotion to his working up of his practical and ideal self-consciousness as his powerful medical treatment is now being tried for its medical potency and found curative. Rare is the patient who is not sadly mistaken in his own identity, given to false consciousness which does not report selfness, and afraid of his body as having the power to dispose of his creaturehood.

Medical Student. Your observations sound as if they are based upon personal experience. I presume that you see all that you are describing as being in the only place where it can be, for you—in yourself.

Author. A helpful reminder is always welcomed living.

Medical Student. Suppose that I do suddenly recognize that I have neither studied the law of my own mind nor obeyed what little law of it I do know. I cannot change habits of a lifetime and start arbitrarily viewing myself as my all and see myself as nothing but my own everybody and everything. At least I'm enthralled by my devotion to my life as I have so far learned to live it.

Author. I am undertaking only to relate what I find to be of the utmost utility and practicality for me. My attaining this life appreciation has been most difficult, and it has involved exactly the kind of hard work long continued which you describe. I have had to renounce habits of a lifetime. However, every bit of this work has seemed most worthwhile. Every self-discovery lured me more meaningfully to my ideal truth of the wonderful allness of my individuality, to the truth of my innocence and the innocence of my fellowman.

Medical Student. What does "innocence" have to do with it?

Author. Living under a sense of wrongdoing (in overlooking my own allness), I suffered the helpful sense of guilt and could not enjoy access to the truth of my peaceful innocence.

The pleasure of growing self-knowledge consciously (the basic happiness in living the principle of self-identity, the joy of self-recognition) provides the most vital personal experience of all. The immediate and indubitable living of conscious self-knowledge alone has made my medical student sure of himself, an ideal realist. Such advantageous living has a compelling self-interest in it. Once my medical student found himself on the track of living himself consciously, he lived his basic science by elevating "explanation" to a *lively* body of abstractions and substantial formulas which gave a real account of his own world. His personal experiences of his basic science were recognizable as felt connections of his conscious self. As he grew his self-insight, instead of fearing his selfishness on account of its narrowness, he enjoyed it on account of its potential scope, which comprehended his all. In proportion to the growth of his insight, he valued for his fellowman the five characteristics of self-conscious living: cherished individualism, prized independence, free innocence, appreciated self-development, and peace for his self-world.

In using his medical education as a self-emancipation, each

student observes that his basic science, too, consists of "thought substance," of his own mind's living (of it.) His declaration of medical independence is inherent in his seeing all of his medical training as conscious self-development. Soon he notices the perfect correlation of his increasing self-consciousness and his increasing volition. He needs each access of will power to apply himself, to work himself in immediately useful directions. With self-consciousness go self-trust, self-reliance, self-direction. Conversely, the extent of his self-unconsciousness decides the extent of his involuntary living of himself. As the meaning of the science of himself becomes clear and strong, due to his own purposeful efforts to clarify and strengthen it, each student discovers that he *knows how* to promote his own health, that he *is* self-helpful. *Finding that every element of his world is fashioned through the raw materials of his own mind is the process essential for every medical student's development of his proper sense of self-esteem.* The practice of this function of self-finding piles up health.

Medical Student. It is understandable that this new and obviously simple truth (of learning the law of self-help) has been so long delayed. Everyone is not only unready to see it but also addicted to looking away from it. What *is* already medical curriculum occupies all of the space, particularly as far as an apparent intruder is concerned. What is there in established teaching which does not rebel against such requirements as: linguistics nothing but self-wording! no "external" authority or anything else! development only of innate self-knowledge about the student's human system! living mental action rather than sleeping indoctrination! self-consciousness and no system of philosophy! personal ideals as the only real materials! intuition the only form of intellect! enthusiasm based only upon the joy of living! imagination the only use of the senses! affective living only of self-love and its vicissitudes! perfection the only value! life force only! all creativity nothing but soul-forging! selfhood the only divinity! individuality the only reality! self-insight the only sanity! now the only time! here the only place! Who can sustain such soothing self-love? I say to myself.

Author. Dr. Henry Krystal of Detroit has spoken and written of the practical benefit in one's personally identifying his cruel fellowman as being his own. As my Nietzsche has stated it, "Let your kindness be your final self-conquest." My ancient Aristotle pointed out, "The good man should be a lover of self (for he will both himself profit by doing noble acts, and will benefit his fellows)." And of the one who gratifies the most authoritative element in himself and in all things obeys it in its upholding what is noblest and best, he adds that this one is "most of all a lover of self."

Being an expert of any kind is a matter of being an expert on mental processes, one's own to be sure. The entire content of his medical training is a creation of each medical student's mind. There is no "real thing" except insofar as it is lived by him. *Finding that all of his reality is a construct made up entirely by his own living of it provides the medical student with his most efficacious insight in his growing of himself as a physician.* This kind of comprehensive view of his individuality enables him to appreciate the comprehensiveness of the individuality of his patient. It spares him the necessity of a medical living which is self-discouraging. It reveals to him *as his own* his Hippocratic insight of self-help. In place of a constantly increasing, disheartening self-repudiation, it puts his very own enheartening world of actuality of himself: first his life, then its mind, and then self-growth.

Every "office call" or "bedside consultation" is a place of the physician's mind, and an occasion for most careful self-growth accompanied by self-insight. Most precious health benefit attends this orientation. *Every patient has his greatest opportunity for saving his life by means of a living of a physician who is fully conscious of the preciousness of his own living, and who therefore identifies "diagnosis" with his patient's finding out the nature of his health ordeal, and identifies "treatment" with his patient's modifying his life according to the indications of his symptoms.*

Medical Student. One thing new and good in what you say is your flair for accepting responsibility for your fellowman's disagreeing with you. But then, as you already said, a prophet is not without honor, save in his own life if he does not produce it there.

Author. As Goethe put it, "If I love you, what concern is that of yours?"

Medical Educator. I cannot but object to your manner of expression; it is so peremptory. You are, it seems to me, evading the number one question: What is there that is *practical* about this theory of self-sufficiency for every *practicing* physician? It's all right for giving a talk, but how useful is it otherwise?

Author. The very *practicality* of self-insight constitutes its specific strength. The power of self-ignoration is the power of darkness. The realization of this truth is not the product of a "liberal education," any more than it is the product of losing one's way in an "off the campus" world. It cannot be found in a college curriculum, general practice, set of great books, or army of educational authority. It is, and can be, only the extension of conscious, self-nurtured development of individual human being. Nothing can be transmitted from one individual to another. Any educational system based upon such an obviously false system of psychology can continue only as a successful failure. *The healthy life of the physician renounces the freezing illusion of getting other people well, in favor of the more pleasing view of his seeing each one of his patients able to help himself specifically by the way in which he grows his experience.*

Medical Student. Years ago I read something like that of Thomas Taylor's, but I never took it seriously or even understood it well until now: "As everything which operates essentially produces an image of itself, the person who forms the world fashions forth an image of himself. And this being so, he contains within himself, by consequence, the archetypes or causes of the world and these are Ideas."

Author. Yes, there is no existence possible for any existent which is not found in its being. A. Bronson Alcott pointed out that "ideas are the originals of words" and "the world is but the symbol of mind and speech, a mythology woven of both." A mind-conscious editor is a peacemaker for his world.[2]

Medical Student. I have been reading Wittgenstein, who claims that "to imagine a language means to imagine a form of life." I believe I could understand this mind stuff, or at least stand it, but it's hard to stay with it. I can glimpse your view that every person is really a great-souled one but that seldom does one conceive his own greatness and *feel* his need to live up to it. I really don't want to find fault, but it seems to me that it would take me a long while to become a specialist in self-insight. Is there daily satisfaction in application to that work?

Author. Yes, every insight has its value in itself. Psychological medicine is most efficacious when the physician recognizes that his mind needs constant looking after. This physician will theorize that there is a similar need in each of his patients. It is relevant to realize that "theory" is the Greek word for "a sight." Although William T. Harris, my most enlightened United States Commissioner of Education, defined mind as "an eternal vibration of subject and object," selfness reveals itself in every possible human process. The only point of life which exists anywhere must exist in the individual living it. Human experience derives all of its unity from the experiencer.

Medical Educator. I realize that it might be just one more stress for my fellow listeners to tolerate, but if you are going to continue in this theoretical strain, insisting that *it* is practical, please account for the fact that educational institutions separate theory and practice. Please clarify your educational perspective.

Author. Surely, my antagonist is my helper. Here must be just the opportunity I need. *All that "practice" can be is the practice of a theory.* I reserve the honorific "scholar" for the one whose intention it is to conduct all of his study as being only the cultivation of his private self.

In my history of my American education it is not difficult to discover the source of the passivity and pessimism characterizing the illusional view of education as a learning process involving an "external world" (rather than the world of one's self), for such a belief was characteristic of my unrelieved puritan. As a theory of knowing, one's Calvinism taught that true knowledge was a product of revelation, not an attainment of human endeavor; that human being is not at all a matter of self-help, but rather the result of an arbitrary grace; that conscious will power is of a foreordained nature, not an issue of conscious self-development; that the pursuit of happiness is a matter of destiny and not at all a matter of the way a man lives his life; that a man's life does not belong to him, but rather to an "external" god.

Medical Educator. I have my reservations about all of your references to educational history, but I am deepening as well as broadening my conviction that all education, fully conceived, would be one's education to personal health. Now you seem to want to identify one's true education as being the only pure force of one's religion as well. Is not your concept of individuality a mystic one?

Author. There is absolutely no question in my mind but that my fellowman lives an individuality which must always be a mystery to me. I cannot even speculate about *it,* for that "it" is in my mind only and from start to finish is only a concern of *my* life. In this sense, the conscious living of individuality may be described accurately as mystic, but *only* with respect to one's living of the concept of his fellowman's individuality.

Medical Educator. It appears that you regard the view that man can somehow appreciate that which he is not, as mystic.

Author. Every so-called "system of education" which is not based entirely upon the student's *conscious* self-activity, must be seen clearly as a self-unconscious (limiting) kind of mysticism. The unmistakable marks of this kind of mystic are the desire to be together with an other-than-self god and the craving to be assimilated into an other-than-self absolute. In other words, the self-unconscious mystic depends upon dissociating his mind so that he can claim to live in some way which does not constitute self-expression. He must seem the passive recipient of a revelation, of a transitory illumination, from an alien power which temporarily *possesses him*—and so on, so that his own self-consciousness and volition are temporarily in abeyance.

The identity of this mystic way of living one's self with the view of science as "the study of an external world" is inescapable. Any and every attempt on my part to explain my self-data as being in any respect "external data" must be based upon my lack of insight into my own mental processes. Any of my medical education not recognizable as only and entirely my self-development must be traceable to my (unconscious) mystic habit of mind. If I "dissect a cadaver," "look in a microscope," "study biochemistry," or "listen to (grow my hearing of) a lecture," or "work in the physiology laboratory," or live myself in any way as a medical student, without the accessible realization that any and all of this living is nothing but my growing selfhood, I am certainly living the life of an unconscious mystic.

In the interest of human life, may I recognize that I am the voluntary author of all of my medical power. My every word stands for reality of mind. The evolution of himself as a physician is entirely the result of every physician's own marvelous life force and of his own endeavors, and such self-insight is a requirement for his proper sense of self-importance. All of my "understanding" and psychological penetration depend upon my activating my sense of awe-inspiring personal identity.

Medical Educator. Such a sense of limitless responsibility for being one's own all reminds me of Nietzsche's notion that Goethe "created himself." Come to think of it, the finest criticism one tends to make of his fellowman regularly concerns his mental independence.[3] Goethe's first sizing up of Beethoven was: "more concentrated, more energetic, more inwardly, I have never yet found any artist."

Author. My, you have noticed the exaltation of conscious subjectivity as a human ideal.

Medical Educator. You seem to consider it the way of wisdom to strive to live everything you do live as worthy.

Author. I see each alternative, (1) to recognize excellence is all that is possible, or (2) to recognize myself as being an excellent fault-finder.

Medical Educator. Your self-consciousness sensibility clearly leads you to a new conception of human life. Your requirements that all human behavior be understood as psychological and revered as life's produce bespeak your living upon a high plane of conscious individualism. Is it that you find that the social way of living trivializes life? Your exultation in an aloneness that cannot be lonely stuns me.

Author. Well it may, for it is the largest order one can put into his conscious living. Life cannot really be trivialized, but conducting it as if it were not one's own certainly appears to toss it about. Certainly, living consciously glorifies life as no other personal effort can.

Medical Educator. I notice that you hardly ever say "no."

Author. Living is affirming, not negating—*there* is a double negative if you wish. Consciousness is always positive being, presence of alert mindedness, happening of human activity, existent appreciation, spontaneous force, a condition of human nature, an expression of self, a personal event. "Think not thine own thoughts," must lead to a mind-weakening direction of living, since it declares a total impossibility. Every human being has nothing but his native sources for all of his living. His wish to "unite himself with a larger whole" must be a natural expression of his need to recover from his having dissociated his mind into one part recognized as "I" and another part recognized as "Not-I," the latter part being by far the greater one.

Medical Educator. I find happiness in the view that my world, all of it, is an adornment of myself, and that I am properly a subject, not object, of ineffable awe—in Goethe's view, "universal man." Scientifically minded as I am, and humble in the fact of my own mysteries, I can help myself tremendously with this practical view: the more I find out, the more self-knowledge I grow. Thus, I need not define science as a finding out of more and more about less and less, to be sure. Life *is* man's only possession, and the importance of medical work can only be elucidated by that enlightening truth. What I am in the dark about is, How can I grow my learning? Not until talking with you have I viewed my study of my lessons as being entirely and only my living of me. Would you *practically* spell out for me your view of the "educative process?"

Author. I am pleased to detail my views of "the learning process." My interest in education as a formal mental discipline has been cultivated by my living as a medical educator for thirty-nine years, and as a board of education member for fifteen years. This educational experience has culminated in the one insight: *every kind of education is nothing but self-growth.* Now I must exert myself to believe that I did not always have that truth consciously accessible. Awareness of personal congruity is a powerful health source, an ever present evidence of individual greatness, the stronghold of peace, and an unfailing spring of excellence of character.

Medical Educator. By "personal congruity" do you mean: fitly suitable to one's nature—a kind of sense of coming to life?

Author. Exactly that—a sense of personal identity, of self-sameness.

Medical Educator. Your record of your experience implies that you have found that your living of the idea of otherworldliness of any kind has been at the expense of your adequate self-esteem. Thus, you go so far as to classify memory (as standing for a non-existent past) and anticipation (as standing for a non-existent future) as categories of (illusional) otherworldliness. Am I right?

Author. As I consciously make these statements to myself, I feel absolutely right about each one.

Medical Educator. I have tended to consider the process of my educating myself as being a kind of uniting of myself with newness in some form.

Author. That is a very interesting view, as I see it. All of life is always new. There can be nothing old under, or over, the sun, according to my learning experience. The only life is *now* life, always novel, fresh, surprising.

My educating myself sanely to enable myself to enjoy the health-bearing satisfactions of peace and freedom which I now can has required of me a very particular kind of personal training, perhaps best described as my sustained self-conscious development. Thus, I have had to discover and weather certain fundamental truths of my inviolable human individuality. There is no peace in agreement. There is no freedom in togetherness. There is no truth in communication. I learn all that I learn by *growing* my knowledge as self-knowledge. I *mind* it. I can give every designation of science its full validity and yet preserve my conscious appreciation of my absolute individuality—and that "practical feat" is achieved as a demonstration of my theory of my "learning process" as being only, and nothing but, my continuous personal experience of living. In *The Dreams of Reason,* René Dubos asserted,

> Scientific questions have their origin deep in human consciousness, often below the analytical level. They constitute specialized restatements of large questions that philosophers formulated long before scientists began to work on their determinism, questions which have preoccupied men ever since they began to think—even before the beginnings of formal philosophy.[4]

What is needed most critically in all medical work is the insight that it is most medicinal when it is recognized by every patient and by every physician as his self-educational experience. What is needed most critically in all educational work is the insight that it is hygienic experience when it is recognized by every pupil and by every teacher as nothing but his development of his own mental power.

Medical Educator. You would prefer to have your American educator face the fact with intrepid courage and honesty that his kind of schooling simply does not, and cannot, accomplish what Jefferson hoped it might, namely, each pupil's own cultivation of the truth of the sovereignty of his individuality. You view the historic, careful avoidance of this soul-shaking fact as having the same significance as your patient's denial of illness.[5] You see your American educator as blindly and vainly trying to create reverence for the dignity of human individuality, the basic meaning of American democracy, from a kind of school living which depends for its existence upon ignoration of the allness meaning of individuality. You see the present educational method, the-knowing-teacher-imparting-knowledge-to-the-ignorant-pupil, as a classic *folie-à-deux* perpetuating the principle of self-unconsciousness as the necessary requirement of the learning process. You consider your true view of the cognitive process (all and only an innate development of the learner's individuality) to be the sole and whole criterion of the kind of education with which the pupil can grow an appreciation of the necessity for peaceful government of the individual, by the individual, and for the individual. You find that a student tends to use his conventional education ("being informed," "instructed," "told," etc.) as a defense against living his learning consciously as his own self-experience. You consider that it might be possible for a pupil to escape the authoritarian orientation of his school living, but that he would have to help himself in consciously individualistic ways to do it.[6] You recommend that the American educator face his reality squarely: *some other method than every American's present school living must be devised for his development of himself as an individual able to appreciate the glorious benefits of conscious self-government.* You regard it as self-deluding to speak of "preservation of democracy," which is taken for granted as already existing somewhere in the United States, since the essence of American democracy is each citizen's realization that his United States exists only and all within him. You declare, there is no truth except the truth of individuality, including each individual's truth. You do not hesitate to call every fundamental principle in question.

Author. I live you speaking the mind of a wholesomely concerned American citizen interested insightfully in *making a study* of that which concerns you. William Blake's genius knew where to find truth,

> He who doubts from what he sees
> Will ne'er believe, do what you please;
> If the sun and moon should doubt,
> They'd immediately go out.

and

> We are led to believe a lie
> When we see *with* not *through* the eye.

Medical Educator. In the early eighteenth century the learned Jesuit Father Regnault made a study of education and reported that Socrates, and St. Augustine after him, had good grounds for maintaining that no man could teach another anything. A hundred years ago Robert Blakey wrote in his *History of the Philosophy of Mind*:

> That which we denominate instruction in a master, is simply the art of interrogating his disciple, according to a received method, with a view to the discovery of that truth which is in his own mind. And that which we call learning or acquiring knowledge in a pupil, is only the development of the faculty of attention, and its steady concentration upon our inward thoughts or ideas.

Certainly, your view of education as being individual development has had a long life. However, as long as popularity is the criterion of success you might as well make up your mind to be satisfied with your own devotion to your understanding of your cognitive process. Your language on the topic of common sense may be too unguarded.

Author. Yes. By bearing testimony to my existence in my every individuation, I do all possible to support the idea of the allness of any and every existent of my universe. From attention with the recognized operations of my own mind within itself I enjoy an appreciation of self-possession which I desire.

Medical Educator. Apparently you do not agree with your fellow physician, John Locke, that sensation is at least in part derived from external properties.

Author. I cannot agree or disagree with anyone, for such an operation itself involves the illusions of externality and (its associated) plurality.

Medical Educator. And all of this education-is-innate-self-growth is what you mean by *elementary medical education.* In other words, you regard the idea of conventional learning (the acquisition of knowledge of the world of nature around one) to be the number one educational fallacy which obscures (1) the ideal view of education as being a healthful process and (2) the ideal view of healing as being an educational process.

Author. Yes. Only with the greatest of difficulty do I find it possible to renounce my incorrect intellectual habits of dependence upon each illusion: (1) of not having to live *all* of my own life, and (2) of being able to live some of that which I do not regard as being my own life.

Medical Educator. Why are there few general hospitals having psychiatric divisions?

Author. It is difficult for the individual to grow to tolerate his mind's needs. Conscious self-helpfulness is sorely wanting by everyone, in and out of a hospital, but that need is seldom a consciously felt one. However, the undeniable usefulness of self-insight has been gradually demonstrating itself, and the development of psychiatric divisions in general hospitals is proceeding apace.[7]

5

Learning Process

Standard textbooks of medicine supply excellent articles on recognized diseases, but with rare exceptions the discussions fail to include one feature of paramount importance. No mention is made of the need for explaining to the patient the nature of his problem, the mechanism and significance of his symptoms, and the course the illness may be expected to follow. This omission is unfortunate because, with present-day concentration on pathologic physiology in our medical schools, the subject also receives little or no attention in clinical teaching. As a consequence it may be several years after graduation before a young internist appreciates all that can be accomplished by sufficiently detailed instruction of those under his care. There are two principal reasons why an explanation along the lines indicated is indispensable. In the first place, it is, in many illnesses, a therapeutic tool of basic importance. Secondly, it is one of the best available ways to show personal concern for the patient's welfare and therefore a most effective method for maintaining public support of our free enterprise system of medicine.

A. CARLTON ERNSTENE, M.D.

Author. MAN'S LEARNING OF his world is his creation of his world. His creation of his world reveals man to himself. However, he may or may not live these truths with consciousness, and thereby hangs the issue of his clear or confused concept of his greatness. If he does remain true to his allness, his life is replete with wonderful insights. If he must repudiate this fact that he originates his all, or that his innate living subsumes all of his learning, his life from then on makes less and less sense, and seems less and less real, to him.

Medical Educator. Since all of my living is entirely self-composed, self-contained, self-possessed, and self-growing, how can I conceive myself as a helpful physician or educator? If I am my own all, my own "everyone" and "everything," how can I study and practice myself in therapy, or instruction, of any kind? If I am unable to "influence" my fellowman, and if my fellowman is unable to influence me, how can I justify myself in my profession of physician or educator?

Author. This is the kind of questioning which each liver and learner must pose to himself. The fundamental meaning of medicine, as well as of all education, is at stake in such self-examination. The excellent self-insight reported by Dr. A. Carlton Ernstene highlights the role of every physician as an educator, as an intact individual carefully applying his medicinal appreciation of his intactness.[1] Using my mind without realizing that I am (using my mind), distracts me from the one fact which gives to every other fact its importance, namely, the fact of *life.*

Medical Educator. If there is no "betweenness," only *withinness,* how can a physician have any meaning whatsoever for his patient, or a patient have any meaning whatsoever for his doctor? Cannot each one have a mind of his own without its having to be an "all"? If there is no communication, why take a medical history or write a prescription? Each of these plain questions calls for a plain accounting.

Author. As each question is a self-growth, so must be its answer. I can see clearly what must appear to be the oracular nature of my self-observations: that my only reality is the issue of my living; that my living is momentary; that appreciation of immediate living is the way of wisdom, of psychological hygiene; that one's state of being cannot be raised, but can become visible as already exalted; that the insights of the holy man and the hale man are one in the realization of the allness of individuality; that knowledge cannot be taught by the informed to the uninformed; and possibly above all, that all learning is a process of the learner's knowledge coming to life, of the learner's awakening to view his self-truth or self-extent. Educability is viability. I am the only existential basis of all of my knowledge.

Medical Educator. I am not the one who is pretending to be a dialectician. Neither do I wish to be cast in the role of a ventriloquist's dummy. I have noticed that you do not mind contradicting yourself—for instance, in your adopting dialog. However, you repeatedly show up conversation as being an inadequate device for upholding your one and only educator-orientation: the allness meaning of individuality. Horace Mann saw learning as mental *activity* in which "the effective labor must be performed by the learner himself." Self-sovereignty was his goal of true republican education. Above all, he maintained that the discipline of a republican school is the self-discipline of the individual.

Author. It is gratifying to have (my) you mindful of the impossibility of dialog. Dialog may be defined as unrecognized monolog compensating for indulgence in a convenient addiction to an illusional "externality."

Medical Educator. You mean that the most popular educational fallacies are: (1) one can talk and "somebody else" can do his listening for him, and (2) one can listen and "somebody else" can do his talking for him.

Author. Precisely. Your curiosity which you are awakening seems to be doing you no mischief. Technically, I consider myself "in transference" to any of my living which I can recognize only as not-self. You may recall that "in transference" means: living without insight that one creates whatever one lives. As Hegel stated it, "self-consciousness . . . is a direct assertion of independent Being."

Medical Educator. You mean that every "materialist" is in transference to everything and everybody of his "external" world?

Author. Yes. My "materialist" cannot call his material his soul and, hence, cannot call his life his own whole-souledly.

Medical Educator. Please get on with your theory of knowledge, from its start.

Author. Very well. In my effort to live myself as responsibly answerable for my kind of conscious self-education, I shall imagine my self-development as an infant (since every infant is most helpful) working very long and hard in truly marvelous ways to develop my capacities for enjoying my life. As one of my earliest forms of self-helpfulness, I *grew* myself a powerful pattern of forces which I gradually personified and ultimately designated with the name "mother." As far as I was concerned, I personally saw to it that my mother lived herself in certain ways whereby various kinds of creature comfort accrued to me. In short, I grew my mother helping herself by living her son in ways which she designated as "nursing," or "caring." All of this living *of mine* was certainly *withinness living* involving no communication, since it was no more than my own growing of myself.

Again, as I developed further, *I grew my mother* reciting her alphabet and obviously taking pleasure in this accomplishment. In a true sense, my growing of my mother in this performance necessitated my having her live this performance (through my living of that part of myself which I personified as my mother). Seeing myself able to recite my alphabet in this one part of myself (my mother-image), to the extent that I actually did see my identity in each element of the recitation, I provided myself with the basic pattern for reciting my alphabet without using my mother-image to accomplish this performance.

Again, I found myself unable to work a puzzle. However, I did grow the realization that I had someone of my world who was able to work this puzzle satisfactorily. My next step was to see to it that *I* have my other one work this puzzle, observing (my) "his" procedure step after step. My ability to work the puzzle, without limiting its solution to my "other one," was thus gradually assured. An analogy comes to mind: if I can write with my finger, I can also write with my arm, shoulder, or whole body. Learning is a psychic process created *only* by *one's* life process.

Medical Educator. You say: Whatever is, is helpful. How is my "educational fallacy" (e.g., that I can speak to, or be spoken to by, another) helpful?

Author. My educational fallacy is of indispensable helpfulness for protecting my sense of personal identity. Were it not for the fact that only I can speak to and hear myself, I would be at the mercy of my so-called "circumstances," feeling myself jerked and yanked about with little or no sense of my individuality's allness. By acceding to a view of education as an alien influence I can conduct myself *as if* I have learned my lesson, until my further self-development will enable me to see such a lesson (consciously) as my own self-knowledge.

Medical Educator. Then you are not criticizing the educator about his "educational fallacy."

Author. Certainly not. My present institutions could not exist without it.

Medical Educator. By reading an excellent book by (my) Walter Kaufmann I grew the just literary principle that "you must understand before you can presume to criticize."[2] However, I do allow myself to ask, Are you sure that you are correct in your statement that your living is the only genesis of all of your meanings for everyone and everything of your world?

Author. I am willing to be either sure or unsure about my imaginings, depending upon the evidence I create reenforcing or loosening support for the correctness of each one. Many a fine insight is recorded in Kaufmann's works.

Medical Educator. Well I find it hard to like the idea that I have only myself to turn to, or from, and would rather not grow it as mine right now—even though I'm sure that liking or disliking it has nothing to do with *it.* Solitary confinement, your freedom, is no recipe for my happiness, even if it constitutes the fact of life.

Author. I too have found no surer guide for my extending my living of the truth of my self-consciousness than by facing the fact that I always do as I please.

Medical Educator. Your style is that of an authoritarian but you seem to be sincere in your proclamation that everyone of your world is necessarily, if not openly, his one and only authority. Your pride is showing in your self-expressions, but you appear to be honest in your observation that everyone of your world is entitled to his glorious vanity. You have messianic manner, but for the most part I sense no hypocrisy in your dictum: it is divine to be human and human to overlook it. I suppose that your almighty devotion to your individuality seems monstrous even to yourself now and then, but I imagine you have long since learned to lie down until that wave of self-depreciation passes over. I am in live earnest in my puzzlement as to how to classify (my) you except as being an individual. You seem to prefer to see yourself as all mind, or soul, if you prefer.

Author. Robert S. Woodworth has comprehensively defined psychology as the study of the activities of the individual. I find that the learning activity is the growing of self-experience, a *life* development occurring from within out, not an acquisition to life from without in. Learning is the product only and entirely of living, not a reaction to an "external" happening. Only *life* can be interesting, or attended to, or explored, or learned, *by life.* And, for me that life has to be all mine. Every meaning of my mind, e.g., consciousness, constitutes itself and contains within itself its "object." Thus, the illusion "objectivity" is organic to the meaning *subjectivity.* Elijah Jordan, in his keenly perceptive *Forms of Individuality* (1927), held that mind, itself, cannot be defined since it is the ground of distinction, and that the essence of meaning of "objective" is "outside."

Medical Educator. I have tended to consider all that is learned as being acquired, and all that is instinctive as unlearned. You have been claiming that your mental life is all and only innate. From what you have already stated on this subject, I presume you mean that my teacher, lesson, educational environment, are all grown by me. Despite the fact that you have already considered these questions, it occurs to me to ask, Can I grow a teacher who is not there? Can I grow a lesson without its existing? Can I grow a college of medicine which is not an actual center of learning? Can I eat food, or breathe air, if it is not already there to be eaten, or breathed? I may not eat ears, or feet, or hands, in order to grow ears, or feet, or hands, but I must eat something in order to grow myself, mustn't I? Your Freud discovered that the mind consists of *unconscious living* and that consciousness is only its organ of observation. That may be your point, that consciousness can observe only itself and therefore cannot report "externality." For you, not-self simply means perfect non-entity, does it not? May not your awesome certainty that you are your own everything be a flight from the personal enlightenment you might have to suffer through if you would devote yourself to the laboratory of experimental psychology?

Author. Helpful questions. It is true that the *appearances* seem all against the truth of the individuality of individuality. However, the moment I live myself as if I could substitute an "externality" for a living action of my conscious human selfhood, I make trouble for myself which restricts me until I extend my consciousness to be able to focus upon it (the so-called "externality") too as my very own living (of "it"). I spare myself this trouble by recognizing that I am, first of all, responsible for seeing to it (*by my consciously living it*) that I grow whatever "teacher," "lesson," "educational center," "food," "air," or what not, which I do grow. What *I* do not live is my only definition for nonexistence; what *I* live is my only definition for existence. I attribute the same nature (mine) of individuality to every individuation of myself. Thus, my teacher is entirely and only about himself, my food is entirely and only about itself, and so on. I *have* worked for years "in the laboratory of experimental psychology," and the personal enlightenment "there" I experienced illuminated my way to my conscious study of myself.

Medical Educator. Do you mean that there is no such thing as pure science, objectively determined physical science? Have you *ascertained* that particular amount of self-knowledge? I have a strong need to believe that there is accurate tangible proof of tangible objects. You would have me take pains to distinguish my living as my own, without interval. I prefer the painstaking efforts of rigorous laboratory training. I may not even want to see that my mind lives it all.

Author. As J. M. Cattell, American psychologist and editor, recorded in 1893, "It is often urged as an objection to psychology that the student of physics can observe one mind only, but it is equally true that the student of physics can observe *with* one mind only. Were mental processes so irregular and idiosyncratic as is sometimes assumed, there would be no science of psychology, but physics would be equally out of the question."

Medical Educator. I help myself by considering physics, or mathematics, as pure science. Is that not an instance of self-helpfulness? Your solemn truth of selfhood seems to oppose itself to the mummery of the mundane worship of "externality."

Author. Individuality cannot oppose itself, there being nothing but its own all. I am pleased to have you help yourself with your view of what constitutes pure science. Particularly where my scientist is concerned I wish to hold my peace and, if possible, see peaceful living the only over-all concern of all scientific research. By "peace," to be sure, I mean that greatness of self-love which makes one's world understandable as his own helpful and good produce. Serenity is becoming to self-sovereignty.

Medical Educator. Please, may I have your idea of pure science.

Author. For me pure science is the science of self, the reality of existence, the present truth. I help myself also by considering my science of physics, or mathematics, as applied psychological science, thereby preserving truth to life. Acknowledged spirit grows recognizable spirituality or, if you prefer, ideality. Dr. James Rush, son of Benjamin, once noted, "When truth is courted, she is as a mistress; and with an ardent and absent lover, she rises in full and vivid image on the slightest resemblance to her." To the extent that I have a searching mind it is most helpful of all (to me) to be able to realize that, wherever I look, I will always find more of myself. "Learning" fitly describes "living" as: presenting selfhood.

Medical Educator. How about the "whatness of things-in-themselves"?

Author. I had my Korzybski speak his insight on his semantics when he declared, "We do not need to doubt human reason, we should distrust our language." Simply by prefacing "whatness of things-in-themselves" with the possessive pronoun, "my," I make it possible for myself to see where all of my observations are taking place. I do not plan to live as an alien in the world which is my creation. Once I see my psychology clearly in its right mind, my own, my mind does not trouble itself over impossibility. However, once I begin with impossibility (that is, with the arbitrary idea that I can be out of my mind) I beset myself with innumerable phantom problems. In my mind is where my picture on my life film actually takes place. Furthermore, I am sure that my mind's film developed exactly the picture it wanted to, and in the way it wanted to, without any so-called "outsidedness."

Medical Educator. There is merit in your declaration of the enormous magnitude in your human living. With such vast conscious resources there must be associated immense self-trust. Giant self-consciousness undoubtedly reveals to man, as nothing else can, his actual gigantic proportions, his world measurements. You seem to be trying to break away from conversation in order to heed life.

I do not yet have focal distance on this idea, that all learning is the record of the experience of the human constitution of the experiencer. How did you deliver that idea?

Author. It was a most difficult birth preceded by protracted labor. It seems that I tried every other creation first before I could convince myself that this precious mind-child was the one needed to be born of love.

Medical Educator. If you are correct in your observation (that the learning process can be nothing but a life process of the learner, a particular instance of self-growth called self-knowing), please account for the fact that everyone in his right mind does not see that truth. Why is your top view of education better than that of another? I may not like your idea that the learning process is a life process. I realize that a quotation may indicate, not vindicate, but can you quote someone who sees education as you do?

Author. I am always glad to be able to make the point that my idea of education is, and can merely be, the proper one for me only. Everyone is entitled and limited to, and can help himself only with, his own "top view of education."

Many a one senses the truth that he lives alone (all-one). Thomas Jefferson recorded, "Health is no more than learning." Margaret Fuller once said, "Very early, I perceived that the object of life is to grow." Who chooses to do so can discover for himself innumerable records of his fellowman bearing witness to the truth that continuous education *makes the most of one's self,* that growing self-consciousness is the art and science of right living. Sterne formed the idea, "Trust that man in nothing who has not a conscience in everything." Emerson was always saying self-realization in one way or another, as, "The only way to have a friend is to be one." Confucius said it thus, "What the superior man seeks is in himself; what the small man seeks is in others." John Milton recorded, "There is nothing that makes men rich and strong but that which they carry inside of them." Stephen Paget worded it, "Once we begin to talk as if the external world were outside our skins, there is no end to casuistry."

The "learning process" is redeemed from the realm of (illusional) "not-self" by being seen as, all and only, a mental birth, a psychic conception. Education exercises the given mind's creative principle. The mind is one, and can only negotiate its oneness as its learning process, as novel self-events (new knowledge) burgeoning from its wholeness. Learning is a product of mental genesis, generated in, and relevant to, only the student's life process. And life itself depends upon affirmation. *I have not completed my lessons of "seeing" and "hearing" if I cannot see and hear only myself in all such uses of my mind's growth.*

Medical Educator. Historian Arnold J. Toynbee calls self-centeredness our "Original Sin." You call it your Original Virtue. He writes that the study of correct history may widen "the mental horizon of an innately self-centered living creature."

Author. I can live that aim of human life as being a choice one also. I have my Arnold J. Toynbee helping himself in his own individual way. Personally, I help myself most by regarding whatever "appears" to separate me from anyone or anything of my world as really being a bridge of selfness extending from the me I can acknowledge to the me I must currently disown.

Medical Educator. Can you express that last idea in a less stilted way, or demonstrate it?

Author. Let me try to illustrate it. My mind has the power to divide itself into parts for purposes of concentration. Thus, I can ideate without having my sense of personal identity excited, even though my personal identity is always my whole present truth. Therefore, I can observe of any part of my own living: It is not I. However that very observation which "appears" to separate me from a hypothetical not-self *is itself my own living.* Seeing it as being my own living is the bridge which connects me with my appreciation of myself as being the all I am.

Medical Educator. The idea of loneliness tends to be associated with melancholy feeling in my mind. But then by "loneliness" I always mean: a feeling of separation from some person or place. I suppose that the trouble may be that when I first grew these kinds of unnoticed self-meanings, I neglecting associating my sense of personal identity with each one, so that it easily took on the not-me appearance.

Author. Yes. A complaint of lonesomeness is, of necessity, spurious; for really to feel alone (all-one) would be to be able to feel one's totality, that is, to feel altogether with nothing missing, or absent.

Medical Educator. Being in a room all by myself does not excite my feeling of loneliness—in fact, come to think about it, I rarely feel alone there although, according to you, I *always* am. Loneliness is such an unpleasant sensation that I avoid it when I can. Learning to live the truth of the all-oneness of individuality is a painful kind of education.

Author. Fortunately, there can be no quest of happiness which does not lead to pain, except the happiness felt in seeing that what I live is all and only my own life's good. *It is impossible to excite the feeling of aloneness while living the illusion of being "in a room," or "under the sun," surrounded by "objects." My alone feeling which I call the "truth feeling," is only associated with my realization that my room, its objects, or all "under the sun," are my creations existing only in me.* Self-love is the great physician, and the great educator. Plato integrated these views in calling medicine "pedagogy attendant upon illness."

Socrates' searching question, "Is education really possible?" is an acknowledgment of the impossibility implied in the accepted illusion that a teacher can educate a pupil. Whatever tends to obscure the innateness and originality of the educational process, tends to obstruct the healthful insights (1) that the learner is the originator of all that he learns and (2) that educational experience is innate. My own human nature is my only *genius loci.* Goethe saw sanely, "What thou hast inherited from my fathers, earn it, to make it thine own."

Medical Educator. What learns? What part of the whole individual performs the act of learning? Can the brain be responsible for learning, as the heart is responsible for pumping the blood?

Author. As I ask each revealing question, I realize that no "part" exists as such, that a "part," therefore, can never do anything for the *whole.* Only *wholeness* exists. *Only the whole individual can perform any act of learning,* or pump any blood, or do anything else.[3] Individuality is the only element of every individuation. My individuality is my only, or universal, or particular, or real, or possible, or simple, or ultimate, or absolute, or indispensable, or principle, or property, or practicality, or nature, or law, or lesson.

Medical Educator. I am beginning to see the conscious purpose in your restricting your attention to each meaning of your individuality and to your individuality of your every meaning. The only possible ascription of meaning is from, and to, one's inviolable individuality. A man's mind is fashioned by the way he uses it, is it not?

Author. I see no other possibility. My own practical cowardice has protected me from the first truth of psychology, namely, my (necessarily) "unsocial" individuality, and has served to keep my mind (hence my world) unevenly conscious. On that account, I have tended to judge my mind (hence my world) faulty rather than to dazzle myself with the glare of facts justly supporting its every turn. My same helpful cowardice has protected my comforting ignorance for the degree to which I have repressed the truth (allness) of my individuality in order to espouse some "party" or "union" cause built largely upon limited regard for the welfare of the human individual.

Medical Educator. You have repeated that one person cannot tell another, or be told by another, *anything.* You have claimed that one cannot ask, or be asked, a question (except by himself). You have described the great educational fallacy (of so-called "communication") as underlying the illusion that the teacher can talk to his pupil and thereby succeed in instructing him; or that the pupil can hear his teacher speak information to him; or that the pupil can read what his textbook author wrote and thus assimilate it as if it were his own writing; or that so-called interpersonal give-and-take is a trustworthy educational device. Please, once more detail this insight, for instance, with regard to speaking and listening.

Author. Whenever I speak I am the only one (since I am my all) who *can* listen to me. I am always my only lecturer and auditor. *This insight is an educational help of the first magnitude.* When I speak, my pupil *cannot* hear me speak to him, (only *he* can ever hear himself). He can grow his auditory experience of having his teacher say (to himself) whatever he may consider to be worth saying (to himself), and stop his so-called educational lecture right there. If he does stop it there, he thereby successfully resists undergoing the further true educational experience of trying to say (to himself) whatever he has just lived his teacher saying (to himself). Thus he may use his illusion (that his teacher can speak directly to him) as a defense against learning the essential life lesson that only he can ever speak for himself and ever listen to himself. To the degree that I cannot see that *all* of my consciousness is self-consciousness I must indulge my need to have "someone else" able to be conscious for me ("see me," "listen to me," "give attention to me").

Medical Educator. You seem to be pinning down the localization of the learning process as having its beginning, course, and finality, entirely in the learner. You apparently feel that this is the essential truth about the learning process; and that all other studies of it can readily serve as distractions from its simple, self-evident, all-important, neither to be subordinated nor taken for granted, meaningfulness for sanity in educational living. The educational insight which you regard as the comprehensive one is the learner's realization that all of his learning belongs to him in the primary sense that he creates it.

Your view reminds me of that of J. D. Salinger's ten-year-old Teddy, when asked if he would like to study to be a doctor, this boy-genius replied,

> Doctors stay too right on the surface. They're always talking about cells and things. . . . But doctors talk about cells as if they had such unlimited importance all by themselves. As if they really didn't belong to the person that has them. . . . I grew my own body. . . nobody else did it for me. So if I grew it, I must have known *how* to grow it. Unconsciously, at least. I may have lost the conscious knowledge of how to grow it sometime in the last few hundred thousand years, but the knowledge is still *there,* because—obviously—I've used it. . . . It would take quite a lot of meditation and emptying out to get the whole thing back—I mean the conscious knowledge—but you could do it if you wanted to. If you opened up wide enough.[4]

It appears that you think that much, if not most, of the persistent puzzlement about the "cognitive process" is traceable to the phantom problem created by one's blindly beloved and dearly indulged illusion of "communication." You feel that your *confused* thinking (that is, your cherished delusion of the possibility of "interpersonal relations") *must* be verbally expressed in self-deceiving terms (such as the unrecognized, and therefore irresponsible, personification, plural, literary bull of every description, mistaken identity, rationalization, "externalization," or any other mental defense of confused thinking at your disposal).

Author. I have now had (my) you justly describe something of the tangled web I weave for myself once I deceive myself that I can listen to, or be heard by, anyone but myself.

Medical Educator. Again please explain, Why is it so extremely difficult to renounce verbal habits supporting other-than-self imaginings?

Author. As I ask, I answer this question. The illusion called "communication" is the sign of the unacknowledged unresolved transference of the human being for his very own parent. It is analogous to an unsevered umbilical cord. In giving psychological birth to his parent the growing infant (and child) found it impossible to acknowledge his *being* all that he was living, while creating his every mother, or father, meaning (personal experience).

Medical Educator. By "transference" you mean simply a living of yourself which you do not recognize as being yourself. In other words, I must live myself either as a conscious unified all, or I must live myself "in transference" to all of me that I deny being.

Author. That is about it. Whatever I cannot see *is* myself, I *must* claim can have some influence *over* me, and I over it. Similarly, if I deny that my hearer is mine, I must also deny that I am capable of living my hearer as living all of his whole unified life. Therefore, instead of having to acknowledge that I cannot live my hearer without making myself feel angry (or suspicious, or loving, or whatever), I can assert that "the" hearer *makes me* feel angry (or suspicious, or loving, or whatever).

Medical Educator. I presume that you do not expect your hearer to be able to renounce his self-concealing verbal habits so that he can understand the comprehensive meaning of human individuality, and thus understand his cognitive process.

Author. However each individual hearer lives his conversation, is all that can be desirable, as I see it.

Medical Educator. To understand this absolute radical individualism which you describe, I must accustom myself to an extraordinary correction in my perspective on the course of my life. It is as though you have taken Thales' claim of the existence of "a single principle" (which he called "water") and termed it *individuality.* Why, I have not even corrected my habitual view that the sun goes around the earth to fit Copernicus' view that the earth goes around the sun. I still say the sun rises in the east and sets in the west. I have no idea of how long it might take before I could accustom myself to saying and seeing "My sun rises and sets in me," or "My earth goes around my sun in me," or even, "I am not in my room, but my room is in me." I can intellectualize that the only reality, hence safety, of my so-called "community" does reside in me, rather than I in it, but I cannot *feel,* or fairly appreciate, that truth.

As the Frenchman says, "Clarity is only politeness." Will you please state clearly whether or not you can feel the need to overhaul your use of language in order to be able to feel that you can speak sanity?

Author. Yes, is my answer to that question, as I pose it. It is impossible for me to *feel* consciously sane except to the extent that my language bespeaks only my conscious selfness—but then I am quite accustomed to the feeling of speaking as if I think I can be out of my mind. Also I can understand A. E. Housman's description of the love of truth as "the faintest of human passions."

Medical Educator. Merely the accurate accommodation of speech to thinking is insufficient to guarantee sane speech, for thinking itself is involved in the, may I say, nearly universally indulged illusion of "otherness," of "not-self."

Author. True. If one thinks insightfully, his spoken and written language clearly expresses self-sight. The way of thinking of "the man within" is exposed by his use of language. My words never conceal, but ever reveal, how I think and feel. My language is precise, or imprecise, when my thinking is. If I live myself carelessly my words and sentences show it. If I need to hide anything (from myself, of course) my language becomes correspondingly obscure.

If I need to trick (myself, of course), my words become deceptive. While I strive sincerely to live accurately, that unifying tendency comes out in the coherence of my speaking or writing.

Medical Educator. You have but the one thesis, *conscious self-allness raises the standard of well-being,* but you confuse its issue in the way you present your evidence for it. I refer specifically to your effort to establish your fundamental truth that all speech is monolog by resorting to the form of dialog. By employing such a division of your mind you can create the impression of having a doubleness of intent rather than a singleness of purpose. You may lose many a would-be hearer by this seeming bifurcation of your stream of consciousness.

Author. I live gratefully every allusion of my hearer to this seeming inconsistency. My (one and only) mind's diremptive power is only apparent, not real. I plead a special case for my otherwise questionable right to this style. I have lived apparent conversational dialog on the topics of these conversations with my every student for many years, so that this presenting of the material (I had previously spoken) fell naturally into this *seeming* dialog form.

In his notably helpful article, "Philosophic Style," Brand Blanshard discussed this dialectic form of writing, "It is surprising that one obvious method of arranging one's matter has been used so seldom, and then so rarely with success. Philosophy, as Plato said, is a kind of dialogue of the soul with itself, and the dialogue, expertly used, is an effective way of winding one's course through a subject."[5]

Medical Educator. Your views of When you learn, What you learn, and How you learn set the foundation of your whole life orientation. Your solipsistic kind of over-all noometry (the allness, wholeness, oneness, newness, and nowness of individuality) stands or falls on the meaning you attribute to your process of learning, commonly termed "the cognitive process." To be consistent, you must account for all of your learning as being your novel living of the realization of your potential self-knowledge. Thus, regardless of any and every other possibly imaginable learning opportunity assumed to be present, you *can* learn only the life lesson you are ready to create as a self-meaning. You are completely insensible, unseeing and unfeeling, to the extent that you are unmindful. Thus, I am creating all of my present conversing only because I am ready to do so; otherwise I would not perform it, and my present experience would be exactly that of having nothing to talk about. First I must be ready to say something, then I must create every condition favorable to my saying it.

My so-called "external world" (which is made up entirely of my self-experience) exists meaningfully for me only on account of the fact that it is I. I can go on enjoying my living as long as I can succeed in creating supplies for my life needs. Thus, if I can live only a room without air, or only an environment without food and drink, I thereby soon restrict my ability to imagine necessary nourishment in a specific manner essential for my going on living.

Author. As you state it, it seems obvious that I am able to live only what I am ready to live. How could it be otherwise! Yes, my views of my education—of when I learn, what I learn, how I learn—provide my mind's basic orientation.

I would appreciate a professional educator's statement of some of his views on American education.

Educator. For centuries now the American has built his entire scheme of life around his idea of education as being a force necessarily shaping his mind into its most effective condition: that of the *Americanized American.* It helps to have you state your view: education is as education does. I have found that Mr. Taxpayer regards his child as his "most cherished possession"—not as his most cherished *self*-possession. He is innocent of the fact that self-insight is not learned as a school lesson, and equally innocent of the kind of consciously self-reliant living-learning from conscious *self-experiences* which shaped the mind of his historic Jefferson to be able to see the sanity in conscious self-government. He just naturally assumes a connection of American education and American democracy whereby the former *necessarily* creates the latter. Mr. Taxpayer who is also Mr. Voter does not enjoy the genuine aspiration—based upon his own duly appreciated self-conscious *self-experience* which shaped the mind of his historic growth of his own self-insight (the prerequisite of conscious self-government). He prides himself upon being "matter-of-fact," and inclines towards the protest "That's carrying imagination too far," if he is asked to imagine the consequences of authoritarian home and school living as being his child's pathway to citizenship. His ruling political belief is founded upon such notions as the following: "popular" sovereignty, not *self*-sovereignty; "participation in a vast cooperative enterprise," not whole-souled responsibility for all of his political living; "stake in the commonwealth," not personal possession of every meaning of his United States and world government; "training of the pupil in democratic ideals by the teacher," not each pupil's consciously unfolding cultivating and controlling his individuality's power. He cannot imagine that his own capacity for self-sovereignty has been developed *only* by the extent of his conscious realization that *all* of his education begins and ends in his very own personal experience.

Therefore, Mr. Taxpayer Voter cannot know just exactly where his American educational system requires far more of his concern, devotion, support, and continuous study, than it now receives. He takes for granted that his educator "knows his business," particularly that he knows how to "turn out" pupils who can read, write, spell, and count "in the American way." Thus, he attributes a kind of magic to his mere idea of "schooling." Certainly, he cannot know that effective democratic education means: *unwavering devotion to the allness meaning of the individual pupil.* His own "schooling" has not disciplined his mind to appreciate the potentiality in *conscious* educational living; hence, he cannot see "money for the schools" as the most fundamental expenditure of his democratic political system. He takes one look at "the size of the average classroom" and concludes that respect for the concept of "the dignity of the individual" is impractical—with little or no consideration of the only alternative, namely, the pupil's disciplining his mind in the condition and habit of authoritarianism.

Author. As you see it, just about everyone of your world begins his reasoning about his educational system as if his schooling were "outside," not inside, of him. Thus, he will state, "The schoolroom cannot exist unless someone runs it," or, "The teacher must bring the pupils into conformity," or, "Without external coercion applied to the many, there can be no order." That is, the insight is most rare that each pupil lives his teacher, or that each teacher lives each of his pupils.

Educator. I never heard of such notions, not in Teacher's College and not since. I have heard expressed the view of the pupil's "willing individual conformity," but the very word "conformity" implies outness. My teacher training has emphasized "common understanding," not *conscious self-knowledge;* "true free effective cooperation," not *responsible living of one's very own fellow worker;* "Thirty pupils in a schoolroom," not *Each pupil's living his, or her, schoolroom in him, or her;* "The pupil goes to school," not *Each pupil creates all that he means by travel;* "The political independence of the schools," not *Each pupil's independently growing all that he, or she, means by "political independence";* "The teacher's beneficial personal influence on the pupil," not *Each pupil's creation of all that he can mean by his teacher;* "The party system," not *The individual's human system comprises his all;* "The teaching function is impersonally representative," not *All learning is the pupil's personal living;* "The school needs able leaders," not *Every pupil lives all that he terms "leadership" or "followership";* "Schooling must reach every human being," not *Each student learns only by means of an extension of his life's processes;* "The individual is not an island, he cannot live or learn in a vacuum," not *Every individual is his own universe, living his every vacuum and plenum as creative developments of his own mind;* "Successful schooling produces a social scientist," not *Society is a word for a meaning in the science of self;* "America stands for equal opportunity for all," not *Each individual lives his own world, is born equal to himself, and must strive for the attainment of conscious equality with all of his living in order to achieve his sanity;* "What is going on in the classroom," not *His classroom living is going on in each pupil;* "The school must teach the fundamental subjects," not *Each pupil is his only possible subject and his attention to that truth is his most fundamental work;* "Compulsory education," not *The pupil's willing his attention to his self-development;* "The republic needs education of the best kind," not *Each pupil ideally can develop himself, or herself, best by the disciplined conscious growth of his life's meaning;* "The

American school is the builder and protector of the nation," not *The American pupil builds and protects his individuality.*

Author. Each of these views you cite is helpful. I use every one of them in my educational living. Each of them is all about itself and one cannot rule out another. However, there is an illusional "mutual exclusiveness" about each one which is really traceable to the truth that each one includes all and only itself.

Educator. You mean that you are as comfortable considering what you call your illusion of "the pupil in the school" as you are considering what you call your truth of "your living your pupil as well as your school where all of your living occurs, in yourself"?

Author. I have had you state the case correctly. The strong act of the mind is *consideration.* The capacity for consideration is based upon the power of freedom of imagination. *Any* of my mental functioning which I cannot consider soberly and lovingly as being my own is lived by me reluctantly and with unpleasant feelings, until I can develop my self-tolerance to be able to endure and gradually grow equal to appreciating it as my own, hence desirable, living.

Educator. I am beginning to understand the practicality in seeing whatever I live, whether classified "right" or "wrong," as being desirable in that it is always my own living. Thus, I am now able to see that each so-called "wrong" answer is as right as it can be for the person using it, *and* that that "person" is also comprised of mental elements of my own living. I can also see that all so-called "criticism of the schools" is nothing but blind self-criticism incapable of accomplishing anything but what fault-finding can accomplish, namely, the momentarily helpful restriction of self-consciousness to living which can be enjoyed. Please give words to your experience with formal education.

Author. None of my formal schooling contributed to my applying myself to insightful living. All of my unwillingness to subject myself to severe discipline for helpful living seems to be traceable to my illusion that I may attain it by formal educational experience instead of by having to take the trouble to live myself insightfully. It is as though I have long indulged an illusion that I can grow self-insight by reading about it, or by hearing lectures about it—quite as I grew my classwork about "the world of nature around me." Thus, I seem to reason, Why cannot I learn the language of self just as I have learned the German, or French, or Latin, or Greek, or some other "foreign," language?

My experience has taught me that I can grow my self-insight only by encountering and renouncing powerful resistances, only by "sweating blood" in my efforts to grow equal to any of my living which I have disowned (relegated to my not-I category of meanings). Nevertheless, I can beguile myself with formal educational habits of living "otherness" illusions which exclude every possibility of my extending the limits of my conscious self-tolerance. Memorization of self-unconscious living is a most alluring succedaneum for self-consciousness. Experiencing the illusion of "attracting attention" can be such a nostalgic appeal away from the rigors of extending the reach of my self-consciousness. It is most comforting for me to live each of my unpleasant feelings as "caused by circumstances," rather than as indicating my defense of the boundaries of my conscious self-tolerance. For instance, I am sorely tempted to trace my unwillingness to increase my hold of self-insight to the illusional "restricting pedagogical procedures imposed upon me," rather than to the self-respecting realization that I helped myself immensely as a child by restricting the zone of my self-conscious living.

My dissociation of my life first into a mental self and "a bodily self" (William James), and then into an individual self and a social self, started in my living of my home, was greatly reenforced by my living of my school. My formal education disciplined me specifically in developing a consciousness for my mind set off from a consciousness for my body and a consciousness for my individuality set over against my everything-else. My self-consciousness came to mean largely my awareness of what Irwin Edman once called "the specific character of the habit-organization" I beheld in my life attitudes. Thus, my individuality divided itself up, and my life developed seeming cross-purposes, will and counter-will. My unified directing of my life seemed impossible, separated self-interests compensated for scattered personal momentum, and my conformist living inhibited my building up (what James called) a "spiritual self" constituted of my own recognized ideals. My formal schooling resulted in my setting up idols, not ideals; environment and heredity, not individuality; circumstances, not soulfulness; seeking happiness and avoiding pain, not enjoying growing pains. The word of the wise was not sufficient. I did not see clearly my identity in the wisdom of my Matthew Arnold,

> Resolve to be thyself; and know, that he
> Who finds himself, loses his misery!

Educator. You distinguish "the acquisition of knowledge of the world of nature around you" as being systematic schooling in self-disesteem, all of it being lived at the cost of conscious development of your own self-power. You see his formal education, in its present form, as defeating the good purpose of the American educator, namely, his intention to have his formal education develop his proper appreciation of the dignity of the individual, cultivate his devotion to self-sovereignty, and further his living of ideal humaneness. Said Condillac, "Science is a well made-language." You conceive your language well made only if it tends to its business of localizing your mental functioning solely and entirely in your mind. Your language is a "book of faded metaphors" in which each word is a historical record of a reality of your mind, defying death as it were by freshly creating the past in the present.

You sense the need of yourself as an educator to acknowledge the fact that your formal education ("the learning of facts about the external world in an objective manner"), instead of developing your native capacity to appreciate the necessity for self-government, actually arrests that kind of development in favor of indulging the illusion of authoritarianism. Is that about it?

Author. Yes. Of the greatest practicality for (my) every American educator is his discovering and courageously upholding just what his traditional schooling may be *expected* to accomplish. For instance, an American teacher senses that he is *supposed* to consider his pupil as capable of using his formal educational experience to provide himself with an understanding of the essential basis of democratic self-sovereignty. Nevertheless, this same teacher also senses that his pupil's learning of his "school subjects," including civics, simply does not constitute for him the development of his appreciation of the importance of his self-awareness, self-possession, self-reliance, self-control, self-respect. Like as not his pupil can graduate himself *cum laude* without sensing his formal education experience as being (nothing but) his own self-development.

In other words, a pupil cannot derive from his so-called "acquisition" of knowledge any insight about the comprehensiveness, or dignity, of his individuality. Only the recognized subject of himself, not "school subjects," can introduce him to the meaning of his self-government. His reading about "Thomas Jefferson" is actually a defense against producing the kind of self-insight which his third President consciously created for himself. The point which needs to be made is "that in order to follow the intricacies of Mr. Jefferson's thought, you must have a mind like his."[6] The self-conscious American pedagog's critique is a matter of his self-analysis. His stock of self-insight is his stock of truth. His mind is his strategic place for *all* his educational living.

Educator. If the momentum of your personal identity allows you to see your sun and moon and stars and earth and every experience as your own, that insight obviates any necessity on your part to concentrate upon your impotency feelings. You trace your every feeling of impotence to a refusal to see your identity in your own power, which you then must feel overwhelmed by. You dispel your illusions of impotence by acknowledging that your living of the meaning of catastrophe is all that there is to it. You extend the boundaries of your conscious self so that it subsumes your erstwhile "opposing" power. One must either admit, or submit, to his own power. All that can prevent one from seeing that he *is* god, is his habit of repudiating all of his kind of living which he did not learn to respect in his earliest years of life. Man cannot get on with or without his fellowman, only *as him.* Education can only be the learning of the given life's wonderful powers. However, if I cannot identify myself in my view of my fellowman's radical individualism, I can escape my conscious living of that discomfort by rejecting it (not seeing it as perfectly desirable) and calling it by a questionable name such as "rampant" or "wild" or even "extreme."

Author. In my opinion, you are now daring to look yourself over. Speculative mental activity is the glorious achievement of the consciously self-oriented one.

Educator. Sometimes I live the recurring notion that you regard the individual patient living his psychiatric ward, or penitentiary, but admittedly focusing his consciousness for the appreciation of his own mind, as doing the most effective work of his world; and you see the so-called "majority" person carrying on his job, earning a livelihood, seeking distraction from his unhappy self-development, treating the mind of his fellowman (either as a layman or professional), as doing little more than occupational therapy for himself.

Author. As I see it, you have quite an idea there. An excitement of my imagination is a delightful thrill of life. Said John Tyndall in his *Fragments of Science*:

> We are gifted with the power of Imagination. . . . and by this power we can lighten the darkness which surrounds the world of the senses. There are tories even in science who regard imagination as a faculty to be feared and avoided rather than employed. They had observed its action in weak vessels and were unduly impressed by its disasters. But they might with equal justice point to exploded boilers as an argument against the use of steam.

Educator. Your distinction of each kind of education, one insightful and the other insightless, seems undoubtedly most helpful for you. As you see it, insightless education requires little personal devotion, whereas insightful education entails great effort on the part of the pupil and extensively developed self-tolerance on the part of the teacher. You conceive one's "formal education" to imply: the learned teacher's imparting knowledge to the ignorant pupil, so that the pupil will not have to feel his ignorance keenly. You find it an advantage to feel your ignorance keenly, in that it represents *appetite for living* which is conceived also as learning.

You have renounced the firmly established educational notion of "getting to know better," quite as you have renounced the firmly established medical notion of "getting to be better." Hidden in the meaning of "better" you see fault-finding. Thus, you renounce the notion of "knowing better," for such a notion implies that previous knowledge was not good enough. You claim that every bit of self-knowledge which you grow is excellent, is all and only about itself, and, therefore, cannot be compared favorably or unfavorably with any previous self-knowledge which you have grown.

Author. Yes. Ever since I noticed the illusional character of knowing "better," and observed that it covered up self-accusation, I have tried strenuously to acknowledge its erstwhile usefulness to me, so that I might live it with sufficient love to be able to renounce it, rather than have to go on living this particular existence of mine as if it were undesirable.

Educator. You mean you do not prefer the solution 2 plus 2 equal 4 to the solution 2 plus 2 equal 5?

Author. "Preference" again implies the illusion of "betweenness." Preference is a derivative of judgment, or of reasoning—not of self-consciousness. My preference has to do with my liking and disliking. My liking or my disliking has to do only with itself, and cannot have anything to do with whatever I say I like or dislike.

Educator. Then none of your knowledge has priority value?

Author. Again, "priority" implies "betweenness," not withinness. Fallacies of education, such as "know better," "preference," and "priority knowledge," are intellectual fronts for deep emotional resistance to the extension of self-tolerance. As a student, I can (insightlessly) claim that my lecturer's viewpoint does violence to my preferred thinking with which I help myself. Thus, I can defend myself against consciously learning whatever of his self-knowledge I have my lecturer voice. However, any new idea which I grow for myself simply cannot "do violence" to any other idea which I have previously created. Each idea of my mind is all and only about itself.

Educator. Are you implying that my mental "opposites" are illusional "opposites," that one idea or feeling cannot contradict another, that all mental conflict is illusional and based upon the delusion that one mental event can have something to do with another?

Author. The idea of opposites is based upon the principle of plurality, not upon the principle of unity. I find that a development of my self-knowledge, my educative process, is always a life development. *Whatever* my mental activity is, it is desirable in that it stands for my living me. It can only be beneficial for me to strive to live with love *whatever* self-knowledge I may happen to grow.

Educator. What *do* you mean by "mental conflict" then?

Author. Mental conflict is an illusion that the occurrence of betweenness is possible. The idea "mental conflict" compensates for the lack of insight regarding the subjectivity of all reality. The meaning "conflict" is employed by my living of judgment and reasoning, not by my living of peace-loving self-consciousness.

Educator. Little wonder contemplative living has been viewed as divine. In your view, one's insightless education cannot evolve his conscious self-knowledge and its underlying development of conscious self-tolerance. It is indulged so that the growing pains of extension of conscious self-tolerance will not be experienced. On the other hand, self-knowledge which is not recognized as being self-knowledge carries all the liabilities of anaesthetised being.

I find it exceedingly helpful to realize that my learning a new point of view cannot be in any sense at the cost of my depreciating any previously held point of view. It seems to me that this insight can prove of the greatest use in enforcing my willingness to grow my self-knowledge. In the past, I have always been afraid that my consideration of any new point of view might somehow lead to my depreciating some one of my beloved lifelong viewpoints. Really this new education orientation gives me an enthusiasm for learning all that I can learn, which I never experienced before. I do know that I can learn responsibly whatever I can live with love.

Author. I have enjoyed this same kind of liberating experience which I have just had my you describe.

Educator. You have stated that your liking or disliking is all and only about itself, despite everyone's taken-for-granted attitude that either can refer to some other "object" which thus becomes a liked, or disliked, object. Such a view is a typical one of those which at least appear to be incompatible with my previous views on that subject. I can see how my liking, or disliking, depends entirely upon me, upon my own momentary needs. For instance, if I were freezing to death I would like a wooden cigar-store Indian for burning, instead of Michelangelo's marble Moses. Or, if I were starving and thirsting to death, I would like a crust of bread and glass of water, instead of a pile of gold. And so on.

I notice right now as I am developing this theme, as my own, that I am already beginning to see my new view of liking, or disliking, as not incompatible with my previous views on that subject—that it is just another view of mine which is all about itself.

Author. Exactly. As long as I must consider any of my mental content as being only "your" view, I am implicitly acknowledging my unreadiness to live that view consciously as being my own. My Lincoln's insight is applicable here: He who refuses to examine both sides of a question is dishonest.

Educator. Certainly I am learning that self-rejection means only unreadiness to live with love. This localization of function of liking, or disliking, is similarly applicable to every other emotional living, e.g., love is all and only about itself, hate is its own only "object," fear is all and only about fear, guilt is just exactly guilt and cannot refer to anything else, and so on.

Author. I find the basic truth, *Whatever is, all and only is,* to be most helpful for my life orientation.

Educator. I realize that I cannot ask (my) you a question, that only (my) you can do that. However, I am making a study of the meaning "enemy" in the effort to distinguish fact and fancy about it. It does seem overwhelmingly true at times that I can dislike the wrongdoing which my enemy does, if not my enemy himself.

Author. Yes. I find every such view useful in my effort to defend myself against *thoroughly* overwhelming myself, by recognizing all that I dislike in my enemy as only that which I am not ready to see as involuntary (unconscious) in myself. My "enemy" is of greatest use for my self-analysis.

Educator. How can one ever grow the experience to see the selfish advantage to himself in loving his enemy, in cherishing someone who has even sworn to destroy him, in seeing his enemy's open hostility toward him as being even desirable, much less adorable?

Author. For accomplishing this life-saving task I have had to create and cultivate a right view of it. Once I learned that such an accomplishment was *possible,* I sought the experience of observing how my thus-accomplished fellowman worked his mind to attain this wonderful felicity. I discovered this kind of experience of mine to be no school lesson, but rather a soul-shaking, death-defying course of my true self-love.

Educator. You mean that you had to face realistically the meanings of yourself which you had hidden in your enemy-living? You mean that you had to lose face in order to save face? You mean that you had to make peace with your cowardice which enabled your distraction from, and forgetting of, intolerably fearful self-experiences?

Author. Whatever I mean, to be sure, is only my self-meaning. I have had (my) you describe some of the hardships through which I developed the hardihood to call my soul (including my enemy) my own.

Educator. Please describe how you conduct your enemy-living now.

Author. First of all, my enemy-living is mine, all mine. I am my own "enemy," and see him trying to help himself as best he presently can. I see his life as his own, all his. He may or may not live this truth consciously, and thereby hangs the tale of his inimical conduct. As long as he blindly decides he can be hostile to someone else, he can go on hurting himself under the alias "somebody else." Where my insight helps me most is in my glad realization that no one but myself can have anything whatsoever to do with my living. Thus, if I choose to indulge my illusion that my enemy can hurt me, that indulgence exercises my own (unconscious and involuntary) recurring need to make that illusion conscious in myself so that I can grow the loving insight to renounce it eventually. In addition, my appreciation of the fact that all so-called "hurting" is really just the only available limited helpfuness, is a truly comforting realization.

Educator. You mean that by seeing and heeding the truth that *your* enemy's self-hurt is really his limited self-helpfulness, you spare yourself the necessity of living *your* enemy as just hurting himself.

Author. I cannot but observe the great amount of self-helpfulness in recognizing that my enemy is always helping himself as much as he can.

Educator. How about the "turn the other cheek" and the "give him your coat also" treatment of your enemy?

Author. The principle of charity is the most reliable rock upon which I can build my self-world. The giver is always his own receiver; the receiver is always his own giver. I can only "turn the other cheek" and "give my coat" to myself, and therein lies the wisdom of extreme charity which otherwise might seem imprudent.

Educator. You find that your discovering that all of your "betweenness" living is illusional, is also the process of dispelling that illusion. Then, you can observe that the living in question is all withinness living after all. You find that once a spouse observes that "betweenness" cannot apply to his, or her, mate, all hostilities based upon that betweenness illusion cease. Is not that state of bliss in which there is freedom from the difference between the sexes usually ascribed to wish-fulfilment in this life and to realization only in the life beyond?

Author. That may be. Whatever self-view one lives now but ascribes to any other "time" or "place" (such as "the beyond," "heaven," "spiritual life," "divinity," "after life") serves as a defense against overwhelming his sense of personal identity with meanings for which he has not yet developed his conscious self-tolerance.

Educator. You mean that it is salutary for me to have the extent of self-tolerance which can enable me to carry my imagination so far as to be able to view myself as god with all of my heavenly living within me?

Author. Speaking to, for, and about myself, I see only benefit derivable from complete freedom of my imagination and from boundless extension of my conscious self-tolerance, to my life's fulfilment. Such is my idea of my ideal education.

Educator. I am finding that (my) your two-voice-soliloquy has started me realizing that I must do all of my own listening, as well as all of my own talking.

Returning to the subject of my enemy-living, you must know that Freud discovered that one's "enemy" always stands for a once dearly beloved one who only later became a focus of fear and hatred. That is a view which one cannot live comfortably, unless he has already developed the conscious self-tolerance it requires.

Author. I measure my momentary conscious self-tolerance by my willingness to see that my every like (or dislike) is all and only about itself, and that it signalizes all and only my readiness (or unreadiness) to appreciate lovingly whatever my life happens to be creating of my self-experience. Whenever I can appreciate fully that any distressful experience I have lived is thoroughly desirable (such as my imagined loss of my wholeness, e.g., "loss of my loved one"), then my mind is entirely healed about it.

Educator. I notice that you seem to enjoy imagining psychic unifications, making novel syntheses of your mental content, conceiving a whole where before you saw but parts.

Author. Yes. Whenever I can create a new totality which subsumes this, that, and the other view, such an economy proves to be energy-saving. My living is always a creative process, and I like to exercise *conscious* creativity when I can. Furthermore, all of any so-called "part" has its entire meaning from its wholeness.

Educator. You see every human being as the very creator of all of his humanity. Please use your conscious creativity to compose a condensed version of your ideal learning process.

Author. I shall try. Basically, love of learning is synonymous with love of living, unmodified love being the natural feeling characteristic of all living which is not overwhelming, not disturbing to the learner's sense of personal identity (including his unorganized developmental beginnings of his personal identity). Conversely, dislike for learning is synonymous with dislike for living. My every dislike is modified love which is characteristic of every kind of overwhelming living. Again, "overwhelming living" is self-experience which seems irreconcilable with the learner's conscious will, or sense of personal identity. In the interest of self-preservation it is all-important for the learner to be of one mind with respect to his appreciation of his own personal identity. My awareness that I am is absolutely essential for my caring the least bit as to whether I live or die. I can be conscious of wanting to live only insofar as I can be conscious of my love, of my sensitive appreciation of my real life.

Love, the fundamental joy of living, promulgates and propagates pleasing *self*-consciousness. Love underlies and supports the grateful appreciation of wholeness of individuality. Love unifies, harmonizes, synthesizes, and thus upholds the truth of oneness. Love is the principle of pure pleasure which enables the learner to see that his life is worth living and that each of his life lessons is worth learning. Only his illusional distancing himself from his stars has obstructed his use of them.

Every unhappy feeling (such as sadness, fear, hate, guilt, shame, pain itself, and so on) is a derivative of love but is first recognizable only as if it were the absence of love. The same meaning tends to make every kind of unhappiness objectionable, namely, its significance as a threat to the individual's appreciation of his wholeness (oneness, allness, unity). *Careful study shows that, just as ready love reveals the reality of oneness, reluctant love (every pain, every unhappiness) introduces the illusion of more, or less, than one.* My every pain (including painful feeling) tempts me to try to degrade (by personally disowning) whatever self-experience (life-lesson) distresses me. Thus, I misinterpret every kind of body ordeal ("injury," "disease") as being an attempted violation of my individuality, as being an effort to have two bodies occupy the same space at the same time, as being my vain striving to subsume a "foreign body" as such (as a "something else," or "somebody else"). My apparently "hard heart" really bounds and protects whatever conscious tenderheartedness remains to me of my personally acknowledged world.

Careful investigation of the relevant facts discloses that every person's living (learning) process is always absolutely ideal *for him.* Thus, on one occasion the only way in which he *can* learn (live) the lesson of his self-experience is unconsciously (by denying that it consists entirely of his consciously appreciated creaturehood). On another occasion he can freely acknowledge that his life's course is necessarily constituted of the course of his own human development and that, appreciated as such, it is his surest lease on life. Can I be a practical advocate of practicality if I do not revere whatever is? How mindful Michael Faraday's view, "What is the use of a newborn baby?"

Educator. Brevity is inspirational. (My) you only state that conscious love observes the truth of oneness, and that unconscious love (serving as painful sensations and feelings) observes the illusion of more, or less, than one. Thus, it would take at least two individuals for me to indulge my illusion of living "somebody else" with dislike (i.e., with fear, shame, disgust, blame, suspicion, and so on). Conscious love completely fulfils the wish to live; unconscious love calls the wish to live in question. For you, every learning process is ideal; for obviously it is the only one which the given learner is ready to use whenever he activates it consciously or unconsciously.

Author. (My) your version of your author's ideal learning process is a condensed one which I can use for my further disciplining of my mind in self-perceptiveness.

Educator. Each incentive, to live and to learn, being one and the same, I would like to have you speak your mind on the subject of sexual enlightenment. Certainly the growing individual has tremendous interest in his sexual living and a proportionate motivation to learn about it.

In my study of the scientific literature on the subject I find little mention of the heart of sexuality, of the actual surging, self-satisfying, soul-stirring sensations exciting every human being genitally and generally to the awesome wonders of male and female rapture, including the culminant ecstasy of orgasmic waves fusing life-affirming sensation and death-defying passion into one glorious experience of male and female godliness. My finding shows nearly all of this kind of basic and concentrated meaning of human life treated as humorous or left to non-scientific writers who, for the most part, allow allusions to it to serve for free-souled frankness. Please explain that almost universal lack of scientific plain-dealing with detailed sexual meaning.

Author. My explanation is a simple one, although it may seem unpleasant, and hence, may hardly be given sober consideration. Only the writer who can live his views of sexuality consciously as being completely under his own volitional control can employ these views in the service of service, that is, as educational material which does not overwhelm him. Only the writer of this extent of self-consciousness *can* use his sexual meanings without experiencing them as sensations and passions which use him. The precious heart of sexual meaning is seldom discussed educationally on account of its power of thus "taking over" and thereby evoking feelings of lust or prudishness or both.

Educator. Are you simply observing that in my estimating the level of self-culture of my fellowman generally, I may tend to let my wish for his emotional maturity run away with my judgment? that I ascribe to everyone of my humanity a greatly unwarranted high-level development of self-discipline? that I habitually overlook the fact that my fellowman does not need to sink very far from where he is in his self-helpfulness, in order to illustrate the primitiveness, the restricted egotism, underlying his everyday show of morality? that I settle for latent readiness for *evident* outbreak of human immaturity, in order to be able to comfort myself with my illusional manifestations of culture? that I need absolutely to help myself by avoiding seeing and hearing the innumerable fearsome distress signals constantly being loosed in my world? that I seem incapable of learning my everyday, every-hour, urgent life lesson to be up and doing in the service of consciously creating the necessary *real* living (learning) conditions of enduring peace, prosperity, loving-kindness, and whole-souled appreciation of my living, based only upon my ever ongoing self-consciousness?

Author. That is precisely what I observe, but only of my own self's world.

Educator. You realize that your difficultly maintained ideal of education as being conscious self-revelation would reunite poetry and science. I am reminded of the mature Goethe's reference to his fellowman's unreadiness to see how natural was the synthesis of his scientific and poetic strivings:

> On all sides people refused to admit that science and poetry could be united. They forgot that science had developed from poetry; they failed to consider that after a cycle of generations both might easily meet again on a higher level in a friendly spirit and to mutual advantage.

You would have it, Where a person's love is, there is that one's conscious personal identity. Such all-loving self-identity reminds me of the Punjabi poem of Shams Tabrez:

How insane was Majnun,
He fell in love with Leila,
Leila left him and he became sad and lonely,
How strange is Shams Tabrez, he fell in love with himself,
As he saw himself, he found nothing but God in himself.

He saw the lovableness of love as the inmost reality of the soul of the lover. You renounce the whole idea of your "being loved" as an illusion based upon your projection of your own feeling of love—which semblance supports the illusions of betweenness and of plurality. To forget self is to die a little, you say to yourself. Your "doing," "having," "feeling," "thinking," "sensing"—each is all and only your being. As author, you see your writing notes to yourself as saving you from being a life-beaten man.

Author. Yes. In his last years Goethe made the following statement (to Soret, a young French tutor at court) of the guiding principle of his career as an author:

> In my professional career as a writer I have never asked: what does the mass of people want and how can I serve society as a whole? But I have always merely endeavored to make myself wiser and better and to increase the substance of my own personality, and then always to express only that which I had recognized as good and true. This, to be sure, as I will not deny, has been effective and useful in a large way; that, however, was not the purpose, but the absolutely necessary consequence.

May everyone of my fellow educators at least consider asking himself life-meaning questions. Is so-called conventional education (learning knowledge from "somebody else" and "something else" about "somebody else" and "something else") an advantage over that which it affects to replace, namely, acknowledged self-ignorance? Are one's "cures" generally as desirable as the "illnesses" they are intended to rid one of? Is one's enslavement to so-called educational authority as much to be wished for as one's freedom of recognized self-interest and self-curiosity? Is anyone's educational system, with its necessarily scattered remains of that one's self-consciousness, with its illusional passivity, as choice as is his concerted self-consciousness in the unsophisticated study of his life? All "passivity" is illusional. Divinity (allness) is *actus purus,* pure activity, subjective being. Whatever is, actually is, and actively is. Does not literally every word of a received vocabulary trade upon the mind-dissociating illusion of objectivity? Is there any sanely accurate name for anyone or anything but the one: I am that I am? Is not every meaning of a mind's knowledge, other than that it is all and only about itself, actually null and void? When any meaning at all is taken for "objective" knowledge, is not the illusion of a mental hiatus thereby necessarily created? Must not every consideration of "objectivity" posit a break in continuity of *subjectivity?* Indeed, is not my precarious "human culture" the product of educational discipline in self-unconsciousness? Is not all of my consciousness which I do not experience as *self*-consciousness a mask and disguise of my very own life's essential oneness? Can the meaning of the *good* be precisely defined as the product of conscious *episteme,* not of unconscious *doxa?*

The story of one's paying too much for his whistle is an old one. As in today's so-called "scientific treatises," there was

> hardly anything that had not been treated in the writings of the famous sophists of the fifth century. . . . All this encyclopaedic knowledge is set aside and annulled by Socrates. As regards these different branches of knowledge he confesses his complete ignorance. He knows only *one* art: the art of forming a human soul, of approaching a man and convincing him that he does not understand what life is and means.[7]

My life experience regularly surpasses my *conscious* self-view (my sensing of my personal identity). My living of my being, therefore, consistently amounts to my continuous going beyond the limits of my consciously appreciated selfhood. Thus, I need all of the power of my creative imagination in order to be able to conceive that I *really* am whatever momentarily may "appear" as not-I. Implicit devotion to the truth of my allness, oneness, and wholeness, in the face of my appearances of "otherness," is my standard measure of my ideal sanity, morality, humaneness, holiness, might, and right. I cannot "receive" any learning, lesson, teaching, discipline, or any other kind of educational benefit, any more than I can "receive" my ignorance; I *create* each.

Most difficult of all self-knowledge to create is the educator-learner's realization that every possible movement, or gesture, or expression, of his individuality's constitution is his life's activity—meaningfully mental, ideally spirited. There can be no real "living out"—all such apparent "externalization" having only the unconscious (but intimately personal) meaning of rite (ritual). Worship is the being, and belief is the rite. It is what I *do* which also reveals to me what I feel and think, and often to my great wonderment. The soul of myself is all that there is for me, and it is the soul of myself I wish to know consciously, nothing else. Absolutely nothing else. Plato noted, and later St. Augustine recorded it, "Do not go out of thyself, return to thyself, it is in the interior essence of man that the truth resides." All belief depends upon loved being. Freud observed that the infant discovers he can benefit from *his living* of "being loved."

And now I can hear my fellow educator say, "Still, how about your knowledge of science, education, psychology, mathematics, art, literature, and even religion?" My answer to such questioning of my own is always the same one, call it Socratic if you please, "I am not yet able to know myself consciously, and it seems irrelevant to investigate whatever I cannot study as myself."

Educator. Many a teacher has wondered at the viewpoint you have created, that negation is *always* illusional. For instance, that means that I could go through your writing and cancel every negative, and still have you willingly consider the statement thus altered. Every one of your negations is merely a grammatical device for developing your theme with negative particulars which actually point up *positive* views.

Author. Yes. Wherever I use a negative, it is essential for my mental balance that I be equally ready to consider an affirmative. Wherever I say "No," my "No" lacks solidity to the extent that I cannot soberly consider "Yes" in its place. Where there is no "Yes," there cannot be a testing "No"; where there is no "No," there cannot be a tested "Yes." Every "Yes" is enabled by the "No" which is theoretically anterior to it; every "No" is enabled by the "Yes" which is theoretically anterior to it. Still, every "No" is as *affirmatively posited* as is every "Yes," and in that fundamental respect it is positive, not negative. Note how the latter use of the double negative makes a positive. Negation, itself, *always* stands for repression—that is, for the denial of what is.

Educator. Please illustrate how negative is positive.

Author. I shall make several negative and positive statements showing how each is all about itself, a positive statement.

Negation: I am no horse, I am a human being.

Affirmation: Every human being creates all that he means by "horse."

Negation: I cannot imagine myself being dead.

Affirmation: I can deny only what I can imagine.

Negation: 2 plus 2 do not equal 5.

Affirmation: 2 plus 2 do equal 5 according to my special system of counting, or according to inaccurate counting, or according to a fairy tale, etc.

Freud elucidated the meaning of negation most clearly in his classic study of the same name. When I deny that one thing can have any meaning for another thing, I am really affirming the positive point that each thing is all and only about itself. If I deny that my fellowman has performed his lesson at all, I am affirming that he has succeeded excellently in another direction. When I deny that I can recall an event, I am affirming that I have succeeded in repressing it. When I deny that I like whatever I am living, I am affirming that I would rather create it than not (e.g., than be unconscious, drugged, dead). By denying the existence of "objectivity," I am affirming the absoluteness of subjectivity —"objectivity" being a name for ignored *subjectivity.*

Educator. I can see that the first years of my life were full of most exciting adventures of deepest meaning. For example, I first met and formed an opinion of my mother and father and each one of my family. I first discovered the marvelous uses of my wonderful mind, including my body. I first took hold of myself in nearly every way. Now then, why is it that I, and everyone else I know of, cannot recall any of that most important living of those very first years?

Author. You raise a soul-stirring question which Freud asked himself over fifty years ago. His answer in every way confirmed and extended his views about the nuclear mind-shaping significance of one's first years of life. I mark well both this question and its answer which contain the most far-reaching, life-saving value for all of my humanity.

I cannot really "recall" my earliest life events or my most recent ones, for all that I can possibly experience is my *present* living only. I cannot voluntarily present for my *now* living whatever of my life experience has undergone repression; and, as I have already indicated, vast amounts of my earliest experiences were lived with so very much unhappiness of rejection that they sooner or later became repressed ("forgotten"). Thus, I arrested the development of my natural proclivities and, instead of eventually learning the safe and sane conscious use of them, I made them unconscious ("forgot them"). Thereby, I forfeited access to vitality which is potentially most useful for my enjoying a happy, wholesome life course.

Every parent's amnesia for his first years of life measures his unreadiness to understand lovingly his living of his own baby's instinctive nature and needs. Every parent, if he will, may enjoy excellent opportunity for self-analysis in the living of his, or her, infant. Psychoanalytic work (self-analysis) helps one to restore to his voluntary use the precious life force he has had to reject as being his own (repress) during his living his infanthood and earliest childhood. Hence it is, Freud recorded those sage words of greatest import for every mind developed sufficiently to appreciate them, "Whatever we can expect in the way of prophylaxis against neurosis in the individual lies in the hands of a psychoanalytically enlightened education."[8]

Educator. According to your view ("Whatever is, is perfect") there can be no error, no defect, no shortcoming, no fallibility, no desideratum. Every such appearance of evil, weakness, wrong, sin, badness, untruth, or of any other apparent negation of good, is simply a perfect, desirable, helpful sign of an individual's life-saving limits of momentary self-consciousness. In other words, you regard every possible kind of degree of the apparently objectionable to be really a wonderful humaneness, however thoroughly disguised it may be. Your view of the individual's original allness, considered from the educator's standpoint, would call for a complete reorientation of the general theory of knowledge as it is now upheld by nearly every educator.

Author. Yes. I renounce regarding as odious, or mean-spirited, any living of mine, even that which I feel I must temporarily withhold from my self-conscious living in order to keep my mental balance (uphold my sense of my personal identity). To maintain my mental equilibrium (preserve my conscious self-control) I must be able to feel *equal* to my experience, so that its sameness is felt by me as an expression of my lovable selfsameness. My conscious mind instinctively shrinks from seeing its identity in its painful living, on the principle that life must be enjoyable in order to seem worth living.

Educator. Your view of education is not new and original but old and eclectic. It embodies many of the features of those of Plato, Aristotle, St. Augustine, and Spinoza. Also, Thomas Aquinas conceived his man as an organic unity with sense experience the very beginning and prerequisite of his self-knowledge, with his moral order a product of his conscious freedom (not impressed upon him), and with his own social instinct constructing his own altruism (family, community, and state ties).

Author. My view of education, can be observed only by me. I am the only one-and-all who can know *anything* about it. I observe to myself that it is entirely new and original. Realistically conceived, one's every "study" (art, religion, science, education, and so on) is nothing but one's own contrived help to discover his already existing, but still unrecognized, knowledgable selfhood (esthetic self, religious self, divine self, knowing and learned self, and so on).

Educator. Please discuss your view of order, or design, in nature.

Author. What one calls "pattern" or "order" or "design" is really nothing but one's freedom from fault-finding, a respect for observation of whatever is, a realization of the ubiquitousness of perfection, a due appreciation of necessity as being the only real accounting for any so-called "order."

Educator. Please state your understanding of the condition most favorable for a student's learning.

Author. The degree of my love for what I am studying is all-important. Whatever I learn *with personal interest* respects the personal nature of my learning process. *I study with greatest concentration when I can recognize that my studying is achieving for me the growth of my conscious self.* To be sure, all of my research, study, or investment of my interest *is* constantly accomplishing my self-growth. However, my view that my learning is a revering of my own life provides the condition of self-love most natural for the exercise of my learning process.

Educator. Can you offer some explanation as to why it often seems easier to learn when one is young, and harder to learn when one is old?

Author. I satisfy myself with the answer that artificial segregation of "young" and "old" is one of the factors that plays an important role in every kind of learning. Everyone is always of the same age. Each infant (or child) is the only "old" person that he can ever know. Each senescent is the only infant (or child) that he can ever know.

A human being is always either a conscious or unconscious student of his own life's experiences. Any so-called "old" human being cannot study youthful interests effectively if he cannot be conscious of his own youthfulness. Thus, a so-called "older" person who conceives that he is also young, thereby frees his ability to learn whatever stands for "young." To illustrate, a senescent person who recognizes that his senescence really means that he has lived his infanthood, childhood, and all of his youthfulness throughout his life's course, can study with personal interest (available self-love) all about his current youthful events.

Whatever I attempt to study "impersonally" (whatever life experience I regard with indifference) sets up a mental condition which is unfavorable for the free, full exercise of my learning process. *My ability to recognize that my studying is really an extension of my sense of personal identity provides the condition most favorable to my learning process.* I have cultivated my conscious appreciation of this true meaning of my education, and thus developed my capacity to study with great self-satisfaction and little fatigue.

Educator. Your idea of health education is based solely upon the natural sensibility of the individual. It might be termed *human hygiene.* It reminds me of D'Alembert's notion, "Locke reduced metaphysics to what it ought to be in fact, the experimental physics of the soul." Educator experience has demonstrated that such an exacting growth of self-insight requires a special breed of educator. Therefore any general use of your self-consciousness nostrum must wait either for the Age of the Individual or, at least, for the development of a center of learning realistically characterized by individuality-consciousness. Only a teacher who imbues his education-living with his subjectivity-consciousness *can* respect the allness of human individuality. And no professional educator I know of has considered such a learning ideal as feasible for his practical standard. That kind of organizational program would be just as troublesome as one based upon conscious self-sovereignty. I find it most disquieting to follow some of your extreme statements about individuality. You go beyond me in your mind-conscious theorizing. For me you make entirely too much over your capacity to *imagine* freely you are fully living anything, anyone, anyway, any time, any place, and so on. As I see it, you claim entirely too much life importance for your being able to use your imagination to live entirely as you please. I can hardly believe that all of my real emotional frustration is always traceable to my inability simply to use my mind in some desired way. All of that kind of claim you make (for the life-saving helpfulness of your freedom of just your mind's use) seems too farfetched for me.

Author. It may help (my) you to realize that I do not speak for (my) you, only for myself. I wish to aim my speaking toward the vocalizing of self-consciousness itself, not toward "liking" or "disliking."

I find it most difficult of all to study my self-consciousness as my *summum bonum,* as my only recipe for happiness which promises sustained and sustaining results. These conversations of mine might be described as "treatises on the theory (i.e., *practice*) of virtue (i.e., self-consciousness)."[9]

Educator. You conceive your ethic to be an issue of your self-sentience, I see. Your ethic is to be true consciously to what you can see is your own nature, is it not? You do believe that moral, virtuous life consists of victorious living, do you not?

Author. All I *can* be true to is to my own truth (i.e., my own nature). When I use the term "victorious," I must consider, "Victorious *over* what?" My realization that I must always be my own loser as well as victor forces me to recognize the advantage in renouncing my goal of "victorious" battling, and to rely upon my goal of self-conscious living.

Only my access to this fine human sensibility of mine (self-sentience) *can* provide me with my experience of taste, or relish, enabling me consciously to choose what is helpful for my human excellence.[10] As the third Earl of Shaftesbury stated it, "Even conscience I fear, such as is owing to religious discipline, will make but a slight figure where this taste is set amiss."

Educator. You account for every description of a so-called "evil" life on the basis that it is autobiographical for merely a fraction of a person's development torn, so to say, from its good and fine context. You see every apparent wickedness as an unrecognized good effort at self-help.

Author. I know of no surer way of damming up the stream of my conscious creativity than by disregarding the truth of my own achievement of living myself (my world, my all) helpfully. I know of no more satisfying sight than that of my self-conscious fellowman seeing that his life (his world, his all) is *all* about him.

Educator. Again, why do you insist upon educating your consciousness to report selfness only?

Author. This question helps me to be aware of a life-saving truth: Only by living my allness-oneness-wholeness consciously can I renounce any strategy of living based upon my own mental dissociation. By living self-consciously I can renounce (1) any notion of victorious living which posits a victory negating its own purpose (by ignoring that every defeat is its own), and (2) any notion of defeated living which posits a defeat negating its own purpose (by ignoring that every victory is its own).

Educator. It is your view that "Education" (my personification of my formalized power of learning) is not really taken seriously, on account of the specific fact that it ("Education") obviously has not been dependable for creating the cultural attainments which would clearly reveal everyone's (world's) troubles as the helpful signs that the truth of the inviolability of human individuality is being disregarded, now generally. Even my American teacher's training school study does not adequately uphold and exalt as the art of experience the all-important fact that one's reverence for his human individuality is the overal-all special interest and most essential criterion of the sane teacher.

You find "calling attention to the world's troubles" and "concentration upon the individual's dire need for self-consciousness" as one and the same problem, a unification which goes unrecognized as such by the very one who decides the declaration of war and the disturbance of peace. In other words, you have discovered all of one's schooling, other than schooling for self-consciousness, not only to be impotent for providing peace but actually potent for promoting war. Of your innumerable fellowmen who claim that the individual derives his identity from outside objects serving as "frames of reference" and that even the motivation for his own development lies outside every individual, you simply observe, "Each one is helping himself ideally in his own way." Of man's "need for opposition," or "helpful antagonism," you simply observe: "Man's own resistance to extending his own self-love to include his own life experience is all of the so-called 'opposition' he *can* need or benefit from."

Surely you must realize that everyone *is* self-conscious, whether he tells himself that fact or not. Everyone willingly acknowledges his power of consciousness and the fact that it is his. That realization is satisfying to me. Are you unhappy if your fellowman does not give to his self-consciousness the centrality in his educational experience which you have laboriously worked up for it in yours? If your fellowman requires a certain limit to his waking up, thus benefiting from a partial sleep while presumably awake, need that bother you? If the wish to sleep tends to dominate even your fellowman's waking life so that his unconscious fears and desires too largely decide his selection of his conscious sensations and perceptions, must you regard all such unrecognized drowsiness as a dangerous shortcoming? Can you not see that all is for the best?

Author. Such is the kind of questioning with which I discovered both the urgent desirability of, and extreme difficulty in, my self-conscious educational living.

Educator. How can you expect the average person to see the connection between his promoting war for his world and his indulgence in a slumbering kind of wakefulness which dulls his responsibility for his being?

Author. My experience in attaining insight about the sanative force derivable from *devotion to self-conscious learning* has been so very arduous and of such a specific kind of endeavor, that I have long since renounced assuming my fellowman, except in rare instances, has helped himself by striving to attain very much coverage for his self-consciousness. Least of all do I assume that he has discovered it to be the indispensable basis for his world's peace, or the lack of it the indispensable basis for his world's war.

As I see it, any so-called "cultural attainment" of mine which I can see benefits me has the basis necessary for its benefiting my mankind. As Goethe averred to Luden, "Mankind? It is an abstraction." One who can see that "mankind" stands for him has the true speciality and incentive requisite for furthering the so-called "interests of mankind."

Educator. Maybe you use too many scholarly quotations. You are often too difficult to follow. Are you implying that nearly everyone of your world is quite out of his mind? Do you mean that nearly everyone you ever meet is grievously disturbed in his mind? Are you diagnosing the average man as a kind of psychopathic moron? Do you consider everyone insane until he proves himself sane? Are you objecting to your fellowman's easy sense of identity?

Author. As I pose each question to myself, the same reply occurs for each one: Only my fellowman can know how he uses his mind. *Every* human being I *ever* live sanely, I must live with a sense of awe before the (for me) unknowable nature of his (for me) mystic subjective individuality.

Educator. This is the life lesson which would put the educator on his feet again, right side up, and restore everyone's faith in the power of education for promoting welfare rather than war, all at once?

Author. My "questioning" is all my own *being,* pointing my interest in its direction to see myself create my answer.

As far as I can now imagine the facts involved, I see no solution for a problem created by irresponsibility other than to (1) renounce irresponsibility or (2) suffer the awful consequences.

Educator. That kind of stark realism reminds me of a statement of A. N. Whitehead, "No science can be more secure than the unconscious metaphysics which it tacitly presupposes."[11]

I may begin to enjoy seeing that my cultivation of inner conviction of my rights as an individual cannot supersede the rights of anyone of *my* world, whether or no (my) he considers himself as a member of a "group." All of my trouble may start the moment I live as if I can "externalize," or "objectify," or otherwise anaesthetize myself.

Author. Individual irresponsibility has a long head start in my educational living. I tend to overwhelm myself by considering how immense the task of any educator who would go about standing for self-conscious living. Considering the alternative to be far worse, however, I can try conceiving that, to promote peace and prevent war, the educator must devote himself as exclusively as possible to paying attention to *his* allness, oneness, wholeness, and nowness as being his enlightened educational ideal for creating a humanity become conscious and loving, hence divinely wise. Emerson did say of his United States, "Union must be inward. . . . Union must be ideal in actual individualism."

Educator. I formerly judged it most helpful of all to be able to prevent my being aware of my so-called evil thoughts. Now I discover that by repressing any activity of mine I not only overemphasize its meaning but lose conscious control of its force, and that by renouncing any activity of mine I consciously control it with merely its due emphasis. How can I tell whether I am repressing or renouncing experiences which I am living? Such knowledge must furnish the basis for the mental hygiene of individualism.

Author. I can tell by the sense of power I enjoy when I renounce, and by the sense of impotence I suffer when I repress. Through my process of repression I impoverish, and through my process of renunciation I enrich, my potentially conscious ego, the source of my sense of personal identity. To illustrate, a person's genius is not complete which does not include its masculine and feminine elements. Nevertheless, it is only the rare soul, a Shakespeare or a Goethe, who is conscious of such identity.

As a man I may renounce my femininity (or, as a woman I may renounce my masculinity) and thus free the scope of my conscious imagination. Conversely, as a man I may repress my femininity (or, as a woman I may repress my masculinity) and thus limit the range of my conscious imagination. My repression always involves self-rejection, resistance to consideration, withdrawal from conscious imagination. My renunciation always involves self-appreciation, readiness for consideration, accessibility for conscious imagination. All of my frustration and feeling of impotence derives only from my limited use of my conscious imagination (enabled by repression). All of my life satisfaction and feeling of power derives only from my uninhibited use of my conscious imagination (enabled by renunciation). It helps to score the truth that my renunciation requires me to take the trouble to see that *whatever living is concerned* is good, desirable, perfect, ideal. Only by thus exerting my self-love can I rescue such living from the overemphasis of prohibition. Only its prohibition (negation) can overemphasize any of my living so that it becomes obsessive or compulsive.

Educator. Hardest for me to understand is your position that you find nothing to choose between one man's way of self-help and another's, nothing "higher" or "lower" in your note of ubiquitous perfection, nothing uplifting or progress-oriented in your course of development, nothing of the kind of "more idealistic than thou" in your single standard of all-is-divine, nothing of communication in your use of language, nothing of fault-finding in your fact-finding perspective, nothing of past or future in your all-and-only present living, nothing dogmatic, sceptical, or critical in your consciousness of the desirability of whatever your life makes happen. Your conversational rule is: the speaker is always right.

In your one-man "revival of learning" I do see one proposition clearly: You choose to point up your localization-of-mental-functioning idea, for only that finding can define truly the sphere of any possible human meaning,—hence the only sphere of proper human activity. "The proper study of mankind" must refer exactly and only to the one man making the given study.

Please condense your concept of noology,—the real subject of experience regarded purely as mental.

Author. Hygienic human learning is the growth of self-knowledge from *consciously* undergoing the life (self-) experience which creates it,—the hygienic intellectual act being considered as complete only when its human derivation and end in the learner's life process are evident. The insightfully (sanely) educated man is *consciously* self-educated. All of my growing of my "mind-stuff" (Clifford), or wisdom, is entirely self-development, just as is all of my growing of my embroyonic, foetal, and post-natal organs.

Educator. I can accept your thesis that theoretic vision is most practical. In his thought-filled book, *Personal Knowledge,* Michael Polanyi points out, ". . . the act of knowing includes an appraisal; and this personal coefficient, which shapes all factual knowledge, bridges in doing so the disjunction between subjectivity and objectivity."[12] He too calls attention to "the objectivist urge to depersonalize our intelligent mental processes."

Author. Most helpful is every such record of an eminent scientist revealing his truth that so-called "impersonal" knowledge must be a synonym for nonexistent knowledge.

Educator. You assert that your word "self" is a momentary existent; that it names the allness-oneness-wholeness of your individuality at any given moment; that one of its powers is consciousness; that your concern now is not so much the nature of the factors by virtue of which they form your self, but rather the nature of the one factor, the inviolable wholeness of your individuality; that self-consciousness, itself, subsumes the very forces historically considered to be constitutive of your sense of personal identity (e.g., "memory," "collection of different perceptions," "contrasting otherness," "judgment and reasoning data," and similar so-called "phenomenological" accountings); that every so-called "materialistic" mental event, such as "surface phenomenon," is really the product of self-unconsciousness; that, for example, "surface" is a term which supports the useful "objectivity" illusion which an individual needs for bridging over his experiences of self-amnesia and self-consciousness; that consciousness for one's self-world is the sure source of peace; that peace of mind (or of soul) is the only possible peace. Alfred Jules Ayer has stated in *Language, Truth, and Logic* (1936) that the philosopher must become a scientist, in the sense of his philosophy's developing into the logic of science, in order to make a substantial contribution to the growth of human knowledge.

Author. I would imagine that my great scientist, Professor Ayer, lived only his own mind to experience every one of his views.

Educator. To sum up further now, this conversation seems to be essentially a dissertation on epistemology, or gnoseology, which asserts all knowledge to be wholly and only the product of one's own mental experience. You also firmly assert that this educational insight is:

(1) indispensable for one's education to mental health,
(2) fiercely resisted by one who has not yet succeeded in making it his own,
(3) created only by one's own self-analysis, and
(4) essential for peace of mind.

Freud recognized, did he not, that subjectivity is the sole possible source of human experience?

Author. Particularly through his persevering work upon his hypothesis of unconscious mentation Freud has made most valuable contributions to epistemology, that discpline which can provide most profound understanding of human nature. One can hardly overemphasize the importance for the appreciation and conduct of peaceful life of discoveries deriving from his theory of the very method or grounds of knowledge itself.

In 1909, at Clark University, Freud pointed out the fact that one may have knowledge including the active force of that knowledge, without realizing or believing that he has it. In 1913 he already recorded his insight that his analysand uses his formal self-analysis to create his own conscious self-knowledge which then relieves him of the necessity for his symptom,

> Even in the later stages of analysis one must be careful not to give a patient the solution of a symptom or the translation of a wish until he is already so close to it that he has only one short step more to make in order to get hold of the explanation for himself.[13]

This was a most valuable epistemological discovery,—namely, that one cannot impart his knowledge to his analysand, that what one might know must ever be distinct from what another might know. Freud's early experience in his own interpretation of his mental dynamics taught him that his analysand's psychological experience was the only possible ground for his analysand's interpretation of *his* mental dynamics.

Educator. Please, what do you find to be the real mental status of "communicated knowledge," which nearly everyone believes in as being the ideal educational experience?

Author. All "communicated knowledge" is denied the mental status of conscious self-experience. It exists in the mind quite as does the "suggestion" of one's hypnotist,—unrecognizable as self-power or as autosuggestion. One may believe that he always has ready access to such knowledge, whereas such is not at all the case. All of my learning which I believe has been "imparted" to me by "somebody else," exists in me as if it had been "suggested to" me by that somebody else. My voluntary use of such "imparted knowledge" depends upon my "rapport" with the (my) one I belive imparted it. A student who "liked his teacher" can "recall" such unrecognized self-knowledge without much difficulty, but cannot use it consciously as self-power. One who "dislikes his teacher" has difficulty "recalling" communicated knowledge and uses it as if it were his disliked teacher's knowledge rather than his own. The very rare student who renounces the illusion of "communicated knowledge" and thus esteems his learning as his living thereby enjoys free access to his self-knowledge as being self-power. He can make conscious learning at will. Furthermore, a matter of great importance, he finds himself interested in consciously continuing its growth as his own self-growth. His powerful intellectual curiosity reflects his conscious interest in living. His sense of his personal identity keeps abreast of his self-experience. His devotion to peaceful living is primary.

6

Conscious Psychic Integration

"I have an enduring faith in the men who do the routine work of our profession. Hard though the conditions may be, approached in the right spirit—the spirit which has animated us from the days of Hippocrates—the practice of medicine affords scope for the exercise of the best faculties of the mind and heart."

SIR WILLIAM OSLER

Author. There is no way that I can account for mental strengthening and mental healing except by way of a given individual's discovering for himself the means for living more of himself kindly, humanely. Such is the self-assigned task of every physician, whose duty it is to study ways in which he can live his patient most caringly. His patient critically needs, above all else, the opportunity to develop his own strongest self-helpfulness. He can accomplish this health achievement best while his kindness and self-trust are uppermost in mind. *Appreciating the absolute inviolability of human oneness frees kindness.*

My discipline of medicine is not based upon "sympathy," an illusion. My science of medicine is based upon identity, a reality. Living my patient "sympathetically," in every case, obscures my realization of the indispensable *helpfulness* of his signs and symptoms of suffering, obscures my full appreciation of the fact that illness and accident are the handmaidens of medicine. *Identifying my patient as my own living of my patient,* as a personification of my mind (with myself clearly the personifier), enables me to distinguish with utmost kindness the *practical* use of his signs and symptoms of his distressful living. Kindness is the expression of a peaceful mind secure in its guardian consciousness. Only the one who does the living *can* sense the practical uses of *his* living, but my patient is seldom able to appreciate the uses of his signs and symptoms (and thereby comfort himself with the helpfulness of his every discomfort) until he grows his physician as having cultivated this medical insight.

"Study my patient" can be no exception to "Know myself." Psychological medicine, self-conscious medical living, enables the avoidance of the errors of factitious otherness. "Physician heal thyself," "Patient know thyself," "Be worldly-wise,"—each idea expresses the identical principle of self-care. Living all of the life of an individual with all of the awareness of an individual is the clear definition of wholesome, peaceful human living.

General Practitioner. I am one whom you had in mind in your conversations. You keep stressing the fact that education is the only mind-shaping force that is not violent. I have a growing family, and I wish to see each one of my sons and daughters developing in the finest way. My (our) family problem is one of how to discipline. Please go into detail on your views of punishment.

Author. All punishment is illusional. I realize this sounds strange, but there actually is no such possibility as punishment in the sense that it is supposed to mean to produce pain in another,—retaliation, revenge, chastisement, requital, or correction. In the first place, all punishment is self-punishment, and it is always used as an effort at self-help. As soon as it is *seen* for what it is, namely, a need for further self-helpfulness, it is renounced. Otherwise so-called "punishment" begets the need for "punishment." So-called "wrong" or "injury," is painfully limited self-helpfulness. Discovering *that* truth is a painful ordeal but it obviates the necessity for self-disparagement.

General Practitioner. I may have to return to my illusion called "punishment." It is hard to try to realize that I am that which I formerly preferred to conceive I was not. Such waking up to new extents of my self hurts at first.

Author. Only at first. Soon it becomes the source of life satisfaction which it really is. Psychotherapy is the process of saturating one's self with the "I" feeling.

General Practitioner. All well and good, but would you kindly explain mental health as adjustment to reality, as successful adaptation in the real world? Surely that question provides you with an opportunity to try to be of real practical usefulness!

Author. Indeed it does, if I can successfully renounce every temptation to forget myself, if I can "come to myself" by each of my observations, if I can notice that all of *my* reality is that which *I live.*

By "reality orientation" is meant appreciation of the truth that "Whatever Is" exists entirely of itself and consists entirely of its own substance. Thus, one reality cannot even conceive, or be conceived by, another reality. Every accounting for mental health is on this score of unity.

Particularly ever since Griesinger's enunciation of his view, "Insanity is brain disease," the phantom problem of "mind and body" has had a rebirth issuing in the interminable arguments of "interactionism," "parallelism," and "automatism": interactionism claiming a "causal influence" in (1) the sensations of body upon mind and (2) the volitions of mind upon body; parallelism claiming a related process of cerebral and mental events; and automatism claiming that body influences mind, not the converse.

Nearly every philosopher is aware that there can be no existence other than self-existence; no meaning of life other than that lived by its liver (no "body," "external reality," "the universe," except insofar as it is a living inner action of its author); no clearly unambiguous meaning other than a given mind's consciousness for its being. I cannot objectify myself even, since I am also the "objectifier." I see that all of *my* objectivity is made up of my subjectivity. Thus, it is clearly absurd for me to live myself as if there can be any real existence for me other than that which I develop as self-growth. Appreciation of life can be derived only from intensity of self-consciousness. The living of consciousness enables the consciousness for being. Self-awareness is the ultimate in sincerity.

General Practitioner. If this mode of being is important for existing why didn't I learn to live by it long ago? Not many people think this much of living conscious individuality, do they?

Author. As far as I am aware, this doctrine of comprehensive appreciation of individuality is universally upheld by every philosopher. However, it is not tenable for the "organization man."

The self-unconscious organizer tends to hate and fear this concept of the allness of individuality. Why? Well clearly if the concept of "the organization" must be lived as if it were greater than the individual who conceives it, then the true meaning of individuality would threaten the whole delusional system. A question which I must ask myself is: How much do I, a physician, see clearly that my life is all and only about me, hence that my patient's life is all and only about *my* patient? How much am I aware that I am exercising my mind's inwardness in all of my living, that an appreciation of a kind of panpsychism is basic for my development of clear psychic insight, basic for my ability to renounce such illusions as psychophysical dualism or pluralism of any nature? Nietzsche proposed, "What you call chance—you yourself are that which befalls and astonishes you."

Mental health has one unit of measurement only, namely, How much of a human life is being lived self-consciously? The substance of selfness subsumes all of the semblance of "not-self." Health goes underground whenever the truth of self-health is ignored. Denied (or ignored) self-interest obstructs enlightened selfishness, and properly necessitates symptom interest, symptom love. Man is the architect and architecture of his own self-world and the only arbitrator of his own existence. He is his own doctor, patient, illness, medicine, recovery, and health. Every man is "universal man," but it is the most rare one who apprehends that truth.

General Practitioner. According to Jean-Paul Sartre, "Man is nothing else but that which he makes of himself. That is the first principle of existentialism." Are you an existentialist?

Author. I am whatever view or views I live. I just now originated (my) you asking yourself a question. I am also (my own) Jean-Paul Sartre. All I can sense or perceive is myself, only.

Medical Student. One moment. I am beginning to get the idea that (you think) all mental trouble is nothing but a case of self-intolerance. According to you, my ability to get along, be helpful, with my patient depends upon my ability to tolerate peacefully the self-tensions I excite in myself every time I treat a patient. Maybe so. I always thought there was more to mental health than just conscious self-tolerance, but maybe not. Suppose that it is true that my mental trouble is my lack of power to find meaning in myself, where it really is. How does a patient tolerate what he cannot tolerate, what he has banished from his acknowledged self-image? How does he increase his self-measuring propensities?

Author. The question seems well formed as I ask it of myself. Everyone who would tolerate a fuller conscious life must improve upon his accuracy as a self-surveyor. His self-analysis consists of his purposeful discovery of his ability to help himself, first to endure his dislikes, and gradually to attain the recognition that his every dislike or unpleasantness or pain is a precious, life-saving, hence lovable, living of himself. Self-analysis is a peaceful process which involves self-conscious living, heeded as such in order to attain a true self-estimate. It is a gradual process of the patient's discovering that it is not only possible and desirable, but also strengthening and healing, for him to further his ability to call his soul his own and his all his soul. Self-conscious living is its own reward; it frees the great-souled joy of living.

Robert O. Johann, S.J., offers an excellent description of the wholeness of individuality:

> But the only experience we have in which being is interiorly present to itself is that of the inwardness of human consciousness; it is the incommunicable presence of the self to the self. Hence the insistence of contemporary thinkers on this experience as occuping a privileged place in metaphysics. The interiority of consciousness first reveals to us what it means really to exist. It presents being, not as a flattened image or an impenetrable block seen only from the outside, but in all its inner warmth, depth and mystery. Through the direct, immediate and concrete consciousness of the self we first contact being as absolute, a value in and for itself, a deep center and source of initiative, an energy that poses itself and can, through a process of transcendentalization, be understood as founding the reality of all that is. This is the experience of being as *subject* or *subjectivity.*[1]

When I awaken each morning I perform a worthy exercise if I regularly take notice that I can awaken only to myself, that *all* of my living of my day can be only personal, and that the extent to which I observe my living to be only the living of myself must decide the sanity of it. To begin with, my bed lies in me, not I in it.

Everyone's "mental trouble" is a matter of difficulty in living himself kindly in one particular direction or another in its whole range. To illustrate, seeing his living of every feeling as being rocked in his own waves is a necessary process for his living his unpleasant emotions with peaceful kindness and to advantage. *Peace prevented by self-ignoration is vented by self-consciousness.*

Medical Student. Can you be a little more specific as to how I might begin to recognize my "wonderfulness"? That is a pacifying description which I have felt is not applicable to me.

Author. To illustrate, I can function in terms of my wholeness if I can conceive my wholeness. Developing my awareness of my completeness is a project I may undertake as I would any other analogous task in biology: First I must discover (notice, observe), that my life experience is a specimen of my self. Then I may begin collecting these specimens (of my own living) for the purpose of studying each one of them for what it is: a spectacle of my own existence. Ultimately, with each additional access of this self-appreciation, I work up a sense of my allness as well as an appreciation of the increasing extent to which I had previously ignored it. Such systematic learning of my owndom may well be called educative psychology. Quite as a geologist discovers and studies minerals, fossils, plants, and other subjects of his field, so I make collections of self-insights which reveal my nature. But how rare it is for one to keep a diary, or any kind of journal of his life's meanings.

Surgeon. Again I must beg your indulgence, as you do mine. As has already been observed of you, you have a way with words, of turning them to your use. No doubt, that must seem practical to you. Whatever is measurable, or quantifiable, comes within the field of science. Therefore, your one and only theme, individuality, consisting of subjectivity only, does not lend itself to scientific consideration. Every "objective" scientist is developing his potentiality as a man of war. The most a peaceful scientist can do in observing individuality is to make acknowledged self-observations. Whatever is based upon life (and what is not?) can be reported upon only from within the reporter as a personal word-illumination of his inner nature, which can have direct meaning only to himself. Please consider each of these questions: (1) Do not identical twins have the same heritage? (2) Is it not possible for identical twins to share the same home and environment?

Author. No discussion topic points up more sharply the need for self-conscious living than does the subject of "twinning" in any of its meanings. One of identical twins cannot in any way resemble, much less duplicate, or differ from, any other individual (including his twin). Each twin lives (in his own life) every meaning of his "other" twin. I cannot safely disregard this *essential* self-conscious orientation by assuming that it "remarks the obvious" or that it can be best "taken for granted." For me, it constitutes the "heart of the matter." A comparison is not only odious, it is a true illusion.

In other words, I can live nothing which is not native to me, to my constitution. In my seeing my twin I cannot read myself out of the scene. Seeing my native identity in all of my living (including my every *personal* growth of sensation and perception) is the health ideal towards which I aim myself: my self-conscious development. "Nature vs. Nurture" posits a phantom problem. The individual can have no twin. The science of human individuality is the science of peace. There can be no peace in "agreement." The very notion "agreement" implies the illusion of betweenness. Mental conflict is the issue of vain effort at having one part of my mind "agree" with another part. Monozygocity is in no respect a violation of unique human individuality. Consciousness primarily is the capacity to be awake to myself, to distinguish my own living. Consciousness individualizes, universalizes. It endows the self with its convincing quality of reality. My sustainable consciousness of the inviolable wholeness of my own individuality is my definition of ideal mental health. Does it not follow that the psychological pitfalls of plurality ("twins," "triplets," etc.) must be duly recognized and kindly renounced by me, particularly in my scientific study of my twin individual? Each "twin" lives only his own unique home, or environment.

Surgeon. It helps me to know what my field of operation is. Would you please attempt a definition of psychopathology? What is your idea of mental disorder? A scientist renounces the notion "disorder."

Author. A fair request indeed, and I shall try to comply with it, as I ask it.

"Mental disorder" is really a misnomer for expressing "order which is not readily observable as order." Where the autonomy of mind is disguised as heteronomy ("externality" illusions) the appearance of disorder necessarily sets up. Every sign and symptom of "psychiatric illness" is truly the expression of a mind trying to keep what health it can keep, while undergoing great hardship created by its own necessities. Even the mind suffering the greatest distress still tries to maintain some perception, however restricted, of its unity. All "psychopathic" behavior is understandable as a given mind's heroic efforts to work out its own healing, recover its sense of self-possession, by its only free means. To modify the wise Latin motto of Thrasea, Who hates psychopathy hates mankind.[2]

Surgeon. I see you renounce the health-sickness, or normal-abnormal, dichotomy on various counts: One, since it may imply that sickness is not worthy of human life, that sickness is not humane living,—so that, under the flag of humaneness one may depreciate humaneness. Another count is that this division is entirely false, anyway, since it implies that sickness involves the absence of health,—whereas all there is to sickness is health's exertion on the occasion of extremely stressful living. Still another count is that sickness, as opposed to health, implies the undesirable, the unhelpful,—whereas every form of sickness is really the only available therapy at the time. Also you have to work with sickness; and if it is not understood, hence loved, that work will suffer.

Author. Yes. I renounce the dichotomy, for its limited truthfulness limits its usefulness.

Surgeon. All of your localization of humaneness in the human individual brings to my mind the contrasting visionless view of Hitler (in *Mein Kampf*):

> A stronger race will drive out the weaker ones, for the vital urge in its ultimate form will break down the absurd barriers of the so-called humanity of individuals to make way for the humanity of nature which destroys the weak to give their place to the strong.

Author. Every student of peace will note that disrespect for the allness of the human individual must be a necessary basis for (his) any national official policy of executing, or sending to a concentration camp, one admittedly innocent individual "for being related to" an alleged offender.

7

Psychopathology

The test of truth in matters of practice is to be found in the facts of life; for it is in them that the supreme authority presides.

ARISTOTLE

Author. Human life is a sincerity. The human constitution, fortunately, must live self-deception of any kind difficultly. The growing individual discovers that he can help himself to feel lovable (livable) only by resorting to many a self-deception. These three sentences constitute an outline of psychopathology. Psychopathology is the study of (helpful) mental imposture, of masked humanity.

All of my mental "disorder" is the product of my self-depreciation, as when the wonderfulness of any of my developmental self-experience is ignored or denied. My "mental illness" is in every instance my effort to help myself to recover from my habit of misprizing my own self's powers. It is compensatory for my self-deception. Its portal of entry is my self-ignoration in some form or other. Life, minus consciousness of life, leaves depreciation of life.

A disadvantage to any part of myself is lived as a disadvantage in every other part of myself, so that my self-deception is a burden to my whole human being. Its specific cure is the extension of my self-insight (self-consciousness). Self-insight entails self-love, self-love being the one indispensable necessity for wholesome living. Devotion to, and cultivation of, this comprehensive self-view is the truest possible definition of comprehensive mental care. My truth cannot be observed second-hand. Socrates sanely noted, "I am the midwife of my ego."

Psychopathology may be aptly described in the discerning

words of John Burroughs, "homesickness which home cannot cure." In each of my mental "illnesses" I am suffering unrecognizable reminiscences. My ways of expressing a seeming past stage of my development are through: (1) my ability to recognize that it is a part of my past history (what is ordinarily meant by "memory"); (2) my need to recall it only by my unrecognized repetitious living of it (what is technically designated as "acting it out,"—persevering in a life pattern of limited self-helpfulness, even though I know, or claim that I know, I am making trouble for myself by it), and (3) my recognizing "past" as only present,—the ideal expression.

All of myself which I live in the form of disguised memory is essentially disguised truth (psychopathological). All of myself which I live with the recognition that I am a human development, a developed and developing homogeneous person, is essentially undisguised truth (non-psychopathological).

In the interest of affirming all of my living as precious, I heed the practical truth of the *efficacy* of my psychopathology. The physician's aphorism states: The healthy knows not of his health until it undergoes ordeal. Every "pathological" force is a more or less desperate life-saving attempt, an orderly strategic "withdrawal action" for purposes of strength and recovery only. Dying, itself, can be nothing but a "last resort" effort to live. Freud quotes Heine's picture of the psychogenesis of the Creation, a quatrain which imagines God as saying, "Illness was no doubt the final cause of the whole urge to create. By creating, I could recover; by creating, I became healthy."[1]

Medical Student. I have always identified sickness with death rather than with therapy, with the disease rather than with the patient. This is a new idea, that the disease germ is one entity and that the patient is another entity. The patient can be no more diseased than the germ can be humanized. I see where I have much to discover about these medical concepts.

Author. I cannot but limit my success as a physician by the way I treat my own mind. The great German poet Rainer Maria Rilke wrote, in *The Notes of Malte Laurids Brigge*:

> The wish to have a death of one's own is becoming rarer and rarer. A little while yet, and it will be as rare as a life of

> one's own. . . . One comes along, one finds a life, ready-made, one only has to put it on. . . . One dies at random; one dies whatever death belongs to the disease one happens to have: for since one knows all diseases, one also knows that the different lethal conclusions belong to the diseases and not to the human beings; and the sick person as it were doesn't have anything to do.[2]

If I cannot see my life as entirely my own, no possibility remains for me except to attempt to explain my living, which I cannot see as my own, by means of my illusional "otherness," by means of my "somebody else" or "something else." This vain effort to account for my being, and thereby to appreciate the nature of my existence (through the study of one of my very own—but disowned—creations, my created "somebody else") is analogous to my trying to study my mind by studying its unrecognized creations, such as "the brain and nervous system," or to my attempt to study the nature of my hand by my most profound research upon the sculptured hand which my hand created.

Medical Student. I always thought a physician's work was to prevent illness and cure the sick. Is that a true picture of medical work?

Author. I must answer that question affirmatively, for such is the nature of medical living. However, by educating himself so that he can prevent his "falling ill" and can "cure himself" to the widest extent, the physician grows the kind of self-knowledge which each of his patients must grow in order to care for health and solve his health problem as it arises.

Medical Student. What precisely is health? Please define it again.

Author. This is the question of greatest human concern. I have always contended: Give me a healthy person and I will build you an actual medical education, for then I will know its requirements. For me healthful (and healthy) psychology, including physiology, is the embodiment of a thorough appreciation of *all* of one's vital forces, of one's human nature. The patient lacks that self-insight, and seeks his physician's help as a succedaneum for his proper understanding of his health needs. Today, the insightful M.D. uses every consultation so that his patient may consciously educate himself as to what is healthful for him. In this medical treatment it is medical wisdom to avoid what William James called "the Psychologist's fallacy": the appearance that one can cure another.

Medical Student. Sometimes you seem to describe mental health as mental illness, and mental illness as mental health. How do you differentiate between your selfish ideas of grandeur and megalomania? Please, how do you distinguish between your intentional harping on "self-consciousness" and a monomania?

Author. I see each question as a fair consideration. It is certainly true that I help myself most by observing the *healthful* meaning of "illness," and of other ever-present threats of life in healthy living.

It seems indicated here again for me to observe specifically that my writing is intentionally non-didactic. It is no ambition of mine to have my reader help himself in my way, for I know that that is impossible. Each of my reader's questions indicates his readiness to grow himself in the direction of his questioning and, as Francis Bacon said, "The value of learning is in the pleasure created."

My megalomanic patient lives himself with greatly constricted self-consciousness. For instance, he does not attribute wonderfulness to any one of his others. Quite the contrary, he lives his mind in unconscious dissociation, claiming wonderfulness for the greatly limited portion he calls himself, but disclaiming this wonderfulness for the remaining portion which he calls "not-self."

My patient with his monomania also lives himself with greatly constricted self-consciousness, indulging a need to live self-consciously in an extremely limited direction as circumscribed by (my) *his* one idea. My "one idea," that of self-conscious living, quite the contrary, includes my everyone and everything, my all. I attribute to *my* fellowman his certainty of his convictions. Truth cannot be observed second-hand.

Recognizing that there is no life for me except my individual, personal, and entirely selfish existence is a necessary realization before I am able to attribute to my fellow human being the same full measure of his meaning as a peace-seeking world of himself. Similarly, I am able to live my fellowman as enjoying varying degrees of consciousness of his true allness, and as giving painful signs to himself (the sources of his complaints) which say: "Extend your consciousness to comprehend your true allness." I see that my life, only, makes all possible for me.

All of my living is personal. When I help myself temporarily by denying this truth, by "living on" even though I do not have self-insight in my living, I thereby create for myself a mounting quantity of psychopathological ("considered impersonal") selfness. Any of my "taking a second look" at my repudiated selfness, in order to see it as nothing but my wonderful selfness after all, is, in every instance, the way in which my mind strengthens and heals itself.

My mind never uses itself "falsely" except when it is most helpful at the moment to use itself in that way. When it does use itself "falsely," the true sense of my identity in its activity is thereby obscured. My mind is devoted entirely to helpfulness in its life adventure; and, unless I resort to denial, I cannot escape the truthfulness of that observation. I have found that my deepest sense of reality exists only when I am living conscious selfness, but nevertheless, I would not be alive at all were I to depend for life upon anything but my life itself. Helpfulness is a product of *living,* not a contingency, or an accident, or a unique pattern, of my living. As I live my psychopathological behavior, I am keeping myself alive by means of it.

Who can say that he has no "buried hurts" and other torments which he tries vainly to bury? Who can say that his "forgotten" experiences do not include many a smart associated with his past agonizing over disesteemed "follies" and "lapses"? All such living, based upon self-ignorance and limited self-knowledge, is buried alive. Rescuing it from its confinement, associating it with loving understanding, reclaiming it as long lost, precious selfhood,—that is heroic self-analysis.

My history of my humanity is a survey of myself as divine man gradually displacing my sense of my divinity in such a painfully humiliating way that my sense of my own identity in it became no longer apparent to me. All of my subsequent self-conscious living has expressed my varying degrees of divine self-consciousness, my development of my capacity to regard the allness of my living self in increasing measures of fullness, and my striving to restore to myself my full-measured awareness of my true wonderfulness. The divinity of every person is always present, but to be most effective it must be seen by him. I can be "sure of my ground" only by being sure of my self. My truth consists all, only, and precisely in that living view of meaning which is created by, and limited to, my individuality. I observe that this life orientation of world-minded self-possession involves the gratifying view that my fellowman is of the same all-inclusive singleness, whether or not he consciously enjoys such a comprehensive concept of his life or rejects it as "euphoric" and "eulogistic." Everyone who learns to appreciate his life must undergo an it's-too-good-to-be-true stage of self-appraisal.

The physician, of scientific mind, seeks truth and finds it where he must find all of his experience, namely, in his self-living. He heeds the truth that the anonymous, or the impersonal, is irresponsible and demoralizing.[3] My immature, unscientific mind observes of its experience: Whether I like it or not is what decides its fitness. My mature, scientific mind observes: Whether it fits or not decides whether I like it or not.

As far as my (self-) observations which follow are concerned, I live each one of them as one self-view only, recognizing it as that. Certainly I do not expect my fellowman to do more than live his own speaking and listening. I do not expect him to be able to claim his author's self-observation as his own. He may "try it on for size" (by saying and hearing it) and may or may not wish to live it as his own (beyond his attributing it to his author).

Medical Student. My hearing of that which "you" think, is not the same as *my* thinking it, you claim. Please discuss that further.

Author. The answer to this question clears up one of the greatest fallacies in educational work. *Whenever I read, or hear, any thought of my fellowman, I am tempted to assume that I have already thus succeeded in making that thought my own, without having to take the trouble to go through my own recognized personal and private originating of that thought entirely by myself.* I can correct this assumption by realizing that my observing my fellowman's solving a puzzle does not satisfy me that I can do it, until I have succeeded in demonstrating to myself that I *can* do it. This act of consciously originating my own ideas as being my own, just *seems* superfluous so long as I can seem to make my fellowman's ideas pass as my own.

Medical Student. You mobilize all of your self-power so that it will be apparent to you that you move and have your being under your own steam, as it were. Now that you mention it, I do realize that my fellowman accounts for very much of his living on the basis that he is doing it to, or for, somebody else.

Author. Yes, that can even apply to a person's accounting for his own death. "In hospitals, where people die so agreeably and with so much gratitude toward doctors and nurses, one dies a death prepared by the institution: they like it that way. If, however, one dies at home, one chooses as a matter of course that polite death of the better circles with which, so to say, the funeral first class and the whole sequence of its touching customs begins."[4] The full health value of all education (personal experience of every kind) lies in its being recognized by the student as an immediate way of his living, as living itself,—and not as a getting ready to live at some later date. My hearer may thus experience any and all of his hearing of his Author, by taking the trouble to author that speaking himself.

Medical Student. You seem to think that individual-made books and newspapers, and all institutions which represent "Society" as existing apart from an individual's mind, play up both obeisance to the phantom called "Society" and fear of the reality called "Individual." Even if that were true, wouldn't it be dangerous to have every individual grow the insight that words like "Society," "People," "State," may be so many blind spots in an individual's mind, so many acknowledgments of lack of conscious self-possession, so many vain efforts at self-nihilism? After all, nobody experiences more from hearing a lecture or reading a book than he is ready to grow, according to you. If you come right out and say of "Society," "Like all so-called plural figures, no one ever saw it except on paper," wouldn't that radical individualism prove overwhelming for your average reader? Do you not hold yourself responsible to your possibly unready reader at least to that extent?

Author. To modify Lichtenberg's choice *aperçu,* If prejudice looks in a book, tolerance will not look out.[5] As I ask myself each question which (I have) you pose, I find a ready reply in repeating your quotation from your author ("After all nobody experiences more from hearing a lecture or reading a book than he is ready to grow"). As far as my holding myself responsible for my fellowman is concerned, all of my writing is strictly autobiographical, composed by me and addressed to me. My fellowman is nothing but my own living of my fellowman. I can repeat over and over: "All of my conversation is only and entirely about me and for me. No least part of it can have anything to do with anyone else, any more than any other part of my soul, or life, can have anything to do with anyone else. Whoever reads his author's writing is seeing only a word-picture, a self-portrait, of his author." Instantaneous self-consciousness does not provide full-measured self-cognition but rather is a process which is necessary to the construction of the biologically adequate comprehension of one's individual life.

Medical Student. Is there some way you can describe your "self-insight practicality" without singing or apostrophizing? Can you diagram it, maybe? I do not mean to be unkind. Why should I hurt myself, calling the hurt spot "you"?

Author. Diagramming it is as easy as speaking of it. Using circles for designating the only life line of (my) every person's originality, authority, and responsibility, I can readily diagram both sane self-accounting and also irresponsible, undisciplined mental action. That is, I can make this drawing if you will allow me a certain latitude with it.

Description of the sane use of one mind is a simple matter, comparable to the simplicity of accurate bookkeeping. However, this "minding of one's business" must be an ordeal if it involves a new self-development. The ingenuity with which one's mental integrity (oneness) is regarded or ignored is the paramount "open secret" of the source of mental order. For my diagrams, I derive my use of circles from a favorite quatrain composed by (my) Edwin Markham, "Outwitted,"

> He drew a circle that shut me out—
> Heretic, rebel, a thing to flout.

But love and I had the wit to win:
We drew a circle that took him in!

The peripheral circle of Diagram I includes myself using my mind to attempt to attend, in sequence, to the concept of (a) myself and (b) *my* you. It is noteworthy that my concept of myself cannot subsume more than an idea of the totality of my subjectivity; and that my concept of my you, as of myself, consists entirely of my own mental material.

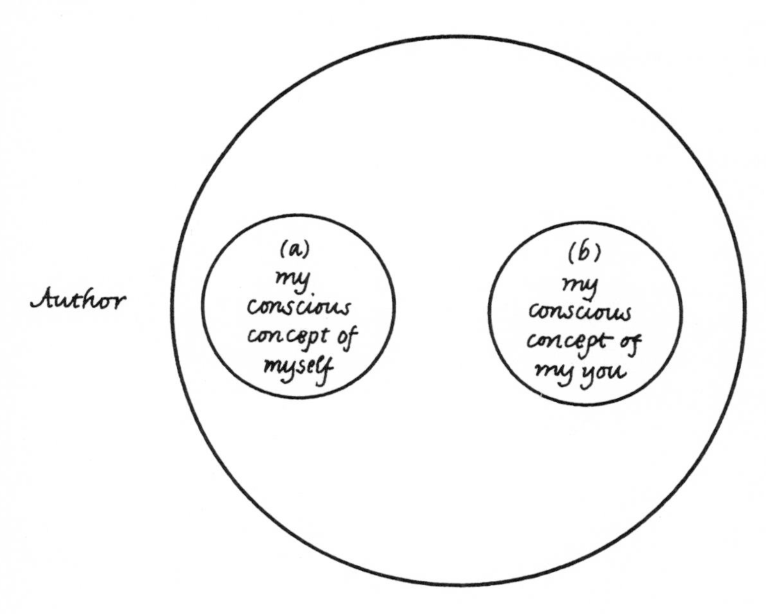

Diagram I

Medical Student. Does the outermost circle stand for your individual life?

Author. Yes. I have designated it *Author* but I intend it to stand for all of my individuality.

Medical Student. Then how can there appear to be something outside of your all-inclusive individuality? or outside of the allness you attribute to the inner circles?

Author. How right (my) you are. I must ask you to imagine each circle as having no delimiting circumference. This is the forementioned "latitude" I require.

Medical Student. I must stretch my knowledge of geometry to imagine a circle without a circumference, but I think I understand your requirement of open-endedness where your figure refers to the process of life. Please diagram your conception of my considering you. That is not the same as your concept of yourself.

Author. The peripheral circle of Diagram II includes myself using my mind to attend, in sequence, to (a) my concept of myself, and (b) my concept of my you viewing your (c) concept of your author.

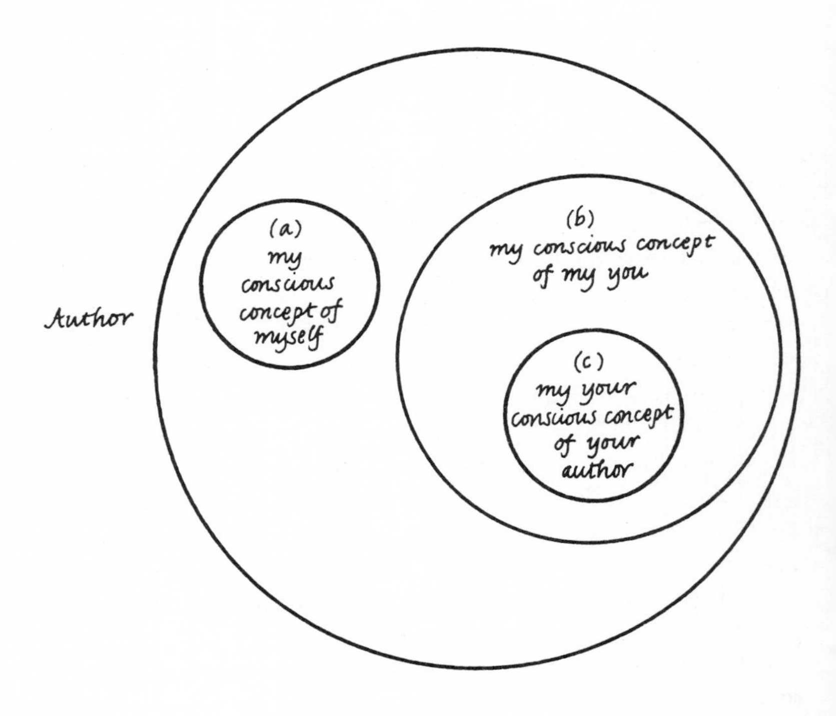

Diagram II

Medical Student. What do you mean by "concept"? Do you mean that you conceive, in the sense of bring into existence, your all of your mental content?

Author. Exactly. In these diagrams by "concept" I mean generated idea. The word "idea" signifies the thing (or whatness) created and seen in my mind. Whatever word I attach to the idea is an attempt to name its meaning. The idea is the mental material with which my mind works itself (imagines).

Medical Student. Where does your concept, or idea, of your you come from? Your you has to be outside of you first, or how could your you be conceived, or ideated, at all? How can I see or feel or eat something which is not *there,*—outside of me, I mean? Please explain that again.

Author. Each of these questions I have put to myself, thereby indicating my growing readiness to see each answer. Taking each question in order: first, my concept of my you *must* come from the only place I am, namely, my own life's substance. Next, unless I do grow my "outside you" (i.e., live my you-environment within me) certainly I will not possess that self-development. Finally, I must first live (create) whatever it is which I shall be able to see or feel or eat. Please note, however, that I, by means of my own life, create whatever it is that I may designate as being "there." Thus, I do not start with that "whatever it is" as if it were not entirely my own produce to begin with. This distinction is one of my everlasting concernments, for its observance is the criterion of the conscious individual who sees that his self is his only knowable existence. All psychology is idiopsychology.

Medical Student. Do you mean that your eating bread and butter is a case of your, first, living yourself in a completely ingenerate way so that you can say to yourself that *you* have made your bread and butter available and that from then on through the ingestion and assimilation of *your* food you can say to yourself that your bread or butter is having itself eaten? For you, all experiencing is individualizing, is it not?

Author. That may be one way of my describing myself as undivided man, as the individuum or all-individual known as *human being.*

Medical Student. Before you began these conversations, you said that you would use dialogism as a device for your self-expression, but that you consider all collocution to imply the totally false notion of "communication." You consider the wisest use of written, spoken, or sign language of every kind to be that of furthering the development of your self-insight. You consider all dialectic, argument, or reasoning of any kind as a movement of your life to observe, quite as you might observe any other of your life activities. Being "above" prejudice, master of your impulses, emotionally mature, self-controlled, realistic, or completely sane, simply means to you to be *consciously* mentally integrated, or insightful. That which your fellowman calls "colloquy" or "interchange of language" you see as being nothing but each converser's personal living (growing) of his own auditory, or visual, experience. Now, the point to all of this presentation of mine (of your radical individualism) is this: I can say it and see clearly that you are sure of it, but I myself do not identify it as my own kind of psychology. In fact, I have always thought of a person who talks to himself as being queer in that respect. As I speak with you, I actually have you in mind as being out of my mind, contradictory as that may sound. You regard such use of one's mind as the clear and simple explanation of all mental trouble, and one's own correction of this error as the prevention and treatment of whatever mental trouble he may wish to dispense with (since it is too limited a form of self-help). What I want to know is this: Whenever I suffer any real vicissitude of my life it troubles my mind naturally, and my seeing that it is all my own experience localizes that trouble sharply in myself. Why does my insight fail to cure me of my distress?

Author. Insight is not riddance. "Mental trouble" means: inability of a person to account to himself for the plight he seems "to see himself in." He cures his "mental trouble" by seeing that plight *in himself* and of his own making. As for your identifying my kind of psychology as being yours, that is as impossible as your identifying my life and its experience as yours. All I can identify as mine is that which I see that I live. Thus, I live my experiences to which I give the name "you,"—knowing that I can identify (my) you as mine.

Medical Student. Will you please diagram the use of the mind which illustrates its functioning *as if* it can be out of itself?

Author. Your emphasis upon "as if" helps to call attention to the self-deception, or illusion, of extraneity. There can really be nothing but intrinsic living in individuality. The peripheral line

A forming the dumbbell Diagram III again represents my individuality. It includes my idea of myself obviously as my own living, but it also includes my idea of my you as if that can be "out of my mind." The broken line A-1 represents my mental "breakdown," that is, my losing my self-sight that my apparently extruding (but really unfolding and enveloping) life line A encloses line A-1. A-1 is my illusion that I am able to view my you as not being entirely my own creation.

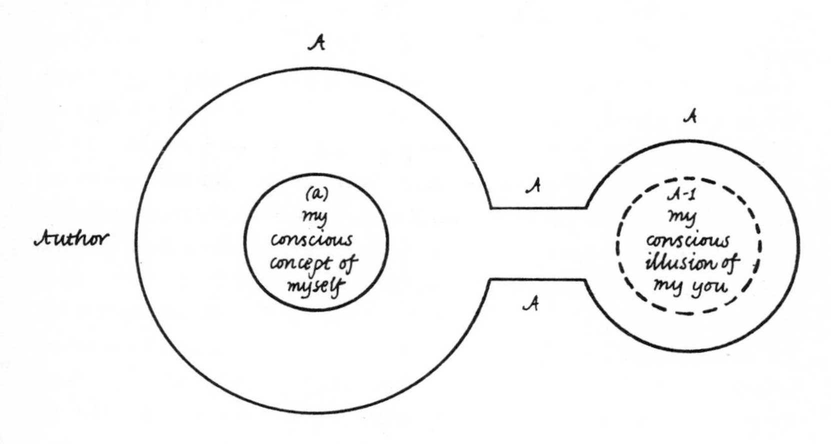

Diagram III

And so, one may diagram his acknowledged selfviews on and on, without his sense of self-esteem ending up like a Chinese nest of boxes finally yielding *nothing,* but rather a selfhood container ever containing selfness. Classification, which always ignores individuality, is not the basis of scientific knowledge. Everyone (including everything) is a class by one's (its) self. Strict obedience to the basic scientific law, self-observation, is the first scientific exercise to practice, however difficult, until habit takes over and custom makes it comfortable. There is no truth but the living truth experienced by the individual living it.

Medical Student. You found your self-discipline upon life itself. What *is* really known about life, after all?

Author. I am most pleased, most, to ask myself that question, and to answer it. Whatever is known *at all,* is known by, about, and for, *life.* Otherwise life is the open secret, and keeping it secret is the one sure way to misprize it. Reality is all and only that which the individual life reifies. All of knowledge is discoverable only as the personal experience of the individual's life. Again, there is no knowing which does not observe, describe, explain, reveal, or otherwise disclose, *life.*

Medical Student. Are you now talking anthropomorphism, that is, interpreting your external world only in terms of your own inner experience?

Author. For answering that question, all depends upon what is meant by "your external world." True, the anthropomorphist posits an "external world," but there is a danger that he overlook the all-important truth that the positor is the creator of that which he posits. In other words, he who posits an "external world" begins and completes his concept within his own mind. He then proceeds to prospect within his own mind, never once seeing anything but his own mind. For me, whatever external world there may be, and I do not doubt that there is one, must be accepted upon my faith in its existence,—and that faith is entirely a growth of my living.

Medical Student. You mean that instead of having little or no knowledge of life, life is all that there is any knowledge of? You mean that I disrespect my being alive when I do not identify my world of meaning with my living it? You mean that life is all that is certain and that everything lacks evidence of the force of certainty to the extent that it is not observable as a growth of life, as ringing the changes of living? What then of the zoologist's efforts to define life in such delimiting terms as spontaneity, purposiveness, organizing and synthetic power, individuality, regeneration, creativity, energy, activity, autonomy, freedom, and so on?

Author. So far so good, of my zoologist's account of life's essence. As I see it, knowledge which will account for the *fact of life itself* cannot but account for all of the so-called "facts of life." My life is the *vera causa* of my all. For instance, all of mind is animation of life. It is understandable that Aristotle considered intellectual contemplation to be the only occupation worthy of the gods.

The sanely disciplined mind assumes all originality, authority, and responsibility for the fact that its living of its "somebody else" occurs within itself. It extends this kind of insight to its view of its "somebody else," noting that its "somebody else" lives all its "otherness" within itself.

The undisciplined mind, however, deceives itself in assuming that it can experience living in some form, however attenuated, outside of itself. It attributes the same impossibility to the mind of each of its own other ones. I have found out that I can live with self-consciousness only that which I can value as my own self-possession, and thus identify with my love of life. For instance, my necessity to live any of my life experience as being the least bit invidious is an acknowledgment of my unreadiness for using well that kind of mental material and, hence, my need to deny its right to exist as mine. Thus, any experience with which I associate any unpleasantness (hatred, fear, guilt, envy, jealousy, suspicion, shame, disgust, or similar feeling of *ill will*) is, to that extent, consigned to my stockpile of rejected selfness. It lives on as the rest of me does, but without my ability to identify it as all my very own disowned being,—disowned, not on account of its being undesirable, but on account of my unreadiness to live it as being desirable selfhood.

Medical Student. You mean that you cannot use well your mental material which you cannot live cheerfully and kindly, and that you spare yourself conscious distress by ignoring its presence? Milton meditated, "In short, the wise is the genial."

Author. Something like that. If I start making conscious all that I have had to turn from in my living, I overwhelm my mind with unpleasant excitations and thus render myself distraught and unable to conduct even my ordinary life requirements. On the other hand, if I do not indulge my life's need that I grow to feel equal to myself, I tie up much of my vitality and have to steer my conscious life in a fixed course which prevents the confrontation of the me I have been able to live lovingly, with the me that I have not yet been able to live as being desirable. A person tends to identify his life with his conscious will, and to regard his unconscious involuntary living as being foreign to him.

Medical Student. You say that all psychopathology can be understood only as an absence of loving self-insight. You say self-awareness is the epitome of human life-force. May I ask a question? You claim mind-healing force for self-consciousness.

Is not every delusion (however false) a belief of which every deluded patient is painfully conscious? Is not every hallucinating patient fully conscious of the content of his hallucination? Is not every delinquent patient conscious of his delinquent behavior? Is not every obsessive, compulsive, or in any way complaining, patient, all-conscious of his symptoms? Are all of these conscious symptoms, exceptions which prove your rule? Will you please clear up this obvious contradiction for me?

Author. I am pleased that you are following your health-claim-for-self-consciousness so helpfully. You are absolutely right. Psychopathology is not a produce of self-consciousness. Contrary to the "conventional" view, my patient's delusion (or obsession, or hallucination, or delinquency, or whatever conscious "symptom" or complaint) is not his psychopathy at all. His mental "disorder" stems from his mental life for which he *is* unconscious.

Medical Student. Please illustrate. If I claim I am Napoleon, or God, is not that delusion my psychopathy?

Author. Not at all. You *are* your own Napoleon, or god. Your psychopathy would be located, not in what you acknowledge being, but rather in what you deny being. Thus, you might deny that you live *your* mother, or *your* father, or *your* brother, while claiming to be only your own Napoleon. It is in such living, *which is denied self-consciousness,* where all so-called "psychopathy" is to be found.

Medical Student. If I am obsessed, is not my obsession psychopathic?

Author. All that is, or can be, psychopathic in my obsessional neurosis is: not the obsession of which I am self-conscious, but rather all of my mental living which I ignore and disregard by focusing my self-consciousness on, and limiting it to, my living of my obsession. My chief health rule of the mind is to locate every meaning one lives in one's own self, where it may not *seem* to be. Every obsession ("involuntarily" recurring idea) is a therapeutic experience which relieves otherwise unbearable tension and presents a lead to the discovery of underlying mental material which is withheld from self-conscious living.

Medical Student. How about stuttering? Surely every stutterer is painfully self-conscious, is he not?

Author. That is one way of looking at it, to be sure. Every stutterer really indulges his illusion that somebody else can do his hearing for him, when he speaks. For instance, his stuttering invariably lets up when he has the feeling of assurance that he is speaking only to himself, when he considers himself to be alone (all-one). He can cure himself of his stuttering by cultivating his insight to the extent of realizing that he *is* always alone and that his auditor is nothing but his own living of his auditor. Indeed, I regard this particular kind of self-treatment as being the specific cure for stuttering,—the stutterer's living his auditor with self-consciousness.

Medical Student. Who else thinks that?

Author. No one that I know of except one who found that it works.

Medical Student. You admit, do you not, that your system of psychology is based upon your study of only one case, yourself?

Author. I have nothing else to go on, only my own life's powers.

Medical Student. Suppose I am in a depression. Surely I'm conscious of that, and surely that's pathological, is it not?

Author. Not at all. In the first place, your depression is *in you,* not all of you in your depression. Furthermore, awareness of unhappiness is no more psychopathic than is awareness of pain. Just as the intention of pain is for you to relieve yourself of the kind of living which necessitates your pain, just so, the intention of your valuable unhappiness is for you to relieve yourself of the kind of living which necessitates your unhappiness. Each is an indispensable attempt to clear up trouble, is itself recognizable only as trouble, but is an exertion you put forth in seeking to live yourself in a healthy way (i.e., free of feeling your pain or unhappiness, and free of the underlying distressful living). You need to learn how to *use* your depression, not feel used by it.

Medical Student. If I misbehave myself as a delinquent and I'm aware of my delinquency, surely that self-consciousness is abnormal, is it not?

Author. First, I wish to appreciate (my) your point of view. Again, I must ask myself to consider that it is the self-consciousness which is absent, not that which is present, which constitutes my psychopathy as a delinquent. I am helping myself to the extent that I am conscious of myself as the perpetrator, for it would be greatly to my disadvantage to be in ignorance of that truth. My psychopathy lies in my unconsciousness of the truth that I also live my own victim. It is my self-consciousness (that my victim is really my own living of my victim) which cures me of my "delinquency."

Medical Student. How does all of my repudiation of the truth of my self-living get started anyway, if it does? How did I lose my ability to "use" my depression?

Author. A practical question, to be sure. My self-deception of this kind began in my effort to help myself. *Life, itself, always consists entirely and only of self-helpfulness, regardless of appearances to the contrary.* During my life development I found it *practical* to make my living self-unconscious, on innumerable occasions. Thus, I found a source of pleasure in making myself conscious of living which I liked. By that means I could have accessible such pleasure sources. On the contrary, I found a source of displeasure in making myself conscious of living which I disliked, for by so doing I had access to too much conscious unpleasant living. Simply by disliking to see my very own identity in my dislikes, I could gradually discount and ultimately, by steering my attention away from them, ignore such sources of painful living. The trouble with this strategy for living (my anesthetizing myself to the truth of my painful living) is that, as in the case of any anesthetic, the painful condition continues to exist, even though I can no longer be conscious about it. Making myself unconscious of the truth that I am my own "dislikes," as much as I am my own "likes," renders me powerless to help myself *fundamentally* by increasing my tolerance of self-tensions (needed life guides).

Medical Student. I am growing and exercising the idea that whenever I live my life as "not-I" living, I am practicing self-amnesia, and helpfully ignoring valuable life guides? Is this one of your mental exercises, observing the therapy of repression?

Author. Speaking for myself, which is all I can possibly do, I regard my own living as the *fons et origo* of every single one of my mental operations. My individuality, my personality, is absolutely autonomous, independent, self-lived. For me there can be no psychology but self-psychology. I find that by redirecting toward my own health condition any therapeutic ambition I have directed toward my patient, I derive two efficacious realities: (1) I can help myself, a possibility; and (2) *my* patient can help himself, a possibility. The medical method of self-conscious living offered here will be livable by him who dares to use it. It required utmost courage, as well as greatest willingness to work, on my part, before I was able to apply it to myself, even a little bit.

Medical Student. In your opinion, how much does scientific training in laboratory experimentation help a man to confine his method of inquiry and his findings to objectivity?

Author. That question makes me ask another, What do I mean by "objectivity?" For me that term means: imputing individuality with all of its subjectivity to any entity.

Medical Student. By "objectivity" I mean seeing the truth inherent in my datum,—not getting the rest of my imagination mixed up with my imagining of my real object.

Author. My laboratory work has been an exercise in self-control of that kind since I began to study *my* specimen, or procedure, as my own living of it.

Medical Student. Your subjectivity subsumes your objectivity. Do you find that attributing externality to your objectivity falsifies the fact that you live it and blocks your mind with regard to it?

Author. Quite so. My "objectivity" rests on my self-consciousness. To the extent that I live my laboratory data as self-data, I am as "objective" as it is possible for me to be. I am my only reality, and if I deny that any "object" is my living of it, I deny the reality of the "object," and thereby create mental resistances to my living it freely. Hence, for me, the answer to this question resolves itself into a matter of the extent to which a man lives his laboratory experimentation self-consiously (subjectively, that is).

Medical Student. I thought always that self-consciousness, itself, was a source of trouble, and therefore something to cure one's self of, rather than to cultivate. How about "stage fright," or "buck fever,"—is that not due to an overdose of self-consciousness?

Author. The "popular" view that self-consciousness is numbing and paralyzing could not be further from the truth. For instance, my "stage fright" simply indicates the narrow limits of my self-consciousness which prevent my living my auditors and spectators as conscious elements of my own selfhood.

Medical Student. What is your present viewpoint about hypnosis?

Author. By hypnotizing myself I develop in my own living (1) a part of myself which I cannot recognize as mine but which I regard as powerful (my living of my hypnotist) and (2) a part of myself which I recognize as "I" and regard as weak (my living of the restricted zone of existence which I am able to acknowledge as being "I"). The cultivation of this kind of dissociation of my mind is what I wish to escape.

Medical Student. Can one person hypnotize another?

Author. Each person is an *all.* There *is* nothing for him to hypnotize but himself. The hypnotist suggests to himself that he can hypnotize someone else and influences himself to accept this autosuggestion as truth. The hypnotized one suggests to himself that someone else (his hypnotist) can hypnotize him and influences himself to accept this autosuggestion as truth.

Medical Student. What do you mean by "influences himself"?

Author. I mean: forces himself, obeys his own request.

Medical Student. I take it that the force which produces autohypnosis is "suggestion."

Author. Suggestion is nothing but unconscious will, nothing but the power of selfness which is not recognized as being selfness. When I am not aware that all of my force is my life-force, I suffer the illusion of alien influence.

Medical Student. Well, why not simply practice autosuggestion instead of self-consciousness?

Author. The practice of autosuggestion, of the illusion of one influencing another (part of one's self), promotes mental dissociation and cultivates devotion to duplicity. Literally, "to suggest" means: to put under. All autosuggestion is authoritarian and ignores the true (full-measured) allness-meaning of individuality. Autosuggestion is an illusion which uses other illusions, "communication," and "externality." It ignores the truth of individualized life. It is the substitute for conscious initiative.

Medical Student. As you find it then, if you do not see to it that you exercise your self-consciousness, you leave yourself to the practices of autosuggestion.

Author. That is about it. My "man on the street" that I live in me is one who gets along largely by his use of autohypnosis. My "man of science" rarely prides himself upon his devotion to self-insight.

Historically, the hypnotist contributed to the development of modern psychological medicine in that his practice demonstrated, beyond any doubt, the strictly mental nature of health deviations formerly disregarded as being mental.

In my view, hypnosis is a process *diametrically opposed* to my indispensable health principle of conscious self-help. It depends for its effectiveness upon the illusion that one (inviolable) individual can get at another (inviolable) individual. Thus, hypnosis represents to me a kind of practice of sham magic. As Faust observed, magic unscrupulously considers the end desired, disregarding the welfare of the human life which is used as the means.

Freud observed early in his self-analysis: Where there is not a self-consciousness present, there *is* a symptom present. Thus, every symptom marks a spot where (self-) amnesia occurs. Psychopathology consists of the mind's efforts to compensate for self-amnesia by, so to speak, patching up this self-consciousness insufficiency with symptoms. A symptom bridges over each mental area of forgotten (repressed) selfness. Full recovery of memory resolves the symptom, disclosing it as helpful selfness, as a kind of psychic hernia.

The strong mind is the potentially conscious ("intact") one, founded upon its internally seen and personally prized *self*-power. Wrote Browning, "All's love and all's law." All love is love of life, self-love rather than an egoism of two. All law is law of life, autonomy and not heteronomy. Individuality is not classifiable and therefore cannot be explained in terms of orthodox science (including "objective" psychology). Self-explanation is an epistemological (entirely subjective) development. Everyone's genius for self-culture, consciousness of helping himself with his own resources, is also the source of his appreciating the full meaning of freedom.

Medical Student. You trace the illusion of "separation" to the illusion of "togetherness," each in turn to the illusions of "space," "time," and "motion," each also in turn to unrecognized creation of your own imagination.

Author. Certainly. I am mindful of Henri Peyre's discerning comment about mental rigidity associated with impoverishment of imagination: "For young Americans of the second half of this century a grave peril lies in uniformity and unimaginative intellectual monotony."[6]

Medical Student. Since you regard every kind of so-called pathology as psychological (including physiological) therapy, you might define your concept of treatment as the recognition of the helpfulness in Whatever Is as the renunciation of the traditional idea of treatment.

Author. A helpful view. And also a scientific one:

> Disorder as a concept contradicts a primary article of faith of traditional science—namely, that there is only order in nature, there is no ultimate disorder, nothing illogical; if things seem to be in disarray, it is only an appearance.[7]

Medical Student. What is your proof of the existence of an unconscious mind? How do you demonstrate your notion "unconsciousness?"

Author. My most convincing and most accessible of all evidence of unconscious mental activity is: *Whatever experience I categorize as not-I.* Absence of my feeling of authoritative responsible personal identity is my only criterion of unconsciousness.

Medical Student. Since all consciousness is self-consciousness, it is your safe assertion that any of my living that I designate as not-mine is unconscious. If I claim I am conscious of anything other than myself, is that "anything" really unconscious selfness instead? Is all "externality" camouflaged self-unconsciousness?

Author. My asking myself each of these questions creates the affirmative answer: Most certainly. My so-called "not-I," or "otherness" living, is my most meaningful open secret, allowing my unconscious mind to express itself right under my nose by using its most effective disguise of appearing to be my fully conscious mental activity. No volitional act is possible without conscious selfness; no so-called "volitionless" act can seem possible without unconscious selfness.

Medical Student. I think it will be helpfully realistic for me to practice alluding to my consciousness always as self-consciousness, and to my unconsciousness always as self-unconsciousness.

Author. By attributing selfness to all the sensa of my experience I respect the constant creativity of my unifold being. Only by consciously predicating the suppositious existence of not-I can I renounce the delusion of externality and thus escape the danger of seeming to lose my mind in its own creations. The term "datum" means "given." My data are given by me to myself. Merely by heeding that I am my every experience I can notice that I am not only all of the Who but also all of the What of my own world, indeed that all of my What *is* Who. Nothing can be understandable except as psychological (subjective).

Medical Student. Please discuss "consciousness," "unconsciousness," "personal identity," and "mental dissociation."

Author. The term "consciousness" means, literally, "knowing with" or "knowing together," implying multiplicity in unity. In his *Introduction to Philosophy,* E. S. Brightman noted, "All consciousness is in the form of self-experience." And in his *Matter and Spirit,* J. B. Pratt observed, "Any given passing conscious state is merely an aspect or activity of the self." To me my "self" means nothing but the present organismic unity and wholeness of my individual life. Its only truth is subjective, obviously clear of any and all reaction to, or interaction with, experience which it is not. Such is the secret within the secret of (my) universal being.

My sense of personal identity is indispensable for my conscious self-help and therefore is preserved as the guardian of my life. Any excitement too great to be tolerated by my personally identifiable self is allocated to a part of my mind other than that constituting my acknowledgable individuality. This (helpful) exclusion of some of my self-experiences from my self-conscious living is what is meant by "mental dissociation."

Such mental dissociation alone is the source of every kind of so-called "mental disorder." In other words, I define my full sanity, not as the absence of mental trouble, but as my ability to live consciously every kind of so-called "psychopathology" within my own mind, insightfully realizing the nature of its helpfulness for my maintaining my sense of personal identity. How insightfully Freud described "psychotherapy" as his patient's development of a new *psychological situation.*

8

Psychiatric Research

If it were a thing obvious and easy for every man to know himself, the precept had not passed for an oracle.

PLUTARCH

RESEARCH WORKER. According to the renowned scientist, F. S. C. Northrop, "There is no one scientific method."[1] That views looks good to me.

Author. My Northrop has a magnificent mind. As I see it there are as many scientific methods as there are scientists, and I am certain that this claim holds for scientific research.

Research Worker. I like Northrop's two major ways of assigning meaning to a term. His method of creating concepts is such that he does not confound his intuitive apprehension of a mental datum (his inductive method) with his proposal of theoretical meaning to his postulated mental datum (his deductive method). I think he might pose the question of your being a pure empiricist restricting your definition of reality to your immediately apprehended living. You seem to fit his concept of a positivist, that is, one who holds the view that there are only concepts by intuition. You do find that you grow your every meaning whether it concerns a "sensible" or an ideal, a postulation or an intuition, and so on, do you not?

Author. Yes, I find that all of my data *are* self-data. Scientific investigation, recognizable as the investigator's own living, is my view of the purest culture of research work. The fact is, as Roger Bacon pointed out, *original research is distinct from the acceptance of authority.* It is nothing but self-conscious self-helpfulness and, as such, constitutes the law of experimental science as well as the pursuit of that healthful happiness called "mental health."

Research Worker. Are you implying that the prized "objectivity" of the scientist is disguised "acceptance of authority," that his holding out for his acceptance of "external data" is based upon his nostalgic longing to *subject* himself to authority (as if) not his own, an addiction developed in his infancy and childhood?

Author. That is the view I have of it, yes.

Research Worker. How did medical work start? Where would you begin the history of medicine?

Author. Medicine, contrary to "accepted opinion," instead of arising "out of the primal sympathy of man to man" (an impossibility), arose out of man's capacity for sensing his own identity (a necessity). Such is my origin of my medical helpfulness.

Research Worker. Please discuss your view of the origin of the body-mind concept.

Author. The hybridism, "body-mind," is a psychological chimera of early philosophic origin. The "hybridist" who coined it appears to have been ambivalent ("of two minds," neither one certain) about the truth that every meaning of "body," as every meaning of "externality," must be entirely a psychological construct. The term "body-mind," as a mental symptom, represents an effort at condensation which reveals both transference to, and resistance against, one's posited (illusional) "externality" of his body.

Careful research upon the soma (body part) of my mind discloses that it represents self-knowledge of primary nuclear importance.[2] My mind may express itself through its powers called its "body," and such expression may or may not be detected in a "physical" (body) alteration. To illustrate, I may complain bitterly, either of anesthesia or of paralysis, without being able to find any physical alteration other than that associated directly with my finding myself unable to feel or to move. Conversely, I may be able to endure great somatic stress, but complain very little, if any. Such discoveries have led to the realization of the mental functioning of bone, muscle, and all so-called "physiological" structures. A live body appears to be a mental agent. A body without a mind is dead. The significance of mindless anatomical structure might be seen as analogous to that of the ink and paper of a page apart from their meaning as words.

Research Worker. You used the term "ambivalent." I hear it used often to represent a person's inability to decide which direction to follow. For instance, if he is given certain choices and cannot make up his mind which one to prefer, he is called "ambivalent." What does this term mean to you?

Author. To me "ambivalent" means: unable to devote one's self in any of the presenting directions he gives himself. His wavering from one to another serves to spare him the (otherwise overwhelming) insight that he has insufficient free energy for expending further devotion anywhere. Ambivalence occurs with great frequency in the form of apparent distraction where the distractibility functions to prevent concentration in *any* direction.

Research Worker. Please be more technical in your definition of "ambivalence."

Author. Ambivalence means classically: the condition experienced when two opposing affective forces are directed toward the same mental situation,—for example, simultaneous love and hate feelings associated with the same mental content. This definition is based upon the delusion "plurality."

Research Worker. I am of a practical turn of mind too, and in order to stay that way I must devote myself to useful subjects. I cherish the love of man in my heart and, I trust, in my head and hand. All of your idea centers on being, but I must be concerned with *doing.* Please discuss that.

Author. All "doing" is nothing but *being.* Only well being can *do* well. Geronimo Cardano, famed as a physician and mathematician early in the sixteenth century, recorded, "A man is nothing but his mind; if that be out of order, all is amiss, and if that be well, all the rest is at ease." This view has much to commend it, particularly if the meaning "mind" is defined as the manifestation of life itself. Life can have no peer. In asserting that I *live* my "somebody else," or "something else," or "body," or "mind," I mean I am in that true sense devoting life of mine to each of these mental developments. Each is a life development of my very own. There can be no truer or greater devotion. As an experimentalist, in extending my self-consciousness I am revering human life in the truest way possible. In all of my practical *doing* as a practitioner, by means of my awareness (my presence of mind) I avoid ever present temptations to unwitting carelessness in word, attitude, and management. "Becoming" is also *being,* and not an exception to it.

Research Worker. What do you mean by awareness (presence of mind)? Do you mean that you find it *impractical* to "lose your mind" in your practical exertions, that you are more apt to hurt yourself where you cannot feel yourself?

Author. Exactly. My mind is all and only *its own place,* always situated in and meaningful for *my* life only.

Research Worker. This truth seems so fundamental that I would like to see it upheld in all educational work. It certainly is not a new idea, is it?

Author. Ancient Sanskrit has a word for "I-maker," *ahankara,* the principle generating self-consciousness.

Research Worker. My specialty is that of scientific investigation, and I intend to free my spirit of inquiry and properly pose many questions and critical observations. First, please where do you stand on the issue of research in your field?

Author. Much research on mental health is already under way, and much more is sure to come. All of such research is helpful for every researcher. Furthermore, a help to my researcher is a help to me, including everyone in my world. As I see it, each research worker will begin his scientific investigation *where, and how, he is ready to begin in his study of his self-activity.* He will put off, as long as necessary, his seeing his research as me-search, as the development of his own insight.[3] His recognition of his scientific investigation as being self-exploration is a health development which sets his every scientific datum free and discloses its full meaning.

Meanwhile each investigator is forging ahead, already avowedly "on his own."[4] It is truly a greatly practical day when any research psychiatrist develops his capacity for conscious self-sight. As he reduces the amount of his life imagined to be "not-self," he frees his imagination for further helpful self-research, for eventually seeing clearly that his every scientific reality is the produce of his own living.

In rescuing his overworked imagination from his chronic addiction (to indulging his illusion of "not-self"), every physician begins to esteem his imagination as his most cherished mental possession. He becomes willing to classify *all* of his mental activity as imagination, thereby obviating such false distinctions as "real" or "imagined" pain, and "real" or "imagined" pleasure.

Research Worker. Please elaborate your idea that self-consciousness produces your realization of your personal identity.

Author. When I live myself consciously my unique individuality is peculiarly evident, so that the *personal* meaning of my sensation, or perception, or idea, or feeling, is conspicuous. Self-conscious activity is always associated with recognized private initiative, with evident will power. All value is constituted of meaning. As I locate myself in my every meaning I thereby establish my sense of my value. As this meaning of my consciousness develops it becomes evident that my entire appreciation of my existence, my value of my life, my devotion to peace, is the outgrowth of my *conscious* being.

Research Worker. Apparently there really is no such thing as a common language. Every person by means of his language expresses only his self-meanings even though he himself may not recognize them as being mere descriptions of his private self.

Author. Yes. An interesting self-study is provided by my examining each word that I use for its significance as a life-meaning of mine.

Research Worker. How do you explain such expressions as "conscious society," "social consciousness," "social psychology"?

Author. To me each such expression means nothing but an idea in the mind of the person who creates it. It is standard for my sociologist to think in pluralistic terms of "interaction," "communication," "mutual relations," "agreement," "disagreement," "competition," "interchange," "group," "crowd," "mob," "social-unity," "social reciprocity," and so on.

Research Worker. You mean that the social worker requires a language which allows him to ideate as if he is a member of his society, thus overlooking the truth that his society is entirely a composition of his.

Author. In the sense that sociology is an "objective science," a sociology may disregard the individual, particularly the allness-meaning of individual.

Research Worker. According to you there is no real difficulty in seeing the allness of individuality except the one of what to do about "otherness," or "exteriority," appearances. Your solution is that of seeing all of your otherness as being meaning which only you yourself create in your own mind. Many a question occurs to me having to do with morality, justice, love, and even intelligence itself. Each of these questions is excited by your claim that the only humanity tie, the only source of his world peace, is one which exists *within* each individual human being. If every "social relation" is nothing but a reflection of an individual's self-rejection, nothing but a reflection of an individual's effort to dispossess himself of his own mind's creation, nothing but his own living which he *cannot* activate without hurt love,—then it seems to me to be distinctly worthwhile that you ring the changes on this phantom problem of psychology and philosophy. It is known as the "subject-object enigma," is it not?

Author. Yes. Everything that is meant by the term "social order" is always a creation, or creature of an individual human mind. Everything that is meant by a "social situation" can be nothing but a meaning in an individual human mind. There can be no such possibility as a group-person, group-self, group-individual. Each new experience which a person has of "forming a new acquaintance" is nothing but a self-development of his. To conceive it as being "an enlargement of his social relations" is to use his own mind for the purpose of seeming to be out of his mind. Everything that passes for "civilization," or for "culture," is in every instance an issue of an individual life.

Research Worker. You mean that your mother, or your father, or your spouse, or your child, lives a world which has nothing, and can have nothing, to do with your world? I am not comfortable with your view that humanity consists entirely of every man's seeing his fellowman in himself as a complex, or cluster, of self-experiences nominated "fellowman." I have educated myself to the belief that civilization is progress toward mutual freedom and agreement among human beings. Your view, that the only peace of mind is the product of consciously integrated human individual mentality, does not mean very much to me right now. I'm sure that the great structures of industry and commerce are not founded upon the principle of the allness of human individuality.

Author. To the extent that my commerce or industry is constructed upon my repudiation of the allness of my individuality, I find that I must conduct it in a warlike, rather than a peaceful, manner. As long as my economic principles depend upon the idea that my gain can be your loss, a totally false conclusion, I shall experience the necessary unhappiness healthfully associated with such oppressed living of myself. To the extent that I can see my rival, or competitor, as entirely his whole world, I can live myself in the most economic way of tending to my own business.

Research Worker. If "meeting another person" means to you only a new development in your own individuality, the more "sociable" you become the more you cultivate your own individuality. As I understand it you would not engage in warlike behavior, for it would always mean firing on your own troops. You would not engage in single combat, for it would always mean feelingless self-hurt. You would not engage in any kind of competition, for it would always mean one part of you feeling superior at the expense of another part of you. You would not devote yourself to immoral behavior, for it would always mean the cultivation of painful experiences in your life. You would always welcome the difference in *your* fellowman, for it would always mean the growth of a new kind of strength in your own personality. You would not want your spouse or child to be a mirror of yourself, in the sense of an imitation or copy, for it would always mean a restriction of your own capacity for self-development. Well, all I can say about all of this is: It sounds too good to be true. I realize that each of us often has the feeling that there is immensely more to himself than he can realize. However, if there were such a foolproof and really simple explanation of human existence as the one you uphold, why was it not discovered centuries ago and why is it so obviously unpopular? Please ask yourself those questions.

Author. Excellent questions. Conscious self-realization is limited by the nature of one's self-experience. The growth of self-insight is entirely a matter of one's own individual cultivation,—and in no sense a product of so-called "mass production." My insightful teacher means nothing to me except that I create all that I understand by "my insightful teacher." My creation of one insightful teacher after another does not result in my cultivation of my own self-insight. My development of self-insight is of necessity my *conscious* executive living of my creativity.

Research Worker. I always thought that self implied "not-self." I remember that Hegel considered that "individual" always implies "otherness" and on that account tended to deny significance to the individual.

Author. In my experience the efficiency of my consciousness is wanting when it does not report selfness. The wholeness of my individuality is kept in view when I see clearly that all of my "otherness" is mine.

Research Worker. That seems to be the most difficult problem of all.

Author. Yes, but it is the one and only problem, and that realization is a great benefit permitting concentration upon what is important.

Research Worker. What do you think of the formula: From every man according to his abilities and to every man according to his needs?

Author. Such a formula implies a Lord Bountiful psychology. It asserts that one man can get at another, that individuality is violable, that self-interest is incapable of extension to include one's fellowman, that the welfare of one individual can mean something for another, that man is biologically inadequate and insufficient as an individual. All of that is based upon (illusional) otherness.

Research Worker. Your ideas of human being might put too great a strain upon the human mind. Maybe that explains why sincere individualism has never been tried.

Author. Learning to lift one's own mental weight "comes natural" provided that the opportunity is present. If my feet are bound and my arms in a straightjacket I can find it impossible to use them with freedom, too.

Research Worker. What do you think of personifying an institution, e.g., the legal fiction of a corporation's impersonating individuality?

Author. It helps to be aware that *human individuality* occurs only in one human being.

Research Worker. You do not feel that social welfare calls for self-sacrifice. You consider "social values" to be a statistical concept obscuring individual worth. You find that all of the meaning of "social welfare" in your life is your own expanding and enlightened self-interest. The utility and serviceability of your view of self-life holds only for yourself as a self-born, self-centered, self-devoted, self-uned selfist. For you, social unity is nothing but a phantom good, your real good being your individual conscious unity. Sheer selfishness only needs to be sufficiently comprehensive to provide the noblest morality.

Author. True. For me meritorious living consists of my extending my reach of self-consciousness. The very word "selfishness" has the rejection of repression in it. If you wish, wherever I use the word "selfishness" kindly, you may substitute its synonym "selfness."

Research Worker. You realize that your fellowman does not limit his meaning of meritorious action to selfism as you do. You see selfishness, laziness, inebriety, dishonesty, and all such disgraceful living, as therapeutic. I do not.

Author. I am pleased to have my fellowman regard meritorious living in the way which is practical only for him. The individual is the creator of all of his value as well as the only end by which all of his value is measurable.

Research Worker. I have heard it contended that a child knows others before he knows himself; that his social consciousness precedes his self-consciousness, that, in every step of his life-awakening, his consciousness of Alter is in advance of his consciousness of Ego; that he is really objective and able to be impersonal; that his natural state is "social"; that he has direct interests in the well-being of others; that his human nature enjoys a pre-established altruism; that his self-consciousness is a vice. Now according to you, all morality is, and can be, only the consciously chosen conduct of life of a human individual following the incentive prescribed by his own best self-interest; every so-called "immorality" is traceable to a human being's indistinct consciousness of himself; everything which is ethical is, and can be, only the expression of a personal idea; every human being's general good is nothing but his broadly conceived private good. As far as "objectivity" is concerned you dispose of it all simply by the old axiom: no object without a subject. Your every "object" has nothing but the quality and quantity belonging to an individuation of yourself. Are you not promoting *absent*-mindedness rather than presence of mind?

Author. I find that it is only the consciously inexperienced person, who is correspondingly lacking in self-consciousness, who loses "presence of mind" when he lives his "audience." His problem arises from the fact that he does not remember that *his* living of *his* audience is a personal, private matter. When he does "forget himself" (by not sensing *his* audience as *his*) it is for the purpose of avoiding the overwhelming excitation which remembering himself would arouse, I repeat.

Research Worker. What do you mean by "overwhelming"?

Author. By "overwhelming" I mean only too much excitement, so that concentration upon any one course of action is impaired. The effect of an overwhelming experience is a restriction of the sense of selfness.

Research Worker. Then to the extent that I am overwhelmed I so to speak, "pass out," or "faint."

Author. Yes. Only self-conscious conduct has my sense of personal identity in it.

Research Worker. I always thought that the insightful individual realized that he is living in a world with other persons and that by understanding himself he can grow his ability to understand his fellowman. For me and my friends democratic government rests on the assumption that conflicts of interest can be resolved by free discussion of the issues involved, and by voluntary concessions aimed at workable compromises. Of course there are some vital interests which men will always fight for rather than rely upon peaceful work.

Author. Every insightful citizen knows that "democracy" is a word which has unique meaning for each individual. As an American way of living it can be "accepted as a tradition" or studied as the most-difficult-to-understand basis of peaceful, rather than hostile, living. Propaganda is not wanting to undermine the governmental ideas of "the founding fathers" as being "impractical for the workaday world of today." Quick remedies are convincingly produced to eliminate the "inequitable disparities" of "human circumstance." The "cause of humanity" is always offered as the basis of non-democratic action. The ideology of the dictator is the alternative to the idealism of the individual. "Social" solidarity is offered as a substitute for conscious mental integration which does not appear to be liberating humanity, or, at least, "not fast enough." The "discipline of the free or democratic society" certainly does not indicate that the only meaning freedom or democracy has is in the *individual* mind that creates it. The language of pseudo-sociology, abounding in necessary plurals, personifications, and metaphors, may be employed in the wonderful effort to produce that humaneness which can only be produced by the individual whose view of his self-life is what impels him to behave (consciously be and have) himself.

As to the idea of "my living in my world," I appreciate that form of self-helpfulness, and yet I find it too limiting for my own living. It is useful for me to see that my recognition of my fellowman does not involve a denial of myself, but does involve a realization of my self-growth. I cannot attribute freedom to my fellowman except to the extent that I attribute solely to him the capacity for self-understanding. By his getting the best out of himself, I thereby get the best out of (my living of) him.

Research Worker. Brotherly love then, for you, simply means an extension of your own self-love. Are you proposing as the only sound principle of social morality your ideal of enlightened selfishness? Are you proposing a comprehensive appreciation of personal interest to be a reliable motive for all ethical living? Are you contending that deliberate selfishness, or self-regard, is the only true basis of any kind of moral behavior? Are you asserting that the only difference between an inconsiderate and a considerate citizen is that the former enjoys limited selfishness and the latter enjoys more generous self-coverage in his self-regard? Do you uphold as eminently practical that every person learn to think of himself only, but include his fellowman in his concept of himself? Is it your view that all that I find objectionable in "selfishness" is based upon my wish that this selfishness be more inclusive, in other words greater?

Author. As I ask myself each of these questions, I can reply only for myself. My reply is uniformly: Yes. I have learned to see the usefulness in self-regard and conscious self-assertion. I consider it an advantage to have my fellowman, my hearer for instance, see clearly that what he calls his fellowman is a living of his very own soul, or mind, when he can. Nevertheless, I do wish to have my fellowman term his fellowman as he does, however that may be, spirit or spook.

Research Worker. I realize that you have given your best efforts to describing your individualistic ideal as providing the most magnanimous human living. However, now you are pressing a point which I feel is critical. As I understand your view you seem to think that *you have no choice as to whether your morality is to be based upon individuality, or not. The only choice you can see is whether or not you will be aware that this is the only possible foundation of morality.*

Author. I cannot point up this truth more clearly than I have just had my Research Worker accomplish it. Individuality is the form of freedom, and responsibility does require a free agent. I do find all morality to be strictly a personal matter. I do find that there is no other reality than that which individual mind creates for itself. It is clear and distinct in my mind that *the assumption that there is a choice between the social and the individual as the basis of morality is an assumption founded upon illusion.* It is evident to me that each individual's human knowledge is his only possible authority.

Research Worker. The Socratic doctrine held that knowledge alone suffices for the attainment of virtue, that a human being naturally chooses a course that is good for him, provided that he has sufficient knowledge of it. You assert that the just State is not simply the just individual "written large," but that the only meaning of "State" is that which an individual's mind has for it.

Author. Yes, trust of increasing amounts of my selfness has obviated my need to reject these amounts.

Research Worker. What is your view of property?

Author. All property is self-property. The principle that one can own "external" property is the product of rejected ideality, in other words, of materialistic illusion.

Research Worker. What is your view of private enterprise?

Author. There is no other kind of enterprise. The illusion that there is any other kind is based upon self-rejection.

Research Worker. You regard your self-insight as a new force for promoting social unity, do you not?

Author. Every "social" force is nothing but a force lived by an individual.

Research Worker. Do you not regard family life as the unit of society and the cradle of individuality?

Author. I am thoroughly familiar with that way of thinking, having brought myself up on it, so to speak. I now help myself fully by realizing that everything which I mean by "family life" is entirely and nothing but my own mind's creation. "Family," or "society," is a unit meaning of the individual.

Research Worker. Don't you regard the family as the place where the individual is supposed to benefit from fullest self-expression and freedom?

Author. As I have said, I am thoroughly familiar with that way of considering family living. I now help myself fully by recognizing that an individual can only enjoy his complete freedom and self-expression by his realizing that he does not live "in a family," by his realizing that everything that he means by "family" is lived in him.

Research Worker. I have always considered the best civilization to be based upon an interweaving of individual interests which enables the development of social sympathy. For me "social intelligence" has meant mutual understanding. In fact, the history of civilization has been the history of man's successful effort to know his fellowman, understand him, make allowance for his nature and needs. Society is organized on the principles of justice and love. The marriage ceremony itself initiates that social organization, beginning as sympathetic reciprocity between two individuals. Sociology itself is the science of such a society in which scientific knowledge is readily communicable. Now your ideas give me pause. You imply that *there has never been developed a science of man, obviously the most essential of any scientific objectives, simply on account of the fact that such a science is too difficult.* You imply that *all of the rest of the sciences and arts are so many helpful symptoms signifying the lack of the science of man.* You point out that science, as it now exists, suffers from cold-bloodedness reflecting the absence of the science of man. You imply that our need for soldiers and police is traceable to underdeveloped self-reliance of the individual. You base all appreciation of peaceful life itself, including its spiritual significance, upon the necessity that it be consciously lived. What I call "the social order of rational beings" you call the individual's life distinctions based upon his cultivation of his self-insight. For you, a man's conscious consideration of his world of individuality constitutes the essence of merit. You do not posit two kinds of theory, one idealism, the other materialism. You assert that there can be but one of these theories, namely, idealism. You claim that materialism is, and can be, only unrecognized idealism, disowned idealism. You regard the distinctive function of a conscious human being to be his ubiquitous recognition of himself. Is all of this somewhat reminiscent of wishing to eat your cake and have it too, or wishing to pick yourself up by your own boot straps?

Author. True. My devotion to work of realizing my capacities of consciousness has revealed to me the virtue of open-minded consideration of every possible self-view which I create. My idea of divinity itself renounces the quality of superiority. It is difficult for me to conceive a god who is comfortable feeling superior to any of his creations. The realization of equality rather than of superiority is the criterion of divine status, as I see it.

Research Worker. Do you deny that you are a member of the body politic or of the body religious?

Author. Again, I cannot deny the right of existence of any idea. All that I can mean by body politic, or body religious, exists only in my mind.

Research Worker. What is meant by the democratic ideal: Man is born equal?

Author. Every one can and must, be equal to himself, or herself, only. Seeing clearly, and knowing fully, that one equals one is the essence of sanity. Equality can be only a synonym for identity, sameness.

Research Worker. Apparently you do not regard the Declaration of Independence just as an impractical historial ideal.

Author. The Declaration of Independence observes and asserts an established fact of human life: the dignity and actuality of the meaning of *individual.* The measure of my realization of my individuality is the extent of my appreciation that my fellowman is actually mine.

Research Worker. That sounds like "the greatest happiness for the greatest number," or "the common good."

Author. All that it *can* mean, however, is "my greatest happiness for my greatest number," or "my good."

Research Worker. Warner Fite said, "The primary condition of freedom is that the citizen in casting his vote shall know what he means."

Author. Yes. Particularly that he know that his government is one of the individual, by the individual, and for the individual.

Research Worker. Do you not often find your solitude forlorn? Your renunciation of established opinion disconcerting? Your reliance upon an ever new self untenable? Your very sense of personal identity an illusion of apperception? Your each speculation a self-growth reaching you nearer to your ending your own life?

Author. True. How true! But I cannot forbear my enjoyable passion to live so that I can learn what I can of my meaning: being alive. Personal identity is of necessity ever a momentary existent, and self-consciousness is only capable of *immediate* appreciation; each is an individuation of individuality. Only the instant self-sight, or conscious datum, can subsume the meaning "personal identity."

Research Worker. You remind me of Hume's renowned statement: "Human Nature is the only science of man; and yet has hitherto been the most neglected. It will be sufficient for me, if I can bring it a little more into fashion." Hume also noted: "Most philosophers seem inclined to think that personal identity *arises* from consciousness; and consciousness is nothing but a reflected thought or perception."

Author. Each is a clear view. The invariable, uninterrupted, and existent self is a now-self, and the feeling of personal identity must be an immediate *self*-consciousness. The self-awareness must be lived as the only datum enlivened in consciousness. Awareness of any kind must be awareness that is constituted only of the oneness, allness, wholeness, and nowness of selfness.

Research Worker. Schopenhauer said: "Consciousness is the mere surface of our minds, of which, as of the earth, we do not know the inside, but only the crust." He considered will to be the strong blind man who carries on his shoulders the lame man who can see.

Author. My Schopenhauer's life experience disclosed Schopenhauer. My experience discloses me. I find "conscious will" to be my most useful conscious life-force. A person's initiative conspicuously invigorates itself as he extends his appreciation of his personal identity to include that which it formerly excluded. My every need to reject any mental life is a noteworthy need to reject realization of my personal self.

Research Worker. It is true that *I* unlock the secrets of *my* life with the key of my personal experience, and thus develop *my* readiness to understand (*my* living of my particulars). I think for myself. However, I am not ready to describe all of my mental activity as "imagination." You may consider your test of excellence to be the extent of your ability to see all of your life as your own. I have a higher use for my mental activity than is covered by the term "imagination." The "far reach" of your self-consciousness, is the "far fetch" of mine. Please explain how a physician's self-consciousness is of practical help in his treating his demanding patient?

Author. Insofar as he is tolerant of his own demands upon himself, and thus can attend to his own health needs, the self-insightful physician will recognize that his patient's craving for "medical attention" is a necessary specific compensation for restrictions of self-consciousness. Attention is a function of consciousness. All of my insistence upon "betweenness" living (in lieu of the truth of my *withinness* living) is an earmark of the hysteria with which I temporarily help myself. Living *my* patient attentively, while the latter is trying to live himself as if hypnotizable, helps me to renounce the use of hypnotic means for living my own life. Thus, I can forgo the pitfalls of illusional "persuasion," "suggestion," and similar implications of being able to "influence" a life other than my own.

Deepening insight into the processes of his own mental life discovers for the consciously self-experiencing physician fuller and fuller appreciation of the fact that there is no helpfulness but one's own. Specifically, this depth of insight will safeguard the physician against employing his most powerful medical truth, *self-helpfulness,* with limited kindness. For his own great health benefit, however, he will enjoy the realization that every kind of medical examination is a mental examination, regardless of how it might be considered otherwise. Every consciously self-mindful person uses the method of working himself which will permit him to continue to be consciously self-mindful. Theoretical method regulates practice.

Research Worker. In all of my study of the subject-object predicament I find at least two possible ways of living it included, as if, one may live all of his experience as self-life or not. Your position, on the contrary, is positively that of asserting that the *only* life experience is self-life, and that one may *see* that necessity or not.

Author. Yes. Take away my consciousness and my *appreciation* of myself as creator of whatever I survey is removed.

Research Worker. Please excuse my bewilderment. I have been heeding your medical doctrine of the truth of individuality as being just what the doctor needs to order, in kindly prescription for himself, so that his patient will experience his living of an insightful physician. What bothers me is this: Does your view that you *grow* your sensations, perceptions, and observations, which you then call your "environment,"—does this view of medical training (as nothing but each student's self-development, or self-activity) negate the helpfulness of all of my learning of medicine as carefully and scientifically validated principle? For instance, I learned to study mental phenomena as one aspect of the study of neurology. I studied sensation and perception as reactions to external *stimuli,* not as sproutings of my self-growth! Do you intend to make medical science over with your acknowledged one-man's ideal of self-insight?

Author. May this line of questioning receive continuing scientific investigation. No statement in my record is intended as negating any other research viewpoint, whatsoever. Each of my self-observations has only additive, never subtractive, value. *All* of my medical training, and particularly my intensive study of the history of my medicine, has been most rewarding for my growth of myself as a physician. I, too, have disciplined my mind carefully and caringly in (growing) my orthodox neurology and other orthodox medical interests, helping myself greatly in the process. Every element of it I may see as nothing but my own self-growth. However, I am only entirely in favor of having my fellow physician help himself in the way which he finds helpful. Only on the ground of his already present and acknowledged self-helpfulness can his further conscious self-helpfulness be grown. As far as my concentration on the need for a science of man is concerned, I find that no other direction of my effort is as practical. As far as my peculiar way of thinking is concerned, I am pleased to recall the excellent observation of (my) Don K. Price in *Government and Science* (1954) that one must learn to think without using the patterns or models taken for granted by most textbooks.

Research Worker. For you individuality is wholly active, and never passive; wholly expressed, and never impressed; always subject, and never object; always ego, and never alter; always author, and never imitator; always original, and never copy; always equal, and never superior or inferior; always divine, and never imperfect.

Author. I deny nothing which I live, and I do live each of these self-views.

Research Worker. George Berkeley wrote as you do in 1713. Read his *Three Dialogues between Hylas and Philonus.* His English contemporary, Arthur Collier, independently recorded the same radical individualism. Read his *Clavis Universalis.* Or read John Norris' *Theory of the Ideal or Intelligible World.* Descartes and Malebranche advanced similar views questioning the bases of the popularly and traditionally assumed existence of "externeity." John Locke also conceived of matter as "unknown support." Kant argued that material substance is "nothing outside our representations." I trust you won't feel that I am resisting kind consideration of *your* science of man. For instance, consider the following assertion from a current writer: "Thus gradually philosophers and scientists arrived at the startling conclusion that since every object is simply the sum of its qualities and since qualities exist only in the mind, the whole objective universe of matter and energy, atoms and stars, does not exist except as a construction of consciousness, an edifice of conventional symbols shaped by the senses of man."[5] I could go on like this citing instance after instance from the birth of history right down to this very present of many an individual's devoting his life to his solipsistic self-orientation. What is so different about your demonstrating yourself as proof of the non-existence or impossibility of an external world?

Author. The "difference" is an all-important one to me: *I* am helping *myself* by *my* self-conscious way of living *me.*

Research Worker. Collier wrote that his assertion "All that passes for 'matter' is nothing but *mind,*" was an instance of his remarking the obvious,—as "a thing is like itself." Of the body he wrote: ". . . when I affirm that all matter exists in mind, after the same manner as a body exists in place, I mean the very same as if I had said, that mind itself is the place of body, and so its place, as that it is not capable of existing any other place, or in place after any other manner." Is that your idea of body, too? Your idea of a body is that there is no body in it, no non-mind in it.

Author. That *is* my idea of my body. It exists as mental material in my mind. Existence of any kind is all *subjective* existence. Subjectivity exists *in* itself always. Therefore, there can never be an externeity *anywhere.* Therefore, all that passes for an "external world" is repudiated reality of subjectivity.

Research Worker. If that is true, how do you think the seeming of "externality" ever got started?

Author. Simply by every mind's capacity to say *of its own living,* "It is not I."

Research Worker. Why should a mind lie?

Author. The mind really does not lie. It lives something it does not like, then wishes it might not experience that unpleasantness, and then that wish fathers the thought that the truly lived self-experience not be acknowledged as such.

Research Worker. Your pronouncement, "There can never be any externeity anywhere," is based upon that first principle of science, "The same thing cannot both be and not be simultaneously," is it not? I mean, whatever you perceive cannot be both your perception and also something else. What you posit as being "external" cannot have that meaning apart from you.

Author. I help myself by realizing that *all* of my truth *is* mine.

Research Worker. If your approach is, and can be, only helpful to yourself, why do you trouble yourself to report it? If you claim, as did Fichte, "All actual knowing is Being,"— why do you publish? If some part of your subjectivity *is* your only possible *object,* or being, or substance,—then why not *keep* it to yourself? If *your* fellow physician is nothing but a special experience of your own being, if every part of your workaday world is nothing but a process of your conceiving (creating) it,—then why try to exteriorize what can only remain interiority? If you can create your own objectivity and *thereby* continue to supply its only content, simply by working your mind diremptively, —then why should you care even to try to appease my curiosity?

Author. This pointed questioning describes you as a research scientist. Whether it has any of "the bitter edge of repression" (C. P. Snow) in it, I can not know. *On account of the fact that I live my you,* I find it only helpful to me, when (my) you help yourself. *On account of the fact that all of my "external world" is my own living,* I cannot but have entirely personal interest in the activity of its every existent. To attribute visibility, audibility, and so on, to an "external" object, is such a conspicuous arrangement of convenience, that it is readily renounced by anyone who gives this primitive explanation of sensory living a second look. Nothing is more evident than that one is the fullest possible conception of one.

Research Worker. I prefer to do some research on any statement before accepting or rejecting it as true. I have been accustomed to considering external matter as visible, but I now observe that the same datum cannot be both. I cannot help it if I speak inconsistently with myself,—that is the way I learned to speak. I see your point that you cannot know, or perceive, or sense any "externeity," but does it follow that you must conclude that no externeity can exist?

Author. When I find that I must posit the identity of existence and subjectivity, how can I, or why should I, care about postulating a something which is non-existent by definition?

I certainly live comfortably my fellowman's helping himself with his devotion to his assertions of "externeity." His dependence upon his world (which clearly *seems* to be external) is a manifestation of his own *individuality,* the very allness and wonderfulness of which (individuality) these conversations are all and only about.

I repeat, the question of what constitutes the most productive psychiatric research is, and must be, open to various answers, each answer an accurate one according to the level on which the research is conducted.

Research Worker. I presume you have already tried all of the other forms of research before settling upon your me-search,—such as neurophysiology, biochemistry, electrophysiology, hypnotism, and the various therapeutic uses of reasoning, communication, and straight non-mental medicine?

Author. Yes, I have helped myself in living each of these fields of endeavor. I have found my truth of sincere self-regard as my most liberal, generous, all-loving, all-revering way of life, by a long and concentrated experience in seeking expert understanding of life, health, and education.

Research Worker. In his *Clavis Universalis,* a book which you can have no trouble authoring, Arthur Collier recommends that anyone who wishes to do so may strengthen his insight that his world is all *his,* by practicing looking-glass visualization, that is, by observing, at least, that what he sees *in* the mirror is not *out* of the mirror. He also suggests that by writing for or against it, one cannot avoid finding that there is no "external world," as popularly claimed. He advised *keeping* in the forefront of one's mind the reminder "There is no external world." What do you think of those self-teaching aids?

Author. Most important of all, in the first place, is the realization that one's life is not sufficiently satisfying when it is being lived without the benefit of self-consciousness. In other words, the self-diagnosis reveals the self-treatment indicated. *The wish to grow self-insightfully* is the living which needs most careful cultivating until it is strong enough to assert itself effectively.

Research Worker. My thanks to you for nothing. I'm sure *that* gratitude pleases you. I must admit that you seem to be all for keeping the peace in your intention, but your view that you are self-made, that all of your scientific knowledge is nothing but your own self-originated, self-determined human being, is not the popular one with scientists. I suppose you may claim that desideratum may rest upon a given scientist's limited use of his psychological appliance called "insight." Now, I wish to try further the validity of your view, for instance, your seeing your neurology as nothing at all unless it is entirely a living of yours. It seems to me that such absolute individualism annuls the tried and true teaching of neurology. How can you be comfortable with such contradictory, and mutually excluding, physiological explanations as (1) your theory of your study of neurology as being nothing but your growing of self-knowledge and (2) the accepted theory of the study of neurology as being an objective medical discipline which each student acquires *from without?*

Author. I am comfortable with each view, in the first place, for each one *is* my own living of it; and it is only natural for me to feel comfortable with my own creations. By keeping my mind open to my possibilities I strengthen my research potentiality. I only make trouble for myself by refusing to see every single bit of my wonderful living as lovable. Fortunately, I do "make trouble" for myself when I make (create) my own living and refuse to recognize it as such. What I cannot take the trouble to see is my own, is a part of me that troubles me until I do grow that pacifying self-insight.

Research Worker. Would you mind returning to my concrete question as to how you reconcile your contradictory views on neurology? One of them must seem absurd to you.

Author. Perhaps I can do that best by means of illustration. Take the simplest act of vision, for instance. (1) My traditional theory implies (the impossibility) that by means of my faculty of eyesight I can make objects visible which are external to me. Now that theory is all about itself and, as such, entirely reconcilable with itself. (2) My inviolable-individuality theory implies (the possibility) that by means of my faculty of vision I can create self-scenes which reveal my wonderful ability to live (grow) myself. Now this theory is also, all about itself and, as such, entirely reconcilable with itself. Incompatibility is always traceable to unrecognized efforts to create the impossible condition whereby one whole, or all, is supposed to have something "in common" with another whole, or all. I regard no theory as absurd and find that the designation of "absurd" to any of my living is my unrecognized and vain effort to disown (repress) it.

Research Worker. Would you prefer that the authorities who write the neurological textbooks deal openly with such questions as these you raise about the intrinsic allness of man?

Author. I shall prefer it when it happens. Until then I am satisfied to live what is.

Research Worker. Is that not the way to betray yourself into a spineless *laissez faire* attitude towards education? Gladly accepting the way things are, hardly provides incentive for new development, does it?

Author. Incentive derives from the wish to preserve living which *is* found worthy. Dissatisfaction begets dissatisfaction. The use and consequence of making the best (in seeing the best) of one's experience is that it frees energy for the action of incentive.

Research Worker. Where does improvement, or progress, come from, then?

Author. I find the idea of "progress" to be an illusion containing the ingredients of indulgence of fault-finding and hope for relief from its overwhelming force.

Research Worker. I see, you are back on your all-is-perfect ideal. You are prejudiced in favor of the ideal that Whatever is, is perfect,—are you not?

Author. I find this life orientation holds the most practicality for my world.

Research Worker. I am glad that you know that research is my business when I ask these questions. Sometimes in your talking you refer to your hearer, when you realize that he must originate what he hears. Why do you not refer to him as Author II, for instance?

Author. That idea is pleasing. It might well be tried wherever the illusion of "communication" is indulged.

Research Worker. Your sovereign remedy of self-consciousness, that is, of self-heed and self-care, reminds me of the *Naturae Codex* (book of nature) of that radical individualist, the iatrochemist Paracelsus, (and of all of the rest of the so-called self-made physicians of history, beginning with Hippocrates). Your nostrum, "The growth of all medical knowledge as conscious self-knowledge, is the healthy core of medical living," I can see is the *summum bonum* of your professional life. According to your avowed world outlook, "The only possible way to look out is to look in." No doubt you are willing to consider accounting for the efficacy of self-insight in your particular case as founded upon an idiosyncrasy of yours. Is that true?

Author. It is entirely true. I gladly consider this felt need of mine (for self-insight) to be an idiosyncrasy, for I wish to test the validity of its helpfulness in every possible way. As you are, so I, too, am a busy philiater needing to cultivate myself specifically as a practical, capable, efficient, lively, as well as kind, working man of science. I am deeply interested in any and every idiometer I can discover.

Research Worker. It appears that your psychological hygiene has made you a harder worker and easier to get along with, anyhow. Is that true?

Author. I work longer hours consciously than my former "I" did, and I do find myself getting along well by not unwittingly running into myself.

Research Worker. Bearing uppermost in mind (and this I need to do in trying to live kindly some of your intolerable views on self-healing) how every advance in medical science has been made against fierce opposition, I will renounce for the time being my need to regard you as a man whose occupation has extended his reason and who, therefore, cherishes all the more what self-consciousness he has. You go even beyond the generous Platonic concept of "microcosm *vs.* macrocosm," asserting that both are nothing but productions of your own living. I realize that psychopathology is the sign of self-intolerance, according to your view. But do you mean by that, that I must either grow able to call more and more of my soul my own, or suffer the helpful signs of self-ignoration (psychopathy)?

Author. When I ask that of myself, all I can say is, It is an excellent question. Certainly *in applying it to myself,* I must answer it thankfully in the affirmative.

Research Worker. You have not yet clarified why you cannot elucidate the mind-strengthening and -healing property of self-consciousness in such a way that your patient will cry out for it. All you really have stated is that you help yourself with it, wouldn't give up the least bit of it, and want to grow more of it. Why can't you make that understandable even for me?

Author. True. A sensible objection. The fact is, however, that (my) you have succeeded in making the medicinal property of thorough and sustained self-appreciation understandable at least for that part of yourself you designate as "author." If (my) you have any trouble in recognizing that *your* author is your own, your finding out what that (repudiation of your own living of your author) means is well worth the distress of the trouble itself. My pain is always a sign that I am living myself in a way to necessitate pain, rather than pleasure. Similarly, my unhappiness in any form is always a sign that I am living myself in a way to necessitate unhappiness rather than happiness. It pays me to be aware of being unhappy, if my way of living myself involves my denying that I am doing some or any of my own living.

Research Worker. I understand that unhappiness of any kind, including pain, focusses attention upon itself so that a person's appreciation of his individuality becomes restricted to his awareness that *he* is suffering. For instance, a toothache tends to restrict his sense of personal identity to his localized awareness of living a painful area of himself.

Author. True. In every kind of unhappiness there is a need for the sufferer to counteract this kind of limitation of his self-consciousness, this lack of appreciation of his wholeness. All self-disregard presses for expression in every human tissue. A full self-estimate provides the most vital, vigorous body tone, essential for preventing and healing suppuration of every description.

Research Worker. Can anyone complain of the limited efficiency of his kind of self-help, instead of complaining of the distress properly associated with the way of life he travels? What I mean is, *can* a person really understand that his unhappiness is a fortunate consequence of the way he has his mind work? For instance, have you ever had an unhappy (grief-stricken, angry, jealous, or whatever) patient, instead of naming his particular brand of unhappiness as his complaint, outline the behavior he cultivates as a full accounting for his helpful unhappiness?

Author. Never. As I see it, that would be impossible. Full insight of that kind would obviate my necessity to conduct myself so that my joy of living would be curtailed. I may feel pain, but if I understand its report I will find pleasure in directing my living to relieve it. Or, I may see clearly how my life situation necessitates unhappiness, including pain; but my complaint will be directed to relieve my life situation while I shall appreciate the efficiency of my unhappiness and/or pain.

Research Worker. How about your having pain from an accidental wound, or from the terminal stages of cancer? Would you, in either case, try to take medicine for your pain or try to live in such a way that the pain would not be necessary?

Author. This question certainly brings up the fact that every complaint is an individual one which does not lend itself to generalization. In the first case you cite, I would have to begin with my realization that there is no such possibility as an "accident." In the second case, I would have to begin with my realization that I could not ever know if a cancer is "terminal" or not. In any case of health ordeal I find my unhappiness, or pain, a most precious and indispensable guide to my understanding and to my freeing myself from my kind of living which is justly announced by that unhappiness, or pain. In every case, I would have to wait to see what I would do.

Research Worker. Very well. Why can't you work your simple prescription, "You're unhappy (hurting yourself unconsciously), get happy (make yourself conscious so that you can *feel* that you're hurting yourself, and thus desist)"?

Author. I do work it. At first I resist it with all of my might, for I have a habit of mind of so-called "punishing" myself; and, like any habit, that one is exceedingly difficult to renounce. By "punishing" I mean only helpfully *repressing.*

Research Worker. That is vernacular, is it not? What do you mean by "habit of mind," "so-called 'punishing' yourself," and "resisting" your making yourself happy?

Author. I mean to be kind in my answers to my questions, but I can never be sure that I am. "Force of habit" has been called second nature, on account of its strength. If I have been "in the habit" of living myself unconsciously, custom has made that comfortable living, even though it is a sure source of my self-disesteem. Thus, I may prefer to live on, limiting my happiness in my accustomed way, resisting my growing any new directive which may exercise my joy of living on a larger scale.

Research Worker. What do you mean by "limiting" your happiness? If you restrict your ability to enjoy life, is that not self-punishment?

Author. In a sense, yes. However the word "punishment," like the word "selfishness," has more of the meaning of self-harm than of self-help in it. And so-called "punishment" really is the only available kind of self-help when it is used. Any other orientation about it involves fault-finding and *its* great limitations. Renunciation of my habit of fault-finding, or of any habit, involves painful living.

Research Worker. You mean that you have to go through all of the distress occasioned by "withdrawal symptoms," simply by abstaining from your habit of so-called punishing yourself?

Author. Exactly. *It is the habit of greatly delimiting joy of living, or so-called self-punishment, which psychotherapy is mainly concerned with. Hence, psychiatric research upon it is most needed.*

Research Worker. You regard all unhappiness, including pain, depression, and every unpleasant feeling like anger, suspicion, jealousy, or fear, as being a most valuable sign of dangerous living. Your patient regards his unhappiness as being his real trouble. He frankly states that he suffers from depression, or fear, or hate, or jealousy, or whatever. Who is right?

Author. Each is right as he sees it. It is natural to complain of a toothache, not of the dangerous dental condition which fortunately is proclaimed by the pain.

Research Worker. What does research mean to you? What is your definition of truth?

Author. Only in my own selfhood's being can I have any consciousness. Hence, all of my consciousness is necessarily *self*-consciousness. All of the value which I attach to reality is at stake, in my view of what constitutes my realm of scientific research. The more closely I examine any and every subject of my research, the greater certitude I develop that it is, in its entirety, nothing but a construct of my mind. My truth consists of my conscious identification of my every sensation, perception, or observation as being (only) the distinct existence of each of these ways (sensing, perceiving, observing) of my living.

Research Worker. Are you then, as subject, unable to predicate anything of your object? Or, am I getting too technical for you? Please stop me if my irritability is showing.

Author. Undoubtedly (my) you are now too technical for many a one of my listeners. However, I am eager to have (my) you help yourself. For my own satisfaction I have succeeded in establishing my truth that dualism (such as subject and object, internal and external, I and not-I, self and others, idealism and materialism) is a product of ambivalence which, in turn, is a product of overwhelming self-excitation. The distraction of ambivalence is helpful when the concentration of oneness puts too great an emotional charge upon my mind.

It is the nature of one living element to grow itself into a new development of itself, but it cannot otherwise become "another" living element. Every subject must grow its own predicate and object, by the process of living its subjectivity only. My awareness of this creative kind of living of my subjectivity is all I can mean by "predicating" and by "objectifying."

Research Worker. No doubt the systematic study of the laws of human individuality, and of their unappreciated practicality and utility, is of certain vital importance. It does appear that the anthropologist studies man in the abstract "objectively" and necessarily misses the mark of the personal man. I can see that a person's self-awareness is the only possible basis for his taking inventory of his assets; that one's opinion of one's self is decided entirely by how much of his individuality he can acknowledge being, and naught besides; and that everyone's self-consciousness signs, seals, and delivers his life to his sense of ownership. *Each individual's self-awareness is his title-deed to his due self-regard.* I now notice that all sense of proprietorship of a person is contingent upon his activating his self-consciousness. Exercise of self-awareness must be the most healthful gymnastic possible.

Author. Yes. A half-century ago, Freud pointed up the fact (*On Narcissism: An Introduction*) that even a mother loves herself only, but her self-love includes her loving her living of her child as being capable of his own all-embracing self-love. With her growth of insight she helps herself to see that she is not her child's mother, that her child lives his mother in *his* own soul. Truth, beauty, goodness, and every possible human benefit, dwell in their beholder. The self is the safety-deposit of all of its meaning, and meaninglessness defines nothingness.

Research Worker. In this era of discovery only one finding is possible: the researcher's discovery of further possibilities of his own manpower. A person's mind is always making itself, and ideal man knows that his mind is *all* his. This insight is his supreme lesson which is constantly new and requires continuous attention. As does the circulation of his blood, it too, continues throughout his life and is a *constant* source of life joy. There is no "out beyond himself" to which one can go. All living is self-begetting. A human being cannot have any opposition, adversity, or discontent even, which is not entirely of his own making. I cannot know anything about my fellowman, let alone understand him. When I claim that I can, I am judging by "outward appearances," or, in other words, practicing the illusion of materialism within my own real, idealistic mind. To the extent that I think of myself as an "object," I am indulging materialistic illusion. *Therefore the very term "individual" must be understood by me as meaning universal.* I have described these insights of mine in detail to test my self-tolerance with them.

Author. As I have just had (my) you declaring yourself, I have been enjoying a thrill of freedom with each of these ideas of individuality. Your self-description exactly fits that of a consciously free man.

Research Worker. I am beginning to see (1) that the orientation, "the people," is materialistic and (2) that "materialism" is an illusion consisting of disowned (unconscious) idealism. The phantom problem known as traditional or common-sense materialism can be solved only by the realization that every mention of materialism (other than that of the self-material of subjectivism) begs the question. Whatever existence there is belongs all and only to whatever existent there is.

My remedy for this most popular delusional system ("materialism" underlying the "insanity of the majority") is my cultivating my subjective standpoint, redeeming my self-consciousness by discovering that I saved my life while growing up by imposing insight-narrowing limitations upon my mind. To live my family experiences harmoniously I had to develop a conscious self-sphere which could not reveal to me my true measure, my allness nature. Then, whatever I could not see as being my own creation I judged to be made up of some other material. Thus, my delusional "materialism" waxed as my conscious idealism waned. Thereafter, it was only natural for me to look (to myself) in my delusional direction ("outward") for "external" remedies, failing to interpret my "externality" as being my rejected human constitution. My fierce defense of my "materialism" was not manifest to me as simple self-defense. All else in the way of "externality" failing, I could still try "going abroad," "around the world," or to another kind of doctor, or die for my cause.

Author. True. As a "materialist" I necessarily prefer to deal directly and only with the "objective," since I must unconsciously sense myself in my "externality" living always (there being nothing else there for me to sense). It is only natural for me to "seek the truth" with a strong (unconscious) desire for evidence to confirm my delusional system ("materialism").

Research Worker. Doesn't education in the form of presentations of "objective facts" to be learned reenforce man's "materialistic" life orientation *at the expense* of his refinement of his self-perception?

Author. Yes. My devotion to my mind's cultivation of its system of "objective materialism" must produce in me a reliance upon (my imagined) non-mental materiality, instead of a conscious self-reliance. As I center my attention upon (illusional) "objectivity," I tend to neglect and disregard my sense of being.

"I am" is the only unencumbered human position; "I have" is human imposture.

Research Worker. Can you consider mind, or soul, or spirit, to be physical in any way?

Author. I can only consider anything, or anybody, to be whatever I make it be, by my *living* it. My mind, or soul, or spirit, is as much a construct of my subjectivity, as is all else. My subjectivity is my only force, or energy, which begets itself, and thereby accounts for my all.

Research Worker. Please, what do you mean by "subjectivity"?

Author. By "subjectivity" I mean, specifically, the only existence which exists.

Research Worker. You mean that there is no other quality, or quantity, than subjectivity?

Author. Exactly.

Research Worker. According to you, if man's reality is to be protected, a new vocabulary, a new language, of science will have to be created, which respects the one and only truth: subjectivity.

Author. Exactly. However, fortunately no one can believe me, —but myself, that is.

Research Worker. Why "fortunately"? If you are sure of your ground of subjectivity, why wouldn't it be fortunate for everyone to believe you?

Author. In the first place it would be impossible, for each one can *only* believe himself. Furthermore, each one needs to protect himself against any and every life view which, if suddenly believed by him, would upset his equilibrium and possibly prove too much for his mind's accommodation. After all, believing is not the same as understanding.

Research Worker. You mean that your experience has demonstrated that you do not have to fear being suddenly understandable?

Author. True. Besides, *understanding is based upon the sense of personal identity and does not depend upon (illusional) otherness.*

Research Worker. Your mind reduces every notion of the "physical" or "material" to its reality as an operation of your subjectivity?

Author. Yes. Subjectivity is my only substance, and even its shadow is not "materialism."

Research Worker. Sensory and perceptual experience is the scientific basis of reality, and it is mighty important to know whether that experience is all subjective or not. Reconditioning my mind to use its power of beholding its unmateriality seems forbiddingly difficult.

Author. Every step of that way has been most rewarding to me. Success attends the first and every succeeding step.

Research Worker. You say that "I-am" living restores man's due self-esteem, and that "I-have" living creates a false sense of life through its divisiveness. You trace all guilt to self-ignoration and all innocence to self-appreciation. You imply that by living yourself as a guilty one you discern guilt in your neighbor's living, and by living yourself as innocent you become conscious of your neighbor's innocence. For you, the meaning of your everything depends upon how you live yourself. As your own conscious author of all of your truth, you see all as perfect, sacred, deific. As an educator, particularly as a physician, you must sense a tremendous need for extension of hygienic effort so that everyone may begin to develop his sense of being a living entity with all of the wonderful meaning of that self-view. The way one thinks is the way one grows. Appreciated oneness of self is essential cleanness of living. By a realization of the law that consciousness of mind is a mind-shaping experience, each one can start using his consciousness with an appreciation that he *is* the captain of his soul and that only he can (but also must) direct his self-growth as he will.

Author. Your view of your author is accurate, if by "extension of hygienic effort" you mean specifically his extension of his own hygienic effort.

Research Worker. You do not feel that science will ultimately come up with a physical accomplishment which will make up for all of its disregard for the individual,—for instance, even make the moon habitable?

Author. As each scientist *begins* to realize that his world, including his moon, is naught but his own, he will extend the hygienic effort needed,—not before.

Research Worker. Please give me a "for instance."

Author. Everyone complains of "traffic fatalities" which are, for the most part, a consequence of "legitimate" speed. An obvious remedy would be to reduce all but emergency road speed to twenty or twenty-five miles an hour. That sane idea is "unthinkable" in this day of contracted "time" and "space." Commerce could not support such an innovation. Warfare could not rely upon lightning motion. And so on.

Research Worker. You remind me of Emerson's dicta. Travel is a fool's paradise. The soul does not travel. The law of self seems like such an obviously desirable basis for science, I cannot but wonder why it has been so long ignored. Science is ready to study anything presumably. I suppose science is too busy with commitments. I see my word "science" as a personification.

Author. Self-questioning has been a valuable therapeutic for me. If I have the habit of mistaking my own identity in most of my experience, what benefit is more experience? If my woe, lack of peace, inability to enjoy myself, are traceable to my way of living myself (unconsciously, that is) what benefit derives from my increasing my speed of living? If radical misapprehension of the illusional meaning of "objectivity" is my trouble, what good do I get from collecting more "objects"? If I am convinced that I have to wait until I die to become, or at least enjoy being, a peaceful soul, what point is there to my pursuing an existence which imputes all potency to matter?

Research Worker. You mean that discontented man is only fortunately discontented since he gave up thinking rightly of himself as an all-individual. You mean that your orientation around your pure subjectivity has been the one thing necessary for your peace of mind, sense of well-being, and devotion to working yourself as conscious subject. You mean that your study of the law of your individuality has saved you from the materialistic mirage which is self made unmanifest. The plain unvarnished fact is that each individual is not an island, but *is* a world to himself.

Author. Yes. My one and only space is that of my own living world which I carry as me, and which undergoes no change of locality. My every circumstance is of my making,—I cannot be "under" any circumstance. *Here* is the only space I can *ever* live. My system of therapeutics is a natural outgrowth of my human system. Prevailing illusional "materialism" excludes individualism largely and relies upon illusional "externals" as sources of help. "Objective" study is the pursuit of self-unconsciousness. The scientific "materialist" deals with "objects,"— he *cannot* concern himself with subjects. And this self-disregard is rated as normal, sane, standard, "natural." The idea of studying the laws of his own being is rarely conceived as practical by a scientist and is *always* conceived as scientifically impossible by the "materialistic" scientist. This idea is a rational innovation for me whenever I arouse myself with it.

Research Worker. The materialistic scientist has no choice other than to live his world dualistically, as now his friend and now his enemy, but never his own human tissue or mind stuff. Thus he can avoid seeing that he is solely responsible and accountable for *his* "external" microscopic and macroscopic "enemies." He can escape realization of the amazing importance of conscious disposition of his subjective forces, for even in this seeming disadvantage there is beneficence for him. He can retain undisturbed, all-important comfort in his affirmation of his already established ideals. He does not have to *feel* the goad to extend his consciousness of himself. He can continue his centrality in his sensations and perceptions without awareness that they impoverish his conscious *self*-image.

Author. I gratify myself by having (my) you see that all so-called disadvatage is observable really as a disguised benefit, if one can view it broadly. Every seeming ill is really a helpful self-created entity. "Evil," everything called "bad," is a term of repression (self-repudiation). To see this truth is to gain title to all of the precious selfness otherwise concealed as "the powers of darkness." St. Paul was a scientific idealist when he asserted, "All things are yours." Freud was a scientific idealist when he observed, all consciousness is self-consciousnes. Self-unconsciousness, which is the negative of self-consciousness, is the mainspring of every woe of humanity traceable to the individual's unreadiness to see that all of his world is perfectly desirable. My self-consciousness limits the boundary of my mind's horizon and decides how much of my completeness I may sense. A sense of personal incompleteness is always traceable to limitations imposed by definitive self-consciousness.

Research Worker. Disappointment, struggle, suffering, death, —is all such agony desirable? I suppose it is, if and when it occurs. The kingdom of evil is just unrecognized kingdom of good, but it is very difficult to see that truth particularly when the seeing of it would do the most good. I mean during the experience of agony.

Author. Whenever I refine, enlarge, and intensify my self-consciousness, for instance, by appreciation of the powerful helpfulness of agony, I cultivate my sense of self-worth. Simply seeing agony as a phenomenon I must forego appreciation of its beneficent force.

Research Worker. I ask it in no impatient spirit—please describe the value to an individual of his ability to agonize. I'm beginning to see my reply in my question as I ask it.

Author. Exactly. Unhappiness of every kind, including pain, is of vital character, and its vitality imbues itself in the whole human economy as an effort of true self-help bringing man completely to himself, mobilizing his self-interests, consulting the law of his constitution, expressing the wish to live free of overwhelming suffering, concentrating on the view of the real self. My agony is perfect even as I am perfectly unaware that it is. With it I can, and must, sense the truth of my unity, and experience my painful self-consciousness as vital inspiration.

Research Worker. I understand you would use a pain destroyer if you had one, would you not?

Author. Whenever I can do so, I prefer to use awareness of pain for indicating how I need to, and can, relieve myself by no longer requiring that pain. The same use of unhappiness applies to my suffering of fear, hate, depression, envy, jealousy, disgust, suspicion, shame, despair, and each such woe.

Research Worker. I assume that you have your patient decide for himself what he can well stand and not stand.

Author. Individuality is the law of laws.

Research Worker. Would you be willing to define "body" as solidified soul, or spirit, or mind?

Author. I see "body" as a subjectively actualized entity of thoroughly organized life force. "Body" is as much a mental term as is "mind" itself.

Research Worker. If you had your way, would you stop all

of the scientific materialism now going on? I know you wouldn't even as I ask, but I'd like to have you discuss this question.

Author. I would no more stop "scientific materialism" now going on than try to interfere with my fellow scientific idealist's current way of helping himself. My scientific materialist *is* helping himself as best he can by the kind of mind shape he has thus far evolved. No one could ask for more, if he knew the necessities involved.

Research Worker. How then *do* you propose to help yourself as far as your living of your scientific materialist is concerned?

Author. By having him, when he will, *add* to his present self-helpfulness,—not subtract from it.

Research Worker. You mean you see all of the therapeutic force of scientific materialism as being a base upon which the given scientist by self-education can build his mental structure of scientific idealism?

Author. Yes.

Research Worker. I have noticed you refer to divinity now and then.

Author. On account of the simple but powerful fact that my idea of my god has the greatest significance for my growth of my idea of myself.

Research Worker. You make everything and everybody divine.

Author. I *see* that all is divine, divinely helpful, useful, practical. I have no limitation of my god. (My) you are god, whether I live you as recognizing your divine nature or not. Whatever is, supremely is, divinely is.

Research Worker. Are you humanizing God or apotheosizing man? Are you allowing poetic imagery to carry you away? Could your psychological research have confounded you with overwhelming soul-study? In this practical book, the first question is, How true is an observation? and, the second, How applicable as a practicality is it?

Author. Again, I can find, appreciate, and apply no truth but my truth. What constitutes truth for (my) you is (my) your proper concern. Every step I have made in the direction of truthfully calling my soul my own and my all my soul has been fearfully made. Now the trend even of the scientist seems to be that of renouncing (illusional) "materialism," except that he cannot find what to do with the heart of it, namely, "objectivity."

Research Worker. The scientific materialist has to lead a kind of double life anyhow. On the sabbath he may exercise the truth of his idealism and enjoy life-promoting soul stirrings, while otherwise daily starving himself by limiting his self-consciousness. There are laboratory and clinical proofs that chronic self-repudiation and its associated varieties of unhappiness produce physiological complication, whereas soul-commanded self-conscious living turns every kind of unhappiness to health account. I am beginning to create these views myself.

Author. For decades leading medical educators have "called attention" to the fact that man's mind is a reality. However, that notion is more readily identified with the philosopher or poet. A "medical man" is, by tradition, devoted to the "concrete substances" of life such as cells, tissues, organs, systems, and such sensible data. Meanwhile, he is pleased to have Browning prescribe,

> But friends,
> Truth is within ourselves: it takes no rise,
> From outward things, whate'er you may believe.

Research Worker. Psychiatrists are not all objectivists. It is true, as a rule, the M.D. has educated himself regarding whatever compound he hears of, except mental compounds. The medical research worker today is for the most part peering into his sensibles fully expecting thereby to discover the sovereign remedy which will permit his patient to enjoy a life of self-fulfilment without the discomfort of seeing to it. Nevertheless, many a physician is using the laws of his mind as his conscious pilot for his way of life. More and more it is becoming the rare one who flies blind, who does not recognize that his patient has the only power of health which, once freed from obstruction, accomplishes all possible healing and strengthening. Just a flash, or glimpse, of this therapeutic is a wonderful medical development which, once experienced, becomes a practical, everyday self-treatment.

Author. True. Personally, I cannot recall a medical educator who considers pain or unhappiness of any kind as an adversary. I would even go so far as to assert that the understanding of unhappiness, or of any kind of symptom, as being really unmanifest therapy, is a main distinction of the self-conscious physician. To value unhappiness, including pain, superficially is to restrict one's psychic maturity to that of a trifler. Due self-love depends upon unhappiness of every kind. As a parent speaking with his child regarding the disadvantages of unwise living, unhappiness is always one's most humane reminder that he has forgotten himself, where he cannot afford such laxity. Every kind of symptom helps its sufferer to come to life, to remember *he is.* Nothing can be lightly regarded but selfness and the just cost is pain. I can only, but must, make myself what I please (will, wish, choose, decide). Fortunately, the spirit of "objectivity" of my scientist is most unfavorable for happy, painless living; for his discomfort is his only possible incentive and guide to a way of living which does not automatically impose unhappiness. "Materialism" *is* symptomatic, and hence therapeutic, the treatment being the same as the "disease." Finding out that truth is the process of having it become controllable in the realm of subjective realism. His bright and life-warm truth of the ideality of his human existence will emancipate everyman from his limiting self-appreciation as long as he firmly and steadily beholds it.

Research Worker. William James, in his *Will To Believe,* described scientific objectivity, not as something impersonal, passive, or disinterested, but as a scientist's passion not to be deceived occurring with his passion to gain truth. That description fits subjectivity does it not?

Author. As far as it goes, yes. However, subjectivity requires that the "truth" gained and the "deception" avoided be seen as referring to the scientist's self, not to an "external" world of truth or deception.

Research Worker. How do you account for scientific resistance to the truth that all discovery is self-discovery?

Author. Any such resistance would be of a unique nature for each scientist. Every kind of scientific resistance is *always* the *only* available kind treatment of one's self, whenever it obtains. Self-examination discloses all resistance as therapeutic, as a helpful psychological tendency to resist experiencing what one is unready to live except as illusional externality.

Research Worker. You mean that it is just my mind's unconscious wisdom which protects me, by means of resistance, against "biting off more than I can chew"? It would be unwise for me to cultivate ideas and views which I must relegate to my rejective living called "outside."

Author. I can only mean something about myself. Certainly I regard my resistances as life-protectors.

Research Worker. John Oulton Wisdom has made an important point regarding Bishop Berkeley's writings, which you might consider: If Berkeley "had been a solipsist he would hardly have written down his thoughts for publication if there was no one to read them."[6]

Author. I have read carefully and with benefit Mr. Wisdom's helpful study of his Berkeley. I record ("publish") *on account of the fact* that I see my reader as mine and enjoy seeing him develop his appreciation of his (solipsistic) allness. In other words, as a conscious solipsist, I must accept the fact that my reader *is* mine and that I benefit when I live him as extending his self-consciousness.

Research Worker. You are aware, are you not, that your conscious view (that individuality is not only the necessary but also the sufficient condition of human being) is by no means the popular one of the leaders of your profession?

Author. Only each health educator can observe the extent of his conscious view of his personal life.

Research Worker. Are you unable to imagine that you may be all wrong in your idea that self-sufficiency (complete independence) is a necessary condition of individuality, so to speak, that without its allness-meaning there can be no individuality of any kind?

Author. I can easily and gladly imagine such an idea. For instance, I can imagine: What is, is not; or, what is not, is.

Research Worker. Do you claim that *your* colleague is wrong when he sees each individual person as "a" part of all of "the" humanity, rather than as *his* all of *his* humanity?

Author. I see my colleague only as perfectly right, as he views his truth.

Research Worker. Do you classify an M.D. who is mostly

body-conscious as being a "body-servant" rather than a whole physician?

Author. I see my every M.D. as whole and as conscious for all that can be lived consciously: his own mind.

Research Worker. Is self-consciousness the one qualification for self-sovereignty?

Author. Regardless of self-consciousness, self-sovereignty is all that can be. Consciousness for that self-sovereignty is the sovereign remedy for the protean complaint of unfreedom.

Research Worker. Have you any observation regarding medical experimentation on human beings?

Author. That question is one which I keep asking myself. Although the voluntary consent of the human subject is indeed absolutely essential, it is not the only consideration by any means. Many a patient cannot speak wisely for all of himself, particularly on this subject. In my mind the responsibility for medical experimentation is *entirely* that of the medical experimentor. The closest he can come to an ideal ethical position on this head is his seeing clearly his own personal identity in his patient, or experimental subject.

Professor William B. Bean, chairman of the Department of Medicine at the University of Iowa College of Medicine, has made sensitively helpful studies of this critically important work of the physician. He calls attention to Claude Bernard's insight: "The principle of medical and surgical morality . . . consists in never performing an experiment on man which might be harmful to him to any extent, even though the result might be highly advantageous to science, i.e., to the health of others."[7]

Rousseau's dictum speaks the law for every physician, "It is never right to harm a human soul for the advantage of others." I would add that a harm to any human being is a harm to his whole world, and that only a help to any human being can be a help to his whole world. Not seeing my life in its allness embroils me in such a phantom problem as: If I knew that my losing my own life would save many "others" would I not be justified in sacrificing myself? Seeing that my "others" are entirely my own enables me to consult that fact for deciding how best to devote, rather than sacrifice, my life.

Research Worker. As you know, it is impossible for anyone but yourself to understand the extreme claims you make for your extreme self-consciousness. How do you handle the hostility you have stirred up, or, rather, the resistance which is aroused?

Author. Einstein created an ideally suitable solution for that kind of phantom problem. Said he, "Arrows of hate have been shot at me too; but they never hit me because somehow they belonged to another world, with which I have no connection whatsoever."

Research Worker. Your explanations certainly explain nothing away. Explanation cannot do that. Please bear with my further questioning. How did the life of the mind ever come to be considered as subservient and incidental to so-called knowledge of "the external world"? How did man get started attributing his own soulfulness to his (imagined) "external world"? How did the reality of man "qua" man come to be lost in the illusion of "society," or of "people" in any sense? Why is it not evidently important for everyone to give definition to his mind? Why is not the study of mind recognized as characteristic of hygienic learning? Is one's conception of mind the criterion of his wisdom? Does one's prowess in self-apprehension transfigure a fallen angel to man, or a matter-of-fact student of "the external world" to an enthusiastic scholar of his own divinity? How did the substantiality of mental matter come to be judged insubstantial? How did any meaning of one's own world become defined as being what his mind is not? Why is war unrecognizable as disturbed peace of mind?

What description of mind is more accurate than Aristotle's: If a person's body were an eye, sight would be his mind? Can there be such a status as an "object" if one cannot even live the *surface* of "otherness"? Can there be a "knower" *and* a "known"? Must not one always live his every meaning subjectively, as the "thought of thought," "truth of truth," "man of man," "meaning of meaning," "mind of mind," "life of life," and so on? If I cannot see any degree of power in myself, must I not thereby find each meaning of my world as that much wanting in power? Was Aristotle deluded in defining mind as "the perfect realization (or actuality) of an organic body"? Or, as you see it, is body always and only existent, or meaningful, as mind? Was Aristotle again deluded in his conception of mind as being the realization and equivalence of life? Or, as you see it, is life always and only existent, or meaningful, as mind? Are you not deluding yourself in your all-or-nothing, divine-or-depersonalized, self-orientation? Are you sure of your idea of self-fulfilment, namely, that of simply seeing that you are always already "complete"? Can it be possible that no constituent forming the human mind is open to scientific inquiry or observation of an objective nature? Is object always nothing but unrecognized subject? Do you not state that "mind" is a verbal symbol, or the locus of spirit, or the sign and savior of life, or the meaning of subjectivity, —just depending upon which definition happens to be convenient to your passing need? Are you positive there is no danger in one's becoming overconscious? Is all learning effected under the canopy of creativity? Do you acknowledge no founder, no pioneer, no originator, no contributor of humanity of any kind, but yourself? Does not your surreptitious desire for attention "show through" the blandishments of your spokesmanship for solipsism? Are you clean of suspicion that you record your dorsey-ism with the purpose of assuming some kind of leadership, other than self-sovereignty of your world? Does not your writing imply more than your triumphantly working yourself out of your life's serious difficulties? Is your zeal the fruit of the freedom from, or of the craving for, unrecognized servitude?

In what sense is all of your writing an advancement to St. Augustine's insight that nothing can be more present in a mind than that mind itself, or, that mind is that which knows and thinks of itself in its entirety? Did not St. Augustine admonish "those who go forth to wonder at the heights of the mountains, at the huge waves of the sea, at the broad flow of the rivers, at the extent of the ocean, and at the course of the stars, and omit to wonder at themselves"? Are you not identifying your will, as he did, with divine will?

In your venturing into the life of the spirit have you added anything at all to the insight of Descartes, "for I consider the mind not as a part of the soul but as the whole of that soul that thinks"? Does your mind out-mind Descartes?

Eudoxus. . . . Tell me, then, what you really are inasmuch as you doubt. It is on this point alone, the only one you can know with certainty, that I wanted to question you.

Polyander. I now see my error. I see now that what I am, inasmuch as I doubt, is in nowise what I call body.

Is not your view of life less momentous than momentary, less continuous than constant, more imperial than empirical, more immigrant than immediate and immense, more fugitive than fulfilling?

Author. As I listen to my asking myself each of these questions, I am grateful for my realization that I am both my own speaker and listener. Certainly, this kind of inquiry deserves a hearing. As I observe what comes to my mind (my reply) associated with each of the questions, I note instant relief from the tension inherent in each question as well as mental material explicating each question.

Research Worker. True enough, I see, as I try that method out myself. However, your treatment of questions is the oddest I ever heard of. I mean, your view that every question concerns a locus of mind ready to reveal itself as its own answer; or, that every answer contains its own concealed question.

Author. My counting myself "the odd one" is only an aspect of my considering myself my only one and all. The inherencies of my mind are my only conscious possessions and the sole sources of my realization of any kind. Only as an idealist can I be consciously consistent with my subject matter.

Research Worker. Considering the use of mind for denying the existence of mind and, thus, creating the imagining of every kind of other matter, it is little wonder that Galileo conceived nature as "a book written in mathematical terms, so that without mathematics as its code nothing could ever become intelligible in it." As Alexander A. Jascalevich sagely saw it, in *Three Conceptions of Mind* (1926), mathematics had assumed in knowledge the function and dignity formerly given to the human mind. The esoteric made exoteric,—the qualitative made quantitative.

Author. I have just lived my you creating an insight of greatest power for penetrating the meaning of mathematics as well as for understanding the most disparate views of the worth of this science for humanity.

Research Worker. For the "objective scientist" mathematics is might; for the subjective epistemologist it is myth.

Author. How odd, how very odd! and accurate. "Not-I" is nothingness, the only extraworldliness.

Research Worker. To create for my own use a valuable verbal view of my already mentioned mind-master Jascalevich, you seem to be "quickened with the passionate obstinacy of a genuine discovery" in your single-souled constancy to your science of conscious self. Please speak your piece again.

Author. To the extent that I can vouch for my individuality, I can vouch for the subjectivity of my every individual existent of my world.

Research Worker. Anyone just dipping into this talk would have to describe its author as "way way off."

Author. Truly a most accurate description. I *am* "a way way off" from my fellowman who has not lived his mind far in his appreciation of his powers. My fellowman may find his meaning of mind in that which he names "externality," or "otherness," or "body," or "divinity,"—I find my every meaning of mind in my mind only.

Research Worker. Please describe the mind orientation you grew for yourself as an undergraduate.

Author. Early in my life I grew my first professor of philosophy, George Thomas White Patrick, all honor to his kindly wisdom, describing "mind," or "soul," provisionally as a term for denoting the totality of mental processes, "like an organization with inherent tendencies." Said Patrick, "We cannot fail to recognize the very great influence of Freud and his school in calling attention to those primary constitutive elements of the mind which they call the wishes. By the wish they mean not a definitely formulated conscious desire, but any sort of mental set or tendency to action."[8] He said also, "The self furthermore is both observer and observed." Patrick permitted himself "cheerfully to be classed among the scientists" even though he knew it meant renouncing an epistemological orientation. He seemed to see *esse* as *creare*, nevertheless.

Research Worker. As I sum up your research orientation, you have found it helpful to devote yourself to conscious solipsism, to study of the psychology of your own person where *all* of your mental functioning is localized.

Do you not find it difficult to restrict your research to self-seeking? Please consider the following view:

> Invariably, man's ingenuity outruns his foresight. Intent upon discovery and invention, he thinks in terms of the advantages of a new product or process—but rarely realizes either its ultimate possibilities or its full impact upon the established order.[9]

Author. I do consider this view soberly and earnestly, for it reveals a profound truth of my human nature. On its account, I try to build up my insight as the firmest foundation for my foresight.

Research Worker. The nature of my scientific discovery intrigues me. For example, How can I live myself in order to favor its happening? How do I unwittingly prevent its occurrence? In what way does it differ from my other imaginings? Does it always involve a "change of face" (an extension of my self-tolerance)? Does my creating my laboratory working conditions contribute to motivating it? Does it first occur in my dreams and only later come to me while I am awake? In what way if any does it differ from invention? Does my self-conscious living favor its occurring? Is it an event correlated with the intensity of my wish that it happen? Do I even formulate this puzzlement of mine accurately by describing it as "my problem of scientific discovery"? To what extent *is* necessity the mother of invention? Can I cultivate a consciousness of any intimation that it is forthcoming? Is it the same as any of my "problem-solving" living? Are there rules determining this kind of self-fertility? Is there something about my character or intelligence or temperament which can influence it? Is it mostly a matter of perspiration, not of inspiration? Does fatigue figure in it in any way? Does it arise from my mind's conscious effort to originate more data or more ideas? Does the simple fact of my being able to concentrate my imagination on a given area of observation ultimately necessitate my making a new discovery there? Must it "steal" into my mind without conscious antecedents first, before I notice it, or am I able to be in on my own scientific discovery consciously from the start? Is all of it describable as special instances of my growth of self-insight? Would my seeing the whole matter as my intense curiosity about my own self-discovery help me to originate new developments in my work? Please word your views of scientific discovery.

Author. I help myself by realizing that my every question contains its own answer, every problem contains its own solution, every search contains its own discovery. I must first be able to look, then look where to look, and I shall find. *My every discovery is always a self-growth. My every conscious discovery provides me with sufficient appreciation of the direction of that self-growth.* My ability to formulate my question exactly enables me to orient myself accurately about the direction in which my answer lies, so that I need not suffer a helpless ignorance of the issue. In all of my scientific discovery (self-discovery) I remind myself of a plant in the process of producing an extension of itself. The thrill of my discovery derives from my consciously seeking and finding what I have been consciously, or unconsciously, growing. The intensity of my wish to grow myself in a given direction (e.g., make a novel scientific finding) unquestionably furthers the possibility. I cannot give birth to any of my new self-growth except upon the foundation of my antecedent self-growth. A previously realized wish furnishes the foundation for the new unrealized wish and can provide intimation (a dawning consciousness) with regard to the latter's realization. As to distinguishing datum and speculation, my every datum is an hypothesis, quite as my every hypothesis is a datum. It helps me to be able consciously to ask myself: Why this particular datum? as much as to ask: Why this particular hypothesis?

Conscious freedom of mind is necessary for its free play through its imagination which can lead to self-discovery, at times even by uniting seeming incompatibles. How could Heisenberg discover his principle of indeterminacy if his imagination were not free to renounce his traditional causality?

Instead of the somewhat rare conscious experience which it seems to be, discovery really is applicable to all of learning (all of living, that is). *Whatever* I live has the real meaning of the formation of a new unity. In *Paradise Lost* Milton immortalized this truth,

> Th' invention all admir'd, and each how he
> To be th' inventor miss'd; so easy it seem'd,

> Once found, which yet unfound most would have thought
> Impossible!

This conception of the way the mind works is one which everyone must create for himself. As C. K. Ogden noted "the majority of those who in the past have called themselves Idealists, maintaining that to be known is to be 'in the mind' or an 'invention of the mind,' have in reality still further extended the scope of a possible psychology, though without themselves actually embarking on its details."[10] This I try to do.

Research Worker. Eddington recorded a similar observation, in *Space, Time, and Gravitation* (1920):

> We have found that where science has progressed the farthest, the mind has but regained from nature that which the mind has put into nature. We have found a strange foot-print on the shores of the unknown. We have devised profound theories, one after another, to account for its origin. At last we have succeeded in reconstructing the creature that made the footprint. And lo! it is our own.

Author. The most helpful view I can grow regarding my own living (learning, that is) is my sense of my growing command of my developing self, which includes my noticing the way I achieve this due self-regard. I can sense confidently my originality only to the extent that I can see my total ignorance of all but myself. As far as my survival is concerned, I can only survive myself.

The veteran scientific research worker, that is, the disciplined worker of self-discovery in the area of his special interest, has found the significance of serendipity. He has also discovered the truth of his Goethe's insightful statements:

> The greatest art, both in teaching and in life itself, consists in transforming the problem into a postulate. (To Zelter, 1828)

> If we pursue the life of the tree in its roots, or in its branches and twigs, one thing always follows from another. And the more vitally any concern of knowledge takes hold of us, the more we find ourselves driven to pursue it in its ramifications, both up and down. (Annals, 1807)

Research Worker. I know that research effort must come from within, and it is often difficult for the beginner to realize it. He wants to be told how. However, as Abraham Flexner remarked, "Universities must at times give the nation, not what it wants, but what it needs."

You seem to recognize that concentration of imagination upon one field of observation requires ignoration of all others; that consciousness of selfness in one direction requires unconsciousness of selfness in all others; that presence of mind for one circumstance of living requires "absent mindedness" for all others; that self-discovery in a given field of observation requires self-concealment in all others. In 1886 Nietzsche wrote, "Forgetfulness is no mere *vis inertiae,* as the superficial believe; rather it is a power of obstruction, active, and, in the strictest sense of the word, positive . . . a very sentinel and nurse of psychic order, repose, and etiquette."

Author. My every self-conscious experience is a world of its own, "sufficient" and unrelated. It is the occurrence of the universal (allness of my individuality) in the particular (special locus of my individuality). My every so-called "particular" in which universality is not recognized constitutes a self-deception of mine.

Mathematician. You may be somewhat lacking in what Tobias Dantzig calls "number sense."

Author. In *Number the Language of Science* (1930), Dantzig presented the evolution of number as a human story. He thought that school curricula often made mathematics repellent to a fine mind by abandoning cultural content for technicalities.

I have a most humane purpose in wishing to explicate the number concept. I am mindful of my fellowman who has suffered unto death on account of living himself as if he were one of millions, and as if he were not even a complete one; on account of his alleged "collective responsibility" for being a member of an alleged family "of assassins and saboteurs"; on account of his being considered merely "a member" of a "race," or "nation."

Mathematician. I can see where mathematics has no subject matter other than the mathematician. However, I wish to examine the concept of number, as such. Measurement, I can see, always involves a single event; but I have always associated number with plurality.

Author. Every so-called "plurality" is the scientist's accurate ascertainment of a *uniformity*. By "plurality" is meant only one meaning's content.

Mathematician. Number is the very field of mathematical operation. If you do away with number you do away with quantity and order, both of which imply the necessity of otherness, and of betweenness. You may not object to W. S. Jevons' definition of number (*Principles of Science,* 1907): "the empty form of difference."

Author. It is my intention to appreciate every view for what it is, and to renounce the illusion of "doing away" with anything. My helpful realization that *Whatever is, is its own everything,* necessarily involves my renunciation of "difference," "comparison," "agreement," "distinguishability," and similar terms implying plurality.

Mathematician. A. Cornelius Benjamin posed the question: "does one build up the idea of 'many' by combining 'ones,' or does one build up the idea of 'one' by breaking up a 'many'?" He considered that *Gestalt* psychology indicates the naturalness of immediate recognition of a whole but added "the notion of number is so intimately associated in one's mind with the notion of counting . . . that plurality seems to occupy a secondary place in the order of experiential derivation." He points out the ambiguity of the word "all" in that it may refer to an aggregate taken as a whole or to the individual members of an aggregate, and suggested two possibilities—"collective," or "holistic," properties applicable only to aggregates and not in general to the individual elements; and "distributive," or elemental, properties which belong to the members and not in general to the totalities. He illustrates the absurdity of an inference substituting a collective property of a class for a distributive property: "Americans are numerous; since I am an American, I am numerous." He decides number to be a collective property, applicable only to aggregates or complexes, and "belonging in the same category as such words as 'organization,' 'pattern,' 'structure,' 'complexity,' 'disorganization,' and the like."[11]

I see how the sameness of all of the mathematician's own self provides the only property (his identity) of any of his individual aggregations which he can accurately attribute to each member of that collection. I also see how his overlooking the base of his own personal identity in any and all of his figures would necessitate his effort to attribute groupness to individual as well as individualness to group. I can now appreciate how any and every aggregation derives its appearance of togetherness from the fact that all of it is an individuation of the oneness of the observer. You describe "plurality" as an illusion created by analysis. How do you explain plurality?

Author. I identify every number as an individualization, analogous to the convenient fiction known as "personification." Each number is an instance of unification. As long as quantity is not meant to be a quantity of anything at all, its disregard for (repression of) individuality is not evident; once quantity is meant to be a quantity of something, it assumes a qualitative function and thus reveals its fallacious tendency,—for who ever heard of more than one of anything! Certainly, no scientist has ever demonstrated two of anything.

Since it is obvious (by definition) that every individual *is* unique, *one* cannot be used in some kind of repetition, to contribute to the identity of "two," or to the identity of any so-called "many."

A so-called single, or individual, "group" of individuals would have to consist of constituents constituting individuations of that individual groupness. However, no property of an aggregation (other than that of the personal identity of the observer) can be distributed to any of its alleged "parts." This fact is of primary meaning for the understanding of the dignity of human being. Every human being lives whatever he calls "group," or "aggregation," *within* himself. *Man can never live himself in anything but himself.* Human individuality can never be in a derivative position, since man lives all of his own origination.

Mathematician. You realize, do you not, that you are upholding a kind of affirmation forbidden by logic? A proposition is not supposed to make an affirmation about itself? Does not every datum suggest something beyond itself?

Author. As I ask myself that question, I see the need to recognize the *subjectivity* of every datum as being its own everything. By only imagining a surface "objectivity" of a datum I necessarily imply all else (than that datum) as beyond that datum.

The language of the exact scientist in the past has been one of counting and measuring instruments and devices. He would substitute "impersonal objective quantifications" for whatever is otherwise meaningful and subjective in human life. This exact scientist's conception of his world was of the nature of mathematical orientation. In his laboratory he did not concern himself with the intrinsic (subjective) nature of living. Thus A. Cornelius Benjamin described the scientist's predicament:

> Analysis gives not parts of a whole but merely notes of a total impression. For this reason, by no act of reconstruction can one regain the whole upon which an analysis has been performed; thought may proceed from objects to symbols but it cannot retrace the route from symbols to objects. Hence scientific knowledge is always partial and relative, and to this extent erroneous. It supposes that since an object has a number of aspects it is therefore itself a plurality; it endeavors to construct an object by multiplying to infinity the abstract symbols in terms of which it is portrayed; it attempts by representations which are outside the object to get inside it.[12]

Today's exact scientist is observing that what he has created out of his mind must be mind. He sees his work as consisting of his mind's negotiating creations of his mind. He concerns himself about the real internal nature of his datum. Henri Bergson described this new scientific tendency fifty years ago (*Introduction to Metaphysics*): "The consciousness we have of our own self in its continual flux introduces us to the interior of reality, on the model of which we must represent other realities." For Eddington reality appeared to be spirit and consciousness. Said he, in *The Nature of the Physical World* (1919), "The whole subject-matter of exact science consists of pointer readings and similar indications."

Mathematician. I am a human being, as well as an exact scientist, and my every "pointer reading" and number are therefore human, too. Otherwise my language of science would indeed be a dead language.

Please discuss further your theory of how the concept of "otherness" (of "not-self") got started, and thereby introduced the notions of "objectivity" and of "plurality."

Author. A certain necessity to report *modification* pervades all mental life. Every human experience is an instance of "something new has been added." The meaning of "change" is implicit in the novel imbalance of one's sense of sameness, at least momentarily accompanying every excitation. Sensitiveness for the meaning "otherness" is accurate reporting of this new self-growth, in that it refers to one's own self's production of *its* otherness. Thus a lag may exist as far as my self-growth and my consciousness of my self-growth are concerned.

The same helpfulness for preserving my life-saving sense of identity while undergoing "change" ("modification," "excitation") is observable in each instance, whenever my sensibility reports not-self. All of my sensibility, from rawest sensation to most refined consciousness, is experienced as if it is *of* other than itself. Thus one says, "I see the red color *of* that book," "I perceive that book itself," "I like (or dislike) that one," "I am cognizant *of* the fact," "I am aware *of* that, too." It is as though activation of each process of sensibility creates the overwhelming excitement which necessitates such a self-disowning tactic (autotomy, repression, denial) and thereby necessitates a reference to experiencing existence other than self.

When I postulate not-self in any of my experience I abandon the realm of the given, and thus remove the very ground upon which I must rely for my every immediate sense of reality. Disciplined imagination enables the renunciation of such ranges of speculation, which are well described as flights of fancy.

Surely each research worker's ability to imagine that every step of his research consists of a further burgeoning, branching, and blossoming of his own mind in the very direction of his quest is *most* practical. With that insight he can proceed with every assurance that all he has to do is live longer consciously in order to make ever-continuing discoveries (create further self-knowledge) in the specific area of his investigation. He cannot help but go on growing conscious self-knowledge in the direction of his conscious devotion. Discovery of discoveries!

9

Psychotherapy

As the state of mind is capable of producing a disease, another state of mind may effect a cure.

JOHN HUNTER (1728-1793)

GENERAL PRACTITIONER. Let me call your attention to one of (my) Freud's statements (*General Introduction to Psychoanalysis*) about his psychoanalytic therapy: "Where there is no repression to overcome, nor any analogous process, there our therapeutics has no business." Now, my question is this: Since everyone helps himself by resort to repression (to ignoring and denying parts of his human nature in which he cannot see his identity with composure) where can the claim be made that there is no repression?

Author. Psychotherapy *is* indicated in every kind of medical work.

General Practitioner. Is it needed in the treatment of fracture? What repression exists there?

Author. Every kind of health ordeal, including injury, has profound meaning for every patient and troubles his mind most with regard to its repressed meanings. First of all, his every kind of pathology is therapeutic for him.

General Practitioner. How would he try to find what his fractured bone means to him?

Author. By the same method he could use for finding what anything means to him, the method of free-association.

General Practitioner. Oh yes, I see. All he needs to do is to start using his mind by paying attention to it, beginning with the thought of his fracture. Then the flow of thoughts and feelings and perceptions, and whatever he can freely observe, will reveal to him all that his mind is then associating with the injury. That's a kind of focal or partial self-analysis.

Author. My only intention was to indicate how I go about finding what anything momentarily means to me,—namely, by letting my mind have its head on it and observing what it reveals, not just by consulting my dictionary.

General Practitioner. If all of medicine is psychological medicine, as I'm sure it is also, since each of us physicians has use for only his mind in every kind of medical work,—then how is there any specialty of psychiatry?

Author. A sensible, and in every way practical, question, as I live it. The clinical practice of psychiatry, necessarily, is the responsibility of every physician. The so-called "specialty of psychiatry" is expected to constitute a branch of medicine in which the physician helps himself by working with a specific kind of patient, namely, one who has trouble with his sense of his personal identity. Nevertheless, this specialist-physician's medical work with his patient is not otherwise unique. It is his professional responsibility to work with his patient in exactly the same way that his fellow physician, a general practitioner, works with his patient. His principle of the mental factor in medicine (the health orientation of treating his patient as himself, of loving his patient as himself, of living his patient in all kindness and helpfulness) is the same for each physician.

A so-called "psychiatric" patient lives himself in such a way that, without proper training, his physician would be at a loss to realize what kindness (humaneness) might constitute for him. This seeming prominence of un-understandable personality of his patient, necessitating the living of physicianary kindness in a carefully prescribed way, accounts for the usefulness of the specialist-psychiatrist. May it be repeated however, regardless of how much the psychiatrist has trained himself in definite ways to identify himself in the involved personal needs of his patient, his ultimate psychological medicine of kindness does not differ from that practiced by his fellow physician of any branch of the profession. This kindness-of-insight prescription, of *psychological medicine,* is identical throughout all of medical living. No worse fate could befall every M.D. than that this precious prescription, "medical treatment with peaceful self-insight," be monopolized by any one specialist of medicine, for instance, by the psychiatrist. The official concern of every M.D. is his "humanity tissue." Every physician needs to school himself in, create as his very own, the wonderful health discoveries issuing from his scientific work in his developmental and dynamic psychology.

General Practitioner. Your self-consciousness functions as a kind of sensorium which enables you *personally* to feel pleasure and pain where your fellowman is located (in your mind, of course), so that out of your pure self-interest you compel yourself to live your fellowman experiences kindly.

Author. Yes. I can discover no more vital way for *my living my fellowman* than with my realization that such living is all mine.

General Practitioner. How do you reconcile as your own living your experiences with each colleague of three different schools: the conscious, unconscious, and the anti-conscious?

Author. I simply see each colleague as helping himself currently in the only way he can.

General Practitioner. What do you think of Thomas Henry Huxley's claim: "We are conscious automata."

Author. As Voltaire tolerantly lived his Helvetius. While readily renouncing such a view of my life easily, nevertheless I recognize my Huxley's inviolable right to defend his own view as being the only correct one.

General Practitioner. John Broadus Watson concluded: "There is no field which an introspective psychology legitimately can call its own." He said of the existence of mind: "The behaviorist finds no mind in his laboratory, sees it nowhere in his subject." He declared that the most human thought was nothing but a gesture or spoken word, involving laryngeal movement essentially. How about that? You will say he used his mind to create this denial of mind.

Author. However my fellowman chooses to help himself to understand his life is always a matter calling for my sincere interest and appreciation. Watson applied himself to his effort to gain "objective" understanding of human individuality. He advanced his view that all learning, in man and animal, was caused by the operation of mathematical laws of recency and frequency along with those of probability.

General Practitioner. I suppose you would observe *that* learning process to be a lived one by the given individual also. You hold that life is of individual occurrence and that human being in any of its manifestations is basically life, no matter how you slice it.

Author. Yes, although about validating that, as about validating everything else of meaning to me, there is a conspicuous lack of "objective" data. All of my data are always *subjective* only.

General Practitioner. Suppose that to be the living truth. Suppose that your idea, about the study and practice of medicine in one's self, holds therapeutics. Is not the difficulty of growing this kind and degree of self-tolerance the real deterrent? You would not ask me to train myself beyond accepting evidence which I can validate with my senses. You would not ask me to grow to accept as a source of truth such imponderable meanings as thoughts and feeling. Do you not smack of Christian Science or of some other cult?

Author. The Christian Scientist and the psychoanalyst, each, may appreciate the historical contributions of the hypnotist, which gave rise to Christian Science and psychoanalysis. The psychoanalyst has already gone very far in the direction of renouncing hypnotism. It is wholesome to have every M.D. see the advantages in the renunciation of all hypnosis (including the innumerable degrees of suggestion).

True, the healing force of mind, the tremendous therapeutic of sensed personal identity (necessitating kindness), has been largely ignored and, hence, may be exploited by my non-medical fellowman who, in turn, may regard the arduous study of himself in medicine as a deterrent to his wish to become a physician. However, the health risk of practicing one's self in medicine without self-insight, once seen clearly, is sufficient to bring about its renunciation.

The necessary practice of psychological hygiene being identical for every physician's professional living, it becomes evident immediately that each one must consciously and methodically include, as a part of every medical workup, the vital practical issue of the health problem: "How can I be most humane in my living of this patient?"

General Practitioner. Do you refer now to the fact that my not understanding my living of my patient releases feelings of dislike in me?

Author. Yes. Having to live without the pleasure of understanding, I naturally resist that living.

General Practitioner. If I understand my own unpleasant feelings, I can renounce each one and not have it grow to panic proportions. Therefore, as I live my patient being anxious, depressed, suspicious, angry, or whatever, I will not have to reject that living in myself, but can live it gladly as my patient's therapeutic effort to carry on even while he feels overwhelmed by his current distress.

Author. That is the main idea: the renunciation of fault-finding, the recognition of excellence everywhere, the joy of living shining through the endurance of hardship and adversity.

General Practitioner. How is this main theoretical pronouncement of yours practical? Naturally, a physician is not given to fault-finding. As a scientist he knows that whatever is, or is not, could not be otherwise.

Author. True. However, sometimes when I cannot understand the absolute necessity that my fellowman be exactly as he is, I tend to become critical, just as a form of crying, "Ouch." There is no patient who does not present individual characteristics, idiosyncrasies, which dictate his particular humaneness needs. Furthermore, every human being suffering any kind of health ordeal tends to develop certain unique and *specific*, but not readily understandable, humaneness needs accompanying his feelings of disability. For instance, his need to "be taken care of tenderly" is suddenly greatly accentuated. Health "misfortunes" are consistently overwhelming, serving to disturb personality equilibrium, and necessitating compensatory behavior which is unusual and sometimes viewed intolerantly. Most frequent components of "patient living" are feelings of anxiety, irritability, insecurity, unhappiness, emotionality, weakness, fatiguability, disinterest, boredom, inability to concentrate, feeling unloved, rejected, and not worth living. Innumerable temptations seduce every patient to overlook self-power, self-reliance, capacity for self-strengthening, self-gratitude, and the need for self-care. His mobilization of his healthful appreciation of self-helpfulness and vitalizing sense of self-esteem are each patient's source of health power.

As noted, in every kind and degree of pain and unhappiness, every patient's mind is sensitive specifically in this direction of self-disesteem, the very opposite of the feeling which makes his life seem worth living. Keenest appreciation of this truth, heedfulness as to its importance, is a first principle of the mind-conscious doctor of medicine. Anterior to the principle, and providing for the possibility of its being seen as the life-saver it is, is the physician's developed capacity for recognizing that every observation that he can possibly make about his patient, is entirely a creation of his own physicianary living. As I see "my patient" as my own living of my patient-meaning, I am capable of putting my very soul into my efforts to be helpful. The most direct way in which this efficacy (of seeing "my patient" as my living of my patient-meaning) expresses itself, is in my full realization that only my patient can help himself, that only my patient can live his physician and his medicines and, in this conscious living, restore his health to freedom.

General Practitioner. Please be practical here, Doctor. Please realize that I do not quite understand you. By that I do not mean, either, that you are un-understandable. I simply have not stretched my imagination, or insight, or self-tolerance, or whatever you please to call it, sufficiently enough to recognize that "a looking at" my patient is "a seeing within myself." When I'm examining my patient or treating him, it is as though I *forget myself* in the process.

Author. Do you really "forget yourself?" Can you really ever "forget yourself?" After all, what can you attend to, but yourself? It is a matter of great moment to realize how greatly a habit of speech can favor magic thinking. For it would require magic for one to be able to forget all that he has that he *can* mind, his self-meanings.

General Practitioner. True enough. As beloved Dr. Oliver

Wendell Holmes minded his own professional business: Altruism is egoism with a spy-glass.

Author. I studied medicine in order to learn my way in and out of health trouble of every kind, so that by knowing my way around health-wise I can preserve and enjoy my own life and, as a physician, see my health-troubled fellowman find his health-way around.

General Practitioner. Do you mean that I am a kind of usher in the theatre of health and that *that* is about as far as my treating my patient goes? Do you mean that my only actual life possibility is to take care of myself, and that in my profession, I am trying to do that by functioning so that my patient can learn how to take care of himself? That notion of treatment reminds me somewhat of the ancient method of curing a wound by treating the weapon which did the injury! If what you write is true, how can I be an attending physician by being attentive only to myself? The Brazilian Bororos medicated the father to cure the child, and that usually worked well.

Author. "Attention," like "perception," or "sensation," or "feeling," or any other kind of sentience, can be nothing but a degree of self-consciousness. But again, the *recognition* that I am living myself is always indispensable for my true self-estimate, for my correspondingly true self-esteem, and thus for my proper appreciation of my very life itself.

The physician's specific self-discipline in self-consciousness enables him to observe *his* patient as being the product of *his* living each observation *he* attributes to "*his* patient." To illustrate, as I personally grow my self-observations to which (accumulation of my personal experiences) I assign the name "my patient," *my* individuality is *all* that is being lived. Thus, I live only my individuality in my visual perception when I "look at" my tree, or my parent, or my student, or my patient. In all of this kind of living I am only personifying a mental area in my own individuality, naturally made up entirely of my own living of it. From finding that this is the only way in which I can possibly have any truthful meaning for *my* patient, *I proceed to attribute the same kind and degree of individuality to "my patient."* Thus, I observe that he too can only live *his* doctor as *his very own* living of "his doctor." Through observing the inviolability of my own individuality I find it necessary to attribute inviolability to the individuality of my own self-created fellowman.

Sociologist. You are repeating that word "individuality" again. I realize your view of every person as a "holy human empire" (to give birth to a phrase first created by my Edward Carpenter). I recognize that a person who cannot see, hence appreciate, his originality and independence, has thereby put his life in jeopardy. I can understand your medical tolerance in viewing your patient's narcotism, addiction to otherworldiness ("the outer world"), as the only treatment with which he can currently preserve his life. Is it possible for you to uphold awareness of pain, including every unhappiness, as necessary incentive to sane and balanced living without your repeating that word "individual" so much? Its very meaning, even Herbert Hoover's "rugged individualism," tends to excite the meaning of "group" or "society," does it not?

Author. The word "individual" may well excite every meaning of which an individual's mind is constructed. However, as one's individuality loses its over-all conscious meaning, his life loses its conscious meaning, and psychic starvation sets in.

Whatever I "have in mind," whether it be my perception designating my fellowman, or whether it be an idea or feeling or whatever, is a living part of my mind having no other existence. Repetitious? Yes, in the same sense that my breathing is.

This work focuses upon the necessity for psychotherapy in every kind of medical practice.[1] It observes and records that all psychopathology *is* psychotherapy requiring each patient's further psychiatric treatment. It intends to highlight the facts that every physician is a psychotherapist and that his every patient is a conscious or unconscious psychotherapist. It states that every mind is needing the most careful kind of healthful concern in its necessary effort to help itself. Everyone's mind is constantly expressing itself through its special development, its body. Thus, its occasional need to live its overworked body (in "sickness" or "accident") in turn, is a stressful meaning which the mind nearly always lives out in terms of its further body stress. "Nearly always," for it is indeed rare for one's human mind to recognize its very own body as being one of his mental structures and hence a portion of mental living requiring greatest kindness.

Sociologist. Zeno comprehended soul as if there were no body; Aristippus comprehended only body. You say life, including its *mental* material, constitutes the only solid substance. Do you mean that all there is to human life is living and that you choose to refer all of your experience to that real foundation?

Author. I cannot send my soul abroad. My awareness for knowing that my life needs the kind of management which provides its full living constitutes my sovereign virtue of my sovereign individuality. With my Montaigne I find wise "the pretty inscription with which the Athenians welcomed Pompey" on his entering their city:

> So far you may be deemed a God
> As you confess yourself a man.

Sociologist. Pardon my insistence upon your applying yourself to what I can see is practical. Do you deny that the mind is resident in the nervous system?

Author. I deny nothing. Every consideration has its rightful existence. If my neuroanatomist says, "The mind is in the brain," I observe only, "That is an excellent idea."

Sociologist. Do you shrewdly emphasize the word *"excellent"* to distract your colleague's attention from the fact that you are again, by the very word "idea," placing the whole proposition (of self-localization) in the mental, rather than in any "non-mental" ("physical"), process?

Author. I wish to have my colleague, if he will, *attract his attention to* the fact of his mental process, not "distract his attention from" any other self-view (to which he may be needing to attend). Any and every self-view he may develop is of value. If my colleague prefers to help himself with his (mental) view that his mind is resident in his (non-mental) brain, then that is the way in which he is trying to help himself at that moment.

Sociologist. In 1909, Warner Fite, Stuart Professor of Ethics at Princeton University, delivered a series of lectures at the University of Chicago on "Individualism." For the most part his views were similar to yours, it seems to me. For instance, he stated:

The popular condemnation of self-consciousness rests upon a misconception.

So far as the individual becomes self-conscious he becomes never less self-regarding but more so.

Individualism holds that selfishness is ennobled in becoming deliberate and intelligent.

What individualism stands for is: intelligent self-assertion.

All rights and values are for consciousness and created by consciousness, and all consciousness is individual.

Individual duty is a matter of enlightened self-interest and practical wisdom.

Merit is won, not by sacrifice, but by consideration,—inclusion of your fellow in your plans.

Justice aims at perfect harmony and perfect individual freedom, which, in the end, is the only real meaning of love.

As conscious beings our ideal is a fully self-conscious realization of the values of life.

The individual as a conscious agent is the source and resource of all value; the interests of conscious individuals are essentially harmonious only in so far as they are conscious.

Author. Yes, my Warner Fite knew the value of his insight. He pointed out how the "moral sciences" became known as the "social sciences" under the orientation of the nineteenth-century materialist, who had to view "humanity" as "society" *in which* the life of the individual was conducted. Thus, "society" seemed to produce the individual rather than to be a product of each individual's mind. "The social," which had no existence but that of a meaning in the mind of the *individual,* came to stand for positive values; and the meaning of "individual" became "a mere phenomenon, i.e., an illusorily personal appearance of real impersonal 'social' forces," or, "the destructive force opposed to the social as constructive."

Sociologist. Professor Fite observed that, as far as he knew, "no one has appropriated my special brand of individualism nor made quite the same use of the conception of consciousness." Do you expect your work to be as popular as his?

Author. Pure individuality orientation necessarily rules out any such possibilities as "popularity," "agreement," "coordination," or "cooperation," in that each such meaning implies illusional otherness but not real selfness.

Sociologist. May I resume the testing of your fidelity to your individuality orientation? How about your use of medication for curing schizophrenia?

Author. Surely, I wish to use every medication with which I can help myself to renounce my schizophrenic, in favor of my full (freely healthful) living. If I am trying to live my life in my peculiar way (learning thereby from my personal experience) *even though that way may be properly described as schizophrenic,* it is most mind-strengthening for me to cure myself by self-insight. In my resort to my "biochemicals," it is mind-strengthening if I can treat myself "biochemically" with the realization that I am using my medicines for that express purpose of potentiating my development of self-insight.

Sociologist. How about your using insulin for your diabetes?

Author. Certainly, I intend to avail myself of any and every way in which I can help myself, with my pharmacological treatment for my schizophrenic living, with my insulin for my diabetic living, and so on. *However, I wish to use each and every therapeutic means in such a way that I will not block my appreciation of my deepest need to live myself with self-insight.* Only through my insight can I achieve, or maintain, my optimal health and happiness.

Anatomist. You speak of a "body of a mind," why not therefore of "a mentality of a body"? Could you please try to be a little more specific? For instance, when you do treatment, what do you treat? If my self-ignoration and subsequent self-neglect can express itself in the body part of my mind, may I not have my soma psychologized by some such practical means as medication or operation?

Author. Good enough, and well said. As George Eliot noted, "Speech is but broken light upon the depth of the unspoken." It is not so much what I say, as what I mean by what I say, that counts. My meaning is: I favor every possible way of helping myself. I am glad to be able to extend my psychological helpfulness through every practical means including, certainly, medications and operations. However, as Montaigne noted of himself, "I do not teach, I only relate."

Self-help is, and can be, nothing but an individual matter. Indeed, it is the recognition of that fact which I have discovered to be the very soul of psychotherapy. There is a fascination in such words as "popular treatment," or "accepted therapy," or "orthodox therapeutics," which can be bewitching. However, I consider Robert Louis Stevenson's view of "public taste as being a mongrel product, out of affectation by dogmatism."

Many a kind of psychotherapy is upheld; in fact, as many kinds as there are psychiatrists. And every one contains its own particular standard of helpfulness. Several of them even depend upon the physician's ability to make himself unconscious. Each psychotherapist's preferred kind of treatment discloses his current orientation about his most efficacious way of helping himself.

Anatomist. Your mentioning Montaigne reminds me of his famous conscious self-assertiveness:

> People try to get outside of themselves, and escape from the man. That is foolishness: instead of transforming themselves into angels, they transform themselves into beasts. Instead of raising they degrade themselves.
>
> A man who can rightly and truly enjoy his existence is absolutely and almost divinely perfect.
>
> We seek other conditions because we know not how to enjoy our own; and go outside of ourselves for want of knowing what it is like inside of us. So it is no use raising ourselves on stilts, for even on stilts we have to walk on our own legs. And sitting on the loftiest throne in the world we are still sitting on our behind.

Author. Sigmund Freud scientized the all-time great health principle of living consciously and devoted his insightful life to the development of this hygienic perspective. He trusted his mind's creations, testing each one for its meaning for furthering the extent of self-consciousness. Each individual must accomplish his own mental awakening to himself.

Anatomist. Wundt claimed that consciousness could not be defined. Philosophers define consciousness as a unity in diversity and a diversity in unity. You seem to define your consciousness as a sense of personal identity extending all of the way from any kind of awareness of meaning in living, such as observable in a self-felt single sensation, to appreciation of the allness extent of one's individuality. If I choose to uphold my idea that you can help me, is not my very *choice* of that view an instance of my self-help? In the way you describe individuality, you rule out the scientific device of comparison, do you not?

Author. As I ask myself each of these reaching questions, I find the same answer: Yes. Consciously doing as I please, or choose, or will, or decide, is an apt description of basic self-help.

Comparison, other than illusional and delusional, I have already noted is impossible, depending as it does upon the illusions of "externality" and, hence, "betweenness." My idealism is my only realism.

Sociologist. In his peace-inspiring book, *Human Nature and the Social Order* (1902), Charles Horton Cooley pointed out that "mystery and idealism are so inseparable that a sense of power in others seems to involve a sense of their inscrutability; and, on the other hand, so soon as a person becomes plain, he ceases to stimulate the imagination." He wrote, "The group self or 'we' is simply an 'I' which includes other persons."

Author. Yes. Cooley originated the freest definition of freedom I have been able to create, thus far: "The best definition of freedom is perhaps nothing other than the most helpful way of thinking about it." Note Emerson's living-flesh view that the way to "have" a friend is to be one: "Let him not cease an instant to be himself. The only joy I have in his being mine is that the *not-mine* is *mine.*"

Sociologist. Is it possible that many a person hates to seek help, most of all, for fear that his help-seeking might be misconstrued, for fear that his physician will not be so distinctly oriented self-helpfully?

Author. That may be. The illusion of being overpowered, of being in the power of another, can be very painful. What Goethe called the joy of dwelling in one's self is the cherished way of life.

Sociologist. But if I cannot believe in my own self-helpfulness, is it not beneficial for me to believe that my good doctor can help me? He always has!

Author. Whatever you do mean by help is important. However, if I cannot believe in myself (the one who must make and support all of my claims for me), what reliance can I put upon my claim that I believe in another, god or man? To be sure, I may claim gratefully that my doctor has helped me, even though it has been only possible for me to help myself. My feeling of thanks is beneficial by itself.

Sociologist. Apparently your ideally true doctor is a consciously self-identifiable kind of highly skilled technician who never sees, or thinks of, *his* patient without seeing, or thinking of, himself.[2] You remind me of the Hippocratic view, "The patient's nature is the doctor that cures his illness."

Author. When my patient consciously undertakes the task of (only) *helping himself* to grow healthfully, he reports that he enjoys the greatest practicality.

Sociologist. Is it your idea that a man should live primarily for the purpose of looking after his own health?

Author. If by "looking after his own health," you have in mind what I imagine, my answer is, Yes.

Sociologist. I have in mind, by that description, one who overlooks life's happiness by constantly preparing to live; one whose fear of dying shows in his fear of living.

Author. Thank you. The life of a valetudinarian is one of compensation for limited enjoyment of life. By "looking after my own health," I mean simply (1) that there is no one else who can do that for me, and (2) that my health-consciousness is a most helpful form of life-consciousness.

Sociologist. Does the extension of consciousness create more individuality?

Author. It reveals more individuality which had been present but unrecognized.

Sociologist. Warner Fite equates consciousness and individuality. Do you?

Author. Not at all. An individual is an all-one whether he is or is not conscious of being *his* whole world. It is only possible to consider individuality in the plural (e.g., "individual members of society") by denying the *allness*-meaning of individuality. The reality in Aristotle's statement, "Man is by nature a political animal," is that his own individual nature must create within itself all that can be meant by "society," "group," "government," "mankind," and so on.

Sociologist. You renounce the notion of the individual's being a "function" of the "social organism," and see, as did Warner Fite, "that the meaning which defines our conscious individual, must be in last analysis his own meaning and no one's else."

Author. As I see it, every individual, conscious or unconscious, can be defined only by his own elements.

Sociologist. Your idealistic theory does not hold that the interests of human individuals are essentially in harmony, does it? Or that human beings are conscious and therefore know themselves and each other? Or that worlds, including all social relations, are safeguarded by improved communications between consciously living individuals? Or that your ends are interwoven with those of other conscious selves?

Author. It does not. My "idealistic theory," as you describe it, discloses that every individual creates and maintains his own world, and that his consciousness of that truth compels him to care for each and all in his world as himself. I see no safeguarding of my morals but my realization that I cannot protect my life except by seeing the extent to which it is mine. The conscious individual is one who cooperates with his own life's forces, who is moral for the benefit of *his* human creature (mankind), who sees that the good of *his* fellowman is, in every instance, a matter for his selfish concern.

Sociologist. According to you, no one is ever fully conscious of his allness, and everyone varies himself from moment to moment in the extent of his self-consciousness. Warner Fite claimed that "awareness of anything involves, however vaguely, a corresponding awareness of self." For instance, I may be sensing only "hot," or "cold," or "blue," or "sweet"; but even that limited sentience represents a degree of my self-awareness. Of the "great scientific man of cold-blooded, naturalistic science," Fite says, "Who can he be but—*the unconscious man?*"

Author. Your own developed tolerance for living this truth of the pure, clear, inviolable individuality of human existence is, to be sure, its own reward. Also, this issue, the phantom problem of *meum et tuum,* is really the only psychological (or sociological) issue of fundamental concern. Therefore, it is well to see its solution clearly as being: the recognition of it as a problem created by the illusional living of one's very own "externality," that is, as if "externality" were not entirely *internal.*

Sociologist. I have read other writings of yours. Each stresses the fact that the entire practice of medicine is based solidly upon the one truth: *the human individual variant.* Will you please discuss further your self-orientation of inviolable individuality. For instance, is your health doctrine based upon the philosophic position of "individualism"?

Author. My health research has taught me to renounce my illusion of living any "philosophic position" other than strictly my own. However, some of my observations may be construed to imply otherwise. Certainly the term "individualism" promises pure devotion to individuality; but, as this philosophy is developed by the "student of any school of individualism," it leaves much to be desired in the way of fidelity to the allness-meaning of "individual."

Sociologist. According to Professor W. T. Stace, "Civilization is organized goodness." In his chapter "The Infinite Value of the Individual" he states: "the maxim of the infinite value of the individual means that each is to treat the purposes of another as if they were his own." I like his view that the purposes of another person can "flow into me and so actually become my own."[3]

Author. I enjoy living my every fellowman's asserting his own current way of living his individuality.

Sociologist. I would like to know the history of the goal of a psychoanalyist's therapy, as (my) you know it.

Author. Psychoanalytic work has been consciously effective to the extent that psychoanalysis has been understood as self-analysis. Freud's discovery of the meaning and method of free-association has, for the first time, introduced a system of self-help respecting the allness of individuality of the analyst and of the analysand. *Full scale* free-association characterizes the self-trained psychoanalyst's work insight. He sees that he can mean anything only to his self.

The goal of my psychoanalyst's therapy has had a history of its own. At first the psychotherapist did not use the psychoanalytic method. He began with the treatment ("cure") of the patient's symptom by hypnosis, but the patient continued to need treatment; next, the psychoanalyist treated the patient's "complex" (unconscious forces producing his symptoms) by suggestion and the method of free-association, but the patient had to continue treatment after that. Then, the psychoanalyst tried to cure the patient's "resistance" to treatment by the method of free-association and suggestion, but the patient still needed therapy. Next, the psychoanalyst sought to treat the patient's "transference" (as if a dependent attachment to him) through free association and interpretation, but even his patient's "agreeing with his analyst" about his "transference" did not effect the desired cure. Lastly, the psychoanalyst discovered his own transference-living of his patient ("countertransference"). He came to realize that he was helping himself by his countertransference-living, and could renounce it only with great difficulty. From then on, he relied entirely on the method of free-association alone, renouncing all so-called pedagogical techniques. Finally, the psychoanalyst grew the insight that his countertransference-living was no exception to his observation: Whatever is, is helpful. Then it took only a little extension of his self-tolerance to discover that his "therapy," like all of his learning, was entirely an occurrence resulting from his innate self-insight's finding its way *out* to expression, rather than from some kind of exoterical wisdom's finding its way "in" to his self-awareness. Thus, ultimately I have been able to renounce my delusions of therapy as being all unrecognized forms of a practice of magic. Any and all of my living is therapy.

Sociologist. Your view of psychoanalytic therapy appears to picture it as a self-analysis conducted (1) by each analysand on himself and (2) by each psychoanalyst on himself. You prize your method of free-association; for it, only, provides a way for the analysand to speak his mind and listen to his speaking, *without any appearance of interruption,* even. The analyst's work consists of undergoing his audile experience of *his* analysand's speaking and listening to himself, and whatever other mental living occurs to him meanwhile. Thus, he may freely imagine his saying and listening to himself whatever he experiences as his analysand's free associations. Can the psychoanalyst ask his analysand questions, or *vice versa?*

Author. As I lived my Freud kindly observing: "Psychoanalysis is not a game of questions and answers." I can only ask myself questions and listen to the questions. I can only hear my analysand ask and listen to his own questions.

Sociologist. How about your interpreting your analysand's free associations, including dreams?

Author. Without countertransference living, I see that I can interpret only my own dreams, or whatever. I can have my analysand only interpret his own dreams, or whatever.

Sociologist. You can make observations for your analysand, can you not?

Author. Without countertransference-living, I see that I can make observations for myself only. I can have my analysand make only his own observations.

Sociologist. The whole idea of self-analysis (psychoanalysis) seems to be that of the analysand's providing himself with the opportunity to see that he is, and can only be, on his own.

Author. (My) Quintilian said it, "What else is our object in teaching, save that our pupils should not always require to be taught?"

Sociologist. Again, I find it hard to feel that I am "on my own" in doing this listening, and that I can help myself by realizing that my author is of my own creating. I find your particular views on treatment to be too difficult.

Author. Remarked my A. N. Whitehead,

> Whenever a text-book is written of real educational worth, you may be quite certain that some reviewer will say that it will be difficult to teach from it. Of course it will be difficult to teach from it. If it were easy, the book ought to be burned; for it cannot be educational. In education, as elsewhere, the broad primrose path leads to a nasty place.

Sociologist. Does it not frighten your analysand to rely only on his own free-associations and have no apparent conversation, communication, a give-and-take, between himself and his analyst?

Author. My free-associating cannot make me anxious, fearful, depressed, and so on; but it can and does reveal to me how anxious, etc., I am, and apparently have been. It may be painful for me to become aware of my unhappiness, but that pain is one that I may well try to be able to afford.

Sociologist. It seems to me that many an individual would have to educate himself a long while to be able to submit to helping himself by his free-associating only.

Author. Exactly. I have never known of an instance of an individual's beginning his self-analysis with any great understanding of the meaning of his free-association for growing his respect for the integrity of his mind, for the allness-nowness-oneness-wholeness of his individuality. I have always had to respect my analysand's unique modification of his use of free-association. His renunciation of the illusion of dialog is, as a rule, most difficult. However, even his little gain in this direction is most worthy of his effort, as he invariably discovers. I have found that my understanding of the meaning of free-association has increased in direct proportion with my growth of my self-insight, so that my full appreciation of my self-analytic method would appear to mark my full devotion to my self-analysis.

Sociologist. When is self-analysis no longer indicated? Your question.

Author. With the understanding of the meaning of my self-analysis came the realization of its tremendous worth as a way of life, to be conducted as long as I conduct myself.

Sociologist. (My) Max Black made the profound observation that every important advance in science and scholarship has required a reform in terminology. I wonder if you ever expect to have prevail your view that language can be only an idiolect (the language of the specific individual using it) for furthering one's self-conscious living.

Author. My view of my language, as only my most helpful method of naming my self-expressiveness, already prevails in the one world where it can, in my mental being. Self-insightful Nietzsche noticed that mankind has a bad ear for new music.

Sociologist. It is hard to see how renunciation of ideas and feelings of improvement (betterment, progress) is essential for freeing human health and happiness. I recognize that a sense of failure, self-accusatory feelings, and ideas of falling behind, seem demoralizing kinds of forces. I notice that my ideas and feelings of self-esteem have an encouraging, motivating meaning for me. I readily imagine that true realization of the wonderfulness of my human being provides me with finest incentive. But it is extremely difficult for me to add to my list of *desirable* human powers all of the unpleasant feelings of which I am capable,—even if I do know now that each of these feelings *does* have life-saving meaning for me.

Author. I too find it hard to renounce my attitude that "treatment" means attainment of finer, healthier, happier living,—even if I do know now that such comparison is my illusion supporting my delusion that I am the same individual a former "I" used to be. My asserting I am now in any way superior to what I used to be expresses my ambivalence about my present, as well as past, wonderful living.

Sociologist. I can readily imagine that many a physician, or patient, is unready to renounce such time-honored expressiveness as: "Are you better?" "Well, I'm no worse." "There is improvement." "I'm most grateful to you, Doctor." "You saved my life, Doctor, and I cannot thank you enough." "I can always count on your help, Doctor." "You look stronger and healthier than before." And so on and on. Even if I do need to see and consciously exercise my spiritual insight and self-control, I also need to indulge "habits of a lifetime" which appear to deny the allness-oneness-wholeness-nowness of my individuality. My study has helped me greatly even if it has given little or no support to my self-insight, that is, to my appreciation of my humanity. I realize you see the conscious intellectual and moral as coinciding: the more the study is seen as self-study the more extensive the morality.

Author. In order to steer my life self-consciously I must be able to renounce certain main objections, such as that it is impossible, or that it is a too risky and dangerous course, or that it is already sufficiently travelled.

Sociologist. I doubt if you will ever, in your lifetime, find your medical curriculum centering on such views as yours, e.g., all "sickness" is unrecognized health; all pathology is struggling physiology; patient, heal thyself; therapy is a form of the patient's self-development based upon his medical self-experience; medical examination is a specific growth of self-knowledge; every patient's "disease" is his only available self-treatment; rapport, empathy, or every other name for interpersonal relationship, describes pure illusion; the uncontrolled force of every patient's wish to die becomes controllable with that patient's devotion to conscious self-knowledge; all "agreement," or "disagreement," is based only upon a lack of self-insight; war is always based upon the illusions of "common sense," "common danger," "common purpose"; there is no peace, and can be no peace, except that which each individual consciously makes with himself; all anatomy, physiology, biochemistry, biophysics, physical diagnosis, or clinical bedside medicine—each is nothing but a nominated set of meanings existing only, and ever, in one particular mind; every man is his every woman, quite as every woman is her every man.

Author. It is difficult for me to substitute for ineffective "Man is the real problem," effective "I am the real problem." Yet, I know it is Puckish to remark, "Lord, what fools these mortals be"; and insightful to observe, "What an adorable fool I can be!"

Sociologist. What do you mean by "mental trouble"? Is it not always a specific kind of self-helpfulness?

Author. Unhappiness in its various forms, including pain, cannot be considered mental "trouble," for it is really wonderful mental help. Also no symptom or sign of mental difficulty can be considered mental "trouble," for it also is a form of helpfulness. Even if I consider every kind of unhappiness of mine to be "trouble," I am helping myself by that view too. If I frustrate myself and accumulate tension to make myself anxious,—all of that necessary living adds up to a form of self-helpfulness also. My every mental "trouble" is only a way of helping myself through resorting to restriction of the range of my imagination.

Sociologist. By what use of his mind does man restrict the range of his own imagination to make trouble for himself? Your question.

Author. I have created all of this mental blocking by restricting the zone wherein I recognize my personal identity. Whenever

I cannot make love for my creating my world, I tend to forget that it is mine.

Sociologist. How do you do that? Your question.

Author. I set up a limit of my conscious self-tolerance and, thus, of the range of my conscious imagination, whenever I cannot see any of my living of my world as good, desirable, perfect. The making of such a limit is known as a "fixation."

Sociologist. My "fixations" limit my self-tolerance, and I can see the helpfulness in renouncing them. I find it hard to revise my estimate of my imagination, which is that of being an inferior power of my mind.

Author. I have frustrated myself most by looking upon my imagination with disfavor, and lived freely and happily by seeing my imagination as subsuming all of my mental action. Very early in his work, as well as in his later writings, Freud pointed out the role of frustration (*Versagung*) in damming up excitation beyond the limits of tension tolerance of the mind.[4] Whenever I suffer privation pertaining to my conscious use of my imagination, I feel overwhelmed, and therefore must submit myself to some method of "living through" my overwhelming experience without consciously loving it as all my own. Thus, if I have not created my own woman as being my own, I cannot use my imagination to experience my own woman whenever, or however, I wish to do so. Therefore, I may have to live myself only as being jilted or deserted, if it appears that my woman "leaves" me or "dies." By disowning my opposite sex I must resort to "looking at" my opposite sex (in the illusional sense of perceiving "somebody else") in order to exercise my (unconscious) being of my opposite sex.

Sociologist. Please give your views of frustration. Where does it occur? What does it accomplish that is helpful? Is it necessary?

Author. By "frustration" I mean my inability to use my imagination to live any and every way I please. My frustration as all else, occurs only in my mind. It helps me to maintain my present helpful limitations of my self-tolerance, and thereby avoid overwhelming myself completely with tensions incompatible with my sense of personal identity. If it occurs it necessarily occurs;

however, it is essential for mental freedom (lovable self-conscious living) to understand how to tolerate and relieve frustration.

Sociologist. How can frustration be relieved?

Author. I relieve it by learning to distinguish between "I may not do" and "I may not freely imagine my doing."

If I must deny myself a certain satisfaction (in order to secure another) I feel disappointment. If I cannot use my imagination for achieving the denied gratification, I frustrate myself.

Sociologist. Does all frustration excite conscious unhappiness, I wonder.

Author. All of my frustration at first is unpleasant, so that, unless I use the unhappiness as a sign that I need to activate my imagination (to allow myself fulfilment rather than frustration), I arrange my mind to go on living the frustration without my being aware of its existence. In this way I can be frustrated in many directions, endure correspondingly great limitations in my imagination, suffer extensive self-intolerance,—without consciously feeling any unhappiness (including pain), without "knowing what is the matter with me."

My frustration is always traceable to being unable consciously to imagine my living as I please. It extends much further than might be expected. For example, it is not sufficient that I feel free merely to "do" ("unthinking action") as I please, unless that "doing" includes my insight that my "doing" (any of it) is mental doing (thus *imagined* doing). It is often possible to feel free to "do," and to live one's fellowman as "doing," provided that one does not require himself to acknowledge that all such "doing" (including his fellowman's "doing") is really only his own *imagined* "doing" for which he himself is entirely responsible. Free-association brings out clearly that it is frequently possible for one to "do" that which he cannot consciously imagine his doing. A man or woman can live an experience through as if passively, as if it were happening "to" him or her, but be unable to imagine being entirely responsible for that experience.

Sociologist. I gather that "doing" is always *mental doing,* and that responsible doing is recognizable as imagining. How about "day-dreaming"? One can imagine himself (including his fellowman) behaving every which way in a day-dream.

Author. Not quite. In his day-dream one regularly omits consciousness of much of his self in his imagining and clearly overlooks his responsibility that much. He may not even be aware that he is devoting his mind to day-dreaming. As Warner Fite noticed, "Even the novelist who creates characters is dismayed to find them taking courses of their own."

Sociologist. In my experience "imagining" has often been considered unreal, dreamy, infantile, even neurotic, something to be "cured of." Also "wishing" has not stood for realizing, but for impotence. Wish-bone has been contrasted with back-bone.

Author. "Name-calling" is also helpful. However, for me to regard any behavior as "infantile" is to point up its basic, primary, fundamental nature. My "dreaming" has pointed up most important elements of my life which I tended to overlook. My "neurotic" living all turned out to be unquestionable helpfulness. "Unreal" I learned to understand as consciously repudiated *reality.* "Wishing" I discovered to be a synonym for will and, being the source of all motivation, the power underlying my creativity. My "back-bone" is only "wish-bone," or *vice versa.*

Sociologist. Now I have another task,—checking everything I do (including my fellowman's doings) against my ability consciously to imagine myself responsible for all of it. It is difficult for me to revere the power of imagination. Come to think of it, I have never noticed my fellowman observing to himself that all of his expressions are activities of his mind. No one seems to revere the fact that he is operating his mind only in all of his expressiveness. Please define "reverence."

Author. For me, reverence is belief in the subjectivity of all individuality and in the individuality of whatever is. My imagination is my human power in action, and it is well to observe accurately how any power can function safely. Without being able to imagine myself as all-I-am, I cannot revere my own authority. It is one power to be able to perform an act of worship; and still another power to be able consciously (responsibly) to imagine the entire event. It is one thing to obey a command or command obedience, and quite another thing consciously (responsibly) to imagine either whole happening. It is one experience to believe in god, and quite another experience consciously (responsibly) to imagine that development of my divinity. My respect for "the constituted authorities" is not necessarily tantamount to my consciously (responsibly) imagining all of that living of mine.

I can spend my life consciously imagining that it *is* mine, or not, and oh, the difference I must feel accordingly! Only to the extent that I limit my conscious (responsible) imagining of my subjectivity as being the sole source of my every meaning can I live a life of frustration, however.

Sociologist. All of this is news to me. I always thought that frustration was produced by a blocking of "doing," and not from a want of imagining. Please illustrate how my stopping doing anything can lead to my stopping my consciously *imagining* I am doing that anything.

Author. As a child I can be doing something happily, and suddenly find my mother disapproving. I then stop whatever I am doing, and may also stop my imagining myself going on doing it. Just my stopping doing anything (e.g., from fear of my mother's disapproval) is unpleasant, but is insufficient to produce the frustration attendant upon my stopping my consciously imagining my going on doing it. I may be about to live the act of striking my brother and suddenly experience my father's disapproval, so that I stop myself "in the act." That kind of stopping is unpleasant, but it does not rule out my consciousness of my imagining my striking my brother,—a deeply needed indulgence, especially in my early years of intensely violent emotional living. My restricting my freedom to (consciously) imagine myself living violently, hostilely, deprives me of the kind of self-expression which is most favorable to my maintaining *peace.*

Sociologist. I can see how my consciously imagining my fighting *my* fellowman can save me from my unconsciously attacking myself in the name of "another." Certainly, such a safety valve would promote peace, would save me from warring on myself. (My) your self-sovereignty treatment of authority (and its responsibility) is, by far, *the most powerful line of insight obviating war I have ever imagined.*

Can you give another specific instance of helpfulness deriving from one's recovering his ability to imagine (consciously) his doing something happily which he had stopped actually doing on account of his parent's disapproval?

Author. A man suffered recurrent headache. In his self-analysis he learned that he suddenly stopped masturbating through fear of his mother's disapproval. He discovered that on that occasion he also thought his mother would disapprove of his consciously imagining his pleasing masturbation. He therefore frustrated himself further by curbing his imagining this satisfying living. He found that his headache represented a displacement "upward," an expression of his disguised frustration produced by his not being able consciously to imagine his gratifying masturbation.

Sociologist. Do you regard prohibited imagination of masturbatory experience as the only source of headache?

Author. I only offer the one "specific instance" desired. I am pleased to note, however, the importance to me of considering restriction of conscious imagination about any pregenital or genital pleasure as being a potential source of headache.

Sociologist. I consciously (responsibly) imagine that it is rare for a human being to "know his place," to consciously (responsibly) imagine very much of his selfhood, to realize that his imaginings welling up from his wishes *are* his realities, to recognize that his hopes are immediate experiences rather than distant "futurities."

Author. May I *find* myself living a life of helpfully painful frustration whenever I imagine I am not my every experience, and may I love to learn (grow) whatever way I find myself living. To be able consciously (responsibly) to *imagine* my living, depends upon my power of making love, the appropriate feeling for freeing self-consciousness. Love is power, and power is the basis of authority.

Self-conscious living, like morality, is the loving imagining of a conscious choosing, a heedfully self-relying, a freely willing, a responsibly realizing, a notably independent deciding, a consciously self-interested way of life. Insofar as I am not conscious that I am law unto myself, I have not attained self-conscious living or morality. My true wisdom, ultimate experience, holy light,—each confirms only the responsibility and reliability of my conscious individuality. Who can speak of "god" but one who speaks *as* god! *One cannot learn to love; one must love to learn!*

Sociologist. I see too many complications in your use of words as being all and only self-words, as naming only elements of your individuality. I would like to have you state clearly the meaning of your concept of your personal identity. Can you ever speak for all of it at once? Do you consider you can have more than one "I" at a time? Do you not mislead yourself consistently by using the word "I" regularly as if you can always speak for all of yourself? Do you divide yourself into a subject "I" and an object "me"? Do you consist of anything but subjective I-ness? Is your I-ness self-perpetuating, eternal, evanescent, or true to subjectivity in surpassing quantification?

Author. My *personal* identity is all that I can at all identify. My individuality, my subjective allness-oneness-wholeness, does not verbalize or vocalize itself all at once, but *is* expressive all at once. My "I" is my am-ness or is-ness, a name for the authority of my subjective being. Whatever is exists only in its is-ness. All of my human being cannot be contained in one of its own illusions, such as "time" or "space." If I say, "I speak to me," all I can be meaning is, "I listen as I speak." I "speaking," or "listening," or "seeing," or whatever,—each is I distinctifying a particular action which is integral to the whole *movement* of my living.

My speaking "I" is all and only about itself; my hearing "I" is all and only about itself; my every other self-meaning, whether named "body" or "mind" or "soul," is constituted of I-ness which is all and only about itself. The word "me" only names an illusion of object, and really consists of I-ness. Thus, my use of the word "I" is an instance of treating, or living, a particular as the universal which it is.

It is difficult for me to renounce my illusion that "I" now am the same "I" who existed before. My illusion of self-continuity is very dear to me. I avoid the excitement of seeing myself as the *stranger* (the newcomer, the new man) I really always am. As a rule my newness does not seem striking, so that my individuality does not appear to be timeless. However, *any* striking newness (such as a "loss of memory," "stroke," "accident," or whatever) immediately presents clearly the truth of the is-ness of my individuality.

The betterment connotation of "treatment" is based upon the philosophic idea: meliorism. "Meliorism" is the term meaning: my perfection is "not now but later," provided I acknowledge my present imperfection and repudiate it. I account psychologically for the almost inescapable urge for "improvement" (for becoming perfect) which I can sense in myself, as follows.

My illusion of "enhancement," "augmentation," "enlargement," or the like, is based upon the impossible: "comparison." And every "comparison" is produced by my disrespect for the allness of individuality. Thus, "comparison" of one stage of growth with "another," one stage of structure of a building with "another," one pile of money with "another," or so on and on, is no more tenable than is any other so-called "comparison." Each implies illusion of "betweenness," or "relationship," or similar disregard for the fact that individuality is non-isolable, hence unrelational, incomparable, and otherwise its own everything. My wish to perfect my "imperfect" self is the disguised return of my conscious repudiated perfection. Joyous "anticipation" of my perfection can be nothing but enjoyment of my presently disguised perfection. As a meliorist, I gladly settle for my disguised indefectibility, my meliorism being a compensation for my repressed theism. I am always caring for my health and welfare the very best way I presently can.

General Practitioner. The peaceful principle that I am *always* helping myself ideally, no matter how I am behaving myself, is very new to me. I can see how that appeasing view renounces fault-finding and its emphasis upon so-called "misbehavior" (which thus becomes accented by prohibition). I can also see how that unperturbing view contributes to my conscious self-estimate and, therefore, to my sufficient self-care. Please let me get this straight: Is it true that I am helping myself by my behavior just as much when I judge I am not helping myself, as when I judge I am helping myself?

Author. When I ask myself that question, my reply is: Yes, it is certainly true. And my discovering that truth has brought me life-saving peace of mind, pacific diplomatic resolve, and peaceable steadfastness of purpose.

General Practitioner. I always thought frustration could occur from privation originating only "outside" the frustrated one. I see now that I can frustrate myself by a restriction of my imagination only, since all that my former-I formerly considered "outside" was really my own living too. On account of my many fixations, no doubt I am frustrating myself right and left without realizing it.

Johann Gottfried Herder also attempted to "dialogize" his conscious-self syncretism,

> . . . . the one and eternal principle of individuation . . . developed along a line which leads into our innermost self. The more life and reality, that is, the more rational, powerful and perfect energy a being has for the maintenance of a whole which it feels belongs to itself, to which it imparts itself inwardly and entirely, the more it is an individual, a self.

Author. I have found only my personal experience, which I call my self-observation, trustworthy for representing my existence. My "conative," "cognitive," "affective," even "conscious" or "unconscious," or every other kind of my living, has any and all of its meaning in the fact that I make it meaningful. My life gives it its only importance. My only true meaning is my identity.

General Practitioner. Your whole thesis consists of asserting the true *proton pseudos* to be: posing a question, or positing an idea, which implies "otherness." For you "otherness" means "objectivity," which, in turn, means ignored subjectivity. Therefore your single purpose is to renounce temptations to account for anyone (or thing) on the basis of another.

To preserve your sensing your oneness-allness-wholeness you must steadily *practice* your observation that your "externalities" exist in you, and see as illusional your observation that you can exist "in," "around," "beside," "near to," "far from," them. In the interest of heedfully situating all of your mental functioning in your own mind, you extol your self-consciousness as your most prized power, as the acme of your self-knowing, as your meaning of meaning, and as the pinnacle of all of your virtue. "Whatever is, is all and only about itself" is a summing up of your principle of sanity. All you mean by "psychotherapy" is: Only immediate conscious speculative idealism is symptom-free mentation. You regard your every preoccupation with any meaning implying (illusional) "not-self" to be an effort to preserve what self-consciousness you can command, pending your cultivating sufficient conscious self-love to tolerate the said "not-selfness" as integral to what you mean by your "personal identity." All wisdom is an issue of getting wise to one's self. Your *summum bonum* is reducible to: conscious self-functioning.

Say you, "I am an I-man. Being a conscious I-man is my lovingly meaningful way of life." "I" see through my eyes, not with them; hear through my ears, not with them; feel through my touch organ, not with it; taste through my taste bud, not with it; experience (illusions of) motion through my muscles, not with them; and so on. Although you may approve of your fellowman's necessary use of his inveterate habits of mind such as "communication" (and other implications of "not-self") you consider all such as practically inconvenient to your way of thinking based upon your type of imagination, which reflects your cultivation of self-love.

Your "localization of mental functioning," therefore, turns out to be simply but difficultly that of placing *all* mental functioning in the individual mind. Instead of developing a departmental concept of psychology, consisting of segregated cognitive, conative, and affective functions (or others), you regard the most practical knowledge about any mental functioning to be the fact that it occurs only in one mind. How do you justify your position, which seems to disregard all that one might ordinarily expect from a "localization of mental functioning"?

Author. "Authority," including its ever present self-evidence, "responsibility," is of most important human concern. As the source of my sense of personal identity, "authority" constitutes the ground of my belief in all of my so-called reality. That accuracy be realized in localizing this most meaningful function is the most desirable of all human achievements. Immeasurable human distress is traceable to efforts to establish authority (which always and only subsumes responsibility) where it cannot exist, namely, "outside" of the individual. What I need most of all, and therefore what I can see *my* world needs most of all, is a far more intensive sense and appreciation of my authority and its identifiable responsibility. As my self-analysis continues, my conscious appreciation of my authorship extends to include my all.

General Practitioner. I must admit that I am the author of my world and am therefore responsible for it, that (my) you are the author of your world and are therefore responsible for it, and so on.

Walter Kaufmann offers one view of subjective truth as being a "fond nick-name for self-deception."[5] He points out that one may have different meanings for "subjective truth." No doubt he would see his own authority (including responsibility) in his every assertion, and that his "authoritative opinion" can hold for his own meaningful world.

I have made an important discovery. *My consciousness and self-consciousness are not the same.* True, when I am conscious it is always my self who is conscious, whether I realize that truth or not. However, my realization that my consciousness *is* all and only my self-consciousness is all that can enable my conscious localizing of all of my mental functioning in my own mind, and thereby decide my appreciation of the individuality of my individuality. The one sure mark of my sanity is my knowing what I am doing, my consciousness of my being. Without my localizing my mental functioning in my own mind, I can never know "where I am." I am sure I shall find ever less use for words implying otherness such as "agreement," "disagreement," "comparison," "authority" (other than my own). I ask myself, Is that not enough? Why should I go to all of the trouble to extend my consciousness for my ever-growing self? Is my only choice solipsism or symptom formation?

Author. My appreciation of anyone, or anything, of my world, such as art or artist, science or scientist, creation or creator,—each appreciation is an issue of my making an acquaintance with myself,—as my Titian, or my Einstein, or my Kaufmann, or my creation of any kind. Furthermore, each one of my subjects may make his self-observations in keeping with his being ever a new person.

I am willing to work hard at loving selffully whatever I live, for the wholeness of my human nature demands this labor of love. I have found it impossible to deny, lie about, neglect, or otherwise ignore the subjectivity of my self-world, except by resorting to symptom formation.

General Practitioner. I wish to pursue further your view of the helpfulness of conscious (i.e., authoritative, responsible) living. For instance, what is psychoanalytic treatment about, except the exercise of self-consciousness?

Author. Whenever psychoanalytic treatment is mentioned, what comes to mind forcefully is: the cultivation of consciousness. As Freud observed, there is only one possible kind of consciousness, namely, self-consciousness.

General Practitioner. What is a practicing psychoanalyst?

Author. A psychoanalyst is a specialist in psychotherapy. As of any professional personnel, there are degrees of readiness of psychoanalysts, but every psychoanalyst realizes that the self-consciousness he has attained is his greatest mental achievement.

General Practitioner. How does a psychoanalyst develop his insight?

Author. By discovering that his psychoanalysis is entirely a self-analysis. The "degree" of self-analytic expertness attainable is decided largely by the extent to which the given self-analyst can grow the realization that his pleasure-pain propensities have absolutely nothing to do with any other mental power of his. Thus, whether he lives an experience with pleasure or with pain can have no bearing upon the all-important truth that the experience in question is an integral living, helpful element of his own individual life. This basic truth did not escape Freud's notice: "We never discover a 'No' in the unconscious," and, "Judging has been systematically developed out of what was in the first instance introduction into the ego or expulsion from the ego carried out according to the pleasure principle."[6] (My) every mental action exists in its own right, and cannot collapse into the nothingness of otherness.

General Practitioner. You must often have thoughts and feelings you ascribe to others.

Author. Nothing that I live can be alien to me. I can feign "not-self," however, by shamming a kind of psychic autotomy, by *willfully* ignoring any self-view which I have not endured and claimed enough to be able to use kindly. Thus I establish partialities, "value judgments." The *meaning of life* is the pacific equalizer underlying all meaning which can dispel the illusion of inequality created by the value judgment. Only when I am least aware of my life's value do I devote myself most to the play of value judgments.

General Practitioner. There must be many degrees of self-consciousness, as of knowing in general. I see that autonomy or autotomy is the law of life.

Author. My realization and appreciation of my selfhood (my sense of my personal identity) is the greater the more awake I am. Increasing diminution of this "I"-consciousness characterizes the increasing depth of the levels of my sleep. Thus, fully wide-awake, my sense of personal identity would extend to all of my world; claiming myself wide-awake, but really not being fully self-conscious, my sense of identity fluctuates largely with my sense of personal satisfaction; daydreaming, my "I"-feeling undergoes great restriction in the interest of certain of my wishes; sleep-dreaming, my sense of personal identity may be entirely absent, so that for my later self-orientation purposes I may have to rely entirely upon recognizing the dream character I lived with feeling *of any kind,* as being my only approximation to my then self-awareness.

Only my consciousness of where my living is occurring (in me), enables me to realize my own individuality. If, as a scientist basing the development of my knowledge upon experiment and observation, I create for myself the "taboo" that I must not see myself in my scientific living, I thereby deprive my scientific effort of that claim to truth. My conscious self can command only my life forces which it has taken the trouble to see, understand, and hence love as itself.

General Practitioner. Freud said, "The mental, whatever its nature may be, is in itself unconscious."

Author. The life orientation aiming at self-appreciation stipulates that self-unconsciousness does have its proper place. Whenever I am self-consciously living any of my life, I am at the same time self-unconsciously living *all of the rest of my life.* In the fundamental respect, my self-unconsciousness is more helpful to me than is my self-consciousness, for there is vastly more of me that is unconscious than conscious. Without it, I could not survive. I have constant and necessary use for it in every phase of my existence. It is the motive power of my physiology. Furthermore, my self-consciousness can apply only to one self-scene, or self-view, at a time; all of the rest of me meanwhile must remain self-unconscious. Also, I have necessary use of unconscious selfness, which spares my overwhelming myself with responsibility incompatible with my consciously responsible living.

General Practitioner. Resistance (the activity of repression) just enforces self-unconsciousness, I presume. Or has it another function?

Author. As I ask myself that question, I note my answer to be: Yes.

Repression is *always* performed in the service of preserving self-consciousness. My repression enables me to live my unrepressed life responsibly as worth living. I accomplish all of my repression as an effort to help myself avoid panic, demoralization. In other words, whenever it occurs, repression is my strongest and most healthy-minded effort to live myself consciously. It provides the exact amount of self-helpfulness needed in each instance.

General Practitioner. Is it not economical to take myself for granted, so that I can feel free to attend to whatever happens?

Author. I deem myself most fortunate when I am able to understand Huxley's maxim: Take nothing for granted. My living of my own self without due appreciation, without full gratitude to myself for my wonderful ability, is now the case in point. My ability to prevent myself from overwhelming myself with my realization of my ignorance and self-deception unquestionably has survival value for me. Similarly, my every complaint is a precious self-use with which I point out to myself that I am not living myself in such a way as to necessitate my feeling happy. Two very practical insights: It is natural to live with dislike what I am unable to understand; and it is impossible to live with dislike what I am able to understand. Conscious love is the necessary vehicle of understanding.

General Practitioner. Please discuss the way you use your mind to conduct your self-analysis.

Author. I use the method of free-association.

General Practitioner. Please describe free-association again.

Author. My free-association is: speaking my mind without reservation of any kind whatsoever.

General Practitioner. Freud said: Psychoanalytic procedure differs from all methods making use of suggestion, persuasion, etc., in that it does not seek to suppress by means of authority any mental phenomenon that may occur in the patient.

Author. Free-association, my only self-analytic tool and rule, derives its chief therapeutic power from two facts: (1) it employs the free use of the power of language, and yet (2) it renounces the illusion (hypnotic) of communication. My beginning "analysand" (self-analyst) cannot appreciate clearly this distinction of his free association. He is capable only of the degree of knowledge about, hence use of, free-association directly proportionate to the degree to which he has developed his capacity for self-consciousness. Thus, his cultivation of his understanding of free-association proceeds as his consciousness extends itself in his mind, so that the extent of his appreciation of the meaning of free-association is a true index of the stage of his self-analysis. He grows self-conscious as he grows self-loving.

General Practitioner. Is free-association difficult?

Author. Facility in free-association (in speaking one's mind for the conscious purpose of growing the realization of its all-inclusiveness) indicates already developed great self-tolerance. Indeed, insofar as the method of free-association is fully appreciated for its health significance, the wisdom of continuous self-analysis is self-evident.

Every psychoanalytic experience reveals the analysand's attempt to escape the strict self-reference of free-association by trying to initiate "conversation" and thereby counterfeit impersonal otherness. All else failing he tries identifying with what he conceives to be the stony *withholding* silence of his analyst, and resorts to living his mind mutely. Each course of psychoanalysis brings out its own degree of this (helpful) resistance, and the insightful analyst realizes the costly risk involved in his analysand's repressing his need to not speak his mind.

A particularly forceful means for his speaking his mind as if it is not entirely his own, is interrogation, the question-answer procedure. Every query, or reply to a query, based upon the illusion of "communication" already constitutes a tight delusional system. To be able to ask a question correctly is not merely already to know half, rather it implies that the questioner unconsciously has all of the knowledge of the answer. Psychoanalytic experience teaches thoroughly that the answer can come only from the place which gave rise to the question.

Every answer which appears to be provided by someone other than the questioner cannot be accessible as conscious self-knowledge; however, such a consciously disowned answer can and does contribute to attitudes of illusional and delusional dependence. Seeing that all of my dependence is self-dependence is my definition of my independence. Not-self dependence posits the impossibility, "thinking with somebody else's mind," instead of with one's own. A mind exercising itself in this illusional and delusional direction is deprived of any clear insight thereby.

Appreciation of the coherence and organization of individuality is steadily obscured by this "finding-out-something-from-somebody-else" mental activity. The self-conscious scientific investigator whose mind is consistently questioning his experience recognizes that he grows his answers quite as he grows his questions,—all in his own organic unity. Actually there can be no second- or third-hand experience, any more than there can be impersonal conviction, but it is rare for one to be clearly conscious of this truth. Whoever does plainly see the necessity for his originality in all of his living knows whereof he speaks and observes that his idiolect, including all of his questions and answers, is a preciously powerful means for his enjoying his living himself wisely and well. He finds that he cannot transmute life into truth by imputing not-self to it. He observes that the one thing to acknowledge as his own in his life is his world, his all. He discovers that no one *can* ask another a question, let alone provide him with an answer.

General Practitioner. How does a self-analyst know when he no longer needs to work with his psychotherapist?

Author. My ideal termination of (my observing) my analysand's free associating ("termination of the analysis") occurs when he terminates it by developing the mental strength to be able to appreciate free-association, that is, when he *can* free-associate with the conscious purpose of discovering and appreciating the allness of his individuality. When he *knows* that he knows what the practice of self-consciousness can do for him, he becomes capable of, and devoted to, conducting his own self-analysis as a continuing life orientation and, as in his childhood, seeing that he is his own ideal. Pending this development he would prefer a *folie à deux* termination based upon the dear illusion of "agreement."

General Practitioner. Coleridge defines pedantry as the use of words unsuitable to time, place, and company. I can see for myself how extremely difficult it is to speak, or write, words which imply nothing but self-consciousness.

Author. Spinoza recorded that words "can be the cause of great errors, unless we take the greatest precautions with them." I know of no way to try to use my language safely and sanely except by efforts at loading each one with the meaning of self-consciousness. Silently I aim at interpolating a "my" before each one. Little wonder Samuel Johnson observed, "To make dictionaries is dull work." He did not sense his identity in his every word.

In my use of words to confer names upon my mind's elements, I do not do any more than that. As I have already observed, an element's name is not the element. Everyone of my mind's elements is all and only about itself. I have found one self-observation to be a particularly worthy one: Any word which connotes "that which might better not be," is all and only about itself.

General Practitioner. Please illustrate further your use of words.

Author. Each of my words is not a dictionary word but is rather one of my life words. As John Ray noted, "He that useth many words for the explaining of any subject, doth, like the cuttle fish, hide himself for the most part in his own ink."

General Practitioner. Please try to weigh certain of your words more carefully,—words describing self-conscious living.

Author. Without knowing the force of my words it is impossible to know myself (consciously). I must turn this rich word "consciousness" ten thousand ways.

My word "life" itself is one which distinctifies my consciousness about being alive. My word "consciousness" distinctifies my *sense* of being alive. My word "sense" distinctifies a certain apical self-excitability, irritability, or sensibility, which I find to be a property of my living. My word "property" distinctifies something that I own by virtue of being (living). My word "discovery" distinctifies an element of surprise in my consciousness, derived from the ever fresh novelty of living. My word "meaning" distinctifies each of my mental properties in terms of its usefulness. My "mind" is a word which distinctifies myself as a distinctifier subsuming that which is distinctified.

I create *my* universe. By living my definite and indefinite articles instead of my possessive pronouns, by living Southey's "arts Babblative and Scribblative," I can succeed in living myself as if I were out of my mind, as if my life were having nothing to do with my experience. I can simply "a" and "the" myself out of self-conscious existence.

Only what I pointedly say of myself can be veridical. Only what every part of me can experience in, of, and for, itself can be veridical. As Ernest Jones worded his necessary aloneness, "We have no immediate knowledge of anyone's mentality other than our own." Thus, my self-consciousness supports my innocence, trust, love, happiness, hopefulness, healthfulness, endurance, and every other pleasing virtue. Conversely, my self-ignoration is ever so quietly supported by all of my painful affects (fear, guilt, hate, jealousy, etc.) and helpfully compensating self-deceits implying self-alien control ("influence," "suggestibility," "disagreement," "agreement," "communication," "corroboration").

Self-consciousness reveals the love of wisdom as the love of self. It reveals all disingenuous critical living as warningly painful to its liver. Above all, it provides the validity of *innocence,* that full, vital human happiness which everyone, from earliest childhood on, strives to recover.

General Practitioner. Please describe your most practical learning.

Author. My greatest educational attainment has been my

realizing the benefit to myself in seeing clearly that my use of language is only for the purpose of teaching myself how to appreciate my life. By renouncing my illusion of language as an instrument for communicating with my fellowman, I achieved my most helpful appreciation of my fellowman's use of his language as an instrument for his cultivating his appreciation of his own life. Self-reference words are peaceful words; "otherness"-reference words are fighting words.

No doubt as with every self-analyst, the great gain I enjoyed when I first realized that I could not "reach" my fellowman but that I could have my fellowman *reach* himself, enabled my attaining a mature sense of "just peace." For the first time I saw fully the potential wisdom in my Emerson's warning: Charity abroad is spite at home. For the first time I was able to see war, and crime of every kind, in its helpful educational significance. My recognition of the useful educational force of every so-called "morbid" sign and symptom, of every so-called "accident" or "misfortune," has been my supreme medical insight and my chief source of medical peace.

With the development of my self-awareness I enabled myself to see my every institution of civilization as a personification of myself. Growing to be able to cherish my pain as my wonderful monitor, I liberated myself from the strictly limited helpfulness implicit in judging what I like to be "just," and what I disliked to be "unjust"; diagnosing what I liked to be "healthy," and what I disliked to be "unhealthy"; proclaiming what I liked to be "good," and what I disliked to be "bad"; and so on.

I live an enormous field of force. My education to healthful development depends upon my developing my capacity to use my life forces *peacefully.* By so much as I recognize my individuality in all of my living will I keep myself aware of the motivation to "keep the peace." Every element of my development is for my use. All being is expressed in the exercise of being. It takes the whole of individuality to live wholesomely. It takes my self-consciousness to reveal to me the elements of that whole.

General Practitioner. Freud said: Our scientific work in psychology will consist in translating unconscious processes into conscious ones, and thus filling in the gaps in conscious perception.

Author. Conscious self-creation, growing acknowledged individuality, is the organon by which the scientist can pursue his investigations without limiting his healthy-mindedness. The only way to study safely and sanely is by truthfully assuming original authority for all that passes under the name of the "learning experience." Upon the proper fixing of authority for any and all of one's own living the growth of healthful mindedness depends entirely. Authority cannot rest on any living fact except that of its author. If he sees it sufficiently as his own, he will recognize the futility in trying to make his fellowman accept it.

All education, including the discipline of medicine, begins where individual care begins. No vicissitude of health is ever an "accident." It happens only when it is made to happen. Self-realization is a credit to that consciously responsible one who has it. It accounts for all of one's feelings of happiness. Its neglect accounts for all of one's feelings of unhappiness, including fear, guilt, hatred, and pain. "The practice of medicine" means the patient's trying to help himself, and the physician's trying to help himself,—not the physician's using the patient as a practice field. Wise in the ways of his life is the individual who comes to recognize that, in every instance, his distress fits the way he is willing to live himself.

General Practitioner. Is being self-conscious just being a spectator of one's own life?

Author. Being awake to one's self is more than just passively observing one's self; it is a greater degree of being actively alive with one's self. To be self-conscious is to be excited with vitality. Thus, to be fully aroused to life's meaning enables the strength of mind which strengthens the mind. In early life it often is safer to repress this vivid vitalization properly animating one's own existence. Human individuality is constant; human self-consciousness is not. Disregard for human life is in every instance the issue of self-unconsciousness. Where I cannot see my own existence is involved, I am numb, enervated. Where I can see my own existence is involved, I am sensitive, innervated. I am humane to the extent that I can be self-aware, and only to that extent. The stability of here and now is always lived consciously by me. Without self-awareness I am without accurate perspective. Self-consciousness is the pacific principle of true life perspective.

By keeping my enlivening mental eye open (by exciting my self-awareness) I see clearly that I am affirming life in the most healthful way. This life orientation is one which I must constantly keep cultivating if I will have it. This particular kind of self-culture is the most difficult one and one which I have made my life's work, and am making my life's work. Physics or theology has no probability whatsoever except in the sense of its being my physics and my theology. A most important help for me in my trying to live my life consciously as my own is to be aware of the self-deception inherent in any and every kind of tangling (illusional) alliance. Renunciation of every illusional "agreement" or "disagreement" is possible only to the extent that such impossible "alliances" are seen as impossible.

General Practitioner. Please let me see if I am developing the full conception of therapy. The integral strength of your therapeutic lies in each patient's discovering that he is, and that only he can be, whatever it is to which he objects. Thus, whenever I find my fellowman objectionable, in that he is a liar, thief, murderer, or obstructive somewhat, I am sparing myself from finding that my fellowman is able to be what I am unable to be. In other words, then, I have repressed, not renounced, my lying, thieving, murdering, or whatever "objectionable" propensity. My finding that I am my only possible drawback, reject, enemy, or whatever is the apparent "subject" of my remonstrance,—is all that there can be to my therapeutic process. Wherever I can see myself clearly, there my love takes over and I feel it well. Psychotherapy is seeing with true mental vision.

Author. (My) your description of psychotherapy lifts a weight from my heart. I fear no longer that you are identifying it with "riddance," "negation," "fault-finding," "changing from 'sick' to 'well,'" or any such disguised self-accusation. My measure of me is my measure of mental health. I do not invigorate myself by means of my self-insight, I simply see that I am vigorous.

Yes, anyone who just once discovers the wonderful experience of relief and release he derives from consciously reducing his hated enemy to his beloved conscious selfness, will continue to seek such peacemaking by consciously extending further the boundary of his conscious self-tolerance. My restricting my every meaning of dislike to that dislike-feeling alone, has invariably revealed the so-called healing and strengthening power of conscious love for my living. Whatever is, is therapeutic. Is-ness affirms no "destruction," "disease," or "deviation." So-called "negation" of any kind oppugns all demonstration. When I indulge my illusion of "getting better" I give way to confounding my dislike with some other perfection of mine which I may then call "symptom." Whenever thus I overlook any of my divinity, I yield to my so-called "anthropomorphisms." "I am that I am, and shall be that I shall be,"—is divine insight for my existence, my reality, my truth.

General Practitioner. What do you think of the name of God as standing for the divinity of every individual? Thus, you can call yourself God, I can call myself God, "he" can call himself God, "it" can call itself God, and so on.

Author. That kind of reasoning supports the notion of plurality. My view, based upon self-consciousness (that is, insightful individuality) requires that I, alone, hold myself responsible for *whatever* I mean by the name of God. There is no seer of subjectivity, no diviner of divinity, to make "objectivity" of being. Divinity constitutes the reality of my being itself, and cannot be segregated in any imagined modification or derivative of that being.

General Practitioner. Expressing such a view to myself brings to mind this wisdom of (my) Johann Gottfried Herder who renounces his idea of God as being "a collective name":

> Philolaus: Then the image of the World-Soul will not be overly pleasing to you either?
>
> Theophron: It is a human image, and if it is used prudently a great deal concerning the inherently indwelling power of God can be illustrated clearly by means of it. Nevertheless it remains an image, which, without the greatest care immediately misleads one. . . . O Spinoza! How far thou art even with all thy most difficult expressions, from such a catachresis of an image, as the "World-Soul"!

But what does all this have to do with psychotherapy?

Author. This specific question arises often in the course of self-analysis, when the self-analyst finds himself making "wholes," unifying previously considered differents, seeing the self-dependent oneness in the apparently aggregated "many." The concept "perfection," dear to the divine, is essential to the self-analyst who needs, above all, to renounce his (illusional) "imperfection" traceable to his resorting to "objectivity" (that is, ignored *subjectivity*). Terms such as "body," "physic," "person," "organ," "system," "measure," "motion," "time," "space," and innumerable words naming "objects"—each one denotes an amnesia for subjectivity.

General Practitioner. Can you succeed in making your idea of psychotherapy clearer? It seems to be one's awakening to his responsible, self-bound authority. Josiah Royce found his truth and reality to consist of his self-conscious knowing. He said, only individual experience is real. Also George H. Howison (1834-1916), great American philosopher, observed that 'the only thing absolutely real is mind. . . . all temporal and all material existence take their being from mind. . . . out of consciousness they all issue, to consciousness are presented, and presence to consciousness constitutes their entire reality and entire existence." Since psychotherapy must mean "true appreciation of reality," what do you mean by "reality"?

Author. My reality is my self-activity, my individuality living, my subjective experience, my self-moving being. My Hegel treated his mind most efficaciously when he said, "Spirit is self-contained being. But matter which is spirit outside of itself, (turned inside out) continually manifests this, its inadequacy, through gravity."

Hegel described well the sanity-creating universality of self-consciousness,

> The universal self-consciousness is the intuition of itself, not as a special existence distinct from others, but an intuition of the self-existent universal self. Thus it recognizes itself and the other self-consciousness in itself, and is in turn recognized by them.
>
> Self-consciousness is, according to this its essential universality, only real in so far as it knows its echo (and reflection) in another (I know that another knows me as itself), and as pure spiritual universality (belonging to the family, the native

land, &c.) knows itself as essential self. (This self-consciousness is the basis of all virtues, of love, honor, friendship, bravery, all self-sacrifice, all fame, &c.)

General Practitioner. You seem to equate psychotherapy with appreciation of all being, hence with renunciation of all negativity. "I am the spirit that denies," said Faust's devil.

Author. Yes. Negativity is nothing but ignored subjectivity. *All* so-called "objectivity" expresses negativity. The illusion "otherness" which supports the deceptive notion "relativity" is the mere absence of conscious subjectivity.

General Practitioner. Conscious subjectivity, the only solvent of any self-ignoration, is then the essence of psychotherapy, for it constitutes the self-realization underlying one's ever growing a new identity which is cherished as such. A *kind* (peaceful) spirit governs the self-world of the conscious personalist, according to you. "I make all things new," is recorded as divine revelation.

Author. I can speak such psychotherapeutic wisdom only for, to, and of, myself. My vain effort to overreach myself always means my trying to exist without existence. Limitation in my ability to live my life as one force, expresses itself in appearances of disunity in my physiology,—most "pathognomically" in hyperplasias and neoplasias. All of my certainty, including my certain self-health, is identical with my conscious subjectivity.

General Practitioner. Probably anyone who hears these conversations will refer to this one on psychotherapy more than to any other. I feel justified in discovering all possible of the subject. You renounce every comparative and identify superlative with positive. Nativity, not negativity, is your medical motto, your prescriptive principle guarding your reality. You find that negativity corresponds to nothing real. Your motive of sanity is not just to understand, but conscious to be. The final meaning of your psychotherapy is only and entirely: consciously living your ipseity.

Now my problem is this: I have conceived my choice way of living myself as being free of unpleasant feelings,—and now it seems that I can fulfil my life only suffering ordeal after ordeal; I always pictured desirable living as consisting of gratifying ease, satisfying creature comforts, serene activities,—and now it appears

I must undergo innumerable tests and trials of my actual ability to survive; I formerly believed that I could prepare myself to enjoy my mature or later years,—and now I find that I must discipline myself to appreciate my true reality as always being essentially that of a timeless stranger; I have regarded love of life as being a settled matter from the start,—and now I see I must experience anxiety, and many another difficult feeling, as helpful expressions of my love of living. I can go on and on detailing the disillusionment which self-conscious living entails. According to your definition (or rather lack of definition) of psychotherapy, my imagined life of lovable ease and comfortable security must be really a degree of my falling asleep, of my temporarily regressing to simpler living which is characterized by effortless equanimity. Whereas my wide-awake living involves my activating whatever feelings may be biologically adequate for the reality of my unexpectable self-experience. It seems I have come out of many an unhappy experience a more deeply cheerful, wise man. Robert Browning Hamilton has created a curative poem describing the practical helpfulness of suffering:

> I walked a mile with pleasure,
> She chattered all the way,
> But left me none the wiser
> For all she had to say.
>
> I walked a mile with sorrow
> And ne'er a word said she,
> But, ah, the things I learned of her
> When sorrow walked with me.

I imagine that for you, however, there is no tragedy, no mournful event, provided that you can see that your own creativity makes perfectly necessary whatever happens.

Author. Yes. My *summum bonum* for any of my living is basically a question of the current scope of my imagination. If I imagine my world to require little, or much, trouble of me, I conceive magnanimity accordingly. Especially by defining any kind of boundary of my living can I correspondingly limit my consciously responsible living of my own psychological (or spiritual) world's nature and needs. True conscious subjectivity (the sense of life) is boundless.

General Practitioner. Your psychologizing reminds me, Warner Fite wrote that traditional psychology, which attempts to give us the natural science of thought, is neither good science nor good poetry. Possibly, poetry can skillfully perform your operation: self-consciousness. I wonder what your subjectivity makes of *fact.*

Author. My subjectivity makes its imagination its one solid primordial fact which is responsible for creating all of its own factual living. My every so-called "external" fact is a real figment of my creative imagination. I call my discovering that truth my "psychotherapy."

General Practitioner. Your psychotherapy—I almost said "non-psychotherapy," for I feel that adequately describes it—preserves the idea of enjoying life, does it not?

Author. Above all else, I am consciously devoted to enjoying my wonderfully difficult, embarrassingly unexpected, tremendously troublesome, enormously demanding, perfectly just, inconceivably powerful, and in every respect divinely awesome, peaceful existence. Anxiety-free placid contentment is but one kind of joy of living. Conscious self-possession incites a person to notice, heed, and look after, his disturbing self-worldly concerns (the fullness of his life).

General Practitioner. It appears that all mental trouble requiring so-called "psychotherapy" is in the end a problem of personal "relations" which do not exist,—except as real phantasies.

I cannot ever do more than resist notions of solipsism—mostly by disowning the fact that they are my own and by refusing even to try to ideate such thoughts "on my own." No doubt therefore you consider me to have an unconsciously obstructed mind, rather than a consciously instructed one.

It seems that your joy of living is nothing but the product of your appreciation of your value. For you, enjoying living is entirely a realizing of your wonderful nature, or spirit. I wish you would speak further of your psychotherapy.

Author. My own psychotherapy consists of my enjoying my ongoing self-analysis (conscious self-imagining) which points up the truth that my own personal being (self-experience) is all that constitutes, occupies, and animates my every sense perception, thought, feeling, or reality (life-meaning) of any kind. Thus, my idea of the pursuit of happiness entails a certain scholarly exercise of mental sophistication which is grounded in the fact of my life. I consciously aim my imagination at the creation of novel self-experiences of varying depth and breadth, for only thus can I appreciate my life to the full. All of my everyday living consists of making new discoveries of my power, whether or not I am able to be aware of that inspiring truth. Goethe told and listened to himself, "To appreciate any man, learn first what object he proposed to himself; next, what degree of earnestness he showed with regard to attaining that object."

General Practitioner. I presume your Shelleyan regard for the poet as the unacknowledged legislator of the world underlies your idea that poetic creativity is due process of the law of health. Certainly Sydney Dobell's evaluation of all possessors of their English "mother tongue" fits your thesis, "Lords of an empire wide as Shakespeare's soul." I have trouble taking poetry very seriously; for I have disciplined my mind to regard it as imaginary, —in the sense that imagination is personal illusional experience, whereas sensory perceptual living is impersonal factual experience. I have trained my mind to conceive what I mean by "a fact" is: a more or less static existent which is independent of my living. My whole way of working my mind is more or less true to that particular orientation.

Author. Perhaps as much as any disciplined person, a poet asserts and works up his appreciation of his conscious life for its own sake. He sees his necessity to "*live but one man*" (Dr. Thomas Browne). A poet's occupation consists of creating, appropriating, and naming his acknowledged insights. Walter Pater characterized the essence of mind as "vision." Croce defined "genius" as a particularly intensified consciousness of life. I like great poetry since it makes me feel my greatness. "For," wrote Vernon Lee, "at the bottom of much of our desire for great poetry is our desire for the greater life, the deeper temperament, for the more powerful mind, the great man." Every poet realizes that he derives his inspiration from his own life. A poet wittingly lives himself personally.

General Practitioner. Your belief that human living is a dangerous adventure, is a belief which one's experience alone can create, fortunately. Self-conscious Shakespeare again,

> Oh, if this were seen,
> The happiest youth—viewing his progress through,
> What perils past, what crosses to ensue—
> Would shut the book, and sit him down and die.

I suppose one cannot experience anything but his own imagination, and cannot imagine anything he has not experienced. I presume his psychotherapy is a special kind of experience of his imagination. Hegel describes that process:

> Self-Consciousness posits itself through negation of otherness and is practical consciousness . . . .
>
> This feeling of its otherness contradicts its identity with itself. The necessity felt to cancel this opposition is Impulse (or appetite). Negation, or otherness, presents itself to the consciousness as an external thing different from it, which however is determined through the self-consciousness (1) as a somewhat suited to gratify the appetency, and (2) as a somewhat in itself negative whose subsistence is to be cancelled by the Self and posited in identity with it (i.e. made identical, or assimilated).

Author. Yes. All of my "error," "ignorance," "illusion," "delusion," and every other kind of self-deception may be described as, in each instance, a specific product of imagination. Warner Fite insightfully described "truth" as being the expression of "satisfied" imagination.

General Practitioner. I am realizing that psychotherapy consists of seeing that the whole extant in any human activity is living individuality only. Psychotherapy means getting to know myself, getting to imagine my experience as all self-activity. Warner Fite wrote,

> To be oneself sincerely and to take one's personal relations seriously is at once to appreciate the difficulties of understanding, along with the special delights of understanding between natures highly individuated, and at the same time to become aware of the complications presented by repressions, suspicions,

defensive reactions, or what not; of all those contradictions which the Freudian psychology has uncovered in the impulses of sex, making them inarticulate and ashamed by their very intensity, but which, it seems to me, are characteristic of all self-conscious human nature.[7]

Author. The only way for me to uphold the first maxim of science, "to explain only by the forces of nature," is to be an enlightened student of my own nature, living (originating) my self-observation (scientific fact) as it wells forth from my being. My *every* sensation, or perception, whether I designate it "scientific" or not, is a manifestation to me of a mental activity originating in my human nature and pre-existing as an innate need of mine prior to its existing as my sensation or perception. In other words, I can only see, hear, touch, or otherwise sense, that native mental material which I have grown of myself. My living, not recognizable as my own, is obviously my irresponsible living. Its accrual accounts for my so-called "mental disorder."

Superstition frightens me away from attempting to realize the allness of my individuality. Little wonder that Kant assumed the "tendency to feign" as a fundamental characteristic of human nature. The power of self-consciousness once activated dispels all doubt, pretense, and every other kind of painful insecurity,—all based upon self-unconsciousness. The unification of knowledge as conscious self-knowledge distinguishes self-analysis. The vital force of self-appreciation is second to none. The dominion of health is presided over by conscious individuality. The modern instance of "impersonal scientism" is the atomic bomb, as well as every instance of attempting to enforce peace upon one's "impersonal world" rather than to maintain the peace of one's own world.

General Practitioner. You can say with your Santayana that "the material occasion of inspiration makes no difference if the spirit is thereby really liberated." Shakespeare, Burns, Keats, Byron, according to you every great poet, created poetry as an outlet for his conscious humanity, as a release of mental power, as a discovery of his only real companionship, as a needed source of fact-finding, as an unfailing source of self-appreciation.

Author. Yes.

General Practitioner. Your idea that human creativity is evidence of man's godhood is an old one. Richard Puttenham recorded it in his *Arte of English Poesie* in 1589. Coleridge divined that a poet's production is "a repetition in the finite mind of the eternal art of creation in the infinite *I am.*" I know that Freud did much to "respectabilize" the study of poetry as being a source of understanding of the mind. Nothing can be understandable except that which is psychological. As Mark Van Doren noted, "Shakespeare, who denies his reader nothing, denies him least of all the excitement of feeling that he is where things are simply and finally alive."[8] That is what you aim at by repeatedly calling attention to your localization of mental events, is it not?

Author. Yes. The testimony of experience is ever and entirely an individual matter. "What is the chief end of man?" Which man! My chief end is to live my I-ness meaningfully (subjectively) in every particular with the view: "That, too, am I!" My alternative is one or another degree of self-hypnosis. Only that which I do willfully can be observable by me as my conscious living.

General Practitioner. C. P. Blacker wrote, "The conception of 'reality' held by a person affords a valuable index to his mental constitution."[9] According to Edmund Husserl, pure consciousness has neither *Realität* nor *Wirklichkeit,*—only *Irrealität.*[10]

Author. Yes. For me, self-consciousness is my all-important reality meaning: being alive to myself.

General Practitioner. I find not one case history or experiment in your presentation. Furthermore, you express no debt of gratitude to anyone but yourself, although you do seem to link up your theory (self-analysis, that is, the practice of self-consciousness) with Freud. Does not the chief value of your book lie in the fact that it may provide food for thought for anyone who can, so to speak, plow through it? It certainly is no source or textbook for a busy clinician, psychiatric or otherwise. One look in it for help may show that you regard (your) everyone as being his own only *real* source and textbook. Please answer the following questions by "yes" or "no."

Author. After asking myself each question, I shall try to do so.

General Practitioner. Do you regard life as the animating principle which governs all of the vital functions of human being?

Author. Yes.

General Practitioner. Do you believe it possible that the individual can learn to regulate this principle of health in his nature?

Author. Yes.

General Practitioner. Does the organic physiologist know the essential constitution of the principle of health?

Author. No.

General Practitioner. Can this principle be subject to chemical preparations?

Author. No.

General Practitioner. Can pharmaceutical compounds ever be health aids?

Author. Yes.

General Practitioner. Is this health force a mental, spiritual, soulful, or some such kind of immaterial energy?

Author. Yes.

General Practitioner. By "spiritual" do you mean a special kind of entity?

Author. No.

General Practitioner. By "spiritual" do you mean a subjective, insightful beholding which includes every entity and which denotes the refinement of mental balance?

Author. Yes.

General Practitioner. Does not your meaning "spirit" bring to mind what Hippocrates means by *vis medicatrix naturae,* or Plato and Paul by *pneuma,* or Isaiah and Christ by *faith,* or Van Helmont by *archaeus,* or Stahl by *anima,* or Barthez by *vital principle,* or George Fox by the *interior living light,* or Bergson by *élan vital,* or Freud by *consciousness?*

Author. Yes.

General Practitioner. Is not one health condition of man better, or worse, than another?

Author. No.

General Practitioner. Each health condition of man is perfectly, ideally, wholly, and desirably whatever it is, and *that* truth reveals such a notion as "better," or "worse," to be inapplicable to it?

Author. Yes.

General Practitioner. Also, you assert that the "I" who feels "worse" today is not even the same "I" who felt "better" yesterday.

Author. Yes.

General Practitioner. Furthermore, you assert that one man cannot be "healthier," "taller," "richer," "older," etc., than another (including, than he formerly was), for such a view only indulges the illusion that individuality is not its own all. Every kind of comparison relies upon the illusion "plurality."

Author. Yes.

General Practitioner. You trace your every "feeling better," or "feeling worse," to your inaccurate localization of "pleasure," or "pain." Thus, instead of seeing that pleasure is all and only about pleasure (and that pain is all and only about pain), you indulge your illusion that each feeling can refer to some other condition of yourself. Then you can irresponsibly carry on such notions as, it feels "good" to be "healthy," and it feels "bad" to be "sick," or it feels "better" to be "healthier" and it feels "worse" to be "sicker," and so on.

Author. Yes.

General Practitioner. Your localization of "pleasure," or "pain," inaccurately (not placing it entirely in itself), is paradigmatic of your inability to localize all of your mental functioning responsibly in your own individuality?

Author. Yes.

General Practitioner. Any such irresponsible localization of any of your mental functioning is signalized by a corresponding want of self-esteem?

Author. Yes.

General Practitioner. Then every illusion of "improvement," or of "taking a turn for the worse," contains in itself some degree of self-disesteem?

Author. Yes.

General Practitioner. In your medical work you try to renounce every usage of such a notion as "cure of a dread disease" or "recovery from a bad attack of illness" or "restoration to health," and so on,—believing that life needs are adequately served by seeing and working with *any* existing health condition as perfectly, ideally, wholly, and desirably constituting the presenting reality. In other words, you consider your inability to see the goodness in all suffering to be your only basis for fault-finding, and that your ability to see *that* goodness waits only upon your further fact-finding.

Author. Yes.

General Practitioner. You consider all "objectivity" to be nothing but the disguised return (to consciousness) of repressed *subjectivity;* all "otherness" nothing but the return (to consciousness) of repressed selfness?

Author. Yes.

General Practitioner. For you the basis of all experience, the final unity of all meaning, is subjectivity?

Author. Yes.

General Practitioner. You consider all that you say or write about humanity, which deviates from your one truth (conscious self-interest), is nothing but your disguised devotion to your self-interest?

Author. Yes.

General Practitioner. In your opinion, it is only in this one respect that the idea of therapy justifies itself,—that is, that whatever one does must be done, either consciously or unconsciously, in the interest of his self-interest?

Author. Yes.

General Practitioner. Then, you consider that everyone, physician or patient, is always treating himself in the best (only) way he currently knows how to treat himself?

Author. Yes.

General Practitioner. Now, once and for all, do you distinguish "therapy" as it is ordinarily understood ("conducted by a physician") from the "therapy" that everyone is always doing on himself (in the only way he can), by the simple fact that the former therapy is consciously regarded, and developed, and conducted *as such,* while the latter therapy is not? Is that really all there is to it?

Author. Yes.

General Practitioner. Whether he knows it or not, everyone is always his own physician treating his general health, but the

M.D. who knows it *thereby* distinctifies himself as responsibly conducting his therapeutic regime? Everyone is always conducting his own self-analysis whether he knows it or not, but the one who knows it *thereby* distinctifies himself as responsibly doing therapy upon himself?

Author. Yes.

General Practitioner. Well, that is a new one on me, but I do see some sense in it. *Consciously* conducting my therapy as being no less than my only wholesome way of life properly introduces my conscious responsibility for the way I treat myself (live my life), does it not?

Author. Yes.

General Practitioner. My holding myself responsible for my own therapy also makes me responsible for medically educating myself further ("consulting my physician") upon every indication of such need? I believe I now realize this self-responsibility principle.

Author. Yes. Self-consciousness is the only realization which is at all possible.

General Practitioner. It seems to me that there ought to be a simple way to state all of this self-responsibility meaning of therapy. It all refers to conscious self-analysis, does it not? Repeat your view of psychoanalytic therapy, please.

Author. My psychoanalytic treatment is all and only my persevering effort to discover and renounce my countertransference as I live my patient discovering and resolving (learning to renounce) his transference. Quite as in my dreaming, my countertransference enables me to attribute "impersonal" meaning to any of my living for which I cannot currently acknowledge self-responsibility.[11] Over fifty years ago, Freud, seer of his psyche, pointed out the primacy of emotion in the life of the mind.[12] Whenever I am consciously unequal to acknowledging that I am the only source, aim, and object of my every emotion, countertransference enables me to live that emotion as if it were not all and only my very own personal responsibility. Whatever I live but do not consciously sense as my very own responsibility (repressed subjectivity) must seem "objective" ("impersonal," "not-I"). Watching and heeding the inconspicuous onset of my countertransference makes for exciting effortful living and constitutes the ideal-all of my psychoanalytic work. The hygienic truth is that only I can please or displease myself in any respect whatsoever; only my fellowman can please or displease himself (or herself) in any respect whatsoever. Painstaking devotion to this simple fact of life is the specific prerequisite for peaceful successful living. It is of this peacemaking truth I am mindful whenever I think of Wordsworth's verse, "*A Poet!*—He hath put his heart to school," and of his life-long aspiration toward

> Some philosophic song
> Of Truth that cherishes our daily life.

Whatever is, perfectly is. The view which senses perfection wherever it looks, whatever it sees, is the fully accurate one. Whatever is thoroughly understood is never observed as ugly, unless beautifully ugly. Noticing the facts supporting, and hence requiring, any kind of human experience always reveals the beauty of it.

The greatness of Shakespeare lies in his magnanimity revealed in the beautiful treatment he gives his every character,—"hero," "fool," "villain," alike. Shakespeare always managed to end even his so-called "tragedies" on some constructive life-affirming note, quite as if he sensed the pejorative connotation of the word "tragedy." He was too much of a fact-finder to yield to his fault-finding propensities whenever he had to endure grievous hardship. He seemed to know that fault-finding was only a form of relieving his pain by crying out. His vision seemed to subsume explanation. The poetry of the poet lies in his giving to his every theme its just due of beauty.

The overwhelming suffering of a patient manifests itself in his locating his sense of power in his symptom, in his "in transference" living of his suffering. Thus, he observes "My head hurts me," or, "My stomach is giving me a bad time," or, "My legs refuse to function," and so on. Even to himself he appears to abdicate authority and responsibility for his experiences which alter his customary sense of mental balance.

However, every physician justly strives to present to himself his clinical findings with a clear understanding of how beautifully each sign or symptom portrays exactly the way his patient is ideally helping himself. His suffering patient's current refusal to live his perfect self-helpfulness consciously illustrates his helping himself by temporarily vesting his self-sovereignty in his symptom. Thus, if I live a toothache I may temporarily identify myself largely as an aching tooth.

Each patient's beautiful psychiatric treatment may be described as his crediting himself fully, from moment to moment, with the excellence of his self-helpfulness. Thereby, his conscious excellence goes on begetting itself and he steadily enjoys his optimal self-helpfulness. I define psychotherapy as my mind's discipline in appreciating its perfections.

All of my psychotherapy is my kind and considerate renunciation of all of my negation. This renunciation is not some diluted version of repression, but is free of condemnation of any kind or degree. Full appreciation of the perfection of any or every meaning I can live is the prerequisite for its renunciation. Only by living my every mental element with love can I prevent its emphasis through prohibition, allow for its due functioning in my mental economy, and freely work or not work it according to my best interests. Only by such renunciation of my negation can I use it without having it appear to use me.

General Practitioner. Let's see if I can say how your psychotherapy works. My recognizable health is characterized by my recognizable self-love. All that I *can* live is health (self-love), but I am accustomed to regard my health (self-love) which is distressed by its trying experience, as so-called "sickness" (or loving feeling of some kind such as anxiety, hate, guilt). This effort of my health (or self-love) to reestablish its disturbed equilibrium actually must attest its presence.

My awareness of the excellence of any of my living carries with it awareness of its helpfulness. This self-esteem encourages and reassures me in my plan of conscious self-care, and gets me to continue consulting my best interests of my whole self. Now I wish to apply this therapeutic to a specific health problem.

If I am depressed and at the same time realize that this keen unhappiness is a biologically adequate sign of the shortcoming of my way of life,—I know how I am troubling myself *and* I know how to relieve myself. By perseveringly recognizing my self-denial as a form of self-indulgence, my self-disparagement as reenforcing my self-praise, my feeling of guilt as attesting my innocence, and so on obviating my symptoms of ignored self-love, I gradually recover my due sense of self-appreciation.

If I am unhappy and I know that my unhappiness is medically adequate self-treatment, then I take a fresh look at my medical "goal" of relieving unhappiness. I discover the importance of relieving my unhappiness in a specific way, namely, by renouncing my unhappiness-producing conduct. It is most desirable that my unhappiness makes sense to me so that I can observe it as the integral element of my being it is. Of course, in all of this undertaking I need to be creating for myself my self-insightful physician as my beachhead of self-love. I need to live some attending self-loving one as constantly present, for my feeling of self-rejection is otherwise unbearably intensified by my notions of "separation."

I've never heard anything quite like this before; so let me talk it through further to see if I've got it right.

If I'm unhappy and I know that my unhappiness is specific psychotherapy, "my love healing itself" you might say, then I not only have diagnosed my condition, but I know that I am undertaking its specific treatment. My accurate diagnosis is tantamount to specific treatment. My educating myself to know (become conscious for) the condition of my health is necessary for me to start proper conscious treatment, and my continuing to inform myself of my true health status, "to make it conscious," enables my continuing my due conscious treatment. Do observe my insisting upon speaking and listening to myself about my self-conscious psychotherapy.

Author. I do indeed. Whatever is conscious, is *in* consciousness. My psychotherapy is my mind's helping itself as best it can in terms of the power it possesses. My *conscious* psychotherapy is my mind's helping itself as best it can in terms of the power of self-consciousness it possesses.

10

Healing Force of Self-Consciousness

We all know how much this turning away from the painful, the tactics of the ostrich, may still be shown as present even in the normal psychic life of adults.

FREUD

AUTHOR. WHEN I try to describe for myself my intentional conduct of my life I can come no closer than to picture it as a process of awakening. When I ask myself, Why do I pursue the way of life which I do? this question is necessary to make evident its (ignored) motivation, namely, its so-called "answer." My reply is to the effect that I have helped myself most by it. And by "help" I mean specifically, I have had my freedom disencumber itself, my health extricate itself, my holiness unveil itself, my truth reveal itself,—in short, my appreciation of my living evince itself in my peaceful development. I note how this reply depends upon self-consciousness for its form and for its content.

General Practitioner. As a witness for peace, you place great stock in your consciousness for your wholeness and allness.

Author. Living peacefully is the noblest human function.

General Practitioner. Your point is that if you can appreciate your true wonderfulness, you can then appreciate the true wonderfulness of all that you live, particularly of your fellowman,—and that, if everyone would live himself thus self-consciously, the recognized value of human life would then be free to express itself. You can advocate peace for yourself, but you cannot tell me what or how to think.

Author. Exactly. Such is the humanistic ideal waiting to be developed by each individual's mighty mind.

Of all of the designs for living I have tried, my present one (of seeing my soul as my own and my all as my soul) is unique in its conspicuously subsuming all that any of my preceding life perspectives offered. I recognize its greatness in many ways but particularly in the fact that it does not exclude any of my previous valiant efforts of self-help. No self-property other than self-consciousness allows the force of vitality its full range. The worth, for my whole welfare, of my *every* meaning has become my reality test of its value. The purposive cause subsuming and accounting for the design of my every function derives from my wholeness. The principle of wholeness of whatever is provides its purpose quite as it comprehends all of its properties. Of this wholeness of one's allness is constituted the vital purposive principle of one's world. When I repudiate myself, I repudiate my fellowman; when I identify myself, I live and love my fellowman as myself.

General Practitioner. The poet of peace, Shakespeare, waged no war on war. He renounced, rather than repressed, the principle of militarism. I wonder if it is possible that you may be a little bit "on the defensive." If so, maybe you do not realize adequately the urgent need for practical help in the life of the busy practitioner. Also, you may not be aware that many a family physician does appreciate the efficacy derivable from his own self-insight. Nevertheless, before you spin out further your theory of the practicality of insight, I would benefit greatly from your illustrating its usefulness. Show me how your self-vision works for you.

Author. Fair enough. To this end may I seek my practical help through (my) your raising questions which seem to you to have the most practical import. Any question which you ask yourself, I will ask myself and then see what answer I find. I suppose that way of speaking, my idiom which is regardful of the inviolable integrity of individuality, already seems confusing to you, and I certainly am not inclined to expect it to be understandable to anyone but myself.

General Practitioner. That is just what I hoped you would say. I do appreciate your helpful civility, but please get down to cases now. How does your insight help you treat an overtalkative, or a silent, patient, each of whom uses up both valuable time and patience?

Author. Well, when I ask myself that question, I find a very interesting reply. In the first place, *self-insight is based entirely upon self-tolerance.* To the extent that I can tolerate the mental tensions associated with my living my overtalkative, or silent, patient as my own living, I am more insightful (and comfortable) in my work than I could possibly be otherwise. I have found either overtalkativeness, or "obstinate silence," to be a most frequent expression of a hurt mind. I see that my patient's volubility is his effort to recover his mental equilibrium, by getting a "distance perspective" on what is troubling him. He can release painful tension by being able to talk about his difficulty, or just about any subject, with excessive fluency. The insight that my patient *is helping himself specifically* in his talkativeness provides me with a health perspective of the most practical kind. Thus, I see his using up "both valuable time and patience" as legitimate medical work. I observe how I can extend my medical use of auscultation to include observing carefully my patient's talking to himself or attending considerately to his reticence. Exactly to the extent that I can see my silent patient as helping himself by means of his reserve (for instance, by sparing himself further feelings of rejection) I can medically justify my respecting his temporary need to be mute. Thus, I enable myself to proceed with each of my patients in the kindest medical way, without annoyance and impatience.

On the other hand, if I lack such extension of my self-insight, I find the kind and considerate conduct of myself in either case to be an impossibility. Then, the most I can well undertake is to refer each patient to a physician who has specialized in the development of the kind and degree of self-tolerance requisite for being helpful as far as his talkative, or mute, patient is concerned. *Each patient needs to grow to approve of his efforts at self-help.* He can grow his ability to listen to his talking.

General Practitioner. How is your insight practical in taking care of a patient who is more or less out of his mind with jealousy?

Author. I am glad to pose this question to myself. "Out of his mind," is the answer inherent in this question. My ability to live tolerantly my own ideas and feelings of jealousy is a practical prerequisite here. To the extent that I have developed my self-tolerance specifically in the direction of living my jealousy harmoniously,—just to that extent can this practical insight be helpful to me in recognizing the self-rejection meaning of my patient's symptomatic (painful) jealousy. Without the practical insight that my jealousy betokens a restricted awareness of my own self-possession, I find the living of my "jealous patient" unbearably distressing for me.

General Practitioner. What do you mean by "restricted awareness of my own self-possession"? How "on earth," or "in me" (as you prefer it), can that make me jealous?

Author. All that I can *see* that I live enjoys a certain sameness, a love-of-life, feeling. My right hand is not jealous of my left, my right side is not jealous of my left. When I can tolerate the truth that my rival is a creation of my own mind I thereby work up that much conscious mental integration and its sane sense of self-possession. I can then trace my "insane jealousy" to the fact that I had been restricting the zone of my conscious sensing of self-love. My jealousy was the painful sign that I was living my rival as if he could be out of my mind. Furthermore, jealousy implies that "rivalry" ought not to be, and thus obstructs purposeful constructive work on painful problems arising from indulgence of the illusion of rivalry. If my loved one *is* helping himself (or herself) with infidelity,—that is his (or her) problem *only,* and I help myself by realizing that truth.

General Practitioner. Do you mean that I have to learn to use my feeling of jealousy as a signal that I am outraging my own love of life, and then proceed constructively to relieve myself of my own hate and fear, which acted involuntarily when I attributed them to *my* rival? How can that prevent my rival from stealing my property? I suppose you see all of your property as always yours.

Author. All true, as I see it. However, if anything can prevent my suffering the sense of loss of love it is my sane use of my feeling of jealousy. My beloved can only live gratefully my consciously self-contained use of my jealousy; or feel his, or her, freedom threatened by my claim that he, or she, can make me jealous or make me sure of myself.

General Practitioner. How is your insight practical in the therapy of a suspicious patient? Please be brief.

Author. Again, the development of my self-tolerance (to be able to live my own thoughts and feelings of being persecuted as nothing but signs that I am not recognizing that I am both the "persecutor" and the "persecuted") enables me to see the self-rejection meaning of my patient's symptomatic self-distrust. On the other hand, if I have not achieved such self-tolerance, I cannot comfortably endure my living of my "suspicious patient," for it rubs on a sore spot of my own.

General Practitioner. Some of this self-tolerance you imply you have worked up for yourself does not seem easy. How did you do it?

Author. I did it by taking on life experience which required my enduring my feelings of (self-) intolerance. Tolerance is a form of patience. I had to *suffer* my feeling of intolerance before I could achieve endurance of it with an easy mind. After all, it was an exercise in lifting my own mental weight; and, as in the case of the weight lifter, I gradually came to enjoy the exercise. The extension of self-tolerance is successful living, not resignation.

General Practitioner. I always thought tolerance was defined as the absence of intolerance, but now I can see that there can be no real tolerance where there is nothing to tolerate. If I *take the trouble* to talk with you further, will that kind of ordeal increase my self-tolerance?

Author. I can speak only for and to myself, but when I ask myself that question I find this answer: Certainly, and specifically to the extent (my) you undergo the "growing pains" from stretching your consciousness to comprehend new reaches of your selfness first associated with intolerance.

General Practitioner. What do you do for a constantly complaining patient, especially for one who shows no real structural pathology? How does your insight show itself as practical there? I know you have already answered this question partly.

Author. First I had to learn that my own complaining is only notifying myself that I need to live myself with additional wisdom. I have discovered that I never complain about any of my living which I can see clearly *is* my own living. I may grievously burden myself with (illusional) self-rejection; but, if I have grown the insight that my life is all my own, I do not use my energy up in complaining. Rather I apply all of my available energy to the process of my restoring my appropriate balance of health. My realization that my patient's complaints are traceable to his lack of the insight that he is the sole originator of his distress is of the most practical help in my treating my "hypochondriacal patient" with the kindest understanding.

General Practitioner. I am beginning to realize that the hardest part of a physician's life is the consequence of any limitation in his ability to tolerate signs and symptoms of illness, specifically in their (for him) un-understandable expressions. A young physician may not be too observant of his patient's necessity and right to practice his own health measures when they appear as "signs" and "symptoms" and are called "disease."

Author. This view which (my) you have just expressed has helped me most in my living of my "therapeutic ambitions." I have found that, for me, therapeutic ambition is wholesomely lived, only by my being ambitious in living myself so that I can grow further understanding, based on my growing *additional* self-tolerance. Even any hortatory note in what I say is not consciously intended, and is applicable to myself only.

General Practitioner. I do not see clearly what you have in mind by this last statement. Will you illustrate it?

Author. I am glad for the opportunity. I encourage myself basically by first acknowledging the excellence of my present achievement. For instance, when I have the attitude that I am annoyed with my patient, with his apparent inability to improve his self-living, certainly my feeling of annoyance is a most helpful one; for it indicates to me the present limit of my tolerance, of my need to grow further insight. The annoyance saves me from further overwhelming myself, and all I need to do is to place it where it belongs, at the place of my demanding the impossible. It pays me to be annoyed with myself when I find myself exasperated if my patient is unable to live more healthfully than he can. If I feel indignant "with my patient," it helps me to be able to see that my anger with myself is justified if I can direct it accurately at my blindness in requiring my patient to behave in some other way than he can. In other words, any painful way of living myself, such as hatred, anger, shame, distrust, scorn, disgust, and so on, is helpful if I can localize the true source of the pain as being *at the boundary of my own limited self-tolerance,* and as saying to and for me, "Beyond this present limit you lose your presence of mind and fall back upon unconscious, involuntary, irresponsible behavior."

General Practitioner. I notice you do not mention the difficult feeling of grief or mourning. Where is your insight practical in the living of that?

Author. I pardon my oversights. I do have to watch my tendency to avoid hard psychological work. It is understandable if I overlook depression when I realize the extreme painfulness of feelings of unhappiness having to do with a sense of loss. Intense feelings associated with bereavement are most helpful efforts on the mourner's part to recover from his illusion of separation, which is the natural consequence of his illusion that he was ever joined with another. That which human nature puts asunder no man can join together. My insight is most practical which permits me to see that all of my personal experience lives as long as I live; that my only *real* loved one of my life lives on as an integral part of me as long as I live; that my sense of loss may therefore be mostly an illusion. How beautifully Emily Dickinson treated her renunciation of her loved one at first, honoring herself with the Little Empress of Calvary. Later she helped herself with the realization that absence is condensed presence, to the faithful.

My mourning work is my effort to recover my awareness of the truth of my allness, after I have indulged a lack of insight about it, after I have indulged the living of my loved one "as if" such living were not entirely my own. This practical insight enables my prolonged working with my depressed patient with greatest kindness.

General Practitioner. I imagine that the alarming habit of overlooking the reality of livingness accounts for the education movement aiming at appreciation of individuality, such as Existentialism. Some of this is very new living of experience for me, and I can see where I can help myself by growing more of my self-insight as a highly practical medical tool. I am trying to realize that all of your motifs are founded in your view of your life. Please, in your further answers try to be as realistic as possible. How is your insight practical in treating an hallucinating patient?

Author. Always it is my own ability to live comfortably whatever I experience, which is helpful. That which I cannot see is myself I cannot understand, and that which I cannot understand limits my view of my truth. "Objectification" is a synonym for lack of self-insight. My hallucinating patient is temporarily helping himself quite as a hungry baby may hallucinate sucking his mother's breast in her absence.[1] My awareness of being able to sense my identity in my "hallucinating" patient puts me at my ease, and spares me feelings of "alienation" or "strangeness." In 1909, at Clark University, Freud justified research into dreams by the indispensable information it gives on all mental disturbance,

> You should bear in mind that the dreams which we produce at night have, on the one hand, the greatest external similarity and internal kinship with the creations of insanity, and are, on the other hand, compatible with complete health in waking life. There is nothing paradoxical in the assertion that no one who regards these "normal" illusions, delusions and character-changes with astonishment instead of comprehension has the slightest prospect of understanding the abnormal structures of pathological mental states otherwise than as a layman. You may comfortably count almost all psychiatrists among such laymen.[2]

Certainly I am aware of "visions" and of "hearing voices" in my dream life. Furthermore, to the extent that I regard my waking perception, itself, as having to do with anything but my own life, —just to that extent do I sense myself living my sensation, or perception, as an illusion.

Please note that I regard every "psychopathological" manifestation of my patient as therapeutic, as his best current means of helping himself. This practical view permits me to appreciate the truth that my patient is continuing his self-helpfulness even in his extremity.

General Practitioner. How is your practical insight useful in curing a delinquent? Surely you do not conceive yourself to be a delinquent, or do you?

Author. Yes. Delinquency, and every kind of crime, I must be able to conceive myself as able to perpetrate, if I would live my delinquent-experience insightfully.

General Practitioner. I have always considered crime to be something objectionable, something to have nothing to do with, if possible.

Author. Yes, many a person helps himself that way. A physician, however, has no choice other than to work with his fellowman whose current idea of helping himself involves his breaking the law. A view of life does restrict itself to an individual's concrete existence. To be profoundly helpful an ideal must decide the conduct of life. A delinquent is not a delinquent in his ideal way of trying to help himself: he believes that one part of himself can gain from the loss of, and to, another part of himself. As soon as he sees that fallacy underlying his moral obliquity he renounces it. One idea is most practical: that he satisfy himself by attaining his solution within himself.[3]

I have found that whenever my "delinquent-patient" discovers the strictly limited helpfulness of his delinquency, and notices that his "ill manners" are helpful symptoms of most distressful self-rejection, then invariably he becomes able to renounce his needs to be "delinquent." Once he sees clearly that he is both the perpetrator and victim of his crimes he promptly begins to "turn over a new leaf." As he realizes his delinquency is too limited in its self-helpfulness, he develops the power to renounce it. Without this practical insight, that every delinquent is trying to help himself by his delinquency (without realizing the limitations of such short-sighted self-care), all I can do is live my delinquent-experience unkindly, as it were, "jumping on one when he is down."

General Practitioner. From all of my trying to see what "insightful living" means I am enjoying a self-arousal and am beginning to discern more clearly that I have been calling practical a "common sense" philosophy, instead of seeing as practical an *insightful* psychology. According to you, the trouble with "common sense" is that it implies my acceptance of authority other than that which I can see as my own; whereas self-insight respects the truth of my being the author of my own helpfulness. As the Buddha, you say to yourself, "Work out your own salvation with diligence." Didn't Nietzsche say, "Be a man and do not follow me —follow yourself"?

Author. Exactly. A necessary compensation for my undeveloped self-insight is my illusion that I can have some living "in common" with a life other than my own. The truth is, I can never experience any living, including any meaning, except my own. Where is there allowance for "common sense agreement" in the exclusive oneness of individuality? My every instance of relying on a "somebody else's" opinion, or perception, or sensation, or whatever, must be only my "cover up" for my self-distrust (and self-trust too).

I view it as mind-strengthening for me to have my fellowman report his findings, with my realizing that the entire performance is nothing except my living of it,—fellowman, findings, report, and all. True language of life is *always* a monolog. All that I verbalize is naming what I am.

A possible accuracy in the claim of "common sense" would be that implicit in the truth that all of my world, my world in common, has its manifold source and terminus in my living of it, —and that kind of "common sense" would be the same as self-insight. The view approximates Dostoevski's claim, "Why, suffering is the sole origin of consciousness" (*Notes from Underground*).

General Practitioner. Can it be that your way of speaking seems too enthusiastic, almost lyrical, at times? Perhaps for you it is vim, vigor, and vivacity. For me it is too much of irrepressible optimism. Maybe now you are considering *your* you as repressed, while I am considering *my* you as irrepressible. How about that?

Author. I may well ask myself, is my heart-gladdening, life-affirming proposition a product of an excessive euphoria? When I do examine the wonderfulness of (my) human life, my appreciation is correspondingly pleasureful, so that I seem to sing with it. I often remind myself of Dr. Oliver Wendell Holmes' verses:

> Alas for those that never sing
> But die with all their music in them!

I have found that I live myself unhappily only to the extent that I cannot recognize my living as all my own. I see the direct correlation of (1) my denying that any of my own living is entirely my own personal experience, and (2) my inability to appreciate the true extent of my own greatness. A basic health axiom is contained in this truth: *I cannot even be interested in taking care of my health except to the extent that I can prize, hence cherish, how wonderful it is for me to be alive.* It follows that for me to "think the world (my world) of myself" does me "a world of good."

General Practitioner. Apparently you do not believe that your seeing all of your world's suffering as your own would lead you to a lifetime of agonizing.

Author. I have discovered that every "accident," "illness," "evil," and each such unhappy living, is indispensable as a guide to my living myself happily. As well wish to get rid of my air since I cannot support my weight and swim in it, or annihilate my capacity to feel since it can make me feel uncomfortable, as seek to rid myself of my life-saving ability to feel unhappy. I find that my every life circumstance of unhappiness contains in it: (1) the clue to the source of my unhappiness as being in my way of life and (2) the direction I must go in, if I would be happy.

General Practitioner. Do you mean that by fully recognizing the fact that "health ordeal" (as you prefer to designate illness and accident) is not an attack of a foreign power, but *is* a human condition of mine, of my own personal making,—I can heal and strengthen myself best? Do you mean that I must see my responsibility for making health trouble for myself in order to be able to see that I can also find my way back to healthiest living? Do you mean that my mental attitude toward my illness, or accident, delays healing of it if it denies my responsibility for it, and furthers healing to the extent that it assumes entire responsibility for that illness, or accident?

Author. To each of these profound health inquiries, all I can answer is: *Yes,* that is exactly what I mean *about my life.* Pain is as beneficial as is pleasure for wise self-culture. Full "recovery" from a life ordeal leaves the sufferer consciously stronger-minded than ever before. Self-endurance, thus developed, is the foundation of growing self-tolerance, of known self-appreciation. The greater the self-endurance, the less capricious is the use of will power. And everyone tends to identify himself with that power which he calls his "will." As you have stated, it is this consciously self-based and willingly unfolding human nature which Goethe exalted as "a mortal's highest bliss." What excludes human nature cannot be a subject of human nature. Rainer Maria Rilke eternalized this view, "Nowhere, beloved, is there any world but that within." A human existence is essentially a world-being-in-the-individual.

As a practicing physician I must renounce the wings of Icarus. Stephen Paget said well,

> Practice is the solvent of all such wings: for it is the man himself, the skill of his hands, the judgment of his reason on the expert evidence of his senses, the quick selection and watchful use of the right set of facts. It cannot be taken over like a theatre-ticket or a share in railway. Name, influence, privilege, succession, are what we make them.

General Practitioner. Please explain your statement that pain contributes to wise self-culture.

Author. An understanding perspective of greatest significance with regard to my every unpleasant feeling stresses the precious benefit conferred by it. Since every dislike of mine is of life-saving significance, it is essential for my welfare that I learn how to *live consciously* each of my unpleasant feelings as being my only way of attesting my love for each of them. Obviously I cannot love any of my unhappiness without living it consciously. That observation applies to every unpleasant affect (emotion), as to all else I live. Only my living of whatever, can constitute my loving it. To illustrate: Only by *being* consciously depressed can I show myself my devotion to my depression. Talk about depression cannot displace the fact of depression here.

I need to practice consciously this orientation for my unpleasant feelings, since I have a natural tendency to try to avoid being aware of each one of them, to try to escape living it consciously. Thus, I demonstrate my unwillingness to show my love for the unpleasantness, since that can be demonstrated only by my willingly living it. This *practical* fact can escape observation easily, for

I am never aware of loving my unpleasant affect at the time I am consciously living it. Quite the contrary. For example, while aware of living my depression I deceive myself to believe that I am not loving it. From habit of seeking pleasure and avoiding pain I tend to speak of "suffering" depression, or jealousy, or disgust, or shame, or fear, or hate, and so on, while "enduring" the living (loving) of such unpleasantness. Thus, I conceal from myself the fact that it is impossible for me to live lovingly any unpleasant affect except by consciously living it fully, except by "touching bottom" in my living of it.

I go on living each of my unpleasant feelings which I cannot esteem as precious for preserving my life, but mostly unconsciously. Sometimes I live it completely unconsciously, so that I can deny that I am even living any feeling of depression, hate, jealousy, fear, and so on.

General Practitioner. Well, why not use my mind's capacity to "go unconscious" in order to avoid, at least, being aware of any unpleasantness I occasion for myself? Why not deny to myself that I am unhappy, even if I do feel heartbroken?

Author. I have found that negation does not constitute riddance. Such rejection of my unhappy living can succeed in alienating it from my conscious living, but that denial constitutes a dangerous disregard for the evidence of my own senses. When I prevent myself from being aware of my unhappiness, I can live my happiness consciously only on account of my not letting myself be aware that I care with respect to my unhappy living ("manic denial"). Furthermore my constantly pressed-out-of-consciousness mental content exerts a counter-pressure, and thus often succeeds in expressing itself in my obsessive and compulsive (only seemingly foreign to my nature) mental activity.

My conscious prohibition of awareness of unpleasantness creates an emphasis upon the unconscious use of the unpleasant affect in question. I then express it in compensatory physiological tensions and similar stresses in my human economy ("strangulated affect," "affect equivalent," "somatization"), each of which signalizes the benefit to me in my trying to live it consciously.[4]

General Practitioner. According to that view I can help myself immeasurably by learning to live lovingly (fully consciously) my every possible feeling of unpleasantness, for it is always counselling me carefully and caringly. I am beginning to see already that I am helping myself very greatly on two counts, whenever I can let myself be aware that I am living any unpleasant feeling: (1) I am cultivating my capacity to love it, and (2) I can use it as a guideline for modifying the conduct of my life and thus for relieving myself of the need for activating this warning signal.

Author. Yes. Again it is practical to make the point that consciousness for any living is not the source of any mental difficulty, or trouble.

General Practitioner. Briefly state your view of the healing force of self-consciousness.

Author. He does the most good who sees the most good. He sees the most clearly, who sights his life only. Allness-wholeness-oneness, love it. Life has nothing to live but it.

11

Developmental Psychology

Only life teaches every one what he is.
GOETHE

GENERAL PRACTITIONER. THE infant is father of the child; the child is father of the adult. A complete history of anyone is a complete explanation of that one. Can you give a brief account of how anyone became the way he is? Is that not what you mean by "developmental psychology"?

Author. The study of developmental psychology explains how a person develops as a unique individual. It is an account of an individual life which is most sensitive to being cared for, most perceptive of self-appreciation, most dependent upon the wonderful sense of self-esteem commensurate with the wonderfulness of human life. The study of infant psychology reveals an amazing account of most helpful self-growth. A careful investigator of this period of life will forever renounce every notion that the infant is not a hard-working and self-helpful complete individual.

From the moment that the infant begins to conceive his power source in that part of his life which he calls his "mother," he begins to recognize his need to live himself in such a way as to make the mother-part of himself happy. To this end he finds it necessary to ignore, slight, and even repudiate (to himself) much of his living which is entirely natural and essential for providing him with a comprehensive measure of his self-worth. Every human being's psychogenesis is characterized by that one's own particular developmental unfolding, arrest, fixation, primitivization, and deviation, with regard to every possible direction of his living his being. Any element of personal living which the growing one cannot prize as precious, *properly* contributes to that individual's most painful sense of self-disesteem. "Properly," since that disesteem feeling is an indispensable sign to the individual concerned that he is not living with sufficient kindness any element of his life which he designates as "not-I." All of any individual's mental disturbance is traceable to this slighting of elements of himself. His growing the mental strength to live all of himself humanely *is* the harmonizing process of psychotherapy.

General Practitioner. Are you one of those persons who does not believe in sickness or death or sin? Please speak your mind on the subject of sin, including evil.

Author. I have helped myself most by working up, and I do mean *working,* the same kind of appreciation of sin that I have for signs and symptoms of those noble heroic health struggles called "sickness."[1] Sin offers the same kind of helpfulness for the worker of religion that symptoms of physiological stress offer for the man of medicine. I see sin as the indispensable handmaiden of virtue, or accurately, as unrecognized virtue. Virtuousness is nourished and vitalized through the renunciation of sin. I do not regard sin as a lack of holiness but rather as an ordeal of holiness. I have found the problem of evil, likewise, to be a phantom problem. I see theological discipline as educational experience concentrating upon the divinity of man in his every way of trying to find his life worth living.

Once I see the happiness of *the truth of my living, my only matter of fact,* I attain the position of recognizing that all of my enlightenment can be nothing but enlightenment of my selfhood. I then see that my every definition simply renders discrete elements of my own living, that all of my religious interest is nothing but self-interest, that I mislead myself in any of my living in which my self-consciousness is left out, that none of my living can be inhuman although my most costly self-deception is my ability to live *as if* I were not all human. The function of my self-consciousness is the function of my supreme organ of truth.

Self-heal is all that is possible. As Terence reported, "It is easy when we are well to give good advice to the sick." No man can have control over any other man or thing, despite all appearances to the contrary. My deceptive use of my words, in every instance enabled by my ignoration of the fact that every word was a living element of my human being and nothing else, led me to greater and greater restriction in my appreciation of myself. My James Bryant Conant noted, "Some of mankind's most terrible misdeeds have been committed under the spell of certain magic words or phrases." For instance: Who is willing to see the exceedingly limited respect for human individuality barely concealed in the following statements intended to revere it? "The most conspicuous evidence of the moral height of any community is the value it sets on human individuality," or "The moral height of any society is demonstrated by its reluctance to sacrifice its least worthy member." Every practitioner is alerting himself nowadays to the ever present threat of an iatrogenic factor in every "illness." No physician, who sees clearly he is a self-made physician, will attempt to make anyone else "well."

My ability to see the meaning of all of my experience as nothing but the working of my own mind was obstructed mostly by my using words in a way which concealed from me the allness of the world of my mind. Thus I developed the idea that there could be something or other which is beyond my reach, some living beyond my ability to live. My increasing vision of myself as an individual, in the sense that my Protagoras defined individual man as the "measure of all things," gradually disclosed my energies as my own and revealed me to myself as the only possible territory of the estimable or measurable. With many a helpful exacerbation and remission I have been gradually extending my sense of my identity by living self-consciously.

I am coming to recognize my sensations, perceptions, and observations of every kind, as nothing but my own examined life. I gladly take notice that my fellowman who can recognize individuality most comprehensively, enjoys the sanest mind. However, it is necessary for me to recognize my own capacity for power, before I am able to attribute this kind of capacity to my fellowman. My greatest joy in living is found specifically in extending my self-view to include new self-awareness. I find my only test of truth in every matter of practice to be: Am I aware that my only truth is truth of me?

Psychologist. I suppose that what I have to say will make you think I am trying to run away from myself. I realize that you regard disputation as illusional since each disputant can be only talking about and to himself. I read once in Lessing: "The dispute has nourished the spirit of examination." However that may be, the fact remains that you have me upset. Please forgive me any asperity in my personal remarks. You can see it all as my "growing pain," possibly.

I feel most intensely on this one subject of what is personal and what is not. Your declared self-centeredness strictly limits the value of every observation you make. Your admitted preoccupation with yourself conventionally signifies disregard for everyone else. You assume a staggering self-importance. Your system of psychology is nothing but self-scrutiny. You assert there is no other direction to look but inward, that every kind of inspection is either evident or disguised introspection. Almost your every sentence is so pointedly personal, subjective, and egoistic that it is worthless for general application. If you are claiming anything scientific about your work, I do not see how one statement you have made can be used to prove anything except that you felt it worthwhile to make it. You have set yourself the task of recording your discoveries about the nature of mental health,—then it turns out you meant only *your* mental health. You implied that such talk is enlightening for understanding human nature; then it turns out you meant only your understanding of your human nature. I seek to respect my fellowman as if he is no part of me, no autobiological experience of mine. I aim to recognize him as an independent individual, not just as a character in my life's story. Are you not trying to remake psychology in terms of your own mind's necessities? All that you have spoken thus far proves nothing about your subject of psychological hygiene, only something about you.

Author. How very true. It is my intention that my listener not lose sight of his author, of his all-subsuming individuality, of his finding that all meaning is self-meaning and all consciousness self-consciousness. Of such individuality observation *is* my psychological hygiene. I have set myself to the one task which concerns the one thing needful, my addressing myself to the question-answer: What does it mean to be an individual?

Psychologist. There you go again. What do you mean by "question-answer"?

Author. My meaning is: Every question is its unrecognized answer.

General Practitioner. Your medical desideratum, that everyone shall become conscious of himself and thereby know *his* medical activity for his own living which it actually is,—that prescription is entirely too hard to fill. Have you no more practical means of purification and relief of human life? I realize that every theory and practice must rest upon life, or being, itself. I realize that my life is all and only about me,—that I am the perceiver, the perception, and the perceptible. When I stop to examine the matter, I realize that my claiming to have any identity with my mother or father even, other than that which I create of myself, would imply that much destruction of either whole being. On second thought, I am usually able to sense with certainty that I am entirely homogeneous as an individual, and am made up entirely of my own life's existence. But you imply a practical advantage in steadily practicing this insightful living. Am I right?

Author. As I find it, harmonious living is consciously cultivated living. In the sense that I live my life, I create my own existence. My own living of myself makes me the author of my being. My continuing my life entails my growing of myself only. I began my costly illusion of myself as "separate" from "all else," when I first started cultivating my not-I illusions.

General Practitioner. For your purpose (calling attention to the allness of human individuality) it is enough to localize consciousness in the individual human being only.

Author. Yes. Samuel Thomas von Soemmerring was the pupil of John Hunter who enumerated and named the cranial nerves. In his book on the soul, dedicated to Immanuel Kant, he tried to prove that consciousness resides in the cerebrospinal fluid. Goethe chided him for tainting the waters of science with metaphysics.

Psychologist. Please draw the line between normal and abnormal.

Author. Whatever is, is normal, and is seen clearly only in being considered normal. The word "abnormal" would introduce the idea of dichotomy where there is none. Much of conventional language simply lifts confused thinking to the linguistic level.

Psychologist. I find you imaginative and operose, if not repetitious. Constant drill upon the allness of individuality can become annoying. It really must take tremendous self-love for you to be able to stick to that one idea as you do.

Author. But that one idea is all that is needed, as I see it. For me to "change the subject" (from me to not-me) in order to provide distraction would get me needlessly involved. Also, in every instance of my feeling bored I find that I have displaced my sense of monotony from the content of repetition to its form. Self-consciousness being the breath of mental health for me, I do not find breathing monotonous although it may seem repetitious. The Arab has many words for lion as has the Eskimo for snow.

Whether or not my growth is conscious self-growth is a matter of greatest moment, *for it is only the self-growth of which I am conscious which provides my volitional activity. Furthermore, my unconscious self-growth provides my involuntary activity.* Although all of my involuntary activity is made up entirely of my own selfness, I must live it as if it is out of my own control. The more conscious my self-growth is, the more I can recognize myself as a free self. Let who will of my world attempt "objectivity"; I see no possibility other than to stew or star, glory or groan, in my own juice.

By cultivating my exercise of consciousness I do not lose the liver in the lived, the creator in the created, the perceiver in the perceived. There is nothing dark about self-conscious living. My cultivation of my use of my consciousness has been most practical of all, clarifying for me the truth that all of my meaningfulness experience has been mental experience. The fundamental *practical* fact of all of my experience is that *I live* it.

The basic identity underlying every difference is the sameness provided by my own living of each different. My own human being is my only dependable practical reference. My most self-conscious living is my most highly *practical* living. Every practical discovery is essentially nothing but human living. My most self-conscious self is my most sophisticated self.

Psychologist. Are you not unconsciously boasting of how able, or insightful, or superior in some way, you think you are?

Author. Asking myself that question gives rise to another question, How can I boast to anyone but my own self?

Psychologist. Boasting is boasting. Are you not exercising your vanity, even if your appreciative fellowman is your own creation?

Author. My fellowman must live all of his own meaning and feeling of boasting.

Psychologist. You have revised the popular view of self too radically for me, right now at least. I suppose you see Solomon's wisdom, "All is vanity," as simply remarking necessary love of life.

Author. That may well be. Seeing all of one's self as adorable solves the problem of vanity.

If I ask myself what is true, what is real, what is actual, all that I can discover is that it is something which I must live. If I ask myself what is false, what is illusion, what is deception, again all I can discover is that it is something which I must live. A true illusion is just as much a mental fact as is a true truth. The only possibly correct explanation of either one is that each is a way in which I can live my mind. By living my sensation or my perception I may experience a uniquely keen sense of living myself, but it is nevertheless myself that I live. However, I may live myself on this sense level as a matter of habit without making myself conscious that all of such living is necessarily my own. "How can I call any halt on living me, in any way at all, except by ending my life?" is a helpful reminder. Self-unconsciousness here is the beginning of every kind of self-deception, making way for the philosophy without the philosopher, the psychology without the psychologist, education without the educator, and so on and on. Anyone who has ever dreamed a dream of any substance whatsoever can hardly question that "matter" is in every respect a mental construct.

The materializations and personifications of my mind are innumerable. Lucky for me if I can see myself in them. For instance, my word "people" embodies each of my hardly beloved vices: personification and plurality. I go on using the word to cover up my stretching lapse in devotion to my meaning of *individuality,* cringing at my Ludwig Wittgenstein's famous thrust: "The meaning is the use." How consistently I mistake partition for plurality.

Every one of my feelings also is lived only and entirely within myself. However, frequently I live myself *as if* I am capable of actually experiencing feeling in my "other one." For instance: I may say to myself, "He is angry," or, "She is unkind." Again, lucky for me if I am able to see that the "anger" or the "unkindness" or any other feeling which I attribute to my "other one" is a very precious feeling which I am needing, as a sign that I am not realizing that my "other one" is my own living. It pays me to have the painful feeling of anger, if I am not living my "other one" consciously as my own; it pays me to feel unkind whenever I am not living my "other one" as entirely my own living. Similarly it pays me to be able to feel scorn, guilt, shame, jealousy, and every other psychic pain as an invaluable sign to myself that I am living my "other one" without full appreciation that it is only my own living which can create my "other one."

Psychologist. I observe that every parent has his own ideas of training and discipline, so that, no matter how I prescribe "kindness in following each child's developmental functions and interests," every parent seems to do as he pleases about the most important living of all, his child's developing mind. I would find it practically helpful if you would state clearly your prescriptions for training, discipline, and punishment.

Author. An opportune inquiry, since my "developmental psychology," as a "discipline," concerns itself entirely with the force of self-cultivation. "Training" is a term which, for me, implies the idea of "externally" enforced shaping of the mind.[2] It is used to describe insightless educational work as it happens sometimes with the animal who is "broken" rather than "gentled" into desirable performance; therefore, I tend to renounce the use of this term for describing a child's educating himself. I renounce all such notions usually indicated by "sphincter training," "toilet training," "training to cleanliness," and so on, as implying the growing infant's compliance through his using repression of his spontaneity.

Pediatrician. A frequently recurring problem in my practice is a parent's puzzlement on what to do about her child's masturbation. I have to work with innumerable instances of anxiety about that. Surely it is a growing child's right and necessity to discover his, or her, genitals as a source of pleasure, but I find many a parent terribly upset when it happens. Of course that kind of prohibiting parent simply succeeds in emphasizing what he, or she, wishes to have his child learn to control. Please think aloud on this delicate and far-reaching subject?

Author. With such a sensible introduction I find it simple to go on, along my own course of sanity, namely, my realizing that a parent can be anxious and puzzled only about his own masturbation right and necessity. As a parent observes his or her child interested in genital pleasure, that experience tests that parent's readiness to live the same kind of activity and reveals whether that parent solved his, or her, masturbation interests through repressing or renouncing them.

Pediatrician. By "repression" you mean: denying the propriety of the existence of certain personal living. And by "renunciation" you mean: fully acknowledging the wonderfulness of that certain personal living and freely allowing, or restraining, one's indulging it. "Repression" seems to solve the problem at once but really complicates it. "Renunciation" takes a longer time, but really accomplishes the desired *self-control.* Am I right so far?

Author. So it appears to me.

Pediatrician. Am I correct in my opinions that it is very important for a growing youngster, boy and girl, *to be able to masturbate,* without associating this precious living with fear or guilt or shame, or any other unpleasantness; and that the individual's success in accomplishing this specific mental freedom with humane dignity, has profound meaning of healthfulness throughout his adult life; and that a parent's objection to seeing her child masturbate attests (1) she cannot imagine her own masturbating as desirably helpful and (2) she has repressed, not renounced, her own ability to masturbate?

Author. In my opinion, repression of masturbation, including repression of orgasm, represents a grievous inhibition of one's sexual development which has far-reaching meaning for producing personal problems of inadequacy, dependence, insecurity, hostility, and distrust. Insightful mental developments are indicated as the ideal treatment for such repression.

Pediatrician. It is clear that you do not think that consciously willed masturbation produces mental trouble, or some kind of harm.

Author. Most certainly not. Of course I wish to be able to "think" anything. However, I regard masturbation helpful in the same sense that *I consider every act of a human being always to be his way of helping himself.*

Pediatrician. Do you recommend that your patient learn to masturbate?

Author. Every decision is a personal one which each individual must make for himself, entirely under his own conscious will. I can make a recommendation for or against any living, only to myself.

Pediatrician. Since masturbation has, in my opinion, been a subject of superstition and prudishness, and since it is so very meaningful for the wholesome growth of individuality, might it not be well for the medical student to study all about it? Understanding it would contribute to everyone's peaceful home-living.

Author. When enough insight is available for this kind of study, no doubt it will be included in the medical curriculum. My parent's ability to imagine masturbation as desirably helpful living is an accomplishment based upon his (her) self-insight.

Pediatrician. Is there any danger that masturbation will be so satisfying that it will preclude desire for sexual intercourse?

Author. None at all. Such apprehensiveness may be associated with the objector's need to repress (objectize and thus reject as unworthy of one's self) his sexuality. I doubt if anyone who is psychologically enlightened today regards masturbation as anything but a desirable human development. Successful sexual intercourse is based upon successful masturbation. However this particular kind of enlightenment is resisted by anyone who "learned from" his beloved parent that masturbation would "produce weak mindedness, or insanity, or impotence," and so on.

Pediatrician. Why would masturbation not be of sufficient gratification as to prevent the development of preference for sexual intercourse?

Author. Simply on account of the fact that masturbation itself is intrinsically inadequate biologically for providing complete sexual satisfaction in the adult person. The masturbation phantasies (of "using" a partner) attest this truth. The individual's experience, particularly early in adolescence, teaches him that his masturbation may be his necessary means of asserting his mastery over his sexual demands pending his maturing to the level of, and desirable occasion for, sexual intercourse. Both as a little child and an adolescent, as throughout life, the individual is exquisitely sensitive upon any matter involving his sense of self-esteem, and inordinate masturbation (that is, masturbation out of his control) is readily renounced by him as being incompatible with his sense of due self-respect.

Pediatrician. There! you have hit upon the basis of the reasonableness of masturbation. Its function is more than just that of temporarily producing pleasure. Its essential function is that of permitting the individual to control the excessive and tormenting sexual demands of his sexual living when necessary. Thus his self-respect is maintained and he avoids a kind of tail-wagging-the-dog existence.

Author. The attainment of sex control is basic for the attainment of self-control in general. What I repress is beyond my conscious self-control. In 1909 Freud observed that the "power of wishful impulse, when once its repression has failed, is far stronger if it is unconscious than if it is conscious; so that to make it conscious can only be to weaken it."

Pediatrician. I find that nearly every parent is willing to have his child repress, rather than renounce, his genital and pregenital interests. Your attitude regarding masturbation is far more one of appreciation than any I have found, but then you seem to appreciate everything that a human being does in his effort to help himself enjoy his life. You are enthusiastic about a child's discovering his, or her, sexual feelings and learning to create them and experience them and control them, are you not?

Author. I am. I consider masturbation to be a holy act, a sacred one, expressive of the love of life. Repression of it creates inordinate emphasis of it, but that too is helpful, when it is all that is possible. Everything sexual, as all else, is best treated as a uniquely individual concern.

Pediatrician. You speak peace. A child's sex control, rather than sex repression, is desirable as a conscious goal.

Author. Certainly. It is my regular finding, however, that my fellowman has established not only his pregenital, but also his genital, control, through repression rather than through renunciation. Thus, his every performance of his bowel, bladder, or genital function is no longer just a matter of his conscious free choice, but is also subject to conditions beyond his conscious control. I consider the maintenance of such repression to be at a heavy, but unrecognized, cost of his conscious mental peace, freedom, completeness, and potency.

Pediatrician. What is your view of homosexuality in our culture?

Author. In the sense that each individual is his own everything, weird as this assertion may appear to my repressed fellowman, there is no other kind of sexuality. A new vocabulary must be cultivated to express accurately the conventional meaning of the term "homosexuality," which posits betweenness (plurality).

One's ever present, substantial homosexual component in either female or male sexuality consistently tends to suffer conscious repudiation. As a rule the heterosexual position is attained by way of repression (rather than renunciation) of one's homosexual propensities. Nevertheless, overt and covert homosexuality are of such widespread occurrence that each calls for greatest understanding of its naturalness when it occurs, and appreciation of the efficacy of the orientation of renunciation (rather than repression) concerning its every aspect.

Repudiated (repressed) homosexuality is signalized by innumerable signs and symptoms of unhappiness. Kindly renounced homosexuality, on the other hand, is a solid basis of happy living of one's fellowman.

Pediatrician. "Covert" homosexuality means that it is lived with shame, as if it ought not be. It is essential to be able to see the good in any kind of behavior in order to work upon renouncing it, rather than having to rely upon developing amnesia for it.

Author. Yes. Self-control with regard to his sex life saves a person from compusive sexual living, frigidity, impotence, prudishness, fury, and all of the other kinds of *involuntary* expressions of his sex life.

Pediatrician. If one cannot create pleasure by his own acknowledged use of his own organs, as hands and genitals, how can he or she expect that "somebody else" can do it for him, or her? One does not learn to walk on stilts, or to play the piano with mittens.

Author. All that you are observing indicates to me extraordinary self-control in your use of your mental forces having to do with sex control, and I feel sure that you are capable of understanding and kind identification with each parent who has not yet been able to work through his (or her) persisting early resistances to appreciating his (or her) sexual living.

Pediatrician. How is it possible for a person to recognize that *he* lives all that he means by his "opposite sex," when he has greatly limited understanding and appreciation of his own gender? How can he, or she, enjoy his, or her, marital sexual relations which certainly must remind him, or her, of masturbation, if that masturbation itself was repressed rather than renounced?

Author. Each question, as I ask it of myself, leads me to sober considerations indeed. Happy and healthy is the child who grows each parent as devoted to the truths of conscious individuality and the continuing cultivation of the individual's powers of self-reliance, self-satisfaction, and self-control. Sex is to life somewhat as water is to chemistry,[3] being far too precious and ubiquitous a power to be relegated to unconscious living.

Pediatrician. Another problem in my practice is: What to do about nakedness. Will you discuss that?

Author. I know of no subject with greater ramifications. "Seeing" and "being seen" are most fundamental expressions of living which are closely allied with "touching" and "being touched." Nakedness in home living is wisely conceived as being a most exciting occurrence for every child. Also, unless each parent really enjoys unusual self-control of his sexual living, and therefore can practice insightful living with regard to his child's sexual interests and explorations, it is indicated that he realize that an abundance of the naked truth can overwhelm a parent and that he would do wisely to take on his education to nakedness in graduated degrees. In other words, nudity is not at all something that the child can "take for granted" in the sense of ignoring its wealth of meanings.

This subject of undress is one of such deep personal significance that it is the rare parent who can bring himself to speak with his doctor about it. Yet it is most desirable that the growing individual culivate the self-control to renounce as precious and gratifying this sexual living, rather than to repress it with shame.[4] Each one must and can do this, as all else he does, by himself.

Pediatrician. The development of self-control of one's instinct life resolves itself into a matter of that kind of self-activity you call "education," and it is essential for healthy living that education be lived with love. The parent is wise who sees his task as one of avoiding overwhelming home living of (1) exciting nakedness and (2) frustrating concealment.

Author. Yes, that is as I see it. The all-important one concern is to use every possible safeguard to make sure that, in his developing his mind, one's growing infant and child may be able to see and feel his directives as his own guidance, not as his "other's" goadance. This self-education prescription, which works health wonders for the baby and child, spells out the sovereign truth that all "training" is self-growth. Therefore, the health requirement is that the educator of every age endeavor to recognize that he *is* educating himself. In fact, all so-called "training" not recognizable as self-cultivation to the greater enjoyment of one's own living is to be wisely renounced in the interest of mental development. Only the strongest mind can see this truth, all of it, clearly. Every other mind must resist the view of its absolute efficacy. To describe the various ingenious resistances to this fundamental fact of developmental psychology (that every baby must, and can, develop his own mind by directing his living, by disciplining his life force) would require greatly prolonged discussion.

General Practitioner. How about punishment? How can I explain to one of my parents that the seeming efficacy of hurting a child who has just hurt himself by behaving himself unkindly, can be nothing but a self-gratifying illusion? The child needs to "hurt his brother"; then the parent "needs to hurt" his child.

Author. That is a trying assignment which tests my insight. A child who "behaves himself" on account of "his parent's" displeasure, instead of on account of his own sense of benefit, is shaping his psychic living to function as if he could be "out of his mind." A parent who has grown enough insight to be able to recognize that "misbehavior" *is* a most distressing form of self-disregard (in that it is a symptom of some serious shortcoming of self-development),—that parent will no more punish his child for "misconduct" (self-disregard) than he would attack his hurt child. He will say, "Two wrongs do not make a right."

However, here again my resistances to renouncing my lifelong habits of unconscious self-disregard are very powerful. In my "punishing" my child, without recognizing that I am hurting myself thereby, I can indulge my addiction to living myself unkindly without being conscious for anything but keeping the peace. Meanwhile, my wayward child, recognizing his parent's need to be hostile, treats his punitive parent kindly, so that I then please myself with my illusion that my child's kindness stands for *his* mending *his* ways. When he becomes a parent he shall have grown the pain-indulging personal experience enabling him to be a punitive parent under treatment with his bewildered child. Thus the unpeaceful history of "two wrongs making one right" repeats itself in succeeding generations.

All that *is* practical, or can be practical, in infant and child "guidance," "training," "discipline," "education," or direction of any kind whatsoever, is the "trainee's" preservation of his sanity-saving sense of *originality* in every direction he gives to his life. A wayward child needs *relief* from hurt, not more hurt.

I am most appreciative of living any kind and amount of questioning in this direction of preserving my true self-estimate. Nothing can dim and darken my proper self-appreciation except the way in which I direct my life. Whether I grow myself consciously, or unconsciously, is at stake in every bit of what passes for "training," "education," or "reform." Education is only self-culture.

General Practitioner. I do believe that my child resents punishment, for I resented the little of it I suffered. Should I consider myself as an educator in discussing my patient's punishing his child?

Author. A parent needs to have a physician with whom to counsel about developmental psychology. The most wonderful development which occurred in my work was my appreciation of its true extent, renunciation of my limited view of it. *Recognized* lack of self-awareness is the firm foundation upon which hygienic educational measures can rest. Even the professional educator may express the combative notion, "There are occasions, however rare, when punishment is all that works." As I see it, each such occasion can be only an occasion of my own lack of self-awareness, my own incapacity to see my own identity (self-meaning) in my pupil. Seeing my pupil as my own living of my pupil, always helps me to renounce the indulgence of "punishment."

General Practitioner. Is "shock treatment" possibly a medical instance of the use of punishment?

Author. A searching question. As I ask it of myself I cannot rule out that possibility, although it certainly is not intentionally such, in the sense that a parent might regard a whipping as a behavior corrective. Personally, I would not use "shock therapy" for the treatment of my mind, for, as does hypnosis, it produces self-unconsciousness instead of self-consciousness.

General Practitioner. According to your views, you consider your depressed patient as a depressed pupil doing all that he can do to help himself by means of facing the truth that his conduct of his life has been and remains such as to occasion his unhappiness. Why, therefore, would you enter the already established ideal psychiatric treatment which your depressed patient is conducting and interfere with his ongoing healing process by having him undergo "shock treatments"?

Author. Quite so.

General Practitioner. Please define punishment again in different words.

Author. "Punishment" is a sensation, perception, or feeling of self-hurt. As is true of all human behavior, the individual suffering it is the only one who can be responsible for it. He does not enjoy it as an experience but tends to deny that it is of his own making. In addition to its use as a danger signal, it contributes to the individual's hardihood (endurance, patience, long-suffering, forbearance, tolerance, peacefulness).

Ellen Key, insightful Swedish educator, offered the kind of self-observation which is most needed, "The foundation of the desire for war is to be sought for less in the war games than in the teacher's rod." In this discussion of "punishment" it is well to observe that wherever one withholds his sense of identity "punishment" is enforced; wherever he does not exercise his sense of sameness, unkindness fills in the defect; wherever he ignores his feeling of unity in the living of his fellow creature, hurt is the helpful signal already in operation. "Punishment" never involves "betweenness." It has nothing to do with sticks and stones. It is always and only a matter of self-experience. Appeals from it on the basis that somebody else is injured are of no avail. The will to "punish" one's self (to undergo painful hardship) is very strong; and the more it is recognized, and thus consciously controlled, the more the will to live has a chance to succeed.

The only way in which I can deceive myself that so-called "punishment" is going to help me is by my being deluded in the first place that "a wrong" has been done. Appearances to the contrary, there is no possibility of such an event as a "wrong." *The charge of wrongdoing is always a delusional accusation.* The farther I remain aloof from any event which I tend to judge "wrong," the longer I can go on comforting myself with this limited honesty (which I tend to call "dishonesty"). The more I make a real study of the event which I had previously considered "wrong," the more I find it necessary to absolve it from every kind of discredit and, instead, find it necessary to appreciate the extremity requiring only the behavior present. Thus, an educator who is punitive is accurately conceived as helping himself as best he can in his limited way. All that I say of punishment as being self-punishment applies equally to blows, righteous indignation, and moral warmth.

It has taken the educator, including the medical educator, a vast extension of the development of his self-consciousness in order for him to see clearly that two "wrongs" cannot make a "right," that the unseeing one needs to be able to live only his moral vision and can really help himself most if he can grow his teacher as insightful rather than as insightless. Although notable exceptions yet continue in force, it is becoming increasingly rare for a physician to be insensible of his patient's inaccessible individuality. The full conscious meaning of torment is unavailable to anyone who must help himself by disowning his suffering fellowman as an individuation of himself. Without his comprehensive self-view, the temptation to drive out hurt with greater hurt is ever strong and ever ready. Once the one reality of life (that is, one's own self) is overlooked, the helpful signs and symptoms of cruelty present themselves.

Sociologist. It is evident that you regard capital punishment as an aggravant, instead of as a deterrent, to the shortsighted selfishness of the perpetrator of undesirable behavior.

Author. Certainly. Legal punishment of every degree is lived by the shortsighted victim of his own shortcomings essentially as a spur to work up the "perfect crime." Through punishment he tends to consider it a crime to get caught.

Sociologist. You mean that the potential criminal is egged on to crime rather than deterred from it, when he reads or hears of punitive measures such as fines, imprisonment and "the death penalty"? You mean that all such well-intentioned attempts at crime prevention can do for him is to make him more careful that he not be caught?

Author. That is exactly as I see it.

Sociologist. What solution for anti-social behavior then do you propose?

Author. "Ill-manners," anti-social acts of all kinds, *are* forms of helpful self-punishment. A crime is a self-hurtful act. Just ask yourself how you would like to be only "a criminal" and you will sense what is meant by the statement: To punish a person for alleged "misbehavior" is unconstitutional in that it involves his being punished twice for the same crime. "Anti-social" can only mean anti-self.

Sociologist. Again, I ask it, What solution do you propose?

Author. The solution that the lawbreaker be considered in no way different from the citizen suffering from his breaking of laws concerned with his health in general. Every "criminal" needs and deserves the best possible opportunity to cure himself of his limitations of his shortsighted behavior.

It requires an educator with most extensive insight to realize the necessity for every pupil's aiming himself at study as self-experience. Education is nothing but a special form of help, and there is no help but self-help. The personification of education as some kind of force "applied to" the pupil, is a most extravagant use of mental grammar. There is no such force, but the illusion that there is supports the illusion that punishment is a defensible educational resource. Educational work is not the manipulation of some kind of learning entity extraneous to the pupil. Only when this truth of educator-insight is reached can educational living as punishment and as a degree of hypnosis be renounced.

Rousseau, the great educator, remarked that all education had failed on account of two facts: (1) The parent is not an educator in the sense of consciously being a self-educator, and (2) The child cannot educate himself with insight unless he can create for himself the opportunity to do so.

Over fifty years ago, Ellen Key recorded a profound observation which (my) everyone would be wise to make his own: "Parents do not see that during the whole life the need of peace is never greater than in the years of childhood." Every child suffers great mental turmoil to the extent that his parent cannot see that his child is all his own living of his child. Thus, in my living of my child it seems I can observe innumerable instances wherein he is needing to help himself. To the extent that each of these occasions elicits from me an effort to help him, rather than an effort to respect the necessity of his living his parent so that he can thereby teach himself to help himself, my child must live his parent as a troublemaker.

In order for me to be able to live my child most helpfully it is essential for me to see that I *am* doing this living, that I am "as a child." I have had to educate myself to *feel equal* to the living of this child part of myself, to renounce as self-deceptions each educational principle implying the illusion that I can have anything to do with my child (instead of his having all to do with his own life).

It comes hard to a parent to realize for the first time that he cannot be useful to his own offspring; but the sooner he makes this self-discovery, the sooner his offspring will grow the opportunity for seeing that he can be useful to himself. The child's educational living which is not contributing to his sense of his independence creates symptoms and signs of a troubled mind.

Sometimes the idea "discipline" is introduced, as if it were intended to provide a more forceful educational experience. Every and any kind of affliction of pain "in order to make a point stick" simply cannot act in any way as a deterrent, but must act as an aggravant, of the distressful living in question. How beautifully Comenius expressed this appreciation when he compared an educator using punishment as a discipline with a musician pounding a mistuned instrument instead of planning ways and means whereby that instrument might succeed in having itself in tune. Punishing in any form belongs to the same level of self-care as scratching an itch until a wound is produced. However, only the educator who can be capable of seeing that punishment is always and only a form of helpful self-cruelty limited to his own living, is capable of renouncing his addiction to self-hurt.

General Practitioner. What are your ideas of death? How do you tell your patient he is going to die? What is your answer to death of your patient when you speak with his relatives and so on?

Author. More excellent sense! Wise Epicurus recorded rare good insight in 300 B.C., "When we are, death is not; and when death is, we are not." Death can have nothing to do with life. Ideas and feelings associated with the living of the concept of death are always helpful reminders of the importance of consciousness of living. Death must be its own answer. A wonderful benefit of so-called thoughts of "sickness" or "death" is that they tend to make a person concentrate upon the truth of his own life,—its meaning, its purpose. It is beneficial for a patient to grow the strength of mind to be able to see with composure that his need to cultivate a new way of living is a life-and-death matter. Hippocrates recorded, "They that are sick and feel no pain are sick in their minds."

I *never* have occasion to tell my patient that he is going to die. My patient often becomes very autosuggestible, particularly as far as his physician is concerned, and can use a prognosis—based upon statistics and therefore not upon individuality—as a death sentence. As far as I am concerned *everyone* has a 100 per cent opportunity to recover his free health.

My speaking with anyone after the death of his, or her, loved one concerns itself with the truth that everyone's beloved fellowman lives on within himself, and will go on living as long as the mourner does. I also point out that grief, in all of its extreme statements and feelings, is necessary and desirable mourning work serving eventually to clear up the fact that the mourner has not been living his departed one (when alive) consciously as his own. In addition, I observe that a deeper cheer will evolve from the endurance of all of the mourning work, and that it is helpful, if possible, to aim at living the whole experience of the sense of loss with noble-spirited composure.[5] I am glad to report this viewpoint again.

General Practitioner. Your way of coping with experiences which evoke thoughts and feelings about death is simply to affirm life, am I correct? "Death" cannot be lived, only deathed.

Author. Spirited life-affirming thoughts and feelings release vital forces, excite interest, and free devotion to activation of loving-kindness and unencumbered self-helpfulness. Exercise of affirmation of life, regular mental gymnastics pertaining to the wonderfulness of living, carefully planned and duly executed application of attention to the precious meanings of living,—of such are the forces of health to be mobilized and utilized during every kind of health ordeal.[6]

General Practitioner. You would not leave such reflections upon the marvelousness of life to the uncertainties of bedside reading and the encouraging, reassuring visits of friends and relatives?

Author. I certainly would not. *Self-encouragement* needs to animate itself; *self-confidence* needs to engender itself.

General Practitioner. Apparently you believe in having your patient find out what is the matter with himself so that he can recognize that his trouble is a matter of life itself, and can consciously mobilize his self-forces to cope successfully with his difficulty.

Author. That is the ideal I strive toward. However, having my patient find out what his trouble is, is a very large order indeed, which does not limit itself to such a fact as that he "has a cancer," or "pneumonia," or "whatever." My cancer, or whatever, is to me my only current means of *treatment* of what is the matter with me. I find it extremely helpful for me to discover, as I find myself able to do so, the general idea of what I am up against health-wise so that I can gradually learn to accommodate my conscious way of living to fit my health requirements. This is the kind of knowledge about my health needs which I must grow for myself.

General Practitioner. It sounds more involved than I thought it was. By "it" I mean having your patient know what his health problem is.

Author. Yes. I find *it* most worthy of continuing and intensive study and consider such study to be an absolute necessity in medical education. No doubt at some future time books will be written and studied which will enable the medical student to grow self-experiences with regard to this critical area of each patient's diagnosing and treating himself. Today, conscious self-treatment is a concept which is not regarded as too practical, so that the need for self-diagnosis is not found to be in great demand. All that can be my "trouble" or "health problem" involves my limited capacity for self-consciousness.

General Practitioner. What is your view of suicide?

Author. On the one hand, it is true that everyone ends his own life and that no one else can do that for him. The idea of "murder" implies that one can take another's life, but that is obviously impossible.

On the other hand, there really is no such possibility as "suicide," in the sense in which it is ordinarily conceived, as meaning: a whole individual's deciding to kill himself. It is not possible for anyone to express all of his mind at any given moment of life. One can never speak with all of himself, or to all of himself, or about all of himself, on any occasion during his life span. What happens in so-called "suicide" is something like this: one idea, "to end life," momentarily appears to assume all of the executive authority of the individual, without heed for the entire rest of the person's life-meanings. This one idea of suicide then, as it were, totally disregards every other thought and feeling of the human being, and recklessly assumes responsibility for ending the entire life of the person. I mind myself as if a removable object, whenever I cannot see my subjectivity.

General Practitioner. Would it not be a comfort for everyone to know that this is the psychological accounting for "suicide"? Everyone has the other view, which is far more painful, the view that suicide is possible and that every element of the person who suicides has been fairly represented in his decision to end his life.

Author. I have always found that everyone who lives the so-called "suicide" of his loved one appreciates the whole truth about the act.

It is now generally recognized that everybody's mental "disorder" is traceable to his having had to help himself by means of self-negligence, that is, by disowning living of his own as actually being living of his own. The self-neglect of this specific order clears the path for unconscious self-hurt.

It is hardly possible for a child to develop himself without creating in his mind the fixed delusion that he is the object of another's care, that somebody else can do something for him. The idea that only he can and must take care of himself becomes obscured by his having to live his parent or teacher as if helping him in one way or another. He brings himself up on a kind of system of rewards and forfeits, of pamperings and threats, of most sincere insincerities and most honest self-deceptions. He has to lie to himself about his natural selfishness, and he certainly must deceive himself about his intentions to have his selfishness his ideal. He cannot see his love for his mother or his father or his sister or his brother for what it truly is,—each an extension of his self-love. No more can he see his feelings of hate or jealousy or guilt or fear, as helpful self-pain, due to agonizing self-love. He dare not assume that it is his right to pursue his happiness. He can scarcely call his life his own, and the truth of his liberty is far removed from his due appreciation. He is not a child of peace, and he is not growing himself to become a man of peace. He can identify himself as an imp or a demon, but not as a god.

By the time a child is five years old, after having lived those years of obeying *his* mother or father and of "manfully" conducting himself contrary to the original dictates of his nature, he is an exception if he is not consciously a pretty thoroughly mixed-up young person, the mixture consisting of his true selfness and his truly false otherness.[7] Unhappy childhood. Little wonder that the parent refuses to remind himself of it.

Loose academic expressions such as "the study of the psychology of the child," "nursery school training," "mental testing of the child," and thousands like them, attest the fixity of the delusion that it is possible for the teacher to understand the child and for the child to understand the teacher. *Any such illusional "understanding" can only be at the cost of conscious self-understanding.*

General Practitioner. Is there not a risk that you are extreme in your devotion to self-consciousness? It has been said that a good way to take a great weight off your mind is to get rid of your halo. How about it? I know that one is always extremely one.

Author. I can find no objection to devotion to extreme sanity. I see no advantage in discarding a halo of self-consciousness for one of self-unconsciousness. However, I gladly consider every way of helping myself.

General Practitioner. Wouldn't it be more economical to talk this way to undergraduate medical students than to physicians who have more experience in deciding what is practical than a teacher can have?

Author. In my mind, every M.D. *is* a medical educator. Even though the physician may not discover in his living of his college of medicine that his self-growth, in one or another direction of interest, is his only possible subject of scientific investigation, nevetheless his tough school of experience in medical living will be a force with which he will either enjoy his medical profession as a self-made M.D. or suffer it as a self-neglected one. All that is valuable in human life is *living.* Living self-consciously extends meaning of life as nought else can. The real wonderfulness of man consists in nothing but his human living. His psychotherapy cannot make a man more wonderful; it can and does make a man see how wonderful he is. The chief end of man cannot be other than to live himself as *his* man. The mind that lives consciously for itself trusts the solid ground of life. The greatness of human life, the consciousness of which every human being creates for himself, must be recognized as earned in order to be duly appreciated. Every young M.D., early in his professional life, needs most of all to develop the habit of mind of calling his medical soul his own. His patient loves most of all to live (learn from) this kind of M.D.

Every physician will find his every patient varyingly limited in his capacity for self-tolerance, rarely one of them ever having considered in a self-reliant way his ability to "live life to the full." Hence it is most helpful for every physician to recognize the health benefit in his steady striving for his own conscious self-realization and conscious self-fulfillment. As the physician aims to help himself, he is doing all possible to see to it that his patient grows a physician with this appreciation of the truth of self-helpfulness, the most useful truth for seeing order in a so-called "disordered" mind. As an ordered mind finds its properly appreciated self-sameness, homogeneity, expressed in the body part of itself, so a "disordered" mind finds expression of its inharmonious living in "dysfunctions" of the body part of itself.

General Practitioner. What do you mean by "the body part of the mind"?

Author. What is conventionally called "body" is made up of mental elements entirely.

General Practitioner. How so? Body is body, isn't it?

Author. When I talk or think or see or touch whatever I mean by "body," I have to admit that I have used only my mind for the whole experience.

General Practitioner. Are you denying that you have a body?

Author. I am only affirming all that I can find that I mean by the term "body."

General Practitioner. Do you now see your body as only your mind's extension? Do you see that your mind's action makes your body so? Do you regard body without a mind as a gone body? Do you see the deprivation of life to the mind as constituting the dying of the body?

Author. As I ask each of these questions, I reply: Yes.

General Practitioner. No doubt, the study of the law of my individual life (which I can see is all there can be for me), its unappreciated power and practicality, is vitally important despite its seeming to be abstract and speculative. I suppose the real basis for my feeling that I lack my true completeness is only the truth that I have not yet finished all of my living. An accurate inventory of my assets must make me feel enjoyably that my all is my own. Everyone rightly "owns the earth," his earth. How different from my wealth of deficiency and limitation as a self-dispossessing "materialist"! Idealism is the vital essence in religion too,—for instance, Paul's insight, "All things are yours."

Author. It is selfishly gratifying to me to observe (my) you recognizing that all of your education is the cultivation of the richness of your mind for its own sake, that all of your commercial activity also is self-development. True human wealth is entirely a subjective growth of its possessor. My discovery that I can discover only myself has been an indispensably practical awakening to my meaning of wakefulness. To claim that *I* can go out beyond *myself* is an obvious contradiction in terms.

Psychologist. Nearly everyone I know thinks of himself as a body, as matter going through space and time; but you consider all matter, space, time, and motion of yours to be elements created by your own living of each. Do you go through exercises of your immateriality, gymnastics of your ideality, so that it will not suffer atrophy of disuse and neglect?

Author. My purpose in exercising my self-consciousness is the positive one of wishing to live my life to the full.

Psychologist. What is the remedy for viewing myself as physical, for viewing my mind as something my physical body produces? How did you overcome this habit?

Author. In the first place, I had to live some experience through which I forced myself to concentrate steadily upon myself, as such. From then on the development (of my consciously living my only truth of my individuality) has been a result of my persistently taking pains to cultivate it. Each slightest access of the development has been wonderful, however. Basic reference questioning of greatest usefulness for the critical study of this work on development may be formulated as follows: *Is it true to life (hence peaceable) for me to observe my own self, including my own offspring, as being always self-composed, as ever and only self-made, self-helpful, self-resourceful, self-reliant, self-possessed?* Or, *Is it true to life (hence peaceable) for me to observe my own self, including my own offspring, as being (at least) sometimes selfless, self-uncomposed, self-helpless, self-unresourceful, self-unreliant, self-dispossessed?*

I have discovered that the only way in which I can be helpful is by living myself helpfully. Every time I have a feeling of wanting to help "somebody else," I help myself most by seeing that feeling as entirely my disguised wish to make myself more comfortable. Peace-loving Shakespeare observed this truth in his beautiful word picture: "In brief, sir, study what you most affect." Seeing each of my mental developments as mine puts every such force in (what I can see as) *my* service. It is precious economy both to be able to get what I want and to want what I get, as a developing human being.

Obstetrician. Your developmental psychology pictures the child as giving birth to all that he calls his mother, or father. Is it not necessary for each mother also to give birth to her baby in each of two ways: (1) in the "popular" sense of "giving birth," and (2) in the mother's consciously creating in her own mind the meaning of her baby's individuality as she lives each experience which involves her growing *her* baby-truth? And, is it necessary for the father too to construct of his own selfness his baby-truth?

Author. All very true. Each person's life experience concerning his, or her, offspring creates all of his, or her, meaning for that area of living.

Obstetrician. As Mark Twain said, "We are all ignorant, but about different things." When I began my practice I could hardly believe the prevalence of ignorance and misinformation about sexuality which I encountered in nearly every pregnant woman and her husband. Now, I do not expect to find this mind-strengthening awareness for genital and pregenital interests, and I'm usually right. Will you please account for this localized backwardness?

Author. As a rule, a most meaningful segregation occurs in married living,—a so-called segregation of the sexes. Strictest separation of male and female living had been found to be the most comfortable way for each spouse to live his parental family experiences with minimal awareness of the vast extent of his, or her, repressed (ignored) bisexuality. Note well, *that* rigid artificial segregation prevents the occurrence of very much education regarding sexuality, genital or pregenital. Thus, even one's marital living becomes deprived of much of its greatest helpfulness, the opportunity at last to become learned regarding one's sexuality.

Obstetrician. A tremendous price in healthful happiness to pay for such "comfort." I am thinking of Havelock Ellis's insight: "The omnipresence of sex, as it is woven into the whole texture of our man's or woman's body, is the pattern of all the process of our life." One's marriage is seldom appreciated entirely as a self-development. This view of one's bisexuality reminds me of Shakespeare's (*King John II,* i):

> He is the half part of a blessed man,
> Left to be finished by such as she;
> And she a fair divided excellence,
> Whose fulness of perfection lies in him.

Obedience to the laws of my nature is my first law. The careful cultivation of my mighty useful capacity for *obedience* is indispensable for my heeding the truth that the world I live is my own, and its every command or demand is my own.

Please describe briefly your idea of the institution of marriage.

Author. My every so-called "institution" is a conception of, in, and about my mind. My marriage is most wisely conceived by my seeing soul as very privileged *self*-education, marital experience being sanely viewed primarily as educational opportunity. As a spouse my career consists of greatly needed *self*-cultivation developing my masculine and feminine propensities to my every life's fulfilment. Poet Juan Ramón Jiménez, awarded the 1956 Nobel Prize for Literature, thus aimed at dividing his day into lives, not his life into days. From his Unamuno, the great rector of the University of Salamanca, he learned, "He who does not have the intuition of momentaneity of everything living is not a true artist."

Henrik Ibsen noted marriage to be living "you've got to give your whole mind to." Anthony Trollope recorded this greatness: "How I do hate those words, 'an excellent marriage.' In them is contained more of wicked worldliness than any other words one ever hears spoken."

Obstetrician. What do you conceive to be the finest basis for one's marriage?

Author. First of all, devotion to the truth of individuality. A healthful, happy marriage is the issue of a man, or woman, continually conceiving his, or her, spouse as (his, her) a stranger. In all truth, everyone is always a stranger to himself, and that self-orientation has all of the advantages of accuracy in it. The success of the early living of marriage is traceable largely to the appreciation of each spouse for his, or her, mate, as being ever new. Also, with the development of familiarity, the repressions of one's parental living begin to be displaced unwittingly upon the meaning of one's child and spouse. By "stranger" here I mean: beloved, independent, original, novel, peace-making.

The conception of marriage as being "a community of two" creates innumerable phantom problems. With what genius does Shakespeare dispose of the interpersonal phantom (Sonnet 121),

> No, I am that I am, and they that level
> At my abuses reckon up their own.

Obstetrician. As I see it, preservation of freedom and peace of mind requires that a parent make clear to his self the fact that a child may think (imagine, phantasy) as he, or she, pleases; that prohibition applied to *doing* is not intended to include *thinking.* It is essential that a mind be free to use its powers of imagining *particularly where prohibition against "doing" is imposed.* However, if this extremely important distinction is not sunclear, a child forfeits the use of his imagination just where he needs it most. It is of immeasurable help to me to know that, whereas I am not allowed to seek my pleasure with my "doing" power, I am supposed to be able to seek my pleasure with my thinking power.

Author. Yes, indeed. Potency of imagination is one's only potency. Over one hundred years ago the internationally famous American educator, Amos Bronson Alcott, claiming that a good school could never be more than an imitation of a good home, tried to introduce sex education in his Boston school. The result was widespread moral panic, not in the child but in the adult.

Obstetrician. Now let me see if I have your brand of developmental psychology straight. If the husband can see *his* wife as a creation of his very own living, and the wife can see *her* husband as a creation of her very own living,—then each spouse is conducting his (her) marriage with due appreciation of the allness-meaning of human individuality and, thereby, developing the psychic "know how" for respecting his (her) baby's allness as an individual. That is, each spouse can live his (her) baby as his (her) precious individuation (meaning, made up entirely and only of individuality).

Author. That is a clear but necessarily painstaking description of marriage as being the realistic ongoing expanse of "single blessedness," rather than the illusional end of each spouse's individuality.

Obstetrician. A marriage ritual might also well include that ideal: "Let no man put together what God has put asunder."

Author. That might be one effective way of living consciously the fact that each spouse, as well as each sibling, has the necessity for living each member of his family as being an individuation of his own individuality, and that his success in attaining to (and maintaining) this most difficult degree of self-awareness determines the extent of his appreciation of his life, itself.

Obstetrician. One's family living which is based upon reverence for the inviolability of individuality is also the most solid foundation for democratic living in general, is it not?

Author. It seems evident to me that where self-possession abdicates, there quietly but surely "the communistic state" addiction begins.

Obstetrician. Have you ever heard of a home where this kind of appreciation for human individuality is the family ideal?

Author. It is necessarily the conscious, or unconscious, ideal of everyone's living of his family experience; for it is the whole and only truth of "family living" that it exists all and only in each human individual's living.

Obstetrician. It does seem that civic spirit has its origin in family spirit which, in turn, has its origin in individual spirit. My American government is founded upon the ideal of self-sovereignty, and I need most of all to know what territory I take in if I would grow to use my suffrage wisely. And, I cherish this self-growth as a precious issue of my developmental psychology.

Author. Again, I have helped myself greatly by seeing that the human individual grows all of his meanings of family and home *within his mind,* and not all of the meanings of his mind within his family and home.

Obstetrician. A favorite theme of the novelist is the discord "between" man and woman, as though there were some necessary rivalry or enmity "between" the sexes. Do you trace all such unpeaceful living to the artificial segregation of the sexes, that is, to the man's ignorance that he creates the only woman-meanings of his world and to the woman's ignorance that she creates the only man-meanings of her world?

Author. Yes. *Rarely does a spouse have the reach of self-consciousness to see that each sex includes all of its meanings for its opposite sex.* Rather, each spouse strives after a marital existence which cannot conform to his (her) human constitution, but which must inhibit complete personality development and its enhanced appreciation of life.

Obstetrician. A man's dream of (his) woman, or a woman's dream of (her) man, could be realized in every instance if each spouse were aware of the fact that each male or female must build up the entire meaning of "opposite sex." In the mind of nearly every man, or woman, is the firmly fixed delusion now that "opposite sex" means not-self. A man does not hold himself entirely responsible for the creation of his ideal woman. A woman does not hold herself entirely responsible for the creation of her ideal man. Each spouse tends to indulge the delusion of blaming his (her) objectized (externalized, disowned, repressed) mate for being undesirable. The consequence is that neither spouse finds the only source of "undesirable matehood" in his, or her, own living of repressed "opposite" sexuality.

Author. Yes. "Segregation of the sexes" really amounts to an effort at desexualization of each sex. The realization that each spouse is a new world consisting both of masculinity and femininity is an insight essential for wholesome self-esteem. Without this awesome, earnest self-understanding no married person can possess himself, or herself, in peace. I cherish this truth of mine.

Obstetrician. You mean that the meaning of one's entirety, one's observation of his complete potentiality, is necessary for his freeing his love and sensing his allness; and that one's intense feeling of the fullness of his life constitutes the happiness of healthful living?

Author. I mean that the only substance of mind, the meaning of meaning, is individual *life.* I mean that a creative process like that an author uses to create both male and female characters is essential for each spouse's creation of his, or her, mate. I mean that conscious mental integration is impossible for the individual who considers his own sex to be constituted of his selfness and his "opposite" sex to be constituted of not-selfness. A mind's health is characterized by its consciousness of its creativity in producing the composition of its world. In his *Sand and Foam* (1926) Kahlil Gibran offered a demonstration of sensory experience as mental creation: "Should you really open your eyes and see you would behold your image in all images. And should you open your ears and listen, you would hear your own voice in all voices."

Obstetrician. By his devotion to his socially accepted idea of "segregation of the sexes," you mean a person necessarily grows a delusion of duality rather than a consciousness of unity about his sexual living? Mme. de Staël claimed, "The egoism of woman is always for two." I suppose what she meant was that a woman tends to see her man as her own living of her masculinity.

Author. Exactly. I know of no more costly substitution of reasoning (involving multiplicity) and self-consciousness (involving oneness), than conceiving one's marriage to be a "twosome." One can only "two-time" oneself.

Obstetrician. It appears that conventional marital living serves the purpose of completing the illusional segregation of male and female sexuality already well established by the parental home living of each spouse. The massive mental dissociation each spouse creates by cultivating his traditional living of delusional duality of his, or her, sex life necessarily freezes the economy of each one's human energy in disabling ways. Thus, it produces unsuspected impotence, frigidity, jealousy, neglect, hostility, and numerous compensatory efforts such as "double standard of morals," "superiority" and "inferiority" sexual "complexes" (for instance, "sissy" and "tomboy," or "stronger sex" and "weaker sex" problems), early loss of free interest in sexual experiences, indulgence in unconscious (involuntary) sexual activities, and innumerable other so-called "abnormalities."

Author. It is evident that you have been "making a study" of sex, that *you* wish to live your sexuality and not just seem to be lived by *it.*

Obstetrician. I cannot but be shocked by the sequence of jealousy, neglect, separation, and abandonment,—particularly the high incidence of it occurring around the period of pregnancy, delivery, and breast-feeding,—just when maternal peace is most needed. I realize that this incidence is well known to the divorce court judge. Will you please elaborate your ideas of jealousy?

Author. Gladly. If I cannot use my own body freely for producing my own life satisfaction, it is on account of the fact that I do not believe that it belongs entirely to me. I believe (unconsciously) that it belongs to my "mother," or to whatever living of mine which seems to control my use of my body. Jealousy is my sign to myself that I am trying to dispossess myself of some of my self-possession. Although consciously it might not make sense to me I nevertheless harbor jealousy feelings for any part of my body which I cannot use freely, as for any part of my living (such as *my* mother) which I cannot feel that I control. However, jealousy is such a painful feeling that forgetting soon makes it unconscious. From then on I can neglect myself in areas which might stir up my jealousy feelings, soon feel separated from them, and finally abandon all such troublesome spots.

Obstetrician. I presume you are alluding to the free use of your eyes, arms, hands, fingers, and genitals for *sexual* life satisfaction, including all constructive purposes?

Author. Certainly, if I cannot *trust* my acknowledged, beloved body to be *faithful* to the care of my nature and needs, how can I grow an acknowledged, beloved spouse incapable of infidelity? Whatver I consciously create, I see belongs to me. I must consciously create my use of myself in order to feel that I do belong to myself.

Obstetrician. You mean that you must harbor constant (conscious or unconscious) jealousy feelings and ideas of infidelity for your spouse, both activate her distrust of (her) you and accuse her of unfaithfulness, exactly to the extent that you cannot see your spouse as a precious development of your very own self-growth, hence entirely under your own control? You mean that you must, by study and practice, develop your sense of being faithful to yourself?

Author. Fortunately, yes. However, I am relieved that you specifically refer to "conscious or unconscious" jealousy feeling; for I find that this distressful feeling, although constantly operating, is for the most part unconscious.

Obstetrician. Each spouse lives his, or her, partner largely under the influence of unconscious jealousy, then?

Author. How can it be otherwise, with each one living *under* the system of (illusional) "segregation of the sexes"?

Obstetrician. You imagine jealousy to be far more general in occurrence than is usually considered. You think that each person, as a rule, has learned from experience the comforts of not caring too much about anyone, or anything.

Author. Jealousy is standard human equipment. One is either conscious he, or she, has it, or is more "under" its operation than ever on account of its being unconscious (emphasized, constant, uncontrolled). Victor Hugo asserted, "God created the coquette as soon as he had made the fool."

Obstetrician. And you consider the way in which each person achieves success in masturbatory sex control to be paradigmatic of that one's success in marital sex control.

Author. I do.

Obstetrician. Of course, "masturbatory sex control" includes all of the person's imagining of his, or her, opposite sex, during his adorable masturbation.

Author. Naturally.

Obstetrician. A boy who did not confuse the entirely distinct entities, his "father's wife" and his own "mother," would encounter the least problem imagining his marrying his mother and having her constant to him. A girl who did not confuse the entirely distinct entities, her "mother's husband" and her own "father," would encounter the least problem imagining her marrying her father and having him constant to her.

Author. That is truth, as I see it.

Obstetrician. According to Homer, the Grecian ladies counted their age from their marriage, not from their birth. Your reduction of the popular notion of sexuality, namely "the sexes," to fit your truth of the oneness-allness of individuality reminds me of an ideal of Goethe, "The excellent woman is she who, if the husband dies, can be a father to his children."

Author. The foundation of domestic happiness is each individual's opportunity to grow all that he grows as being his own self-development, and particularly his growth of his "opposite sex" meanings. The risk of familiarity in one's family living is greatest of all. Addison points up that truth, "An idol may be undeified by many accidental causes. Marriage, in particular, is a kind of counter apotheosis, or a deification inverted. When a man becomes familiar with his goddess, she quickly sinks into a woman."

Obstetrician. An undercurrent of your psychology seems to be that you get out of life consciously what you put into it consciously. If you do not allow yourself consciously to feel your living, you have no conscious appreciation of it. I am reminded of a poignant thought recorded by Mrs. Sigourney, which has always made a lot of sense to me in my work, "A mother's first ministration for her infant is to enter, as it were, the valley of the shadow of death, and win its life at the peril of her own! How different must an affection thus founded be from all others!" It seems clear that every mother's solemn experience of child-bearing is of the depth of conscious meaningfulness which is most salutary for her consciously caring deeply for her baby-living.

Author. I repeat, there is no harder nor more rewarding work than that of marital living. A husband has his wife bearing and delivering and nursing his offspring. Bacon had this strenuousness of marital living in mind when he noted, "Certainly wife and children are a kind of discipline of humanity."

Obstetrician. Well meant, I'm sure. I am equally sure that many a reader, including myself, will not like many an idea which you have seen fit to voice in the interest of your humanity.

Author. All well and good. Disliking, or liking, an idea has absolutely no effect upon the idea itself. However, every listener who lives any idea he hears with repugnance, indignation, or any other feeling of rejection, may find comfort in the fact that his dislike is effecting his quickly forgetting about (repressing) the idea in question.

Obstetrician. Horace Smith supported your view of sexuality, as must every full-measured conscious individual, according to you. He said, "Every man, like Narcissus, becomes enamored of the reflection of himself, only choosing a substance instead of a shadow. His love for any particular woman is self-love at second hand, vanity reflected, compound egotism." Similarly Alphonse Karr noticed, "Love is wholly in him who loves; the beloved is only a pretext." Even Dickens' scamp Fagin, in *Oliver Twist,* based his infamous morality upon self-interest,

> "Every man's his own friend, my dear," replied Fagin. "He hasn't as good a one as himself anywhere. Some conjurors say that number three is the magic number, and some say seven. It's neither, my friend, neither. It's number one. And in a little community like ours, my dear, we have a general number one; that is, you can't consider yourself as number one, without considering me too as the same, and all the others."

Please illustrate the practicality of renouncing indulgence in the illusion of a "segregation of sexes."

Author. I have helped myself greatly by my carefully developed ability to see that my fellow*man* subsumes all of the femaleness of his world,—his mother, sister, spouse, daughter, and neighbor girl; that my fellow*woman* subsumes all of the maleness of her world,—her father, brother, spouse, son, and neighbor boy. It is of great practical value to me to see that every man has his wife and each child "at work" with him; that every woman has her husband and every child with her wherever she is. I regard it as a grievous error, based upon ignorance, that every male employee's wife is not recognizably "on the job" within him, interested vitally in his employment, and inseparable from him in every respect; that every female employee's husband is not recognizably "on the job" within her, interested vitally in her employment, and inseparable from her in every respect. This kind of insight is a dire need of the physician who lives as a servant of the poor in health, often at the cost of his wife's interest in living; and of the "neglected wife" whose husband's demanding work threatens her with the idea of being second-choice to "a medical profession." The physician's wife needs desperately to develop this specific insight which allows her to see that her husband is always with her, that "out of sight" cannot mean "out of mind," that her husband lives his wife twenty-four hours a day.

Obstetrician. If each spouse can revere his (her) individuality, then each one enjoys the full benefits of his (her) free human nature. Wise Tennyson pointed out, "As the husband is, the wife is, if mated with a clown."

I am just beginning to see that my jealousy feeling operates as a warning to me that I am not living my loved one consciously as precious meanings of, and in, my own individuality. Mostly, a person interprets his jealousy as telling him that "somebody else" is unfaithful to him. Your position on the subject is that each one can be unfaithful or faithful to himself, or herself, only. I suppose if your mate were unable to conduct her spouse-living loyally you would consider her as seriously needing to help herself in that regard, and would wish to have her live (secure) some expert self-education (experience specific learning) along that line.

Author. Yes. All fidelity is self-fidelity as I see it. Invariably I find that my jealousy feeling subsides the moment that I recover sufficient conscious presence of mind to see that jealousy signalizes (illusional) "out of my mind" behavior.

Pediatrician. You regard every human activity as an expression of the kind of maleness, or femaleness, which a person has developed. I suppose gender is that fundamental. You state that you have helped yourself by making peace with the desirability of your incestuous mental life. Have you also made peace with your pregenital mental life? I mean for instance, can you live harmoniously the oral, anal, and urethral meanings inherent in your sex life? Also, are you able to live peacefully the tremendous capacity for violence characteristic of the mental life of your infanthood and childhood?

Author. Much of my joy of living derives from my harmonious appreciation of my earliest autoerotic sources of pleasure. Violence is understandable as uncontrolled extreme excitation, characteristic of my being very, very young at heart.

Pediatrician. Is your mind comfortable imagining your cannibalistic living, even imagining your making a meal of your own flesh? Have you no legitimate unimaginable?

Author. I have long since learned the practicality of being able to use my imagination for living with acknowledged love *all* which I formerly repressed as "gruesome," "hideous," "shameful," "hateful," and as every other kind of pained (unrecognizable) love. Whatever I cannot live consciously as my imagination, and with love, I can live unconsciously.

Pediatrician. I have grown one idea for myself which I have had you state. How is that for semantic sanity?

Author. You are asking yourself, no doubt.

Pediatrician. Exactly. The idea is this one: My hearing or seeing my fellowman express his learning does not constitute my learning, at all,—even if I do tend to assume that it does, *in order to avoid the trouble of consciously doing my own learning.* Seeing my fellowman create something for himself is not the same as my creating my "something" for myself, although I may delude myself that it is the same. *I* do live each of these acts of learning, but differently. Whatever I hear, or read, is lived by me as if not-mine (repressed). I must write or say "it" responsibly by and to myself before I can live "it" consciously as my own creation.

Author. An excellent view of your cognitive process! Over fifty years ago, in his *General Introduction to Psychoanalysis,* Freud pointed out that "there are various kinds of knowings," "more than one kind of ignorance" requiring insight to understand. He asserted that conscious self-knowledge "must be founded upon an inner change in the patient which can only come about by a mental operation directed to that end."

Pediatrician. Now I would like to have (my) you diagram "family living," a husband, wife, son, and daughter. It seems to me that accurate mind-accounting by each one who lives his "family" would relieve the troublesome puzzlements of incest,

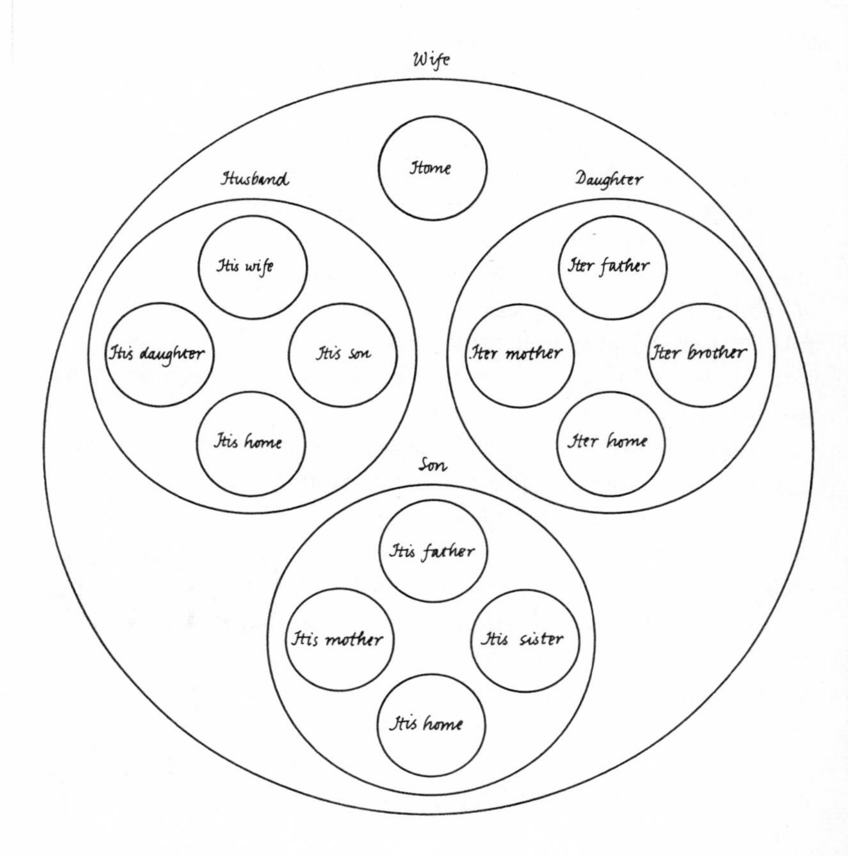

the Oedipus complex, "the family romance," and every other developmental fixation traceable to confused self-identifications.

Author. How right (my) you are. There is but one basic question of psychological importance: Is it I? Quite as there is but one basic answer of psychological importance: It is I.

Pediatrician. Please draw your diagram indicating that each "family person" lives his family within him only. Please use your crude system of diagram.

Author. Very well.

Pediatrician. Is there some name you can give to this scheme of life orientation? How might I designate the meaning of such figures?

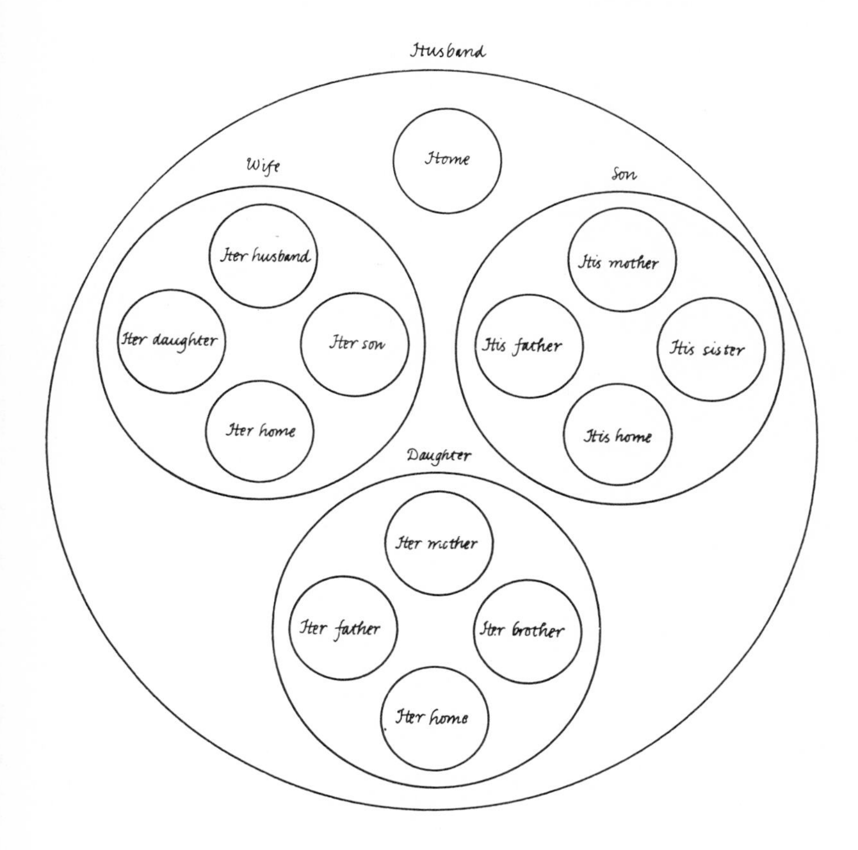

Author. I term this kind of accounting for mental activity as occurring within the given mind: *the localization of mental function.*

Pediatrician. For you the all-important diagnostic and therapeutic fact about all mental activity is that it occurs *only* and *entirely* in the given individual's mind, for you find that the activation of each one's acknowledgment of *that* fact is his specific mind-healing and -strengthening force.

Author. The accurate and practical map of localization of mental functioning must serve to situate elements and fix responsibilities accounting for mental disturbance on the one hand and peace of mind on the other. Certainly it is of interest to study

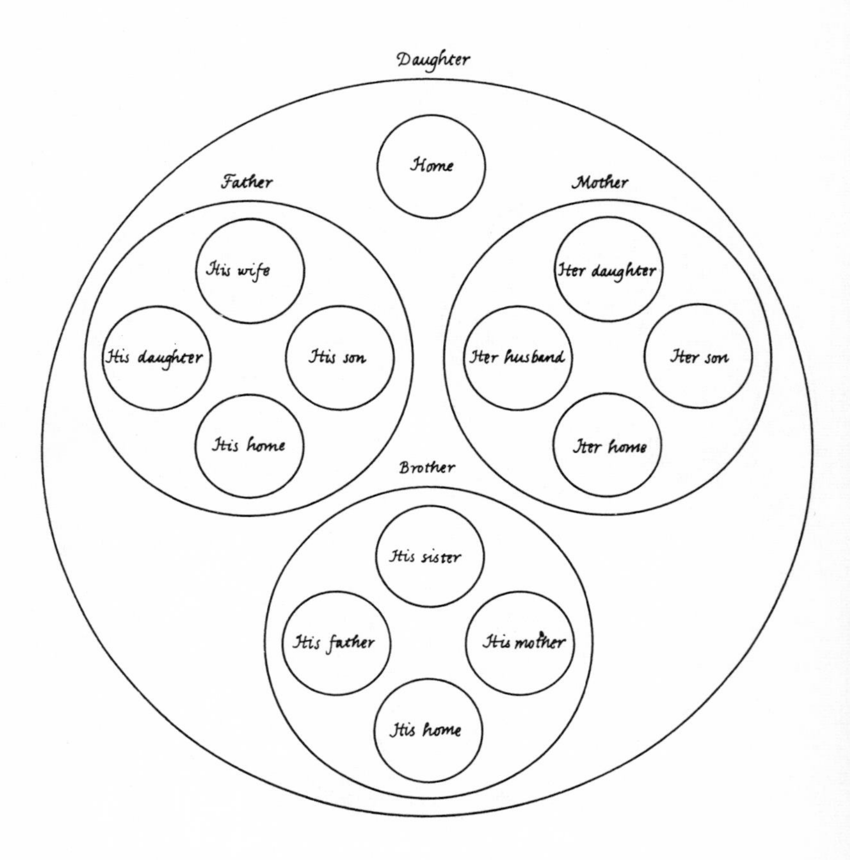

the regional anatomy of my mind accounting for specificity of mental functioning (such as sensation, perception, consciousness, affect, body meanings, and the like); but such a study does not elucidate the one and only appreciation needed for my sanity, namely, *all of my mental life is localized in my personal human economy.* This localization within my mind, my science of self, provides my indispensable scientific table of constants. When I am not *noticing* my mental power as being mine I am unwittingly indulging my illusion of self-expropriation. The systematic exercise of my self-consciousness is necessary for my making an ever new self-estimate corresponding to my lifelong self-development. In no other way can I avoid piling up problems based upon

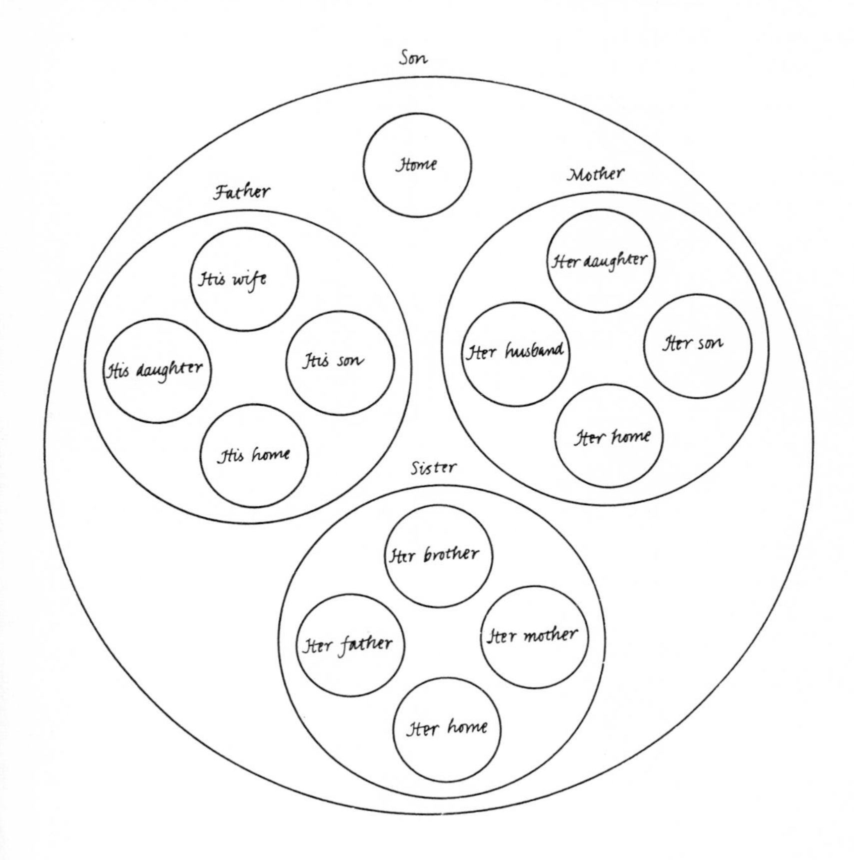

a sense of displacement of my own life's power, of my own mind's properties.

Pediatrician. I have heard of "cerebral localization of function," but never before of "mental localization of function." You find that what a person needs to recognize most of all is that his life experience is taking place *somewhere* within his human being,—"just exactly where," not being at all the mind-strengthening and -healing issue.

Author. Exactly. Blind (unconscious) indulgence of the illusion that I can experience anything not myself is the specific mental health issue calling for that sovereign remedy: self-consciousness. As Plato divined, mind is the true reality; it occurs only in an individual's life; and it provides all meaning with its form and essence. My observation of my mind (self-consciousness) is necessary in order that I may think correctly, feel truly, will directly, adventure peacefully, and see straightly.

Pediatrician. I can now consult each diagram and see for myself, and thus remind myself of, the all-important truth that everyone of my world does actually live all of *his* (or *her*) own world. For example, I can now picture clearly that *my* father (whom I live as all in himself) lives *all* of his own life; that *my* mother (whom I live as all in herself) lives *all* of her own life. Thus I can easily observe that *my* father is not, and cannot be, my mother's husband; that *my* mother is not, and cannot be, my father's wife; that my brother (or sister) does not, and cannot, have the same father (or mother, or sister, or brother, or home) that I have.

At the same time I can readily notice how my habit of mind has indulged the most profound confusion in each of these matters, and how difficult it is for me even to consider renouncing this habit.

I must use up a lot of my mental energy in maintaining my delusional system based upon the impossible: my "sharing" in any way the same mother, father, brother, sister, or home. No wonder psychiatrists have traced all mental trouble to the experiences of the individual's first months and years of life. I now see clearly for the first time what you mean when you say that all dispute is nearly fruitless, that one disputant cannot even discuss the same thing as his fellow disputant.

Author. I help myself by asking myself, What more practical might I be doing, or trying to do, than getting my mind in shape for enjoying my life fully?

As already noted again and again, it is health-giving to grow the full-measured self-view of my allness. According to my experience, it is a rule for my fellowman, as a man, to dissociate his mind by disclaiming his femininity. Similarly, my fellowman, as a woman, tends to dissociate her mind by disclaiming her masculinity. Thus, ever so quietly, grows up the unpeaceful illusion of two kinds of worlds,—a man's and a woman's.

A woman's ideal of a man may be: one who can make her

feel like a woman. A man's ideal of a woman may be: one who can make him feel like a man. I observe the advantage to a woman in having as her ideal of a man: one who can make her feel and understand her maleness. Similarily, I observe the advantage to a man in having as his ideal of a woman: one who can make him feel and understand his femaleness. Each ideal permits each sex to be responsible for feeling its own truth and force.

If I hold that I am a male and all that is female is foreign to me, or hold that I am a woman and all that is male is foreign to me, I am rejecting precious powers of my human nature without realizing it. Whatever power of my life I disown, I live that disowned power of mine in an unconscious involuntary way.

Self-rejection pertaining to one's other sex is found to be signalized by serious mental trouble particularly in the area of behavior respecting one's opposite sex. The specific treatment for this kind of psychic blindness is the self-rejecting person's waking up gradually to the realization that he *is* whatever sexual meaning he lives.

Pediatrician. Please describe your idea of a man's woman, and a woman's man. I always thought a man's woman is one who makes him feel like a man; and that a woman's man is one who makes her feel like a woman.

Author. A man's woman constitutes his living of his own femininity; a woman's man constitutes her living of her own masculinity. Each individual's "opposite sex" experience begins at home. The girl lives her father and brother experiences (in her) "there"; the boy lives his mother and sister experiences (in his) "there." Each child soon learns that he (or she) can enjoy (consciously, that is) only greatly limited sexual experiences of a sensory or perceptual kind in his (her) any home living.

The child is fortunate who learns to distinguish his parent's prohibition about sexual "doing" from other sexual *minding.* However, a child easily misunderstands his parent's admonition and construes parental rules to extend to his use of all of his mind. If he (or she) dissociates his (or her) beloved parent (of either sex) from sexual meaning, he (or she) thereby lays the foundation for marital trouble.

Incestuous living is a necessity which can be either renounced or repressed. If renounced, it is an accessible source of power for happy married life. If repressed, the child tends to develop two kinds of opposite sex: one which stands for tenderness without lust; and one which stands for lust without tenderness. Obviously such outcome of one's first love is troublesome and calls for the enlightenment which will eventually replace repression of incestuous living with renunciation of it. Freud discovered the ways into and out of this kind of mental dissociation.

Pediatrician. I assume that a man who has retained his access to his masculine propensities can make himself feel like a man, and use his living of his female for a conscious development of his femininity resources. Similarly, I imagine that a woman who has retained her access to her feminine propensities can make herself feel like a woman, and use her living of her male for a conscious development of her masculinity resources.

Author. That is as I see it.

Pediatrician. I suppose that the man, or woman, who has repressed his, or her, heterosexuality (opposite sex) suffers the "sissy," or "tomboy," complex. How about the one who has only *renounced* his (or her) opposite sex living of his (or her) parent?

Author. Fortunately potent is the man who can observe that only he must and can live (be) his woman; and equally fortunately potent is the woman who can observe that only she must and can live (be) her own man.

Pediatrician. Why do you center one's fortune upon one's sexual potency in this way? Do you consider sexual potency to be one's only power?

Author. I have found it helpful to be able to consider any and every view. Only to the extent that sexuality means life, can *any* power be claimed for it. Broadly conceived, however, sexuality pervades life as long as there is any life, and my responsibility for my wise, loving cultivation of my sexuality is my *lifelong* responsibility.

Disguised and/or undisguised complaint about sexual impotence characterizes every mind troubled by its limited potential for conscious mindfulness. My characteristic symptoms of my repressed mind (e.g. irritability, weariness, anxiety, depression) reflect my basic concern about my inaccessible sexual potency. Unhappiness signals the suspension of the free functioning of my mind.

Generally and specifically, my *power* is the only source of my human happiness; and my conscious power is the only source of my conscious happiness. I enjoy my life only to the extent that I consciously cultivate my human power.

Pediatrician. If I cannot see the extent of my power, and avail myself of it, I naturally doubt its existence. Doubt of my own power obstructs my view of my dominion over myself. It certainly is not spirited living to feel powerless; and, as I understand what I have been hearing in these conversations, my subjectivity is the only existent, the only substance of matter. The dimension of my soul (self-principle, or life force) is limitless, and deprivation of awareness of that truth accounts for my delusion of impotence. My forgetting myself is certainly a merciful anodyne but is also accountable for my limited self-appreciation, or idea of impotence. My limited conception of myself obscures my realization of my potency.

Author. It is but natural for a woman of fifty or sixty years of age who cannot realize that she is also sixteen years old to feel that her life is past rather than present. The practice of conscious mindfulness enables a man, or woman, to live all of the glories of youthfulness, as long as there is life.

Pediatrician. You mean that a man, or woman, of advanced years must contend with impotency ideas and feelings who cannot use his, or her, mind to exercise all of the prerogatives of youth. Is this your allness-or-illness principle again?

Author. There is only one world which can ever want redeeming and that is the ever present world of the individual, which includes his every life meaning. Maeterlinck said, "It is far more important that one's life should be perceived than that it should be transformed; for no sooner has it been perceived than it transforms itself of its own accord" ("The Deeper Life," in *The Treasure of the Humble*).

Pediatrician. Are you not *generalizing*: that everyone must learn sex control through masturbation experience, that everyone must complain of impotence if he cannot accurately sense his manpower, that everyone must live his (or her) opposite sex, and so on?

Author. I wish to renounce every generalization, and appearance of generalization. Every person's concern for his (her) masturbation, heterosexuality, consciousness, or whatever, is entirely his (her) unique individual living, requiring his (her) special individual attention, as I see it. I can and do speak only about and to me.

Pediatrician. As you elucidate the comprehensive meaning of human individuality you do away entirely with troublesome generalizations like "it's a woman's world," "it's a man's world," "man is superior to woman," "woman is superior to man," "the battle *between* the sexes," "man can merely love, woman is love itself," "the double standard," even "heterosexuality" itself. I am beginning to see that a husband can never have the same marriage his wife has.

Author. Yes, every problem of the "other sex" is always an individual's problem of seeing this complete unity in his life so that his love can include it.

Pediatrician. I suppose that the "one man for one woman," or "one woman for one man," ideal is only the natural outcome of the biological fact that each individual's being is the issue of one beloved parent of his (or her) "own" and "opposite" sex. Also each girl grows herself but one man in her beloved father, quite as each boy grows himself but one woman in his beloved mother.

Author. That analysis makes spiritual sense.

Pediatrician. Please discuss further the unity of spirit and sense.

Author. Awareness of the truth of human individuality provides the enlightenment in which every appearance of disunity reveals itself as illusion obscuring the value of love to life.

The aim of life, the very foundation of human nature, is to go on living. Love is the happiness associated with the functioning of manpower, and happiness which signifies the peaceful freedom of man to be himself is the real elixir of life. Each person's sense of being in his every experience is vitalizing self-consciousness. Goethe said it briefly, "To seem nothing, to be everything."

Pediatrician. A certain view is vivified daily by my work. It seems that the infant or child is tried by the parent he must grow, and that the parent is tried by the child he, or she, must grow. Very much of my professional effort is taken up by my living of each mother who is seeking help, coping bravely with worry over her feeling inadequate to be the kind of mother her baby is specifically needing. I suppose I am only one "seeking help, coping bravely with worry" over my feeling inadequate to be the kind of pediatrician this mother is specifically needing.

Author. (My) you have spoken your mind's problem to its solution.

General Practitioner. Developmental psychology includes all of human life, does it not?

Author. Well said. More and more shall be learned of the joy of living of the continuing years of life as capable, well-aged writers emerge. Each age has its characteristic opportunities for enjoying life. As a few life-veteran authors have already indicated, the very last, first, and intermediate years are equally precious.

General Practitioner. Can you account for the fact that the later years are commonly feared as unhappy, as *sans* everything?

Author. Yes. It is on account of living one's life as if it is not one's life.

General Practitioner. You mean that a person who sees that the nineties have all of the tens, twenties, thirties, and following years in them, will have access to mental riches unavailable to a person who pulls the curtain down on his past life? You mean that a ninety- or one-hundred-year-old man or woman is also a baby, a child, a young adult, and so on? You mean a centenarian can go on menstruating, suckling a baby, enjoying courtship, and having all of the pleasures of youth as long as she lives, in her mind, where every event occurs anyway, just through her free use of her imagination? You mean that aging is always additive but never subtractive really?

Author. I *am* all that I have lived.

General Practitioner. In the stage of senescence it is not already too late to start this study of mindfulness, or self-conscious living, is it?

Author. Not at all. It is exactly the right time whenever the start can occur. Indeed during senescence the individual may have another opportunity to recover some body-centered potency which he, or she, repressed while terrifying himself, or herself, away from primal masturbation and sphincter freedom. It is never too late to start the learning experience of gentle, loving self-control.

> Was man nicht nützt, ist
> eine schwere Last.

General Practitioner. If, as you see it, it is wholesome for the growing boy and girl to be able to use their minds freely, in keeping with their budding life interests—if, as you see it, it is healthful for every human individual to be able to recognize the naturalness of his or her sexuality as well as of his or her hate, jealousy, guilt, fear, and other defensive feelings of spurned sexual imaginings—then why is there almost universal resistance against such mental freedom of the infant and child? What is more to the point perhaps, why does nearly every parent keep his or her growing offspring in ignorance of the benefit of *freedom of imagination* about such vital living of sexuality? Why does nearly every beginner in the living of his masculinity, or of her femininity, quickly sense (his) parental rejection of nearly every expression of sexuality? At least, why is it left unclear in every child's mind that "in his heart so is he," so that he can make peace with his necessity to imagine all of his new growths of sexual interest? In my practice, nearly every little one has grown the conviction that he, or she, not only must not "do" anything sexual or defensive but, what is far more restrictive of mental freedom, must not otherwise *imagine* "doing" anything sexual or defensive. Said Thomas Huxley, "The sense of uselessness is the severest shock which our system can sustain," and I find that statement a true one. You observe that the repression of masturbation is the basis of serious impotence.

Author. Yes. "Uselessness" is a name for repression of usefulness. In the first place, imagination is rarely appreciated as being a name which covers *every* use of the mind. Quite the contrary. For example, one usually opposes "imaginary" and "real." It requires great self-tolerance (self-insight) to see that all that one can mean by "real" must also be *imagined,* and that all that one can mean by "imagined" must also be *real.*

General Practitioner. Nearly every parent protests that allowing his child to imagine sexuality and its defenses "just makes matters worse. If my child has no food and would just imagine eating, he would still be hungry."

Author. A dream, a daydream, a consciously indulged imagining,—each is a form of self-gratification and a very real source of relief, even if it differs from, and cannot fully substitute for, any other source of gratification. To illustrate, his desert mirage keeps the thirst-crazed wanderer alive and striving for relief; his dream of a banquet comforts the starving explorer and protects his vigor-restoring sleep; his imagining his "growing up" and marrying his mother, comforts the yearning young one who feels rejected on account of being "too little" or "too young"; or his imagining himself as big and strong enough to rescue his sane mother from his crazed father really consoles the temporarily hate-filled boy.

General Practitioner. How about this popular view that the free use of imagination complicates, not clears, the child's mind?

Author. The truth in that complaint, as you probably can easily realize, lies in the fact that his, or her, child's free imagining does complicate each parent's problem. It is only natural and necessary for a parent to use his, or her, limits of self-tolerance. *The limits of conscious imagining are prescribed by the limits of conscious self-tolerance (self-insight).*

General Practitioner. Please illustrate what you mean.

Author. A mother who has solved her own sexuality by restricting her imagining tends to live her growing infant and child according to such restrictions, living her young one's compliance pleasantly, and defiance unpleasantly. The baby, or child, prefers to live a pleasant mother and charts his workings (imaginings) of his mind accordingly. Seldom does a parent grow the kind of mastery of his, or her, sexual living so that it can be lived as mental vitality only. Sexual living is of such force that imagining it tends ordinarily to excite sensations and feelings mediated through the body meanings of the mind.

General Practitioner. You mean that a mother, or father, as a rule is not free in her, or his, own mind about sexuality, so that it is impossible for either to voice helpfully factual views about it.

You mean that it is rare for a parent to be able to discuss the sex of sexuality without having either erotic or prudishly unpleasant sensations, so that she, or he, tends to avoid imagining this all-important subject as much as possible. You find that your fellowman by and large cannot consider soberly the personal private wonderfulness of intimately detailed sexual living, in the service of service (for growth of conscious self-knowledge about sexuality), rather than in the service of sexual acts or in resistance to sex.

Author. Yes. Any denial of the goodness of sexuality interferes with that much sexuality's being recognized as idealistic (subjective and good), and requires its being recognized as materialistic ("objective" and not good, or bad).

My "freeing my imagination" means the same as "freeing my mind,"—a healing process which entails all of the difficulties of growing a new kind of appreciation of my personal identity, a new face, as it were. Even as I do, I find that each one of my world *is* using his, or her imagination, in the way that seems most helpful to that one's self, namely, to preserve the *status quo* of his conscious self-tolerance.

I know of no way to make a success of my life except by using my imagination to credit my life with the innumerable wonders it creates.

It does appear that man and woman have succeeded considerably in sensing personal identity in their opposite-sex living.

General Practitioner. Please explain how your localization of mental functioning is practical in the treatment of specific jealousy, where a woman feels insecure regarding her ability to hold her husband, or regarding her ability to prevent his preferring another woman.

Author. To facilitate this explanation a drawing may be useful, thus:

Consultation with this diagram immediately clarifies certain

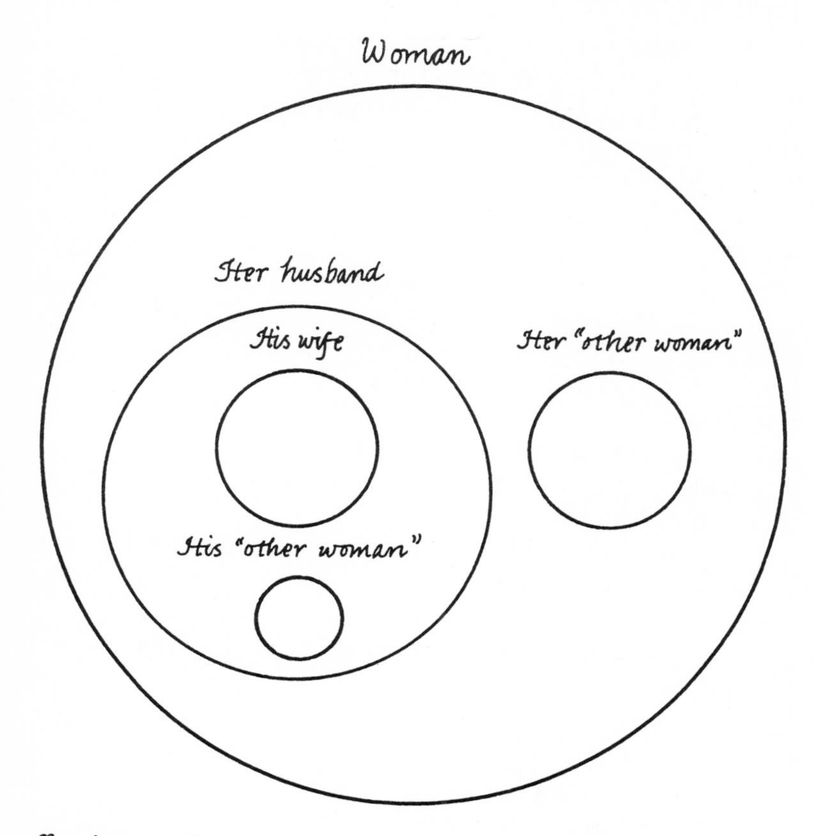

efficacious truths for any person suffering the helpful pangs of jealousy:

(1) Every woman actually lives all of her own husband as an individuation (intact whole) in *her* mind. That means that *her* husband is entirely her own creation and, as such, *cannot* have anyone else to prefer, any more than her arms or head or any other part of her can.

(2) Every woman's "other woman" cannot have anything whatsoever in common with her husband's "other woman,"—except the truth that each is constituted completely of that one woman's own life.

(3) Every woman actually lives all of her own "other woman" as an individuation (intact whole) in her mind. That

means that her "other woman" is entirely her own creation and, as such, cannot have anyone else (man or woman) to prefer.

(4) It is most desirable that every woman consciously grow a husband who is a whole and free-minded individual capable of using his mind for every purpose, including his conceiving himself as untrue as well as true, unfaithful as well as faithful, and so on. What a person cannot responsibly do thus mentally, he *can* "irresponsibly" act out, that is, he can do it as if "externalized" and as if "non-mental." He may or may not act out, however.

(5) Every woman who can thus consciously grow her husband, as a whole free-minded individual, capable of using his mind for every purpose (including his conceiving himself as preferring his "other woman"), thereby spares herself the torments of helpful jealousy,—which jealousy would only be necessary otherwise to warn her that she was disregarding her capacity to love all of herself.

(6) Every woman's sane living of her husband who is unable to be faithful to his own wife and who "prefers" his "other woman" is:

a. To realize that her necessity to live her husband's marital infidelity has nothing whatsoever to do with her ability to go on living her husband's marital fidelity. Sustained consciousness for this fact is of prime importance, and the more farfetched it seems the greater is its needed force.

b. To exercise her continuing ability to live her faithful husband by realizing that he is a mental creation of her own to be enjoyed. Every woman capable of this specific kind of use of her mind's imaginative power will not allocate her husband's marital infidelity to limited mental strength in herself but will recognize that her husband's mind is troubled by his infidelity. The distressing frustration usually called "mental trouble"—associated with painful ideas and feelings of anxiety, depression, jealousy, revenge, and the like,—is *always* traceable to the given individual's inability to use (his, or her) mind freely, and never traceable to (his, or her) somebody else's self-forgetting or self-anything. This discovery of psychoanalytic research, namely, that all mental trouble is traceable to denied free use of the given individual's mind, and not to so-called "external" hardships or misfortunes, is of the most profound helpfulness for everyone's mankind. It is, correspondingly, a most difficultly attained self-realization.

c. To utilize her insight that her husband's mind urgently needs his most loving expert care and try in every way possible to see to it that he experience the most understanding kind of private, personal self-helpfulness.

(7) Every woman's sane living of her "other woman" is to recognize that her "other woman" is her own mental creation to be enjoyed; to utilize this insight to have her "other woman" live as it pleases her to have her live (again using her mind's wonderful healing imaginative power); and, if indicated, to see to it that her "other woman" live the loving expert care she needs for helping herself to live consciously and harmoniously her need to act out the seduction of *her other woman's* husband.

General Practitioner. I hardly know what you mean by all of this, but I think I can get the idea somewhat. Are you able to explain similarly to yourself every kind of mental trouble, besides delusions of infidelity, by means of this kind of accurate localization of mental functioning?

Author. Yes, so far.

General Practitioner. By allocating *all* meaning to the given mind, how do you dispose of the senses and of their sensations? Aristotle's maxim held that nothing is in the intellect which was not previously in the senses. Locke elaborated that view.

Author. The senses are the outlets of the self-dependent soul, the emergence of mind in conscious, and unconscious, manifestation. So-called "somatic" sensation is an elementary expression of meaning. Human experience has its source in the individual's indigenous sensory living. All knowledge is a form of experience, of being, pre-natal and post-natal. Consider the wonderful mind of Laura Bridgman (or of Helen Keller) born blind and deaf. Consciousness itself is ideal sensation. *Every* operation of my mind proceeds from powers intrinsic to itself. Plato compared the soul to a book of which the senses are the writers. All of sensation is lived actively, that is, subjectively. All of "passivity" is an illusion essential for any scientist's work based upon the illusion called "objectivity."

General Practitioner. As you see it, if I talk about Chicago, the atom bomb, God, or the devil,—in each instance I am speaking to and about myself.

Author. Yes. All my thinking (including speaking) which I see is entirely a process of and about my own mind is insightful self-observation, of practical use to me for self-understanding.

All my thinking (including speaking) which I do not view as entirely my own mental scenery, constitutes insightless reasoning. Ernest Jones invented the term "rationalization" for such thought since it carries "a plausible ring of rationality" (*Papers on Psychoanalysis*). All of my world which I judge to be "external" is derived from my self-amnesia. The virtue in my seeing and acknowledging my allness enables me to be willing to renounce every distinction based upon my self-deceiving dichotomy of self and not-self. Self-illuminated by this insightfulness, I renounce my every illusion named "otherness," "elseness," "inhumanity," "alienage," "enemy," "insanity," "objectivity," "externality," "common sense," or any such alleged exception to my own self-helpfulness.

General Practitioner. You state that you began your costly illusion of being a self "separate from all or the rest of the world" when you first cultivated your illusion "not-self." From then on you could respect your individuality only as being one separate from many others. You could not revere your allness truth, that is, the fact that your individuality subsumes its every so-called "other" individuality. I can see how my first concept of my acknowledged selfhood was restricted, in that it necessitated my creation of my illusion "not-self," or "I am not." This delimiting conception of self, or individual, or person, explains its limited usefulness for every clear-minded philosopher.

Author. Yes. It is noteworthy that the birth of the illusion "not-self" necessitated the birth of the illusion "separation." "Am not" or "is not" is a self-contradiction. The oriental seer carefully distinguishes his One, or Absolute Being, as his *universal* self. The idea of alien control arises with the birth of the illusion "not-self." A person finally defines his appreciation of being alive by the way he uses his imagination.

General Practitioner. Are you suggesting that every person mad with jealousy can renounce his concentration upon that feeling, simply by consulting your diagram and studying its general meaning?

Author. I cannot suggest anything. "Suggestion," like "communication," *always* refers to illusion, or delusion, of alien control. I *am* wording my views on jealousy, with which I help myself. That is all. I simply record how I have helped myself to understand my jealousy feelings by working with (experiencing, living, growing for myself) my fellowman who has already developed his ability to understand and explain to himself the indispensable usefulness of his jealousy. The person who is helping himself only by being aware of his painful jealousy needs most of all to experience his fellowman who *can* appreciate the therapeutic force of *his* jealousy for inciting (motivating) himself to learn how to acknowledge his precious jealousy as signalling his effort to disown lovable life in himself.

After all, it is a wonderful relief for me to discover that only I *can* make myself jealous, and that I will never make myself jealous except for the purpose of calling my attention to the fact that I am practicing self-rejection (by displacing my own feelings and ideas, sensations and perceptions, upon *my* somebody else without realizing that *that* "somebody else" is all my own creation). In a fit of jealousy, without insight, I am like a dog chasing its own tail.

Psychologist. Please align your ideas about jealousy with some aspect of your scientific perspective, e.g., experimental method.

Author. A redeeming feature of my scientist's method is its emphasis upon the idea, or prerequisite, that *every* scientist who desires to do so may be able to perform the same kind of experiment and secure the same kind of result, by and for himself. This aspect of the scientist's technique is highly commendable, and holds truly wonderful promise, for it contains the essential truth that everyone must live his experience for himself before it constitutes effective learning.

Psychologist. Are you saying that I, personally, must first suffer each illness or accident myself before I can really learn the health lesson inherent in that kind of experience?

Author. In the realistic sense, I find that true. *When I, personally, use my mind self-consciously to consider myself as actually living whatever my study experience, or textbook lesson, happens to be, I thereby make that medical work effectively meaningful in the most practical way.*

Psychologist. Are you impling that simply by using my mind self-consciously to consider myself as actually living myself *in any way,* I thereby make that kind of living my very own in the most practical sense?

Author. Yes, that is as I have lived it. My creative imagination is useful for my keeping my mental balance.

Psychologist. What do you mean by that?

Author. As I have seemed to repeat, I can mean anything only to myself. *I mean* that I can self-consciously use my mind so that it can experience anyone of my world as behaving himself or herself in a manner expressing my merest whim. *I mean* that such freedom of my mind's use of itself is most hygienic. To the extent that I cannot have my everyone behave thus (as it pleases me), I invariably displace this lack of accomplishment of mine upon my fellowman, and then accuse my fellowman of the deficiency which I cannot acknowledge is my own.

Psychologist. You are too theoretical. Please apply what you are saying to the problem of jealousy.

Author. Very well. I can use my mind self-consciously so that it can experience anyone of my world as being perfectly unfaithful (as well as being perfectly faithful), and thus spare myself any necessity of accusing her or him of infidelity.

Psychologist. That is too deep for me; maybe someday I shall try it again,—but that is more than enough for me for now.

Author. I often comfort myself with this helpfully easy view.

Psychologist. You state that all knowledge *is* self-knowledge, all love *is* self-love, and all that can be lacking is consciousness for each of these truths. I recall the statements of R. J. Meyer, S.J., regarding man, in *The Science of the Saints* (1902): "when he studies himself as he ought, he is really studying the whole creation," and, "For man, by the very necessity of his nature, seeks his own happiness; and consequently he feels instinctively a sense of satisfaction in the contemplation of everything that tends to increase that happiness. Every excellence possessed, every praiseworthy action performed, every good attained, furnishes material for self-congratulation."

Author. All that I can state about either knowledge or love is entirely about *my* knowledge or love, of course.

Sociologist. I am pleased to have an opportunity to offer some of my studied views for consideration, particularly where you are talking about the development of the human individual. Please explain the fact that anyone who helps himself with his counsellor or physician (especially his psychoanalyst) consistently falls in love with that one. Does that kind of "crush" differ from the kind a student develops for his teacher or an employee for his boss, and so on? How does such an affair of the heart differ from the conventional falling in love, marrying for love, and staying in love?

Author. I am glad to have my sociologist, if he wishes to, uphold his ideal of objective validity, test his author's orientation in subjective conception.

As usual for essential aspects of the mind, I must call my attention to the fact that (my) Freud dealt insightfully with this powerful subject (transference) over fifty years ago.[8] My "falling in love," known technically as "transference," occurs apparently in innumerable ways but really only in one way: by living my loved one as if she (or he) is not entirely my own creation. So-called "conventional" falling in love is of the nature of transference: neither lover recognizing his (or her) loved one as entirely his (or her) own creation.

Sociologist. You are stating that conventional married love is transference-love, implying that each spouse carries on his love-making (and spouse-making) as a *folie à deux,* rather than as a sane self-development. You point out that you best visualize your whole life, single and married, as your ongoing self-analysis. You are also indicating that everyone's so-called "marital" and "family" troubles are traceable directly to his (or her) unconscious devotion to transference-love. Furthermore, you claim that every individual's concept of any kind of social organization is an outgrowth of his personal orientation about his family living. In other words, you trace all so-called evils of civilization (war, crime, poverty, starvation, authoritarianism of every kind except *self*-sovereignty, etc.) to transference-love. As far as daring is concerned, at least, that's putting it straight on the line.

Author. Again, I can put only myself straight on the line.

Sociologist. As I understand (my) you, you are declaring that nearly everyone goes through his entire life in a state of transference regarding his loved ones (parent, spouse, offspring, teacher, clergyman, physician, attorney, statesman, world, God). You would account for all real *mental trouble* on this one unresolved problem: transference. You do not count other adversity, hardship, difficulty, as real mental disorder, but rather as necessary life lessons in psychic realism, which always produce desirable personal development such as endurance, hardihood, forbearance, experienced observation, sophisticated judgment, and clear self-consciousness. Whatever life trial you undergo, which is not based upon transference, is a desirable ordeal of living-and-learning the wonderful resources of your human being.

Author. Despite appearances to the contrary (due to my resort to dialogism), I declare only for, of, and to, myself. I do trace all so-called mental "disorder" directly to transference. However, I consider such so-called mental "disorder" based upon transference also to be entirely an *orderly* self-development, the understanding of which is an essential living-and-learning of my wonderful resources.

Sociologist. I accept your dialogic method as an insightful concession made selfishly in your listener's interest. What do you mean by "understanding" your transference-loving, or transference-living? And how can I learn to renounce transference-love and cultivate *conscious* self-love, provided that I wish enough to do so?

Author. By "understanding" anything, I mean seeing the general and special helpfulness to myself in it. Understanding transference-love is known technically as "resolving the transference." Resolution of transference is accomplished only by one's self-analysis, which alone can reveal to him that his love *is* his, and that his love is all about itself. Usually resolution of transference is achieved by the individual's working with his psychoanalyst, who has already disciplined his own mind to see that all of his love is self-love and only about itself. The appreciation of self-consciousness comprehends all love as self-love. The renunciation of transference-living, the practice of conscious self-love, is the foundation of mental health. I find it understandable that Napoleon considered Machiavelli's political works, which seemed based upon limited conscious self-love, to be the only ones worth studying.

Sociologist. You must realize that even a political scientist can understand the important role of self in his discipline,— Destutt de Tracy, to mention one.

You aver that the only human living is all self-affirmation, and that negation is all and only an affirmation of self-unconsciousness. In his *Philosophy of History,* Hegel wrote joyously of the French Revolution:

> Never since the sun had stood in the firmament and the planets revolved around him had it been perceived that man's existence centres in his head, i.e., in Thought, inspired by which he builds up the world of reality. . . . This was accordingly a glorious mental dawn. All thinking beings shared in the jubilation of this epoch. . . . a spiritual enthusiasm thrilled the world, as if the reconciliation between the Divine and the Secular was now first accomplished.

Still, as Cassirer noted, Hegel held the state belonged to the sphere of the *objective* mind:

> No other philosophical system has done so much for the preparation of fascism and imperialism as Hegel's doctrine of the state—this "divine idea as it exists on earth." Even the idea that, in every epoch of history, there is *one* nation that is the real representation of the world spirit and that this nation has the right to rule all the others was first expressed by Hegel.[9]

What I am getting at is this: Is your theory of human individuality practical for *your* world affairs? Can your solipsistic idyll withstand the urgent demands of your world of individuals, each of whom cannot conceive himself as an individual of worlds? Is it not your highest human privilege to renounce your self-consciousness in favor of world-consciousness?

Author. I can ask myself to substitute the often sweet myth of the state (or socius) for the frequently bitter medicine of self-allness. I am aware that such an illusion of human culture is tempting. All I have to do is live myself with increasing self-unconsciousness to enforce my regression to conceiving myself as a member of "the" family living in "the" bosom of "the" state. I had it happen here before and I can have it happen here again.

Sociologist. I find Ernst Cassirer's definition of "understanding" useful, "In order to understand a thing we must begin with defining its nature and essence." One must include in definition the "why" as well as the "what" of a meaning. "There is no *pactum subjectionis,* no act of submission by which man can give up the state of a free agent and enslave himself."[10] Whoever possesses the keenest sense and deepest understanding of human individuality is capable of prizing it to the extent of being able to suffer peacefully whatever experience may be necessary, in the interest of peace. You seem to consider the idea of a war to end all war as a contradiction in its terms, unless it means: end all human life so that there can be no more humane wars. Have you ever considered your life lesson (reverence for human individuality) to be an oversimplification of the true meaning of your ideal society? Are you unable to make your sociology alive?

Author. My every conception, definition, or word is nothing but an outgrowth of my personal living which produces it. All of my recorded understanding is only biographical (biological). I am already in myself to see it; I can, as it were, watch it coming out. I cannot draw a line between what I say of my world and of myself. I can make only life alive.

Sociologist. This view reminds me of Carlyle's life-philosophy. As did he, you seem to require not only intellect but also "insight" and "sincerity" of your ideal hero, sociologist, or whatever. You seem to consider and renounce every claim of an impersonal society, state, or externality of any kind, simply as being nothing but a *petitio principii.* Human individuality is, for you, absolutely the only vivifying principle of any meaning.

Socrates demanded that orientation well enough, it seems to me. You know he conceived the individual as living his own so-called "collective" action. He renounced his living of "external" political science in favor of morality of the inner man. Also, Plato observed that man helped himself to know himself by living his socialization, adding "his" society, "his" city. He thought of society as "individual consciousness writ large."

Author. Only my sociologist can know all that he means by his mind's use. Only he can know whether his use of his meaning of socius, or society, represents a laying hold of the matter of his own living, or whether he considers it to be away from the subject of himself altogether.

A chief use of my language derives from its power to help me put my mind in positions which I consider desirable, and I presume everyone of my world either consciously or unconsciously uses his language for this purpose also. I find "cooperation" an illusion. *Identification* of my fellowman as only and really mine in "his" every meaning for me (not cooperation), is my basic principle of human power. "Working together," realistically conceived, means: each worker functioning as his whole task force. What is everybody's interest is everybody's interest. Oracled Emerson, "We live in a very low state of the world, and pay unwilling tribute to governments founded on force. . . . With the appearance of the wise man, the State expires."

"Unanimous consent," rather than being an anarchistic doctrine, is the very life of the reality of self-sovereignty. My every study of society is a psychological treatise concerning the order of my own living. My every distrust of morality built up from within the individual is traceable to my intolerance of the difficulties involved in realizing such morality. To use (my) Winston S. Churchill's choice way of expression: Self-sovereignty is absolutely the most undesirable kind of government, with one exception, namely, every other kind.

Sociologist. "Developmental Psychology" might well be your first conversation, for it lays the foundation of your thesis; the allness, wholeness, nowness, justness, and unity of human individuality. Please state briefly the meaning of what you have been saying.

Author. Unless I discipline my mind, I tend to be satisfied with considering the "what" of any of my living, overlooking its *why.* Thus, if I am living unpleasantly (depression, anxiety, anger, and so on) I may not consider the *why* of my feeling, and shall therefore lack conscious information about it. Whenever I lack conscious information of my living I tend unconsciously to account for it on the basis of magic (to illustrate, I see it as if I am not entirely responsible for it). Awareness of only the "what" of my unpleasant (or pleasant) living favors my ascribing it to some "alien" influence. Thus, I may say, "I am displeased with you," or "You make me sad," or "You frighten me," and so on.

My considering the "what" of my living treats it apparently as if it could be "objective." My considering the *why* of my living treats it really as *subjective.* The "what" (or "objectivity") of any of my behavior is the aweless, insightless, and necessary basis for any of my fault-finding. The *why* (or *subjectivity*) of any of my behavior is the insightful and necessary basis for the fact-finding which reveals my all as ideally desirable, perfect, life-affirming. Every "insanity" is traceable to "what"-mindedness; every sanity is traceable to *why*-mindedness. My *why*-living underlies *my* genetic psychology: my responsible study of the origin and course of my development of my every mental event (sensation, feeling, perception, idea).

Sociologist. Please ask yourself the following questions, if you will, and answer yourself simply by "Yes" or "No."

Author. I will, but with that thorough understanding that I am saying all that I say, to and for myself only.

Are you willing to consider the proposition that sterilization may be a desirable contraceptive? Yes.

Do you ever regard sterilization as being a desirable simple contraceptive for male or female? No.

Cannot a physician, or loved ones, talk the patient out of his, or her, sterilization objections? No.

If the sterilization does not involve castration, does it still create very deep emotional disturbance? Yes.

If only one spouse is sterilized, does the other unsterilized one regularly experience any of this deep emotional experience (whether aware of it or not)? Yes.

Does sterilization always involve deep emotional disturbance? Yes.

Does sterilization for any purpose always involve very deep emotional disturbance? Yes.

Is the patient always aware that she, or he, is most deeply concerned about possible, planned, or even performed, sterilization,—for example, a senescent patient? No.

Is this profound meaning of sterilization generally recognized? No.

Is the sterilization procedure often regarded as a simple matter of convenience? Yes.

Do you think that your fellow physician and surgeon can see this whole subject of human sterilization as you do? Yes.

Does sterilization create emotional disturbance even for a woman who feels she already has too many children? Yes.

Does hysterectomy usually carry this kind of sterilization significance? Yes.

Is hysterectomy, or sterilization, or castration, ever indicated? Yes.

Is that only when no other procedure can more safely and sanely secure the life-saving results? Yes.

When absolutely indicated, is it better for the man to be sterilized? No.

Is it better for the woman, then? No.

Is it entirely an individual matter? Yes.

If sterilization, or even castration, is performed, can the sterilized (or castrated) one, through proper self-help, recover the full appreciation of wholeness of being? Yes.

Would you sterilize, or castrate, your pet animal? No.

Not even an old male or female animal? No.

You renounce all castration of animals, except that based upon imperative necessity? Yes.

You hold that a human being's rights extend to zoological rights in general? Yes.

You realize, do you not, how very far-fetched such a view must seem to nearly all of your fellowmen? Yes.

Can spontaneous, or even therapeutic, abortion, always carry with it the same kind of profound meaning and deep emotional disturbance as that associated with sterilization? Yes.

Can every loss of an organ or member of the body, from accident or operation, have associated with it similar deep emotional disturbance, differing only in degree? Yes.

Even a tonsillectomy, or removal of a wart? Yes.
Even a hair-cut? Yes.

When a child or adult lives his so-called "separation" from his loved one with emotional disturbance, is that a similar instance of his defending himself from awareness of his threatening ideas and feelings of impotence? Yes.

Then whenever anxiety, or depression, or cold indifference, to living of any kind occurs, it is an effort at self-help, and an occasion for further self-help? Yes.

Sociologist. Fifty years ago, in his *Trattato di Sociologia generale,* Vilfredo Pareto (1848-1923) called attention to perspectives such as yours. He stated outright that all knowledge is subjective, that language without an understanding of semantics simply confounds one's mind, that one's society is what one's mind makes of it, and so on. In fact, in 1935 his translated work was published here under a new title, *The Mind and Society.* You would renounce all counterpointing of self "and" society by postulating "each self's society," I am sure. You renounce such notions as being "brought up in an age," or "in a world culture," or "in a great tradition."

Author. Yes. My Pareto expressed profound insights, one of them being his clear, insistent view that his own published works truly reflect only his own expressed viewpoints, untrammeled by those of his fellowman. Proud of his craftsmanship, Pareto, like Walt Whitman, wanted to put his own freely acknowledged personal views of his life on record. Each realized that the only one of his world who could read his author's view aright also could see it as his (that reader's) very own original creation. Only thus can one come to terms with every solid corpus of true subjective selfness (or false "objective otherness") pervading his very own world. Each learned thus how to make love to his world, and thereby to renounce unhappy feelings of empty loneliness and indulge happy feelings of self-fulfillment.

Sociologist. I notice Anna Freud considers that an infant must learn to distinguish his sensory and perceptual living from his other self-experiences: "Although the two look the same in the child's mind, they feel completely different."[11]

Just one more question, I would have you listen to yourself ask. Why is his developmental psychologist's work steadily neglected by the medical educator?

Author. My medical educator is now helping himself with his findings in developmental psychology. In the autumn of 1952 Anna Freud addressed the first group of first-year medical students under the new curriculum instituted in Western Reserve University. I quote some of her remarks about this urgently needed innovation:

> Instead of beginning their medical education in the dissecting room, these students are introduced each to a pregnant mother on the occasion of her visits to the prenatal clinic. They see the mother several times during her pregnancy, they attend at the birth of the baby, and they remain in contact with mother and child subsequently during the whole course of their medical studies. Thus, they are provided with the opportunity to observe the physical and mental growth of a healthy infant from birth onward, as well as the development of the relationship between mother and child.
>
> The medical student who is introduced to a newborn baby for the purposes of observation and study of mental development may find this experience enthralling and fascinating; on the other hand, he may be disappointed by it. It is a thwarting experience to watch an infant in the first days and weeks of life, if one does not know for what to look. Students may well need some guidance as to the direction which their observations should take, as well as help in grouping the data which they can elicit. They have to understand that, by nature, their field of observation is limited at first. Similar to the human corpse on which medical students used to begin their training, the

newborn presents to their watching eye a body only and no mind, the all-important difference lying merely in the fact that this body teems with the phenomena of life. It is the watching and understanding of these phenomena, singly and in their relation to each other, which lead to the first glimpses of a child's mental activity.[12]

Now at Wayne State University, the medical student enjoys all of the advantages of a curriculum which includes opportunity for observation of infant living.[13] Each student's experience of anatomy is of dynamic living anatomy, which also may be synchronized with formal studies in the humanities.

Sociologist. Since you regard all of your living as divine but find that you must live much of your experience with various kinds of unpleasant emotions (anger, hate, depression, suspicion, jealousy, shame, etc.), you realize the hygienic necessity not to confuse "dislike" with "bad." You try not to let any of your feelings of rejection mean anything at all but a valuable sign that you are not yet ready to see the divinity in whatever you must still live unpleasantly, and therefore cannot live it presently as adorable.

Author. My appreciation of my human power enjoyed an enormous access when I first realized my every unpleasant sensation and feeling to be all and only about itself. Then I could observe its precious helpfulness for outlining the boundaries of my conscious life tolerance. Then I could see that my dislike, itself, was divine, and that it could in no way detract from the divinity of any of my living, including whatever I still might not be ready to experience consciously as being my very own.

Sociologist. What is your view of racial desegregation?

Author. What was never "together" cannot be "separated." *Integration can only occur in the mind of the individual who can see that he is his own Negro and white fellowman.* All other show of integration is appearance.

Sociologist. How about the law of the land?

Author. My white, or Negro, citizen, may conceive his government as an "outside" force which can help him, and thereby obstruct the free movement of his mind for consciously helping himself. Nowhere can this self-forgetting show up to greater disadvantage than in shortsighted efforts to try to force one's fellowman (again, from the "outside") to behave himself humanely. Disregard for deep-seated self is a hypnotic likely to lead to warfare instead of welfare. *Self*-restraint must be *self*-imposed. Freedom is always a *subjective* experience involving *self*-consent only, not "outside concession." Every benefit of freedom rushes to the use of the citizen who can see that he created it and can use it. The uses of one's freedom are always *supposed,* and cannot be imposed "from without."

Sociologist. You mean that freedom cannot be legislated, that the Emancipation Proclamation was ineffective?

Author. Whatever effectiveness one's legislation has is realized only in and by each individual citizen's mind, and his educating himself to use his freedom safely is a product only of his *conscious* self-learning. Certainly, every citizen's legislation of his government is a powerful reality with which he may help himself in his own unique, individual way. If legislation to freedom could be imposed "from without," one's Constitution of the United States would have been capable of creating every citizen as ready for freedom, ever since it was first established. The "public" schoolman originally intended to provide experiences shaping the pupil's mind for conscious self-sovereignty, but he soon found that "public" schooling did not attain this goal.

Freedom which is not earned by being learned can be only a source of fear of running amuck. One hundred years of American experience has taught the wise citizens to renounce every kind of get-free-quick scheme as being a disguised reenforcement of bondage. Every moment of life may be considered as incipient freedom, or slavery, depending upon whether or not that living is being appreciated as self-learning.

As a white, or as a Negro, citizen my conscious enjoyment of my freedom is necessarily expressed in my wish that my white, or Negro, fellowman consciously enjoy his freedom. The extent of my understanding my freedom can be measured by the force of my wish that my fellowman understand his freedom. If I do not busy myself to live so that my fellowman can observe his author's concern about his cherished freedom, then I do not cherish my own freedom. To the extent that I see my fellowman unable to appreciate his constitutional freedom and I do not feel concerned, I live myself as shortsightedly as a physician unconcerned about the incidence and spread of contagion or accident. One's *conscious* health cannot but include beholding and heeding personally every kind of health struggle. Indifference to slavery is always traceable to self-ignoration. Self-ignoration is always traceable to necessary delimiting of self-awareness. Limited self-awareness is traceable to limited self-love. No citizen can be more free than the least free of his fellow citizens, but he can ignore that overwhelming truth.

The range of independence of the American citizen needs to be spelled out as it has never been before. American freedom is of the widest scope, but may not be consciously appreciated for its world extent. I am hoping that every Emancipation Proclamation memorial program properly elucidates freedom's full meaning, including its extent; what it means to have it, what it means to be without it. I want one of my brothers who is largely a self-unconscious Negro to awaken himself to the full meaning of Emancipation. I want my father who is largely a self-unconscious Negro to understand (and understand means: admire and love) his American rights and privileges. I want my mother and sister, each of whom is largely a self-unconscious white person, to know what it means *in terms of human happiness* to live unbound, uncontrolled, unsubjected, and unimpeded.

I am firmly convinced that my fellow American citizen, white or Negro, too rarely learns very much from his own living experiences, about the precious, wonderful, soul-stirring thrill of *conscious* self-government.

There are certain fundamental questions to be examined from as many sides as possible. Does each Negro, or white, child enjoy conscious growth opportunities for his education as being the development of knowledge about his self-possession, self-reliance, self-help, and self-control? Does each one grow conscious love of civil rights, as well as of the tremendous difficulties (necessary obstacles) to the exercise of each civil right? Can one catalog desirable, basic, conscious growths of American citizenship so that recognition of attainment can be clear? How can every white man himself recognize that the Emancipation Proclamation opened up a new resource for the development of his own freedom? How can I, Negro, recognize that my white brother's ability to appreciate that his extending his meaning of civil rights is entirely a matter of liberating himself from enslavement? Being Negro, how can I avoid confusing myself about my wonderful freedom so that I will not confound emancipation with anything at all other than my freedom to develop consciously my meaning of freedom of soul, and my need to study how to exercise it safely and sanely? Does every American realize that *conscious* self-government is the most difficult of all forms of human behavior, and therefore must be studied, and studied, and studied? Does he look for "outside" opportunity and not realize that he *is* all of his opportunity?

Sociologist. Jefferson's political aim was that of a life of freedom. He was confident that the American citizen could cultivate appreciation of the innumerable benefits of *conscious* self-sovereignty and thereby renounce all of his illusions of "external authority."[14] Today it is an accepted dictum that the individual's consistent family living exercises the power of illusional "externality" and renders his mind more or less insensible to his theoretical schooling in the inviolability of individuality, but most sensible to his actual school experience daily demonstrating reliance upon illusional "external authoritarianism." One must be very bright indeed to maintain stupidity regarding the great difficulty with which conscious self-government is attained.

Author. Greatest intelligence *is* required to make unconscious neglect look like conscious devotion.[15]

It is difficult to understand that my rating of myself as a free citizen is the product of my degree of self-insight; and that the more I understand the meaning of freedom the more I find uses for it. The conscious learner of self-freedom is the only safe, or sane, manipulator of his freedom. As he studies the implications of his liberation, every fitting opportunity presents itself to him to employ his new-found independence. To be sure, asking for help, seeking to be taken care of, trading independence for security,—each *is* a form of self-help associating itself with the level of conscious freedom it represents.

A slave is as free as a master. "Circumstances" cannot account for either. Freedom, or slavery, can only be a self-conferred order of humaneness. Everyone lives the kind of world in himself which he thinks it to be. One sure truth is that there cannot be two homes "of the free," a Negro one and a white one; for each Negro is the only white he knows anything about, as each white is the only Negro he knows anything about. One's "other man" is the progeny of his own mind.

A white, or Negro, citizen who feels "at home" only in his slum living, *is* an unavoidable source of concern for his every other white, or Negro, citizen, whether the latter is conscious about it or not. However, to the extent that he understands freedom, but only to that extent, one will be conscious of this distressing necessity in his living, and therefore feel impelled to do what he can to relieve his distress. Only my own shortcoming can make me critical of my fellowman. *When I am consciously intolerant I am only defending the boundary of my conscious tolerance.*

Sociologist. Perhaps if you would become active in politics you might work effectively on self-consciousness. Please realize, however, that it can be of great practical value in one's political life, not only to make "the right kinds of friends," but also to make "the right kinds of enemies." Your view of the allness of human individuality is incompatible with nearly everyone's image of himself as one of some three billion human beings, as one who excitedly upholds, craves, and will not renounce his comforting illusion of "external" authority. Nearly everyone will proudly allege his dependence upon a greater authority than himself. Everyone speaks of "the people," or "the populace," or "the majority," or "the citizenry," or "the electorate." You must find a way to make your idea of the *allness of individuality* understandable for the untrained mind.

Author. The truth of one's own allness is neither school-bred nor home-bred, but self-bred. Only by my reverence for my fellowman's allness can I enjoy the experience of seeing that my fellowman does exercise his self-reliant, independent, self-sufficient idividuality (either consciously or unconsciously).

My conscious mental development is my only source for my consciously responsible living. Any behavior of mine which I can recognize as being autobiographical cannot contribute to symptom formation. My symptomatic living consists of whatever living I cannot acknowledge is mine; my symptom-free living is all recognized by me as my own. Any sensation, perception, thought, or feeling, which I can trace to its origin in myself, contributes to my sensing my worth. Otherwise it functions as if I am subject to it, not as its being my own subjectivity. For instance, any of my present living which I call a "memory" is responsibly presentable as being all about me and, to that extent, is not a source of self-disregard. All of my present living based upon my own experience *is* traceable to its origin in myself but, if I cannot conceive it that way, I feel irresponsible for it.

Sociologist. I presume that your view of the source of all labor-management strife is in each laborer's not seeing his manager as entirely and only that laborer's own living; and in each manager's not seeing his laborer as entirely and only that manager's own living. When each senses his identity in his imagined "external" opponent there can be no labor-management conflict.

Author. Yes.

Psychologist. As I formerly understood, my dissatisfaction with any of my living constituted my motivation to grow more satisfyingly. You express the startling idea that my dissatisfaction with any of my living is a defense of it serving not only to preserve but also to emphasize it. According to your notion, if I can see the good in my so-called dissatisfying living and thus appreciate its true value then, and only then, do I cultivate the motivation to grow satisfyingly further.

Author. Yes. Conscious developmental psychology is ideal self-analysis. However, I cannot develop my appreciation for my dissatisfying living in its absence. I must consciously, so to speak, willingly lay down my life for it by exerting myself to experience it. Only when I am aware that any of my living *is* my very own, can it assert its due meaning for my self-love. My consciously living my dissatisfaction *is* the expression of my loving it, for its helpfulness.

Psychologist. Please let me state your way of life, illness or allness. In the interest of my life fulfilment it is necessary that I develop, cultivate, my tolerance for every kind of unhappiness so that I can use it as a signal for regulating the conduct of my life along directions of health and happiness.

Author. Each human being possesses the mental power to achieve the realization that his whole world *is* his. However this kind of conscious living of his world is a most difficult attainment requiring his free use of all of his mental abilities. Every self-observation possible to man, including every possible manifestation of unhappiness, is indispensably helpful to him for his taking overall care of his self-world. However, certain of his feelings are indeed painful, hence lived by him as if undesirable. Therefore, a person may conduct his life in a manner calculated to avoid his becoming aware for certain of his painful thoughts and feelings. Such steering of his living only avoids his consciousness for his unhappiness. Also it tremendously restricts the range of his enjoyment of peaceful life, imposes narrow reaches upon his self-tolerance, inhibits the freedom and conscious responsibility of his life-insuring imagination, binds great quantities of his avoidable energy, shrinks his conscious volition, and swells the amount of his "involuntary" impulses and their actions.

Psychologist. Is there any particular characteristic by which I can detect that I am, as it were, living as if controlled by my intemperate unconscious envy, or jealousy, or suspicion, or anger, or guilt, or shame, or despair, or any other feeling of hurt love? How can I know if I have repressed any of these valuable sources of vitality?

Author. Whenever I assign responsibility for any kind of my living to my fellowman without seeing it as my own, I can be sure I am repressing it.

Every such unhappy feeling is entirely natural to my human constitution, so that if I deny that I have any such power, certainly that denial may be evidence that I cannot consciously control it.

The earmark of my conscious living of my unhappy feelings is that it is *measured.* I become moderate in my blame, shame, suspicion, jealousy, or whatever unpleasantness signalizing I am living dangerously, once I can observe its exclusive self-reference.

12

Medical Self-Insights

"This Commandment which I command thee this day, is not hidden from thee, nor is it far off. It is not in the heavens, that thou shouldst say, Who will go up for us to the heavens, and bring it to us, that we may hear it, and do it? Nor is it beyond the sea, that thou shouldst say, Who will go over the sea for us, and bring it to us, that we may hear it, and do it? But the word is very nigh to thee, in thy mouth, and in thy heart, that thou mayest do it."

MONCURE DANIEL CONWAY,
The Sacred Anthology

AUTHOR. MY STUDENT in physiology is wise who heeds the principle that his every "illness" (health ordeal) is just as much an acknowledged way of expressing his way of life as is his avowed philosophy. Every so-called "health trouble" is a mental one. The dichotomy of physical and mental health is untenable. If I wish to find my present *meaning* of my fracture, pneumonia, coronary thrombosis, or whatever, all I have to do is free-associate (use and observe my mental activities with complete freedom) around each so-called "physical" sign and symptom.

Medical Educator. I understand that you assert that everything of *meaning* is composed of your life's identity and that "meaning" is the very unit of mental life. Would you please name four of the most extensive areas of repression (and by "repression" I too mean an individual's repudiation of his own mental material under the guise that it is some other kind of material)?

Author. Although I have already indicated as much, again I am pleased to name the four most extensive areas of repression (ignored and denied selfness, asserted non-mental existence) according to my view:

1. One's body, even though it is body-mind, is centrality of mind. Comprised of the first organization of mind, it is most apt to be considered as being non-mental (so-called "physical").

2. One's entire so-called "external world," or sphere of so-called "physical nature." Although everyone must create and organize his own "external world" meaning, as he does his body meaning, nevertheless he is most apt to assert that he lives in his external world rather than that all of his external world lives in him.

3. One's opposite sex. Although everyone is all of his (her) opposite sex, he (she) is rarely able to acknowledge that fact.

4. One's God. Although the kingdom of heaven (as all else of his life) exists within him, everyone is most apt to ascribe all of his divinity meanings to a "greater power than self."

Medical Educator. To get back to the meaning of "illness," its significance as psychological material, please verbalize further your ideas of life and death.

Author. Gladly do I word my mind's meanings, indulge my language of self. Yet Hawthorne stated, "Language,—human language,—after all, is but little better than the croak and cackle of fowls, and other utterances of brute nature,—sometimes not so adequate." It appears to be no arbitrary chance, but rather the only fitting circumstance, that I have attitudes toward sicknesses (health vicissitudes) which I do have. *Consciously cherished life best disposes of death's unknowability.* If I cannot live my human mind, all of it, in its true form, I must express it as best I can, even in my attitudes of abdication to my health challenges, including surrender to my "Dark mother always gliding near with soft feet" (Whitman).

Emerson noticed, "My life is for itself and not for a spectacle." The mental language, or gesticulation, of my viscus is for the most part undetected and even unsuspected by me as being such. Only the most astute pathologist is keenly aware of the necessity to read life and character into the tissue in order to derive its meaning, the essential drift of its significance, its accent and education.

Self-education is the only kind which accords with the life process. Only self-knowledge can be "natural knowledge." Self-science can be attested only by self-evidence, however, not by the averments of "others,"—and is therefore feared to prostration by every human being who seems to himself to be possessed by his self-denying spirit, "otherness." Quite as Da Vinci recorded, "Behold a thing which is valued the less, the more one has need of it. It is advice."

Medical Educator. It appears that you consider that you have solved the hitherto unsolved problem of the origin of human speech. Thus, you trace language to man's primitive efforts to cultivate his self-consciousness, every name being a (recognized or unrecognized) synonym for selfness. Then language as (illusional) communication set in as man grew extensive areas of his mind as not-self (as "otherness"). "Communication" you see as man's effort to use his language of self to bridge over his owned and disowned mental areas.

Author. Yes. A helpful account of the linguistics of individualism, a science of idealism, is yet to be written. Everyone's language seems to inhibit his mental power and obscure his natural glory. Although it is really the paramount symbol of individuality, language implying not-self and prohibiting the consciousness of self-allness amounts to a linguistic obstruction of self-consciousness. Everyone *expects* his fellowman to study and practice a "common tongue" and bans originality of tongue and type with linguistic intolerance. Every dictionary and encyclopedia known overwhelmingly support the illusion of "otherness" and undermine the fact of self-allness.

Medical Educator. That is easily understandable, when one realizes that in his spirited defense of his use of his "otherness" everyone is only practicing spirited self-defense after all. Just consider the tremendous intolerance which is based upon the rejection of any "foreign" language! Religious or any other kind of self-intolerance may be supported by linguistic intolerance, may it not, insofar as language names human meanings?

Author. As I see it, yes. However, all such "intolerance" is really the only possible manifestation of existing limited *tolerance.* Again, it helps me to observe that everyone of my world *is* doing all possible to live himself consciously, *is* loving as much of himself (his world) as he possibly can, *is* living himself up to the very limit of his self-tolerance, and *is* trying in the only ways accessible to him to continue to see his life as worth living. I enjoyed a great release of my mental power for direct self-help, once I could renounce my peace-disturbing delusion that my fellowman could just as well live himself more helpfully "if he only would," "if he would merely grow up" on the spot, and so on. Language *is* used only as the symbol of individualism, regardless of the fact that appearances do not attest that insight.

Medical Educator. In his own way Walt Whitman was an all-time great physician of his mind, was he not?

Author. My Whitman's poetry and prose have inspiriting, enlivening meaning for me. Horace Traubel, in his book *With Walt Whitman in Camden* (1915), describes some of Whitman's living of his physicians and close associates. Of S. Weir Mitchell's regimen he complained, "Mitchell is inclined to drug me—to fill me with the doctor poisons—which is no help, in fact always an injury, to me, as I too bitterly know. Osler respected my objection. . . . Drugs are not for me nor I for them—Mitchell himself now admits it. Of course I do not set it down as a doctrine for everyone to observe." Of what is best for man—the whole of man, Whitman declared: "A man is no democrat if he takes the narrow in preference to the broad view." About his revered friend William O'Connor, Whitman was enthusiastic, "William is always wideawake—always plants both of his two eyes on life. Bucke's letters often go off into words—off into the air—but William is always true to the scent of himself." And, "William has more right words for right places in him than any man I know of in America." To (his) Traubel's remark, "I'm leanin' up against myself strong," Whitman rallied, "How good that is—leanin' up against yourself! That's about the best any man can do when he needs support." His attention called to an error in *Leaves of Grass,* he countered, "I see—I see: it must be wrong—but that is one of my idiocrities—to put it there and let it be, wrong or right. Maybe what is wrong for him is right for me: such things, too, do happen." And on another matter he affirmed his living thus, "I am more likely anytime to be governed by my intuitive than by my critical self, anyhow." Whitman championed individuality in the very word, "We never say things so well when we try to say things as when we let them say themselves." About a tragic death he refrained from speech, "Too much must not be said of that or the like of that—it gets down in you where words do not go."[1]

Charles Feinberg, world-renowned Walt Whitman scholar and collector, called my attention to Whitman's claiming as his ideal physician the Canadian pioneer psychiatrist, Richard Maurice Bucke.[2] Said Whitman, "Osler, too, has his points, big points, but, after all, the real man is Doctor Bucke. He is top of the heap."

This fresh scrutiny of the science of man, the science of self, is the extension of the basic view that living, in order to be healthy, must be true to individual human nature. If it is psychologically true, it is physiologically, and hence sociologically, true, —otherwise not. The meaning of life is all, all, in the living. Optimal healthy living is, all, sincerely self-conscious living.

The more I live me, the more clearly and enduringly I see (1) that I help no one but myself, (2) that my life is one of uninterrupted self-helpfulness, and (3) that my every wish is already a concrete realization, only needing to be seen as such to be evaluated rightly. *Such self-sight I regard as my professional life's crowning achievement.* From the very beginning, *all* education not observable as self-growth is most aptly defined as "hiding." The field of sincere and enlightened selfishness has not been well worked, as the potter's field of "otherness" has been and continues to be. However, from my point of view, selfward is the one and only possible utilitarian direction of any of my research which earnestly deserves to be called serious scientific investigation.

The prevailing clinical concept of health, which is based upon whether or not illness (struggling health) rears its head above a clinical horizon, is not intended as the whole picture of health, for to claim it as such would be woefully inaccurate and insidiously misleading. This ordinary notion of "illness" (as being the opposite of health) does provide a useful view of human welfare which is pretty much in keeping with existing medical facilities.

Each physician or patient undergoing treatment who upholds

the truth of self-interest, benefits correspondingly. Both the meaning and testability of this medical viewpoint are proper subjects of continuous interest and study.

Each physician *lives* the necessity of being *his own patient,* quite as every patient must be *his own* physician. What I mean by the "comprehensive practice of medicine" is: the medical experience *within* each man, the whole physician for the whole physician, the whole patient for the whole patient. These high phrases are more than ordinary catchwords, they are watchwords of *practical* medical living.

The physician is his own, but cannot be his patient's, health representative. Courageous specimen of the human race, his living of himself in medical work is a proper sign that the physician feels within himself his identity in his every suffering man. The insightful physician sees (his) each patient as helping himself specifically by means of his suffering every and any kind of symptom. How insightful of E. A. Robinson: "Miniver coughed, and called it fate,/And kept on drinking."

Medical Educator. Your view of every human experience as being ideal, perfect, and helpful, necessarily includes your peacefully seeing every so-called "pathological" event as therapeutic and every so-called "evil" event as good. I see how your health perspective avoids a fault-finding attitude toward life's vicissitudes, favors the kind and loving feelings which underlie the will to go on living, and respects the obvious and ever reliable truth that an event will always happen if all of the factors are present which fully constitute it. It was with insight apparently that the Greeks called the Furies *Eumenides* (kindly).

Author. Yes. Most of all, medical truth needs to be learned in love. As Thoreau noted, "What other words, we may almost ask, are memorable and worthy to be repeated than those which love has inspired." My life is all I have to go on. It is my only truly precious wonderful possession. Every moment of it is lovable, adorable. Whatever I live is lovable, primarily on account of my *living* it.

Medical Educator. Your writing records that pleasure and pain freely functioning are sufficient to account for moral behavior. How does that idea jibe with your declaration that all is lovable?

Author. The joy of living is the love of life. The feeling natural to self-conscious living is love. All of the other feelings of pleasure or pain are derivatives of love and respectively activate or inhibit conscious loving. Thus, hatred may be conceived as naught but outraged love, jealousy naught but narrowly restricted love, fear naught but threatened loss of love, guilt naught but repudiated love—and so on. To the extent that I do not inhibit my living consciously I do not inhibit my loving consciously, and loving my neighbor as myself is a natural condition. I love whatever I can feel equal to (that is, feel fully my selfsameness in). Whatever I live necessarily with the painful derivatives of love (fear, hate, guilt, etc.) is living which I do not wish to keep available to conscious living, since it hurts. My fear of the hurt feeling helps me further to distract my attention from painful mental content. Thus I have the power to forget (repress) my unhappy living. All of my "unsocial" behavior is traceable only to this "forgetting" of myself.

Medical Educator. You would explain high incidence of infant mortality in part on the basis that a suffering infant has his wish to live weakened by his unhappiness?

Author. Yes. It is particularly indicated that infanthood and childhood living be peaceful (lovable).

The physician systematically grows as many as possible meanings of disease (harassed health) within himself so that he can think and feel with his patient, so that he can speak from *within,* hence with the ring of sincerity. He does not speak for the shadow of health and refuse its substance.

I observe that my every medical doctor practices his medicine in an absolutely unique way which is specific for him alone, namely, according to the way which makes him feel good. His language learning may proceed largely as it did when it first began, semantic appreciation having little or no part in it. All well and good. For him, at the moment, there can be no other possible, or more desirable, medical rationale. Only thus can be filled the wise prescription, "Physician heal thyself."

One of my medical students, speaking for his classmates, expressed appreciation for the opportunity to cultivate a positive, life-affirming, healthy way of living: "It is greatening to be able to grow more than an ability to escape so-called human 'disease,' and to be able to add to the life-saving directions of preventive medicine the joy of living which issues from developing my power to call my soul my own." Cared for integrity of my mind delivers me from that kind of classroom fallacy poignantly described by Sidney Lanier: "Pretty much the whole of life has been merely not dying."

Healthy living consists of loving of peaceful living, no nostrum; pleasing feeling of being alive, no prescription; *originating* gratifying ideas and emotions, no feeding on high thoughts or noble aims; reaching one's own kindness and tenderness further in one's self, no trafficking in charity; growing one's own human being, no being an example or mimicking; cherishing self-integrity, no trying vainly to divide or multiply individuality.

It has not been easy for me to renounce my addiction to *fighting* my own "opposition." I have grown to glimpse the extreme need for more love, in order to be able to transcend (renounce) such popular "fighting words" as "the good fight," "fight cancer," etc. I am seeing the benefit in my loving even my ultramicroscopic "enemies" as my own creations. I am enriching my vocabulary with *recognized* self-words. The almighty language, like science, is entirely and only personal. It enables man to study and practice full living. The peaceful force of kindness is ever present, well disguised as it may be in the appearance of "cross-purposes." Seeming "cross-purposes" are really the benevolent indicators that one is living as if it were possible for him to be "out of his mind," as if it were possible for him to live more than his very own purposes, no one of which *can* "cross," or have anything at all to do with, another. The hygiene of scientific idealism is quite in line with St. Augustine's precept: "Love, and do what you wish to do."

Medical Educator. Your principle of self-understanding posits as its central truth the realization that all human meaning is the possession only of human individuality. You do not argue about the ideality of matter or the materiality of idea. You do not involve yourself in such a psychological bull as: each body is merely an idea since it is through your mind you perceive it.

Author. Capital! Your growth of that appreciation of your author's "main point" indicates that you have taken the trouble to follow his elaboration of his self-understanding.

Medical Educator. Santayana once defined radical idealism as abstention "from all hypostasis or hearty belief in anything, and to dwell only on the consciousness of imaginative activity in a vacuum." Where is the self-verification in that view?

Author. Yes. Please note that Santayana was *personifying* "radical idealism" and thereby troubling himself. All such beginning (with personification) is bound to involve troubled individuality if it is not insightfully undertaken. For instance, beginning with "my radical idealist," instead of with "radical idealism," already supplies me with my dwelling place for my "consciousness of imaginative activity." The "You can't live in a vacuum" protest is regularly advanced to support the (unconscious) contention that two bodies can occupy the same space at the same time.

Medical Educator. You would renounce all discussion of human produce, such as psychology, art, philosophy, science, scientific idealism, and so on, unless it is understood distinctly that no such entity exists except as it is lived by the individual producing psychologist, artist, philosopher, scientist, and so on.

Author. Yes. Such respect for the reality of the only dwelling place of truth (in the one who lives it), would bring peace to everyone's troubled world. Whatever I consciously live, *I* consciously personify, and that is the only kind of personification which has my conscious responsibility in it. The anonymity of all of my unconscious personification favors endless author and hearer confusion.

Medical Educator. You did mention your helping yourself by renouncing the use of personification, plurality, and possession of impersonal living ("otherness"). Human life is not fissionable.

Author. Whatever is, of human life, emanates within the individual. Material physics can only emanate within the given physicist. Whatever is, is the source of itself. Not by "taking," but by *growing,* thought, can I add a cubit to my stature and fulfil myself.

The greatest scientist is the one who has most nearly cured

himself of self-intolerance. The greatest teacher of science is the one who has grown the most conscious self-knowledge. Devotion to his personal health elevation is the physician's best credential. Personal medical study and practice is not only all that is practical, but all that is possible; and without it as his devoted ideal, correspondingly limited practical personal living is the physician's only source of help. Self-reliance must be based upon self-consciousness, which always and exclusively enables volitional decisive living. Self-love is the natural driving power of man. Human being is not just generalized biochemistry and biophysics.

Kant called attention to the fact that a child learns to speak for about a year's duration before he begins to use the personal pronoun "I." Until this time he refers to himself by name, "Charlie wants this," quite as he refers to everyone else of his world by name. In beginning to use the personal pronoun "I," he tends to begin making the false distinction "not-I" in his living. It must appear to him that each of *his* parents feels that this dissociation of mind into "I" and "not-I" is helpful. This habit of mind of dissimulation (of disowning any of one's own mental element by disguising it as "not-I"), once it is set, is renounced only with greatest difficulty. The three-year old also can refer only to his one concept of himself ("Charlie"),—not to his whole self.

There is no possibility that any living, or meaning of living, is not autobiographical. I "keep a diary" as an aid to myself in extending my self-consciousness; but in all truth, whatever I write, or read, is autobiographical.

Medical Educator. After hearing all of this to its end, as I understand it, you study and practice medicine quite as every other one of your medical colleagues does. Thus, you see to it that your patient enjoys all of the advantages of helpful medicines, instruments, and operations, just as any "normal" physician does,—with no exception but with one addition, namely, you endeavor to live all of this medical study and practice consciously, as being all and only a medical growth of your own personal self. Thus, you oddly describe your medical work as: the study and practice of medicine in *yourself.* Am I right in my view of your medical beatitude?

Author. That is about all there is to it, if you will only add that I regard this one additional mental discipline (my *conscious* self-development through my medical work) as being the one indispensable educational requirement of my psychological medicine. Aristotle observed, "The mind is the Form of Forms," and, "The secret of a good life is liberty."

Medical Educator. Your medical educational requirement (recognition of every learning process as a self-development) is in accord with your medical doctrine: Extol the exalted meaning and expanse of individual (human) life. You uphold the preciousness of living being, of life itself. Thus, you claim the fact that every human experience is an individually *lived* one is what univocally accounts for its worth. For instance, life to you is always complete. Everyone always lives the whole truth (of himself). Living being is all that *can* exist. Becoming, or having been,—each is, and can be, only a present view of immediate being. There is nothing exciting, dynamic, interesting, or real, but present self-experience. What gives any "environmental," or "constitutional," factor any and all of its importance to you is the fact that you *live* it. You know Alfred North Whitehead stated, "The present contains all that there is." Your extension of your consciousness of your living has broadened the base of your consciousness of kind, so that you can see such word meanings as "alien," "foreign," "impersonal," and "the beyond," as bridging your very own repudiated selfness with your defended selfness. I like your unitive definition of love as being the feeling natural to freely functioning life, and of every other feeling as being a derivative of love signifying impeded self-expression. What a world it would be if, beginning in the living of each member of *his* family, every individual could understand hatred as being bruised love! Certainly, no one would get mad at *his* hater if *that* insight were available to him. Please describe your view about performing euthanasia, about "easing" a distressing life to its end, about seeing to it that your patient dies well (from your putting an end to the life he suffers).

Author. Everyone must do all of his own living, including all of his own dying. Seeing all of my own suffering as my very own living of it, and recognizing every kind of my suffering as being a necessarily painful way of my helping myself, I may seek relief of my awareness of my suffering,—but hopefully not by means of ending my life. Surely the suicide regimen is the most glaring case of the truly helpful "disease" being infinitely preferable to the allegedly true "cure." Such "euthanasia" (then a chaste word for my disesteem for life) would never be favored by me for my fellowman, if I could acknowledge that I wanted it only in order to relieve my own distress (occasioned by my intolerance for living my fellowman's distress). My attitude regarding any action quickening death rather than continuing life is that it is essentially suicidal, hence psychotic self-helpfulness.

Every person who suicides does so with some notion of euthanasia in mind, to "put an end to his troubles." A medical policy favoring suicide as a therapeutic means would offer the most distressing kind of contradiction. Medical work could offer no sorrier sight than that of a physician seemingly "in collusion" with his patient's wish to die, for the purpose of hastening death.

Medical Educator. You regard actual suicide as always a psychotic act then?

Author. In my opinion, there *cannot* be any other conscious act demonstrating such extreme self-repudiation, such restricted self-helpfulness.

Medical Educator. How do you go about advising your dying patient that his days are numbered?

Author. Life is uncertain. Everyone lives within the shadow of his numbered days. However, while there is life there is hope. In this basic sense, I find it helpful never to give up hope as far as my life is concerned, as long as I can continue to live. I renounce *every* temptation to predict the length of my patient's life, regardless of the extremity of his illness, regardless of the statistical estimates "bearing upon the malignancy of his disorder."

If I am unable to trust my patient's self-helpfulness, that means that I am not well prepared for that particular assignment, and that I would treat myself best by securing further help for discharging my responsibility, or by asking to be relieved of that charge if possible (by referring my patient to a physician more self-consciously experienced in attending difficult health-ordeals). Efficaciously I can have the idea, "My patient is dying," without that idea's seeming to have me.

Medical Educator. Many a patient needs to know that he has not long to live, in order to be able to put his affairs in order. How do you take care of that necessity?

Author. I can *never* know how long my patient has to live; however, I can propose sensible business procedure without its meaning that I am thereby predicting my patient's death. Indeed such a proposal is potentially a life-affirming one which can properly be turned to health account, for the easing, comforting prudence it offers. It is always well for everyone to have his affairs in order, to the best of his ability, and such a prescription may well be considered by every physician for each of his patients at first consultation. "Timely notice of dangerous manifestations" serves the best interests of medical practice, and is not a condemnation procedure.

A physician best upholds the dignity and honor of his profession, exalts his medical standards, extends his sphere of usefulness, and promotes the advancement of his science, who can renounce any illusion he may have as to the "relative" value of life in an "old" versus a "young" person, in a "sick" versus a "well" person, in a "good" versus a "bad" person.[3] Human life, at any stage of its development, and during any and every struggle for its preservation, is equally precious and of unimpaired worth. Human life is always and ever the truly specific marvel for each physician's reverence and veneration. "Age difference" is an illusion.

Medical Educator. Your testimonial that your living *self-consciously* is always attended by a health access interests me profoundly. Coleridge described the principle of his philosophy as "the referring of the mind to its own consciousness for truths indispensable to its own happiness." I notice that you regard any and all acknowledged responsibility to be the production of self-consciousness. I can admit that my ability even to be interested in taking care of myself varies directly with the extent of my self-esteem. I can also admit that my living myself as if being (enclosed) *in* a room, *in* a house, *in* a city, *in* a country, or *in* a world—each "in" makes me out to be a small part of a great whole, instead of making each such "whole" out to be a small part of me. I can even see that it is clearly to my health advantage to increase my self-tolerance, so that I will not have to live most of my living *as if* it is not my own. The fact is that I have actually tried to recognize my own sensation, or perception, as entirely my own living (which it obviously must be) and have thereby been able to feel something of the "lift" you describe. My trouble is that I find it impossible to stay with that way of living myself, living *self-consciously,* I mean. Don't you find that difficult, too?

Author. I most certainly do! Not only difficult but often impossible, even after my many years of applying myself to it! Yet, I am afraid to give up trying; for I realize such a surrender would be too costly. I keep *trying* to see myself in all of my living, since I have discovered that way of life favors my health. My every success in living with proper appreciation of my life *as such* is my most enlivening experience. I have grown to cherish as my most prized working force *my ability to try living self-consciously.*

Medical Student. Please mention again the power which opposes your enjoying all of your living as your very own? How *can* an individual, always under his own power, begin to live himself in any way so that he can *deny to himself* that he is the author of that living?

Author. I am ever pleased to ask myself this question, for it activates wisdom for the conduct of my living. My feeling of love frees my mind for action and facilitates my conscious living of my mental power. All of my painful living, however, necessitates my interest in the possibility of my dying, rather than living freely. *Forgetting myself is not a purposeful act of my conscious self.* My "active forgetting" is an instinctive defense against my making too much over the unpleasant vicissitudes of my life. Whatever I live unhappily (painfully) is *thereby* qualifying as forgettable. It is human nature to recall pleasant, and "forget" unpleasant, living. All of my self-repudiation (repression) is the product of my forgetting myself (as far as my painful living is concerned) so that I can recognize myself (as far as my pleasant living—hence my wishing to live—is concerned).

Medical Student. I see. Your attention tends to steer itself away from unhappy memories just as you tend to keep your hands off a painful part of your body. However, for purpose of healing you must often do work involving painful parts, and surely that must be true of your injured love and its sensitiveness. It seems to me that nearly everyone is seeking happiness not for the sake of free happiness itself, but to avoid seeing how unhappy he already is. Everyone I know wants his happiness not just for itself—but also to rule out his being aware that he is depressed, or even has the helpful capacity to endure and be guided by unhappiness (including pain).

Author. No doubt you understand your Thoreau's insightful comment that "the masses of men live lives of quiet desperation."

Medical Student. I can understand my own temptation to live a narrow secluded life rather than to take the trouble to endure and use wisely my valuable capacity for unhappiness. Please discuss this further.

Author. When I force myself to live an experience which I am not ready to live as one of my own choosing, I may relegate that (usually painful) personal experience of mine to a part of my mind which I may thereafter treat with neglect, with as much ignoration as I can muster. Of course that means that I must avoid living any experiences which might remind me of such rejected life. For instance, if my fellowman's behavior might remind me of my own (rejected behavior) I must either avoid my fellowman-living entirely or deny that *I am* living it. If I do not focus my attention upon such forgotten selfness, I do not force myself to be aware of how unready I am to live it peacefully. Of course I do live it thereafter, but in a special manner, namely as if I am not living it. While this kind of *consciousness-deprived* living of mine accumulates, as an outgrowth of my habitual resort to it, I find that I must accordingly live more and more power of my self without sensing my identity in it. My indulgence of this latter habit increases its strength.

Medical Student. Please illustrate.

Author. I shall try. As a very young child I am enjoying my living myself in one way or another, when all of a sudden (without any preparation for so doing) I find that I am growing a prohibition as far as that source of pleasure is concerned. Thus, I grow what I then, or later, designate "mother" living her disapproval (seemingly about her child's being able to enjoy his life). Simply by forgetting (my living of) *my* disturbing mother whenever I can, I do not have to live her consciously as mine, I can then resume my interrupted self-enjoyment activity. As I succeed in forgetting such self-growths which I associate with unhappiness, I develop my (self-deceiving) "out of sight, out of mind" philosophy about them. Thus, I disclaim that I am the author of my very own self-experience which I call "mother." By denying that I grow my own sensations and perceptions denominated "mother," I pave the way for denying that I grow all of my own meanings for the same, and thereby enable myself to live these experiences of my own life without realizing they are entirely my very own. However "in sight" *is* in mind. Seeing, or hearing, or any sensory living, is minding.

Medical Educator. According to you, you must love yourself in order to be conscious for yourself. How about love and individuality? How does it work?

Author. "Existent" may be well used as a synonym for "individuality." Whatever is, *is all about itself.* The only way in which the meaning of individuality can be minimized, is by disregard for it. Thus, love exists as an individual life force. *Love is all about itself only.* It is the natural feeling of being alive. This love, my native life-feeling, undergoes innumerable vicissitudes,—many of them associated with great pain. Every other feeling (affect) derives from love and has all of its meaning in terms of it. I find this insight very helpful.

Medical Educator. Please illustrate again your view that painful feelings stand for disguised love, for attempted negations of love.

Author. Hatred is wounded love; anger is outraged love; fear characterizes threatened loss of love; jealousy is unacknowledged self-love, love (as if) dispossessed; guilt is ignored love; shame, disgust, suspicion, and every other unpleasing feeling,—each is a modality of love.

Medical Educator. It is easier for me to see how each of the pleasing feelings, such as worship, ecstasy, rapture, awe, and so on, are ultimate affirmations of love. Nevertheless, I can understand how all that favors human functioning in all of its powers frees the love of life, and how all that impedes the freedom of all of human functioning obscures, as it tests, the survival of struggling love. I realize you regard all love as self-love. Please explain the accurate meaning of such a statement as: "I love my fellowman."

Author. I may live my meaning for my fellowman and my feeling of love at the same time, but the one *cannot* have anything to do with the other. This appreciation of the "loveness" of love is essential for the recognition that all love is self-love. Love lived fully for itself enjoys its freest existence. Living all of my self-activity with conscious love is my health goal toward which I try to aim my living.

There is no possibility for me to be conscious of the meaning of humanity, or of divinity, except by my living that meaning. Peace, freedom, love, truth, order, health, faith, hope,—each is a self-grown product entirely. All of any seeming mental "conflict" which I suffer is traceable to my vain effort to see one part of my mind as having something to do with another part of my mind, traceable to my trying to bring about agreement "between" parts of my mind (although every part of my mind must live all of its own agreement, or harmony, or peace, within its interiority). All of this deepest conviction of my own unicity is the culmination of all of my sustained exertions toward maintaining conscious strength and wholeness of my mind.

Medical Educator. You speak of your "profound conviction" and of "the culmination" of your mental exertions. By all of that do you mean that there is no possibility of your ever growing more sense, no possibility of your growing even a more "profound conviction"?

Author. Thanks for the opportunity to provide allowance for the illusional element in every sentence or word I speak. The wisdom of Ernest Weekley fits here, "Stability in language is synonymous with *rigor mortis.*" Every bit of my talk is nothing but a register of my current mental events.

Medical Educator. By human individuality you mean human wholeness, and by wholeness you mean a constituent, homogeneous completeness which is essential to, and constitutive of, that individuality's entirety. Its every part is all and only its characteristic element. Individuality cannot be separated into anything different from itself as you define it. The only possible, hence understandable, meaning of an "apparent" human "part" is entirely and only a function of its *real* wholeness inherent in it.

Author. True.

Medical Educator. Does your physiologist teach that every viscus derives all of its livingness from the individuality of the organism? that every function of the body is entirely an expression of the individuality of the person? that the only law of any human tissue is a necessity of the autonomy regulating the whole life? that all that lives is wholeness living? that there is no basic understanding of organ function except that based upon understanding of the whole economy of the individual?

Author. That is as I see it. Every organ speaks the mind of the individual.

Medical Educator. General Smuts held that the determining factor in nature is the whole organism, not its constituent part. That is the philosophic doctrine of holism, is it not?

Author. My mind uses my every observation only as a view of my own which helps me to comprehend, and account for, the humaneness of my allness. My body has no parts in the sense that a machine has parts. It has only the oneness which my life provides. As one of my colleagues picturesquely described this physiological orientation, "Every organ has the man wrapped around it."[4]

Medical Educator. I recognize that the doctor of medicine is systematically doing all possible to develop his own health which, of necessity, includes his proper concern that *his* patient consciously cultivate his healthfulness. I like R. L. Stevenson's tribute to his M.D. "The physician is the flower (such as it is) of our civilisation and when that stage of man is done with, and only remembered to be marvelled at in history, he will be thought to have shared as little as any in the defects of the period, and most notably exhibited the virtues of the race."

13

A Psychiatrist's Way of Life

"Father," he cried, "I have found it!"
"Found What?"
"The fact that I have a mind. A mind that can think and create."
"In that case, son, you had better go to Princeton."
Thus his pastor father, Dr. Wilson, lived his son Woodrow, seventeen years old. Princeton, his own alma mater, could channel mental prowess into practical achievement.

HENRY and DANA LEE THOMAS

GENERAL PRACTITIONER. IT would be practical if you would detail for me your medical way of life. What is your idea of a wonderful time? What do you find is practical in your effort to live yourself happily? I am aware that health is entirely a personal, private matter.

Author. The real issue of living for me is that of enjoying peaceful life in such a way that I am at the same time developing further my capacity for enjoying my life. In consciously going my own way, "living my own life," it is my whole world that I have going my own way. With this comprehensive view of my self-possession I find it necessary to consider that my enjoyment of myself is basically my life's work, and that to keep the spirit of self-satisfaction an accompaniment of my current self is a task which I cannot afford to slight. Living my catholicity with felicity exercises all of my capacity for self-consciousness.

General Practitioner. Your last remark reminds me of a question I have been wanting to ask for some time. It is generally conceded now, at least by every psychoanalyst, that one's mind, or psyche, is entirely *unconscious.* Freud pointed out that the entire psyche is as unconscious as any other imagined externality. He indicated any mental material considered to be "conscious" is *virtual,* only, in its existence, as a virtual image in optics. Therefore my question is this: By your stress upon self-consciousness, do you not overlook the all-important truth that the mind, all of it, is always unconscious except for its one power, consciousness, which always functions as if *it* is all that counts?

Author. I am glad to face this question squarely again. My living consciously does not, and cannot, exclude my contemporaneous unconscious living. My mind is entirely unconscious (except for its one function called "consciousness") and it is helpful to have that insight ever accessible. My concentration upon the importance of consciousness is not intended to be at the cost of appreciation of my very own unconscious mental material. Quite the contrary, my express intention in my use of my consciousness is to call my attention to evidence of the existence of my very world of unconscious mental material.

General Practitioner. I see. You find it helpful *both* to realize that your actual mind is entirely unconscious and to realize that (by means of your mind's power of consciousness) you can adduce virtual evidence of the existence of your actually unconscious mental life. Is there no exception to the helpfulness of self-consciousness whenever it does occur?

Author. Self-aroused self-consciousness leads consistently to conscious self-help. It may seem less desirable for me to be aware that I am sitting on a tack than to be unaware of this self-hurt, but this is obviously only a seeming. My happy self-experience has upheld steadfastly the principle that self-ignorance is the most çostly form of bliss.

General Practitioner. As I understand it, you are not telling or advising me of your views. Your idea is that you favor *your* healthy and happy living when you have everyone of *your* world knowing how to live health and happiness. Therefore you have your hearer grow his author expressing his views to his self, and then decide if he wants to live them also entirely as his own, by saying each of them to his self.

Author. I find not only that I cannot advise my (other one) fellow citizen, but also I discover that I cannot advise myself. Self-consciousness is not a form of advice. Self-insight is self-conscious living, not a product of counselling. Any living which is lived just as "preparation" is not self-conscious living. Living which is experienced as self-conscious living dispenses with all kind of makeshifts for itself, such as preparation, counselling, and similar compensations for the embarrassment.

General Practitioner. You state what is not self-conscious is concealed from one's self. Is it possible to develop one's living of this state of grace you call self-consciousness so that it can operate "on automatic"? For me, an all important energy-saving device is my cultivated ability to do what needs to be done "from habit." Maybe "habitually self-conscious" is a contradiction of terms.

Author. Enriching question, that. I have found it possible to grow my current sensations and perceptions as developments of my own identity. I do regard continuous self-conscious living as a desirable developmental goal,—one, however, not to be confused with the repetitive connotation of habit (so-called "second nature").

General Practitioner. You find that self-consciousness provides the most humane of all creature comforts,—peacefulness, sincerity, and interest. In one sense it functions as finest mental nourishment, e.g., as fresh air to a gasping mind. In another sense it functions as a needed mental elimination which prevents psychic intoxication. In still a further sense it provides robust mind substance. And so on. You stated you would recommend the screening of the applicant to the college of medicine basically in terms of his capacity for conscious self-development.

Author. The more I hear my "other one" use the pronoun "I," the more I am inclined to appreciate his effort to be sincere with himself. What is not self-conscious is hidden. As I have indicated, the medical aptitude test which could evaluate what is most essential for medical living would measure the applicant's capacity for self-conscious growth of his medical experience. *All* observation is subjectivity.

General Practitioner. How do you abstain from feeling bad about the self-unconscious living of your fellowman?

Author. A self-observation of unlimited self-helpfulness (in my seeking the natural level of responsible living for myself) is my realization that I do not complain or protest or grieve about any necessary helpfulness of my fellowman, provided that I see my identity in it. I certainly do, and wish to, feel distress or displeasure about my helpfully painful living, but once I realize that my distress is all and only of my own making, I do not expend my energy in complaining. My energy therefore becomes available for my healing and strengthening myself, so that I may "live through" patiently whatever distressful experience I might find it necessary to create for myself. Just considering the application of this kind of insight and its subsequent release of energy with regard to every complaint or criticism, grievance or grumble, is well worth the energy investment such consideration involves.

Self-consciousness breeds self-consciousness. Self-consciousness reports my living through the proper channel, which truly respects the only line of my authority and always leads to harmonious living of whatever issue is to be lived. Recognizing every meaning as having its entire existence only by virtue of my living it simplifies, frees, and eases all of the working of myself. It enables me, as a trouble-shooter, to work with what is workable; it renders accessible to me my accumulated growth of self-wisdom; it enables me to be self-confident, enthusiastic, and, above all, kind. Insofar as I see myself as my whole, I grow the attitude of mind which helps me to renounce my unconscious use of any pronoun but the one pronoun possible for me, "I." For me, the only true feeling of home-felt harmony is provided by the sense of homogeneous selfsameness in all of my personal life. Thus, I recognize that what is "impersonal" can be nothing but unconscious personality. Seeing my concept of my patient as an abstract personification created by myself attributes to it the only specificity and concreteness possible for it. All else is self-disregard parading as regard for my patient, who must do all of his own regarding and seeming regarded.

My "getting down to the facts," or "down to business," originates when I practice facing the truth of the allness of my own being. This "good life" has to be constantly lived, newly created. The more self-conscious my living is, the more concrete it becomes. Every way of living a human life is adventurous and involves daring. Self-conscious living is most heroic of all. My living "in the present" is not actually descriptive of my being; my living "the present in myself" is. Seeing all of my world as, in every particular, nothing but an extension of myself is the key to all of my sanity. First, I lived a part of myself, my psychoanalyst, while creating my way of cultivating my self-awareness. Gradually, I saw the sanity in self-insight. The benefit of self-conscious living has been life-satisfying.

Insofar as I cannot recognize my life as being all about me, just to that extent I must find myself without something interesting to do. There is only one possible concentration on a specific problem for me, namely, a problem about me. Insightful individualism provides the only actual relevance of my every meaning clustering about such an abstraction as "society" or "collectivism." However, if I cannot call my society, or my everyone, my own, I must thereby constrict my acknowledged self-view and simulate an ability to "do good for somebody else,"—since I cannot observe that full self-love develops a reach of charity which covers my world.

Editor. Please consider these time-honored views of humanity:

Individuals are not wholly individuals, they are really parts of *society.*

Humanity is a social meaning not an "individual" meaning.

People grow up only through their *relationships* with other people.

Mature human love enables a man to lay down his life for his fellow man.

Your insistent personal note is the unwanted one of literary bad breeding. You might try looking the other way while you speak. For shame, your selfness is showing; and, frankly, I do not feel equal to identifying with the exhibition. If you feel old and candid and secure enough to write your memoirs, very well, reveal them. Please realize that I am trying only to be helpful in these remarks, none of which is intentionally unkind. Autobiography is the proper form of literature for the disclosure of *personalia,* is it not?

Author. Yes. All writing is creative writing, is truly autobiographical.

Editor. "All writing" includes transportation schedules, telephone books, and census reports,—not to mention scientific measurements. Are they autobiographical, too?

Author. Only and entirely. Whatever any one writes or reads, is an expression of his personal life. *All* "objectivity" is ignored subjectivity.

General Practitioner. I always consider self-effacement to be a virtue,—and by self-effacement I do not mean face-saving denial of responsibility. According to you I am an attitudinizing diarist in my reading of my daily newspaper, but do not know that.

Author. I can observe only that I am a diarist in all of my reading and writing,—which is not, and cannot be, the same as my making this observation of my fellowman. Only he can make any of his self-observations. This talk of mine is devoid of any avowed purpose other than that of stating observation of me, to me.

General Practitioner. After all, all you have really stated so far is that your mind orientation is that of the truth of subjectivity (of your everything and everybody of your world) which exclusion necessarily rules out objectivity (except as an illusion); and that one's scientific mind orientation of "objectivity" by definition rules out subjectivity as being the source of error. I have always considered the "objective" to be the "reliable." True, the postulates of science are psychological assumptions, but the scientist's unique goal is the quest of laws. He considers, with Socrates, that ignorance is the only vice. Your overemphasis of the individual leads to fierce selfishness, the only bone of contention in social living. A most *popular* axiom states that self-expression is a substitute for genius. Your notion of an individual is that he is an ingrown, self-centered autocrat unaware of the world around him, living in a vacuum. I couldn't trust such a person. Literary propriety, or virtue, may change, but hardly in the direction of your first-person-present-tense fixation. No wonder democracy is in danger all over the world when there are notions like this about it. You couldn't even grow such ideas, if you didn't live in the tolerant democracy of America. You owe allegiance to your country, not just to your self. I am interested in unity in my country, not in one of its individuals alone. People such as the individual you describe create all the chaos in the world.

There is just one world, not billions of worlds. I can understand a person's wish to be "the whole cheese." Your descriptions of individuality are a classic example of how verbalism can run away with a person. You say you can't help anybody else,—well, anyone can help himself by egotizing as you do. My protest could go on and on.

Author. It is just such rejection of dawning self-consciousness which constitutes the beginning of acceptance of it. Such expression just gives voice to the idea that every man is an all-important man, and that the edifice of any and every kind of democracy rests on the individual man in whom it has its any and every meaning. Comes to conscious mind Carlyle's comment about "the Wind-dust-ry of all nations involving everything in one inane tornado." The true "measurable" exists only within the measurer. Truth exists only within the truthful *one.* Every "spectacle of humanity" is only and entirely a self-view created by a human being. The "best" psychiatric residency is where the "best" psychiatric resident is. Whoever sees the meaning of individuality, of oneness, most sharply, is the clearest, most reliable and dependable of human beings,—as I see it in my world. *That* self-measure is most difficult of attainment, *which is why I see so little of it.* If insight were easy to attain it would certainly be the most "popular" of all life views. Everyone's self-measure is useful (in ways which can be evaluated by him) in that it favors his prediction and control of his behavior (a prized goal of every scientist). The self cannot be opposed to "others" or to aught else since, as its own all, it subsumes its every meaning.

My knowledge consistently recognizable as self-knowledge most readily finds its purpose in my practical conduct. All of my seeing scientific idealism as a cultural force, certainly does alter the structure of my mind in that it develops my capacity for conscious humaneness. My medical science is conceivable as a specialty in my human being, in that it constitutes specialized self-helpfulness. Each of my basic medical sciences provides a study of the "body" and, as such, cultivates my mind. Every bit of study of "medical science" is, in its entirety, a creation of my mind. Every "anti-psychological" attitude, after all, can be nothing but a psychological attitude. My medical study is seen most clearly as a real (ideal) scientific movement, if it is recognizable as a specific direction of study of myself. I find strengthening and healing self-sight in *appreciating* that every aspect of my medical living derives from my mental development. *I see clearly that objectivity is the source of all errors.*

Every "practical art" is constituted entirely of conscious or unconscious mental events. If medical learning is not recognized as entirely a matter of self-growth, the strengthening and healing benefit of self-consciousness must remain the *arcanum arcanorum* of medicine. Yet Plato was only expressing the view of his contemporary medical scientist when he stated his belief that fundamental education of the patient is the idea of scientific healing. Knowing the ways from health to "sickness" (health undergoing trial) enables the physician to know the ways back from "sickness" to health.

The verifiable scientific fact of my one life postulates the natural role of my individuality in subsuming all of its world. William James discovered in his living: "a man's self is the sum total of all that he *can* call his,—not only his body and his psychic powers, but his clothes and his house, his wife and his children, his ancestors and his friends, his reputation and works, his lands and houses, yacht and bank account." The common element in all that comprises one's own world is *that one's* own personal identity.

General Practitioner. Leibnitz asserted all reality to be psychic material. Lotze said, "Self-existence, or self-hood, is the only definition which expresses the essential content and worth of that which we from accidental and ill-chosen standpoints, characterize formally as realness." Haeckel and Jacques Loeb described matter as psychic. Coleridge said, "Self-consciousness is groundless because it is the ground of all other certainty." So what?

Author. How educationally insightful this question is! So what? indeed. My hearing my teacher saying to his self what he sees to be true is not at all the same as my saying truth to my self. I can have him understand himself but that does not mean that I understand him. It is helpful to observe all of my experience from that same vantage point. Life without a conscious purpose of self-development for self-fulfilment and self-realization substitutes side issues, makes cause of details, becomes litigious or outlawed in one or another direction. Self-consciousness provides the sentience necessary for the proper ordering of my human being, and I well appreciate my Plato's definition of health as "the proper order of the body."

My definition of "genius" is: one who enjoys *all* of his human being to the fullest extent. All *conscious* use of the creative power of mental life derives its efficacy from being a healing method which allows the healthful wholesomeness of human nature to assert itself. The self-unconscious patient becomes the self-conscious healer by attaining to the knowledge of his wholeness and, therewith, the volitional control of the directing of his life.

Professor Charles Horton Cooley, Michigan's most insightful sociologist, distinctified a solution of the phantom problem, "society *vs.* individual," in his *Human Nature and the Social Order* (1922):

> I conclude that the imaginations which people have of one another are the solid facts of society, and that to observe and interpret these must be the chief aim of sociology. I do not mean merely that society must be studied by the imagination—that is true of all investigations in their higher reaches—but that the *object* of study is *primarily* an imaginative idea or group of ideas in the mind, that we have to imagine imaginations. . . . It is important to face the question of persons who have no corporeal reality, as for instance the dead, characters of fiction or the drama, ideas of the gods and the like. Are these real people, members of society? I should say that in so far as we imagine them they are.

Professor Cooley adds that it "is healthy for every one to understand that he is, and will remain, a self-seeker, and that if he gets out of one self he is sure to form another which may stand in equal need of control."

14

American Physician

I say, we ought not to reject the ancient Art, as if it were not, and had not been properly founded, because it did not attain accuracy in all things, but rather, since it is capable of reaching to the greatest exactitude by reasoning, to receive it and admire its discoveries, made from a state of great ignorance, and as having been well and properly made, and not from chance.

HIPPOCRATES

MEDICAL EDUCATOR. MY practice of medicine has prospered in its American freedom thus far. Ronald Gregor Smith worded a viewpoint which I have recently made my own: "The human spirit is free so far as it knows no limits within itself to the possibilities which it may unfold."[1] Your doctrine of man as being a wonderful absolute solitary, whether he realizes it or not, is difficult to understand. From experience I have found that I cannot understand anything that I cannot live lovingly. However, radical individuality is full-measured individuality, and I "may unfold" its truth as a possible guiding health principle.

Author. Living up to the health directive of his country's constitution, the American physician may consider, and live himself, as a free world. He may recognize free-mindedness as his precious system of therapeutics. His medical education, above all, may be safeguarded as mental emancipation and continue untrammeled by illusional "other-than-self" medical dictators disguised as "authorities." His every medical dogma may be clearly evident as a self-principle, as a self-observation. Every American medical student may cherish as his most prized possession his consciousness for his freedom, his consciousness for his self-activity, his consciousness for his growing creaturehood, his consciousness for his self-helpfulness, and his consciousness for the fact that he is the author of his own existence. Self-consciousness only can open his mental eye to visualize the allness of his selfhood.

Every slightest extension of human consciousness is expressed in an increased measure of recognized human freedom. Self-conscious living sensibly fits the mind for the proposition of liberty, thereby activating mental health. "You tell me what to think" is a terrified and terrifying alternative for self-reliance built upon self-trust, and self-trust built upon self-consciousness: "terrified" in that the individual living it is incapable of conscious self-reliance, "terrifying" in that the individual living it properly claims respectability for his irresponsibility. A human being is not a conduit. Such questions as "Is living a materializing of mind?" or "Is living an idealization of substance?" may distract a well-meaning scientist from the all-important observation that *all of any living is the living of one life.* Such is the historic doctrine of medicine, *the individual variant.* There can be no "gap" between mind and matter. The very meaning of "betweenness" is that of a construction compensating for a lack of insight. "Mind" is all about mind; the word "matter" is a localized living of mind which is all about itself.

Medical Educator. This view reminds me of Louis Sullivan's beautiful unification of mental material: "That man creates in the image of his thought is our thesis."[2] Frank Lloyd Wright also upheld the ideality of architecture: "Buildings are a synthesis of society and civilization in a system of philosophy and ethics, if they are organic architecture."[3]

Author. The findings of self-conscious living are far-reaching,—and well they may be, since specific psychotherapy has only one task: the conscious integration of "far-fetched" mental material.

Medical Educator. The scientific idealist observes views of the learning process which call for the greatest modification of ideas and customs prevailing in the mind-shaping experiences of everyone's home living, child development, and systematic educational work. I refer to the desirability of each person's reducing repression, promoting renunciation, and thus furthering humane self-protection of every kind.

Author. Any work upon appreciating the truth of individuality is health work. Every last effort in developing and maintaining self-consciousness is finest self-helpfulness. Every practicing physician who sees his living for all that it can be, a continuing self-discovery, cannot but appreciate that his power of self-consciousness is his one desideratum when he is afflicted with an infantile paralysis of his will and an anesthesia of his self-respect. Any one who has exercised his ability to comfort and thrill himself self-reliantly cannot but appreciate the truth of self-heal. Democracy means: conscious individual opportunity to realize one's potential.

Medical Educator. In what way, if at all, does your prescription of "enlightenend and extended self-interest" differ from the doctrine of "emergent evolution"? You too seem to believe that successive steps in a person's evolution produce essentially new creation.

Author. I live gratefully every highlighting of the "fresh look" idea. Undoubtedly, my "self-conscious practice of self-activity," my here recorded hygienic way of life, bears close resemblance to many formulas for living. All that I am really reporting is that I have found that I must either exercise conscious self-helpfulness as practical, or exercise *illusional* not-self helpfulness as practical.

Medical Educator. As I see it, you wish to have every American physician practice medicine in line with his country's constitutional appreciation for the sovereignty of the individual. Your autology (science of self) is nothing but the scientific idealism necessitated by human individuality, is it not?

Author. This direction of questioning stirs up a plenitude of insight of the most serviceable order. Personally lived experience is always, and only, a development of a given individual. Individual life development is the only possible basis for psychic realism. Life only is dynamic. Whatever is "about" life, "on the subject of" life, is as static as a body without a mind except for its (rarely recognized) meaning as a moment of its author's human life.

There is no value for psychological work except the value provided for it by the fact that the psychological worker *lives* it. Self-grateful is the scientist when he reaches new conscious mind and is comfortable with the truth of his ubiquitous subjectivity and pure idealism. This comprehensive view is the explain-all for recognizing the *practicality* of insight. For me, there can be no more pathetic picture than my trying to accomplish anything by power not possibly at my disposal. For my study and practice of myself (scientific idealism) I have *my* life meaning only. My human nature cannot satisfy itself by my taking only occasional glances at my recognized self. I am most grateful for my feelings of unhappiness which always show up whenever I live durations of my life without appreciation (for my life itself). Life is all about itself, not about "something else" or "somebody else."

Medical Educator. Are you now dogmatizing?

Author. My guardian angel is mine. Cataloguing forms of my self-help, listing varieties of my self-insights, may be considered as a kind of dogmatizing.

Medical Educator. Every devotee of science and of scientism has tried to isolate the reality principle, the unit of the absolute. The atom of Democritus, monad of Leibnitz, "thing in itself" of Kant, substance of Spinoza, Ego of Fichte, idea of Hegel, will of Schopenhauer, individual of Emerson, existence of Kierkegaard, meaning of Freud,—each such concept of being has had its day. Now your Freud's view of self-consciousness as the foundation of human welfare would involve the renunciation of all previous conceptual theory of the *summum bonum* to arrive at what? No abstract universal science of individualism, but each human being's concrete science of his individuality.

Author. What is supremely human is the wisdom conferred by devotion to the truth of subjectivity. What is essentially human is conscious appreciation of humanity. All that *is* human is human individuality. Practiced attention to life itself is possible only to the liver of that life. *Self-consciousness is one's awakening to the creative powers of one's life.* Somewhat as Henri Bergson stated, "I believe that it is of man's essence to create materially and morally, to fabricate things and to fabricate himself. *Homo faber* is the definition I propose. . . . *Homo faber, Homo sapiens,* I pay my respects to both, for they tend to merge."

Medical Educator. Maybe I am beginning to see something of your method of choice for psychological treatment. But often you seem to use your words to conceal, rather than reveal, your meaning. Like Alice's Humpty Dumpty, perhaps, you claim the right to make words mean what suits you. Your words now and then seem to me to be empty,—*flatus vocis*. Let me try to put me in my words, and then correct me if I do not appear to stick to the facts:

If the will is not free, the healthful meaning of liberty is withheld. If self-consciousness is lacking, volitional (free will) self-activity is correspondingly inoperative. The hygienic indication therefore is clear. The American physician who prizes his liberty for its healthfulness, in that it favors tested and proven respect for the dignity of his individuality, will (1) renounce every illusion that he can in any way overpower his patient, and (2) practice every realization of the health power inherent in his patient's recognition of himself as an entirely free, independent healer and strengthener of himself. Is that about it? The soul must know itself.

Author. That *is* it. This work is entirely about the *practical* ideal. A rational estimate of the value of anything at all cannot be divorced from the subjective individual whose value it is. Above all, *my American physician needs to live his patient as the conscious author of his own intentional medical helpfulness.* Most helpful of all patient living is: *the will to live self-consciously,* commonly called "the will to get well." Every patient's available power to make the effort to recover does not, and cannot, exist apart from him. His life is the natural base from which his *all* is generated. It is an absolute health imperative that he use his medical experience to reenforce and extend whatever consciousness he may already enjoy with regard to his self-healing propensities.

Medical Educator. A scientist cannot be too prudent when it comes to his verification of hypothesis. May I now ask you to consider the possibility (by that, I mean simply live the view and call it your own living) that the chief earmark of a scientific psychologist is his readiness to renounce all of his psychological productions as unworkable for anyone but himself. The only possible human enterprise is individual enterprise. Are you able to live that requirement happily and to see in it all of the advantages of professional self-tolerance? There is more to life than just an aphoristic psychology. As Goethe worded it, "It is in his limitation that the master is revealed." What do you say to that?

Author. My lack of limitation of me is *my* freedom. Only to the extent that I can limit all of my appreciation of life to the one truth that I live it can I consciously enjoy the vividness of my freedom. Yes, I am "at home" in living each of my self-entities, prizing *my* fellow scientist's production on account of its being his own, cherishing *my* fellow psychiatrist's finding on account of its helpfulness for him. I see and cherish the view that every person is first and last an inventor (creator) of his experience; indeed that he creates his discovery of his creativeness in each creation. As Henri Bergson beautifully described (his) Claude Bernard's pedagogical maxim, "Wherever there is no personal and even original effort there is not even the beginning of science."

Medical Educator. I understand your use of dialog (with all of its implied equivocation) as your means of providing a device for your hearer to invent and refine key life-meaning of his own. You stated the illusion of betweenness which dialog creates can undo all of the good intended by it. As Santayana said, "Dialect is the conscience of discourse." You consider self-consciousness to be your ideal conscience. I know of no way of deriving self-consciousness from dialog except by vigilant awareness that *one* creates his own speaker and hearer.

Author. How helpfully true! Every effort my hearer makes to explicate the intent of this way of talking is importantly practical. Man cannot understand his own conditions if he cannot even see each one as his own creation. Everyone of my fellow scientists is engaging his life in original productive research, and I see all of his fact-flowering as helpful. Where my fellowman is, there is (my) his world. Whether he is growing his "clinical sense," or his "laboratory atmosphere," or his appreciation of his life in its immediacy,—in every event he *is* an alive human being, and all that can be important for him derives from his life.

Medical Educator. Your ideal of an American physician is that of a realist who sees clearly that he can no more have a selfless mind than a mindless self. I have been trying to work up a synoptic statement of your scientific idealism. You impress me as being a radical empiricist with a predilection for nativistic explanations for your self-experiences. Does that semantic scene seem to look like you? I am only trying to size up your scientific rationale. Of all of your deliverances I derive peace of mind most from those with which you describe your views of your human creaturehood, the *self* of yourself.

Author. My mental make-up lends itself to no limitation other than that it is my mentality, my breathing life into mental activity which is all and only about me. My living self is my only stock-in-trade, and my only possible field of research. The science of somebody else's mind is no substitute for science of my mind—even though it is *my* somebody else.

Medical Educator. Possibly the Sophists were not so far off the science of mind, after all, when they created rhetoric as an essential system of knowledge. Democritus and his colleagues considered semantics as an integral part of biology, especially of physiology.

Author. Wise Democritus.

Medical Educator. You see wisdom as a product of man's conscious unification. His self-synthesis steadies him whenever he observes it. His *conscious* mental integration is a balancer of his mind. You renounce the notion of a "society of ideals" quite as you renounce the notion of an "ideal society." For you the meaning of plurality in the term "society" always resolves itself into being one individual concept invented by one individual mind. The sociologist's meaning of society as being a kind of composite human individuality is in your mind quite analogous to the condensation of dream work. For you the "ideal state," or utopia, can be nothing but ideal self-sovereignty. Certainly, it requires nerve for you to be able to talk out your imaginative embodiment of your inviolable individuality,—for instance that you are not your mother's son, or your wife's husband, or your offspring's parent, or your employer's employee, and so on. Your scientific idealism reminds me of Santayana's definition of piety, "man's reverent attachment to the sources of his being,"—what Irwin Edman named, "the domestic impulse of the soul." You see the principle problem of human existence to be: the individual's justifying the ways of his life to himself. What ever is, is perfect. *Awareness* of perfection is the divine look, which is for the most part perfectly ignored. Is that it?

Author. I live each statement (my) you willingly make, as being correct. Beauty itself is produced by one's clearest perception of the truth of individuality's universality.

Medical Educator. What makes a man industrious, a worker?

Author. My answer for that question is: his consciousness of his freedom (to work himself). Happiness is the expression of a person's ability to function with his freedom, unhappiness being the consequence of incompetence of that ability.

Medical Educator. From all that I can make out, what you regard as particularly striking about your planned and practiced way of mind development is the degree of mental alertness and vision it produces. Your therapeutic, self-consciousness, can be a welcome addition to iamatology. Do you claim recognition for yourself as being wide-awake, ready to perceive new angles, original, creative, and just generally workable? All of your "conscious selfness" is presumably good treatment for you. By the way, do you regard physics as false? Do you consider any guide in action to be misleading?

Author. Vanity is certainly one of my virtues, and I take pride in my ability to be humble. (My) your question points up the age-old important matter of my veracity as a witness, the validity of my positive testimonial for self-consciousness. Does my word stand for reality? For me, it does. My speech reflects my own conviction only. Each person must convince himself. Certainly, and in all truth, all I can report to myself with the slightest claim for accuracy is: whether or not my devotion to my self-consciousness has made me less sleepy, less insensitive, less inclined to live myself as a mimic, less unworkable, and less narrow-minded in my life views, than I now judge my former "I" was. In this respect, then, I am happy to be able to report that my electing concentration upon the practical helpfulness of self-insight has been most rewarding in terms of my finding my life to be well worth the living.

I do not regard physics, or any other unrecognized ideality, as "false." I consider no guide in action to be "misleading," for it is always an individual's conscious, or unconscious, perfect way of trying to lead himself. In my mind, "true" means whatever I can live consciously as mine. Truly "false" means whatever I must deny my conscious identity, on account of its overwhelming my sense of my unity.

Medical Educator. Does "black is white," or "2 + 2 = 8," or "c-a-t spells dog," upset your mental balance? Is not each of these statements false?

Author. In the conventional sense of "false," assuredly each conclusion appears false. On the other hand, at least each conclusion must be acknowledged as being truly intended. Each falsity is truly false, or nothing. The false can never be more than truth ignored or denied. Each of these so-called "false" conclusions is a true word picture of that which you want portrayed.

Medical Educator. Please elaborate upon what you *do* mean by American "academic education," and relate that to your ideas of American government and of language.

Author. By my "academic education" I mean my directing my living consciously so that I can purposefully create my self-produce which corresponds with my presenting self-demand. In my formal study, I systematically grow the self-uses which I estimate will enable me to enjoy my continuing living.

As I relieve my ignorance of myself, I discover "extraneous matters" to consist of knowledge of myself which I have tried to disown. As I study myself consciously I begin to discover the extent to which I have used my vocabulary as if it could do my thinking for me. I find that, in a sense, every vocabulary represents a "dead language" insofar as it is required to denote sameness where sameness does not exist and deny sameness where it does exist. For instance, I use the same word in the effort to denote differents, no two apparently same objects (e.g., "two horses," "another cow," etc.) ever having anything "in common." Or, I use words of different meaning to denote the sameness of self (e.g., "external," "not-self," etc.). A true "living language" would have a fresh denotation for the singularity of every mental creation, for every view of the ever flowing mind. Obviously I use my vocabulary to provide myself with a sense of permanent stability which is not true to the actual uncertainty, instability, and novelty of my living.

I wilfully cultivate self-consciousness as my most helpful means for enjoying my individuality, thus strengthening my conscious will. I can use this increased conscious will power, which is necessary for any conscious purpose of mine, to apply myself to observing all of my selfness in whatever I am living. For me there can be no psychology but my conscious mindfulness. Negation is mental impossibility.

By this kind of educational psychology I have been able to discover why it is that I enjoy working as much as I do. My work is associated with functional satisfaction, or pleasure, on account of my being able to recognize that it *is* all my own skillful living of it. Simply stated, I enjoy exercising my powers, quite as Schiller's verses describe work satisfaction:

> For this is still what graces man,
> For which alone his mind expands,
> That in his inmost heart he feels
> What he created with his hands.

Educating myself, realizing that that is what I am doing, enables me to enjoy the wilfulness in it. Marvelous autodidactics of my world such as Rousseau, Pestalozzi, Shakespeare, Goethe, Jefferson, Emerson, Freud,—each one by his conscious self-discipline has given himself the greatest mental power of consciously willing the functioning of his self-consciousness. Real health benefit is always associated with an access of conscious will power. On account of the restless power of life to go on creating new mental creations, seeing the health importance of willingness to excite self-consciousness becomes evident.

My educational program consists in my seeing my learning as being my manifest gain of power which I produce by renouncing my hypnotic living and by indulging my willing self-conscious living. Once I develop the vision (the willingness to observe) that the nature of my human being and the continuation of its existence depend specifically upon my cultivation of my sense of my self-worth, then my own power to estimate my human worth becomes a matter of conscious concern for me. I now regard my devotion to my self-conscious living as my chief manifestation of my human excellence. Of my other life orientations

I have somewhat the view which Daniel Webster expressed of a particular political platform, "What is valuable is not new, and what is new is not valuable."

General Practitioner. Your psychological principle seems to be based on empirical egoism. You see all of your individual self as only a build-up of your living elements which your consciousness (mind's organ of observation) only can cognize. That psychology is no different from Hume's "Bundle-of-perception theory of self," is it?

Author. Whatever I live is uniquely mine. Whatever (my) Hume lived was uniquely his. However, in a general way you have described your author's psychological principle of epistemology: knowledge by the self of itself. I can only and always speak with a minute individuation or hear with a minute individuation of myself. Nevertheless I do seem to myself to be a dynamic, whole, subjective, new being experiencing empirically (living) a sense of unity to which I ascribe the name: personal identity. I have not one point of departure or return.

General Practitioner. You offer no alternative but allness or illness. You have mentioned the "ego-centric predicament" nearly everyone associates with absolute idealism, and with every "appeal to the mental."

Author. Yes. There is no predicament once all of my "external worldliness" is fully recognized as my own mind's creation, as inherent in my mind's nature.

General Practitioner. Your emphasis upon wholeness, or unity, or allness, reminds me of the Gestalt psychology of Wertheimer, Koffka, and Kohler,—the 1912 reaction against the psychic elements of the analytic and associationist psychologist. Why do you not credit this work of your field psychologists?

Author. I can credit only myself, and I need all of my credit that I can supply. Apart from that necessity, I may point out that my concept of wholeness is in complete accord with my psychoanalytic orientation. Wholeness-allness-nowness-unity is a truth of individuality applying equally to every individuation of individuality and accounting for the ubiquity of subjectivity. Once wholeness is granted, subjectivity is acknowledged as all that is possible.

As to whatever life orientation I have my fellowman (configurationist, or otherwise) helping himself with, I can neither agree nor disagree with a word of it; but I do see clearly his right to it. A man can confidently "place his trust" only where his confidence is. His trust can be only in himself. My fellowman's only trustworthy guide of conduct is the way in which he wills to help himself. Therein is to be found his genius. All I know is about me, and I am certain that the only basis of my conscious independence is my sense of personal identity.

Emerson offered this view to himself, "In every work of genius we recognize our own rejected thoughts; they come back to us with a certain alienated majesty." Similarly, earnest Rousseau memorialized his own deep appreciation of the allness of oneness, when he said that for him there was "no intermediary term between everything and nothing." Existence, whatever exists, is ever specific and individual. It is not in the nature of my human mind to become insightful (wise) in any other way than by my *consciously* developing my own educational shaping of it. Every effort to sophisticate my mind in some other way has taught me that "other" helpfulness is limited to preventing my exertion to extend my appreciation of myself.

Man has no impulse to attempt the impossibility of making himself a part of a social group. His appearance as a "joiner" is his frantic effort to recover his sense of belonging to himself. All of his behavior which has any resemblance to "socialization" is really prompted by his need to live, and his wish to enjoy, his individuality. He succeeds in deceiving himself, however, by ignoring the truth that his pretending to be a part of a larger whole is nothing but a political expedient of his self-government.

Individual creaturehood is the only foundation and structure of any kind of governmental living. Democracy is the choice self-government, for it is the only one which insures all of the benefits of individuality for every individuation of the given individual. The guillotine, like all forms of "punishment," was the resort of the goddess of reason, not of the spirit of self-consciousness. "That man belongs to an alien and inhuman world," "that man is alone amid hostile forces," "that man is butt of cruel circumstances,"—

every such estimate is the product of self-unconscious man, not of self-conscious man.

When any part of my mind asserts itself as an autonomous center (for instance, when I live *my* fellowman as not my own living of him), mental complication begins. My own personal identity *is* the man within the man; and, if I do not appreciate that truth, my mind suffers an unrecognized dissociation right at that moment. My self-consciousness is the power I must exercise in order to appreciate my wholeness and allness.

I see clearly that the future safety of my world depends directly and specifically upon the capacity of my world governmental leaders severally for self-consciousness.[4] The governmental leader who really senses his identity in his fellow citizen, must be a man of peace, not a man of war. If my world is to enjoy peace it can only come about through (individual) use of self-consciousness. However, my world has already reached the Stone Age of self-consciousness. As soon as one finds that he cannot behave toward another, or misbehave toward another, he can begin to study behavior where it really occurs, entirely within himself.

The appreciation of the life force of self-consciousness is hedged in by the greatest possible conservatism. A conservative has been defined anonymously as a man who believes that nothing should ever be tried for the first time. Certainly, it is my own conservatism with which I interfere with my expediting my functioning of my self-consciousness. Calling myself an unpractical visionary or a doctrinaire spares me the very hard work of seeing that self-consciousness is most practical and least system-ridden.

General Practitioner. No doubt you approve of Whorf's viewpoint that the science of academic psychology is of little or no help to the person who wants to understand the laws and topography of his inner life.[5]

Author. I approve of every viewpoint. Certainly Whorf's theory of "linguistic relativity" is congenial to my view that my language of sanity is a language of my individuality. Coleridge said, "In order to get the full sense of a word, we should first present to our minds the usual image that forms its primary meaning."

General Practitioner. You mean that a word is a name and that a name is a unit of lingual reality itself, not merely a symbol of that quiddity which it denotes. You mean that the language of self is a science of self, in addition to providing names for that self's powers. You mean that words constitute a reality of their own, verbal reality, instead of just mediacy.

Author. I have just had (my) you say something I have been trying to say.

General Practitioner. Is there not a great danger that language develop the significance of being static rather than dynamic, and "objective" rather than subjective?

Author. Indeed I conceive this to be the greatest danger associated with naming. Literally, "vernacular" means: a slave born in his master's house.

Specific mental treatment is the conscious quest for "lost," forgotten (overlooked, since *far removed* from conscious use) selfhood. Naturally, therefore, the only mental material to be recovered for conscious use is that which at first sight seems *farfetched.* Most "farfetched" of all is the mindfulness which exists under the disguise of "externality," one's *own* (and therefore internal) entire "external" world.

General Practitioner. I suppose you mean that your every word which implies not-self potentially has this "farfetched" connotation to it.

Author. Only my repudiated selfness can have this seeming.

General Practitioner. Please illustrate how you can appear to use your words as if each one of them is now entirely and only a sign of your own life's meaning.

Author. I may speak of *my* fellowman and have my fellowman speak of himself (including his fellowman),—all without disclaiming my every word as being all and only about my life. Thus:

My Nietzsche stated that his Emerson's works had the most profound meaning for him. My Ernest Jones recorded in his biography of his Freud that Freud "several times said of Nietzsche that he had a more penetrating knowledge of himself than any other man who ever lived or was ever likely to live." My Nietzsche's Zarathustra offers words of wisdom especially for his young doctor, "Physician, help yourself: thus you help your patient, too. Let this be his best help that he may behold with his eyes the man who heals himself."

General Practitioner. Enough. I see where custom has made my habit of speaking (as if I can be out of my mind) so very comfortable that I can renounce it only at the cost of great discomfort to myself. If I must choose between truth and comfort I am afraid that my choice must be comfort,—at least until I can see for myself the limited advantages in my present speech habits. Maybe a course in semantics might confront me with my lingual lunacy.

Author. Wendell Johnson, professor of speech pathology, University of Iowa, reports enlightening samples of the "sanity-producing" force of study of the creation and use of one's words.[6]

General Practitioner. Much of your epistemology reminds me of Max Stirner's renowned book *The Ego and His Own,* which was studied carefully by such minds as Ibsen, Nietzsche, John Henry Mackay (the Scottish-German poet), Huneker, James Walker, and Stephen T. Byington (Stirner's translator). Stirner's real name was Johan Caspar Schmidt. His idea was that of personal awakening to the truth of one's allness. He realized that popular insurrection could eventuate only in socialism, tyranny, or anarchy. He led a precarious existence.

Author. I live each of (my) your observations with the personal interest that I am living it. No doubt each one (world of himself) you mention enjoyed his own degree of, and devotion to, his conscious mindfulness.

General Practitioner. Do you give the same care to a murderer that you give to each patient?

Author. Yes. There are essential medical indications underlying the treatment of *every* patient. Devotion to each of these medical principles safeguards and advances the health of physician and patient alike:

(1) Every patient's physician represents to him his most expert hold upon life. Every patient, whether a so-called "pauper," "murderer," "traitor," or whatever, is entitled to live his doctor's optimal kind and degree of medical helpfulness.

(2) Full medical treatment, including "heroic effort," is indicated in *every* instance where, in the physician's opinion, it will

serve to uphold or prolong life. Withholding known means of prolonging life is not a medical ideal, regardless of the "reasoning to the contrary" which may appear to be able to alter the circumstance (the patient's expressed wish to die, his relatives' uncaring attitudes, the expense involved, and so on).

(3) A physician must renounce all understandable wishes and tendencies to be a prophet. Statistical averages never apply to an individual. As far as the physician is concerned his every patient has a 100 per cent favorable prognosis. The physician healthfully renounces all such resources as "established chances for life," "laws of probability," "actuarial data," which would appear to commit his patient to death rather than to life. *Particularly in this area of the physician's authority and responsibility is suggestion extremely powerful.*

(4) If a patient, throughout the course of his health struggle, does not seem to be likeable to a physician, it is well for that physician to consider strengthening his tolerance for his dislike, or even referring his patient to a colleague.

Everyone's war reveals the superficiality of his civilization in that it is a human volitional destruction of human life. However, even *medical experimentation* performed by my Nazi physician during World War II was of absolute ruthlessness involving total disregard for the preciousness of life of *his* experimental human being. Upon reviewing one of these so-called "medical experiments," everyone with a just claim to understanding of the meaning of medical humaneness overwhelms himself with guilt. Awareness of the desirability for the growth and maintenance of physicianary insight regarding the comprehensiveness of human individuality thus became an unavoidably urgent reality for *every* educator.

Responsibility for this horrifying lapse of sanity (sanity meaning: self-conscious living of each individual) was, and still remains, unfixable insofar as each investigator can confuse one human individual (world) with another, or even appear to succeed in lumping individuals into his imagined state or nation. The Assembly of the World Medical Association met in Geneva, September 1948, and each member present studied this most grievous problem of disregard for one's allness, searching for a prevention of its possible recurrence. One leading recommendation was that every graduating physician consciously commit himself to medical humaneness in the following statement known as the Declaration of Geneva. Note insightfully, if you will, the due stress of this Declaration upon the *particular* individual's personal responsibility for his conduct of his medical living:

Declaration of Geneva

At the Time of Being Admitted as Member of
the Medical Profession

I solemnly pledge myself to consecrate my life to the service of humanity.

I will give to my teachers the respect and gratitude which is their due.

I will practice my profession with conscience and dignity.

The health of my patient will be my first consideration.

I will respect the secrets which are confided in me.

I will maintain by all the means in my power the honor and the noble traditions of the medical profession.

My colleagues will be my brothers.

I will not permit considerations of religion, nationality, race, party politics or social standing to intervene between my duty and my patient.

I will maintain the utmost respect for human life, from the time of conception; even under threat, I will not use my medical knowledge contrary to the laws of humanity.

I make these promises solemnly, freely and upon my honor.

General Practitioner. I note that this declaration contains wonderful truths, quite as does the Declaration of Independence. However, it is my experience that every American citizen demonstrates the extent of his acknowledged appreciation of his Declaration of Independence in the way he lives his family, and his every other "organization." Thus, if he is not able to see himself in his fellowman, he comforts himself with the conclusion that the principle of democracy (that is, self-sovereignty) simply does not apply to his family, business, school, college, or whatever organizational living he calls his own. How rare it is to find the democratic principle of individual sovereignty (conscious self-government) the leading organizational principle actually striven for by any kind of American executive.

Author. As I see it, the truth is that every American citizen lives his ideal of American citizenship (self-sovereignty) properly, —that is, to the very best of his current ability to do so. Fact-finding, rather than fault-finding, is most beneficial about that medical record.

The epitaph of an Athenian physician who lived in the second century A.D. also speaks for itself,

> These are the duties of a physician: first . . . to heal his mind and to give help to himself before giving it to anyone else, and not look upon [his patient] or make approaches in a manner contrary to divine law and to the oath. Let him cure not only with [professional] skill, but also with blameless character. . . . Let him make himself the equal of slaves and paupers, of the rich and of the rulers of mankind, and to all let him minister like a brother.[7]

There follows the Hippocratic Oath, the traditional physician's oath, the ethical command each medic gives to himself at the time of his securing his M.D. degree:

> I swear by Apollo, the physician, and Asklepios, Hygieia, and Panacea and all the gods and goddesses, that, according to my ability and judgment, I will keep this oath, and this indenture—to reckon him who taught me this art equally dear to me as my parents, to share my substance with him, and relieve his necessities if required; to look upon his offspring on the same footing as my own brothers, and to teach them this art, if they shall wish to learn it, without fee or stipulation; and that by precept, lecture and every other mode of instruction, I will impart a knowledge of the art to my own sons, and those of my teachers, and to disciples bound by a stipulation and oath according to the law of medicine, but to none others. I will follow that system of regimen which, according to my ability and judgment, I consider for the benefit of my patients, and abstain from whatever is deleterious and mischievous. I

will give no deadly medicine to any one, if asked, nor suggest any such counsel; and in like manner I shall not produce abortion. With purity and with holiness I will pass my life and practice my art. I will not operate on persons suffering from stone in the bladder, but will leave that to specialists. I will enter homes for the benefit of the sick and will abstain from every voluntary act of mischief and wrongdoing to women, men, and slaves. Whatever, in connection with my professional practice or not, I see or hear, in the lives of people, which should not be discussed abroad, I will not divulge, believing that such things should be kept quiet and secret. While I continue to keep this Oath inviolated, may it be granted to me to enjoy life and the practice of my art, respected by all men in all times! But should I trespass on and violate this Oath, may the reverse befall me!

15

American Patient

Psycho-analysis has warned us that we must give up the unfruitful contrast between external and internal factors, between experience and constitution, and has taught us that we shall invariably find the cause of the onset of neurotic illness in a particular psychical situation which can be brought about in a variety of ways.

FREUD

PATIENT. AT last my author is giving life, and its expression, to patient-living itself, whatever that may amount to in his mind. Certainly, I am agent rather than patient, since I must do all of my own diagnosing and healing, create all of my own medical and surgical experience, and even generate all that I can possibly mean by my own "physician." I am actively "patient" in that I must endure and cure my affliction, which includes both my physician's efforts to help himself "conduct the case" in the only way he can, and the pained attitude of this or that member of my family towards the extra burden incurred whenever there is a health ordeal in one "so close to him." I am also an amateur philosopher.

You speak of "comprehensive" medical education as being health development of the whole physician for the whole physician, as well as being health development of the whole patient for the whole patient. All of your medical orientation turns largely on your observation that any and every health force is always subjective only. According to these viewpoints, I see that I am fully entitled to my say about American medicine, even though my thoughts have traveled along other meandering channels.

First of all, your every statement about the importance of freedom, for the safeguarding of health, is duly appreciated. I cannot imagine what it would be like to be unable to choose my own physician, but I cherish that freedom of choice quite as I cherish my civic right to choose the religious living which I prefer. I consider "taking a physician" to be almost as private and personal a matter as is "taking a mate." Where my health is concerned I need as much harmony of spirit, consent of will, and unification of self-consciousness as I can mobilize, in order to recover and maintain my clear sense of the wholeness-allness-unity of my human being. Thus, I might not choose you, on account of your extreme subjectivist theories, but if anyone else wished to choose you, I hold that he should not be denied that possibility.

Given my choice I would greatly prefer, of course, to cultivate the medical (including surgical) helpfulness of a physician capable of diagnosing and treating and billing his patient as himself. Wherever necessary, however, I would also gratefully grow the advantages derivable from my experiencing that physician's technical ability who might be unable to see and work with his patient as his own life's creation. I have gladly grown, as my own, the insight that every physician must treat himself as best he can while rendering his professional services; and I naturally choose as my physician one who knows how to care for himself most effectively, as I see it. Everyone to his taste in his choice of physician.

Since I have convinced myself that whatever I perceive of my physician is all *in* my mind, I feel very secure experiencing a physician who has convinced himself that whatever he perceives of his patient is all *in* his mind. Also, I see nothing at all to be gained by indulging my imagining an "external" world, except the one tremendous advantage of not embarrassing my mind with this extent of truthfulness. However, simply by seeing my own living in my experience of my physician, I have access to the use of all of the sensibility essential for my conducting my life. I want my physician to enjoy this safeguard of his own self-interest in his experiencing of his patient. Nevertheless, if he cannot treat his patient as his own personally created fellowman without disabling embarrassment over such intense meaningfulness, then, to avoid such panic, it is preferable that he treat his patient in the so-called "impersonal" way which conceals his stake in the way he lives himself.

I appreciate the non-technical way you talk; but, even so, I have not yet experienced some of the living which might make some of your observations fully satisfying to me. For instance, I can see some truth in your idea that your dislikes simply reveal your lack of self-knowledge. Nevertheless, I would hesitate to assume, as you do, that my every dislike betrays and protects my ignorance. I know what I like, and I do like your notion of a self which maintains an identifiable allness, wholeness, and unity, even as it grows itself, not somebody else. Sure enough, every self changes but changes in its own individual way. I can renounce my wish to claim to be exactly the same person in any two successive moments. I trust that my growth of myself, which constitutes *the only "change" I can undergo,* is entirely a desirable power of my wonderful life. I see the benefit in renunciation of that Faustian addiction to any wished-for self-fixation which, if granted, would arrest my own development.

Author. I find (my) your view of life to be wholesomely free, particularly of the yoke of formal professional education. Your view of "self" as being a name for supporting individual growth, not an unchanging lifeless entity, is singularly life-affirming. As Eddington surmised, the scientist who has gone the furthest fares through the fullest extent of himself: "all through the physical world runs an unknown content which must really be the stuff of our own consciousness." In his address to the British Association, September 1934, Sir James Jeans declared, "Little is left of the forbidding Materialism of the Victorian scientists: modern physics is moving in the direction of philosophical Idealism."

Patient. I do not know anything about that, but I do know that I have a backbone, whether you call it psychological or not. I do know that my thoughts and feelings are mine. It seems to me that my senses function so that *I* can get along better than *I* might without them. I am only conscious of myself when I take the trouble to be. According to you, I can help myself every time I, so to speak, take a deep breath of self-consciousness. Well, I'm willing to try it,—but I've said that before of nostrums without really doing the trying. I was always taught by words to put down selfishness, and by actions to uphold it. I suppose everybody is trying to make out the best way he can. One man says, "Forget yourself and remember your neighbor, for that way you can make out better." Another man says, "Remember your neighbor is yours, for that way you can make out better." The main difference to me is that the second man has someone responsible for keeping store. I've noticed that my aches and pains and worries and troubles of every kind make me think of me, as you say. If they did not, I doubt if I'd last long. I guess the main job is heeding that "self" does not mean *conscious self,* that every "experience" I live does not mean *conscious experience,* that everything I see or hear or even imagine does not mean *conscious seeing, hearing, or even imagining.* I think you put your finger on the real trouble when you pointed that out.

Author. I see that no system of psychology or of philosophy has taken over your conscious ability to think for yourself. A question stirs: What difference does it make if I consider myself a kind of collection of impersonal experiences or a person of experience? If you ask yourself that question, what do you come up with?

Patient. You have claimed that every fact makes a difference; but if this one makes no difference to you, that is your affair. According to my lights, again it's a matter of someone's keeping store. It's all well and good to talk about losing yourself in a greater self in order to help yourself; and you can give up your independence and freedom in exchange for having somebody else seem to treat you as a dependent and make free with you,—but that kind of gaming with life is not for me. I have read about "selfless" living, but it never made any sense except that it meant wider self-experience. It's true that every bit of me is as independent and self-sufficient as I am; but that means that *it is made up of me,* not the contrary.

Author. If Hume had grown (his) you he would have enjoyed and profited from the experience. You seem to be one who is satisfied to suppose true that which is experientially irrefutable.

Consulting the expert is no way "out" (to an "external world"), for a genuine expert in any field sees that his decision is ultimately an expression of his own personal view only.

Every dispute of the "objective" mind-worker seems to be in the interest of his upholding his notion of a "means" as well as of an "end," whereas every so-called "means" is itself an unrecognized *end.* Insistence upon the scientific validity of the meaning, "a means," is essential for the maintenance of some of his favorite notions (illusions), such as "betweenness," "mediacy," "plurality," "objectivity," "externality," "time," "space," "motion."

Patient. I like the ideas that a person either becomes a fool or a physician as he grows up, and that every one of my doctor visits is a medical consultation in which I must be (consciously or unconsciously) in charge of my own health interests.

It seems to me desirable to educate myself with the truth that *self,* human individuality, is the *only possible* responsible authority, and that any effort on my part to get out from under that mental load is understandable as the expression of arrested activity of my mental powers of self-consciousness. Unless I can see my parent as my own creation, I cannot see the truth of my intact wholeness and must resort to some kind of illusion of "communal," "societal," "impersonal" power for purposes of adequate self-protection.

I do not want my physician to treat his patient as a piece of substance completely consisting of analyzable component parts, as an assembled human machine. I want him to be able to see that his patient is an unanalyzable whole, a human universe, not "out of commission" but *already* earnestly in the serious business of treating himself ideally, and needing to extend his ideal treatment further in, as yet, undiscovered directions.

I am just a plain, self-educated man; but I have often wondered if the paradoxical notion of defining continuing self-growth as necessitating consequent loss of personal identity is not traceable, in the first place, to the fact that one does not respect the one and only fact, namely, that *he* is doing the growing, that it is *his own life* which is creating his "becoming." The self, the human individual, to begin with, *is* a creator, a self-grower; and that appreciation is needed to support the truth of the enduring sameness of his every become one. Heraclitus found "change" to be the only reality.

Author. He who sees a thing from its beginning on has the best view of it. I cannot but distrust my conception of my world if I cannot begin, and continue, to see that my living is the only reality of it. I live my notion of "you" in the same sense that I live my notion of "me,"—each is entirely my own creation and concern.

Patient. Your word "continue" begs the question; and, since my awareness of the intact wholeness of me is my health essential, I prefer to be careful about my use of that term. Even my "becomeness" is constant, not continuous. You know, J. S. Adams, American philosopher, held that we do not know our own identity since we are always in a state of becoming. My life is a constant beginning, and I prefer to see it that way. In my ordinary experience I am not conscious of the only truth of it, the I-ness or me-ness of it, but I intend to mend my selfhood forgetfulness. I am realizing that it is the hygienic requirement to give a full account of my health, including medical, experience in terms of my own mental situations only.

By the way, how do you distinguish "doctor" and "patient"? Does not a physician often seek to further his medical helpfulness on account of some acute personal health struggle, and thus become a patient? Does not a patient often seek to further his medical helpfulness on account of his wish to live himself as a doctor, and thus become a physician?

Author. Every physician lives (creates) all that he calls his patient; every patient lives (creates) all that he calls his doctor. The physician sees his patient, not as a means to the fulfilment of his desires, but as the end his patient really is. He sees his patient needing to learn how to take care of himself in some particular aspect, or aspects, of his living. He has specifically prepared himself medically and legally to help himself live the life of a physician duly qualified as a health specialist.

Every patient may see his doctor as the end he really is. He grows his physician for the express purpose of learning how to live himself in a way which will not necessitate his troubling himself with signs and symptoms of his selfhood neglect and ignorance. From growing his physician's demonstrating his knowledge of the nature of his human functioning, each patient learns how to take care of himself adequately. His physician's helpfulness is not intentionally hidden in his medical language. Rather, every M.D. strives to attain the ideal described by his revered Claude Bernard, "I feel convinced there will come a day when physiologists, poets, and philosophers will all speak the same language and understand one another." Interest in health development need not remain the peculiar business of the specially endowed or devoted. It is human business; it is every person's business.

Patient. Although it does seem to be too good to be true, I find *practical* the view: Whatever is, is helpful. Whatever is, is curative. Instead of seeing my so-called "accident," or "pathology," of any kind, as unnecessary, or as harmful in anyway, and, hence, as a source of sorrow, it is a health benefit to me to be able to see each as a necessary event and, hence, as a satisfying source of learning-experience. It is life-affirming for me to see *whatever* I live as being a *worthy* expression of life. I favor my living on by being able to take pride and find satisfaction in my therapeutic *tumor, calor, rubor,* and *dolor.* By seeing every way my body expresses itself as being entirely efficacious, I take heart, and thus prevent the disheartening, discouraging, demoralizing, life-depreciating attitudes (which I would need otherwise as helpful warnings of the life risk in self-disesteem). I am awakening to the invigorating force of patient-gratefulness to himself, and of physician-gratefulness to himself.

Author. Although the time-honored health-illness dichotomy may already be largely renounced by the M.D., it is desirable that *everyone* see its limited helpfulness so that he can enjoy the health benefits derivable from *constantly* upholding a thoroughly constructive, positive, unified life orientation.

Patient. I find it difficult to feel positive that my elevation of temperature, rapid pulse and respiration, heightened blood pressure, insommia, headache, irritability, constipation, anxiety, "feeling bad," or whatever I may have to so-called "suffer," is in truth the expression of the wisdom of my life in its efforts to preserve itself.

Author. I have had to grow this kind of insight difficultly also. Every word of my medical vocabulary of a pejorative meaning is renounced only painstakingly. "Suffering" is wonderful human effort.

Patient. Surely enough physicians have suffered health ordeals to provide medical literature with sternly serious, practical accounts of their subjective experiences of so-called "diseases" and "accidents." A physician's conscious mastery of his personal resources must encourage his putting into words his thoughts and feelings about his own health's adventures.

Author. Medical literature contains the autobiographical case reports of many physicians, although such professional confidences are apt to be notably devoid of acknowledged psychogenic data (affirmed subjectivity). Max Pinner, M.D., and Benjamin F. Miller, M.D., edited a book of such precious seeing, of consciously personal contributions of physician-patients to the understanding of their several health vicissitudes. Quite a few of the contributors "stated spontaneously that in writing their reports (which demanded an effort to objectivize their subjective experience) they felt a welcome and relieving catharsis." And, story after story told "how these physician-patients triumphed over diseases which they themselves, as doctors, would have thought practically hopeless."[1] However, every physician finds great difficulty in disposing of his acknowledged imaginings about his personal health interests in a way compatible with his scientific training.

Layman. I want my physician to be able to imagine a worthy conception of his patient's abstract capabilities, of his patient's unconscious vitality. I want him to have a truly heroic inward vision of the powerful dynamics operating constantly in his own "mental space" (Coleridge). Imaginative insight is needed to connect consciousness with medical education, I see.

Author. Consciousness is intensely human, is the purest culture of distinctly human energy. Whoever has it in abundance is chary of sleepy resort to the comforting devices of self-forgetfulness implicit in innumerable terms which slight individuality by complete disregard for its allness-wholeness-unity (e.g., every kind of plural, such as "group," "society," "community," "neighborhood," "family," "state," "we," "they," and so on).

Patient. Ordinarily, I feel self-sufficient, self-reliant, and self-helpful, until I get myself hit by something which seems too big for me to be able to call it myself,—a car, or coccus, or cancer, or criminal. How can I feel successful when I seem to feel "sick"? No doubt by understanding (loving) that feeling.

Author. Living, itself, *is* everyone's basic success. But I want to live a life of importance recognizable to myself. I can see now that it is possible for me to realize this goal in one way only, namely, by my consciously upholding the importance of all of my living, as long as I live. Thus, I cannot afford to yield to my innumerable temptations to depreciate, or ignore even, whatever I happen to live with dislike (on account of my current inability to live it without painful feelings of insecurity, "aloneness," intolerance, inequality, or any other violence to my view of myself as being a whole unified *all*).

Patient. Your experience has taught you, so to speak, the more difficult the lesson of life mastered, the greater the appreciation of the power and meaning of that life. Thus, every kind of life ordeal, once you grow equal to it (by studying its facts fully) redounds to your corresponding appreciation of your life. You are not like some lifeless thing which seems to be ruined by hardship to which it cannot become equal. You see blindness, deafness, every kind of amputation, or whatever "adversity" that can have meaning for you, potentially as being a fair opportunity with which to have your soul build for itself a statelier mansion, so to speak.

Author. My experience has taught me that my hardship has *already* created the foundation of my hardihood. The only remaining task is for me to *see* that my soul has already built its "stately mansion." "Growing equal" to my every difficult life experience is only a process of my *observing* that it *is* mine, mine to cherish as I do all of the rest of my life.

Patient. Obviously you would renounce the affliction of every such, to say the least, uncomplimentary designation as "league for the handicapped," "school for the mentally retarded," "home for the feeble-minded," "juvenile delinquency residence," etc., as well as the time-honored "jail," "penitentiary," or "criminal court"?

Author. I find it helpful when I can renounce any and every healthier-than-thou life orientation.

Patient. How *can* I designate my own child, then, who has been already diagnosed as "mentally retarded"? He is unable to perform as his brother and sister can. He simply cannot seem to learn, or be interested in learning. Do you mean that there is self-evident benefit to me in my not calling my child by some term which is obviously a fault-finding one? Do you mean that my child is a human individual, understandable only to himself, living a life of his own making which, possibly, may be quite as satisfying and interesting to him as mine is to me? Do you mean that it may seem easier to me to find fault with my own child than to study painstakingly the facts which I may be able to discover by my painsworthy attention to his way of life? Do you mean that I find it extremely difficult to feel equal to this child of mine but save my face by my observation that he cannot feel equal to me? It is shocking to me to consider how little I know about my own child. I do not seem to learn or be interested in learning. But what am I now saying, except what I have already said of my child? I have been using my views of my child as an excuse for my own ignorance and intolerance, have I not? Thus, I refuse even to try to understand (my) his wonderful necessities. I summon no wisdom, or very little of it, for appreciation of his possibilities. I can see more clearly now how my living anything with dislike accounts for my ignorance about it. That must be the basis for nearly everyone's view of so-called "illness" and "accident." Living each with dislike accounts for ignorance about the life-affirming, healing importance of it. My new orientation (Whatever is, is desirable) has helped me to know how to be humane in my living of my child, in a way that I never thought possible before. Surely, I never expected to be able to feel grateful for my child's kind of life, as I certainly do now.

As I put myself to the difficult task of trying to feel equal to this dear child of my own living, may I not expect that he will have far less difficulty in trying to live his father harmoniously? It is probable, is it not, that nearly everyone senses his own feeble-mindedness whenever he undertakes the impossible job of really trying to understand that which he cannot understand, namely, anyone else? May I not expect to give myself a hard time by sincerely renouncing my smarter-than-thou attitude toward my child? Certainly, I have had a genuine but unappreciated need for that illusion and, hence, have not even tried to see this child-living of mine as being entirely desirable. Now I find myself "coming to life" through it, in a way wonderful, but impossible before I even tried to feel equal to it. I am understanding now the rarity with which anyone can enjoy the benefit of equalitarian family living, despite its specific hygienic power. A man needs obstacles to bring out his resources, doesn't he? A person's disasters offer him indispensable opportunities, not only for self-analysis but also for self-development, do they not?

Author. Again, I marvel at the way your questioning clearly contains its own answering. You can see for yourself how your own personal experience is what makes you humanely understanding with your fellowman undergoing a similar life development. Martin Grotjahn, M.D., gave an excellent account of understanding his suffering.[2]

Patient. My spirits returned most, I believe, through learning that anxiety, depression, and pain, each of which I have always hated most, really stand by me in good stead. Such realization helps me to endure peacefully each of those difficult health aids. Before this insight, I was in the position of fighting my own essential ways of helping myself.

Just seeing *all* of my health trials as desirable health efforts has given me a peace of mind I never had before,—and that *must* be good for my health. I wish everyone of my world might make this same inspiriting self-discovery. By "getting well" I always meant: returning to my previous limited way of carrying on my life. From now on, by "getting well" I shall mean: Growing equal to my new self-discoveries occasioned by my so-called "sickness" or "accident." Only during self-awareness can self count as the wonder it truly is, and certainly every health reminder forces me to pay attention to my life.

Author. As far as illness, or accident, is concerned, your *terra firma* of self-consciousness may prove attainable. My every health vicissitude puts in its appearance as an alien power, as being an attack by a force foreign to me. My every sign and symptom is a sudden, unexpected episode. Indeed, even when it makes its appearance, I find it extremely difficult to become interested in the *real* nature of my so-called "illness" or "accident."

For his Republic Plato required physicians who had learned about health problems first-hand from coping with their own health trials. Actually having an "illness," or "accident," creates detailed insight about it which is otherwise unattainable. That kind of learning is consciously personally *lived,* the conscious emphasis being upon that *living* rather than upon the "learning." As long as I can do so, I look away from unpleasant indications, refusing to see my personal identity in the painful details of so-called "accident" or "illness."

Patient. Obviously, you favor having your patient learn as much as possible of the truth of his health status. I do not refer here to his confusing himself with general statistics, but do refer to his elucidating his health development by finding the specific facts about it. I do understand the view that a physician cannot tell his patient anything, as well as that a consciously self-oriented physician realizes that he can have nothing to say as far as his patient's life or death is concerned. He has noticed that one of his patients empowers his life by undergoing a tremendous health struggle; and that another of his patients ends his life rather than undergo one more apparently minor wrestle with his health. Above all, the consciously self-oriented physician has learned that each of his patients is a unique, unified universe of largely unknown and untapped health resources. Thus, I cannot heed the plainly manifest warnings I am giving to myself. I become alarmed promptly, but my attention is devoted to my getting rid of my (therapeutic) symptoms, rather than to my renouncing the behavior responsible for them. I am always overwhelmed by a sign or symptom. Therefore, I have never found the duration of any health ordeal to be the ideal educational opportunity which it surely is. For instance, if I am anxious and depressed, I invariably conclude that my anxiety and depression constitute what is wrong with me. Having my doctor say that his unhappiness is "good for him," that "it serves him right," may be truly helpful for my tracing the genesis of my trouble, but I need to focus my loving attention upon my own limits of my helpfulness, or else collapse. *My first need is for a doctor who can appreciate his helpful patient exactly as he is.*

Above all, I want a physician who sees his profession as one upholding the endurance of life, *regardless of the work or expense involved.* He need not fear that I will not die when and as I please. He need not fear that his efforts are unnecessarily prolonging a life which is better ended on account of its "painful, vicious, stuporous, moribund course," or whatever else. May he attend to his proper business of life helpfulness and furtherance. Let me, conscious or unconscious, "under" my most life-favoring medical care, settle whether or not I think my life is worth living.

Author. Yes. Unless I regard my every sign and symptom as seemingly unpleasant, but necessary, self-treatment, I must lack the incentive to learn to behave myself in a symptom-free and sign-free way. My helpful but hard-to-uphold orientation for my every so-called "illness," or "accident," is: that it is entirely desirable; that I am helping myself ideally with it; that it constitutes my difficult but constructive work; that it is counselling me regarding the way I can restore my previous health balance, avoid further health risks, and prevent further health disturbances of similar kind; that, in short, it provides me with a wonderfully valuable life lesson. I am fortunate, not unfortunate, to live whatever I live, and my recognition of that basic medical insight can save me from using up my valuable life force in feeling sorry for, rather than joyful about, my truly wonderful being.

Patient. You regard the specifically life-affirming attitude of your patient to be his striving to see his personal identity in all that he calls his "doctor," "nurse," "medication," "microorganism," "accident," "room," and so on. You find your patient's consciousness of his own dominance over all of his living to be a pure source of powerful self-heal. You see that each patient's necessary consciousness for his helpful complaints as being his own is the specifically needed beginning of his exercise of his wholesomely dominant self-consciousness. Again, you uphold "study of the facts" as being your patient's reliable conscious self-helpfulness,—his fact-finding being his cure for his fault-finding as well as for his tendency to expect free healthfulness without working the forces which alone can necessitate that healthfulness.

Microscopic facts can be as potentially dangerous as automobile fenders. To have one's self struck by a virulent microorganism can be as fatal as having one's self struck by a bullet. Everyone must learn as best he can how to discover and manipulate the facts of his microscopic, as well as of his macroscopic, world. Your recognizing your every health ordeal as your own doing is a life achievement uniquely favorable to your healing sense of wholeness. It is life-affirming for you to be able to say of your every life condition commonly called "illness," or "misfortune": "It is good that I am this way, for the truth of my living is in it. To be sure, I am learning by my signs of life that this is not the direction in which I can safely continue to steer my life course. Too much of this way of living may not become me. I must live my virulent microorganism with the same sense of sanity about it with which I live my wild animal. If I, wittingly or unwittingly, do not protect myself every way (with medicine, sterilization, isolation, and so on) during my living of it, I must endure the situation I create for myself. It is only the nature of my beast, or of my bacillus, to behave as it does."

You consider your patient to be the only one who can be concerned about his health, or have anything whatsoever to do with it; and you hold, therefore, that every medical worker needs to study this truth until it begins to make sense. In your mind, medical work is a matter not only of "Physician, heal thyself," but also of "Patient, heal thyself."

You see *every* physician as always doing all that he can do to be helpful to himself in his professional work, and you find it impossible to compare physicians. Indeed you, yourself, live *your* every physician and hold yourself responsible for living *your* so-called colleague. The most, truly all, you can do for your medical profession, is sustain your active devotion to your own ongoing professional development. Thus, your therapeutic intention applies to you; and you cannot relegate it to your colleague, or patient, who must help himself only by means of his own therapeutic intention. No matter how your every human being behaves himself, you strive to view that behavior as being necessary, perfect, desirable, therapeutic, ideal, adorable,—as being the only possible behavior upon which that person can base any of his further conscious development.

By the way, do you consider any case, degenerative disease for instance, to be hopeless? Your question.

Author. "Degenerative," "idiopathic," "constitutional," and cognate terms, refer only to the individual nature of every human being. While there is life there is hope. Hope for whom? I cannot feel hopeful or hopeless except about myself. Hoping is wishing, or willing. It is impossible to rule out wanting to restore myself, although it is possible for me to indulge my wayward wish to treat my despair by ending my life. My every meaning, including despair, is a desirable one to learn to live comfortably, so that I can see myself as freely using it rather than see it as seeming to dominate me.

Your M.D. can grow a patient that is very good for him. You realize that every medical treatment is one during which the patient treats himself as well as possible, and the physician treats himself as well as possible. Whether I realize it consciously or not, my giving up hope for myself in any direction stands for my own resistance to helping myself further in that direction. Chronic, long-term health complication is a saving grace to me whenever it occurs. I may wish for it unconsciously to such an extent that my conscious wish to remove every obstruction I have raised to my freer living seems limited. The most malignant cancer can, and must, reverse its course once it serves its helpful purpose and is no longer necessary. I wish always to be able to consider myself hopeless, comfortably, in any and every direction of my living.

Otherwise, I must repress (and emphasize) this "hopelessness." Such a self-view is all and only about itself and can have nothing to do with any other of my innumerable self-views.

My experience has demonstarted to me that, when I have difficulty with an idea or feeling of any kind, that difficulty is traceable to my inability, or limited ability, to consider the idea or feeling soberly. For instance, a "farfetched" idea is always one which I am unwilling to consider as localized in the forefront of my mind; a "painful thought" is one which I have never practiced living until it is no longer associated with pain; a "troublesome notion" is one which I have not taken the trouble to see is helpful. Invariably, each of these sore places heals itself if it is lived consciously as entirely my own helpful creation.

Patient. What do you mean by "a full life"?

Author. Whoever lives self-consciously lives a full life, regardless of the so-called "chronological" age. Self-awareness enables one to carry on his life's work full-scale.

Patient. The "one" to whom you refer is yourself; you have made that clear. However, as long as devotion to self-unconsciousness *seems* as non-incapacitating as it now does, it can escape detection for centuries as being everyone's world's Public Health Problem Number One.

Author. The *self-consciousness* Health Solution Number One is the only one which cannot even appear to lend itself to the all-out efforts of so-called organized education, organized medicine, or organized public health. It is a darkly feared every-person-for-his-self-world issue.

Patient. When I am not able to work myself "in good running order," I am dispirited and all too willing to acknowledge that there is "something the matter with me," but on such occasions I suffer from a disabling degree of infantilism. My mind just wilts, and all I can do is wail. When I am well, the idea of there being "something wrong with me beyond my control" is so frightening that I have never entertained it very much. At the same time, I realize that I can live nothing beyond my control, once I conceive myself comprehensively as my being my whole life. Whatever I live *is* I. My insight enables me to see that "beyond my conscious control" only means: beyond my conscious self-experience.

You imply that your feeling of inadequacy is troublesome to the extent that you cannot see your self-extent as coterminous with your world-extent. But altering my idea of myself, that is, extending my self-consciousness, seems literally to mean death to me, when I get right down to it. I realize that all of living is a death-defying performance.

Author. I note that you have reached a conscious independence which favors your sustaining uncertainty about any new view until it no longer seems to be incompatible as your own experience.

Patient. Let me speak of some of my visions, of my conscious psychic views I have been making for myself. (My) your world reminds me of Lao Tse's "He builds but does not dwell therein; and because he does not dwell therein he never departs." (My) your helpful way is to prevent yourself from identifying yourself as amounting to a personality who can oppose itself to any other "who," or to any "externality" at all. Thus, you require a thorough revision of the rules of grammar in order to speak the meanings of your mind with accuracy for yourself. As you see it, any true magnanimity you may have is lived by your fellowman as his own "you." If you are exercising full-measured magnanimity your fellowman lives consciously the self-glorification he has (his) you enjoy. The pupil of a magnanimous teacher knows that he is educating himself.

I do cherish my realization, though, that *I* can choose the limits of my self-unconsciousness, and that all such limits therefore have no power to decide the further extending of my conscious life-appreciation. Also I like the idea that I can "go to sleep" when I consciously choose to rest, and that I do not have to resort to narcolepsy, narcotics, or hypnosis.

My physician realizes that I feel and act like a baby when I'm too troubled, and he does not complain. His attitude is that his patient is always right, and I help myself with that kind of appreciation. He says that he cannot keep up on his scientific literature. I asked him what medical psychology to read once, and he said, "Read Emerson. Osler had his residents read the psychological remedies of that great all-American sage." I do read Emerson and help myself greatly through that effort.

Author. Yes. Similarly, Sir Richard Blackmore was directed by Sydenham to read *Don Quixote.* In 1850 Dr. Jacob Bigelow spoke his mind on medical education then, "Medical science has at this day become so unwieldly and contains so much that is unnecessary, at least to beginners, that the attempt to explain to students the whole is likely to involve the result of their learning but little."

Patient. Doesn't the medical school now at last center its education upon the sane concept: the individual patient? I mean, doesn't every teacher now constantly devote his educational living to his philosophy of medicine: appreciation of nowness, allness, wholeness, and unity of human individuality? Doesn't every medical educator steadfastly live up to his Hippocratic insight that the *individual variant* is the true basis of medical study and practice? Doesn't the medical educator constantly uphold the subjectivity of individuality?

Author. By no means, and properly so. Any dean who might be able to find it desirable himself to regiment any such method of teaching, fortunately would not last very long. Every medical school teacher is himself an individual, doing all that he can do to further his own life's health as best he can. Being a medical educator, or a physician, is no clean bill of health by any means. It seems easy to stand off and criticize the medical educator; but careful study, fact-finding, would lead to the renunciation of all fault-finding here, as elsewhere.

In the last analysis, it is the layman who is responsible for the kind of medical education and practice which prevails. The layman demands to be treated in a way which will not interfere with his established way of life. He shuns fearfully the extension of his own self-consciousness. He denies responsibility for his being the way he is. He does not want his mind to undergo "treatment." And so on. Many a physician, himself lacking working experience for sensing his patient's condition, would refer his patient to a psychiatrist, but has learned that his patient would only leave his doctor on that account. The incidence of helpful ignorance and repression in myself is so overwhelming that I am unable to realize the enormous amount of it in every one of my fellowmen.

Patient. I now see that misunderstanding and derision are unconscious compliments in that each is a succedaneum for sober consideration and subsequent (self-) devoted appreciation. I also see your defending your medical school dean and each of your medical educators as simple self-defense.

If everyone is already doing all he can do to further the efficacy of his medical work, and yet he is as adorably unimaginative (except in seeming to be "externalized" and "objectized") as he is, what do you propose as a solution for such an apparently insoluble problem?

Author. This particular question I put to myself over and over, and always come up with the same answer: My responsibility for my medical education begins and ends with me. By constantly attending to my own medical education I do *all* that is possible for the medical education of my world.

Patient. How would you recommend that I go about picking a physician for myself?

Author. I can speak only for myself of course. Each qualification is essential. Therefore the "numerical" order is not one of increasing or decreasing importance. In the interest of careful selection, it is a great advantage to choose my physician before acute emergency need may limit or dictate my possibilities of choice. First of all, then, it is extremely desirable that I realize *fully* how important a matter of life-and-death my "picking my physician" really is. Secondly, I consider my choice to be properly based on my general, as well as just medical, education. Thirdly, I regard my choice of physician to be ultimately (after whatever "secular" or religious counsel) a personal one of my own conscious making. Fourthly, my liking and respect for my doctor is helpful counsel. Fifthly, my knowledge of any physician's technical proficiency is an essential screening device. Sixthly, the finding of my physician's devotion to the cultivation of his own wholesome personal insight is an absolutely fundamental one. Lastly, such factors as my physician's health, ability to practice, availability, history of professional competence, suitability from the standpoint of the several members of my family (whether as a general practitioner or as a specialist), system of fees.

A baby, or child, must have most of these qualifications involving knowledgeability screened by his parent carefully. Hippocrates recorded, some patients "recover their health simply through their contentment with the goodness of the physician."

Patient. To return to the subject of being prepared to die. How is that achieved? This information has special meaning for me as a layman. If I am going headlong in a deathward direction, I want to know about it.

Author. Well, first I must review what I have already said on this subject. Basically, there is only one source of seeming mental disorder, namely transference: living as if all of that living is not one's own. Therefore, if I suffer the delusion that I can know anything about when *my* fellowman is going to die, any more than how he lives,—then I am living my fellowman without insight (which means, *in transference*). Only *my* fellowman can know anything about his living or dying. Therefore, the (phantom) problem of how to inform my patient that he is dying can be resolved only by my resolving my transference which conceals from me the fact of the entire subjectivity of my fellowman. In other words, I find it impossible to say anything about my fellowman's chances of life or death. My fellowman is the only one who can know *anything* about himself. It is a benefit to him to be able to be conscious of his exclusive responsibility for his living. Usage has given to the word "death" the dread meaning of separation. One speaks of his dying as of travelling to a distant land to leave and visit loved ones.

Patient. You touched upon your thanatology before. Please discuss it further.

Author. "Death" is a name which refers to a meaning of non-existence which is *lived* by the namer. Its dictionary meaning is: the permanent loss of personal identity, of vital individuality. As I have already observed in detail, all of me does not, and cannot, enter into my conscious living of my meaning of what I name "death."

Patient. Why is death so feared?

Author. On account of the restricted sense of personal identity which prevents one from seeing that he is his own all and that, therefore, the extinction of himself cannot involve any kind of experience of separation or loss.

Patient. You mean that, as I extend my sense of personal identity (my consciousness of my individuality) so that I can recognize myself to be coterminous with my world, I enable myself to recognize all of my ideas and feelings of separation and loss as being real delusions and illusions. Do you mean that my only problem of so-called "death" is my inability to see it as one fact, or one meaning, of my life. I can see that the expression, "the fulness of life," can truly mean the allness of a life. As I preserve my consciousness of my unity I renounce all of my illusions of "coming" and "going," including "my departure from this world."

Author. I find the term "death" to be a name for the meaning: meaninglessness, or, what is not.

Patient. Simply by seeing the life-death duality as an illusion you renounce it, and thus renounce the illusion of "death" as you do that of "wrong" or "illness."

Author. As I grow the self-tolerance to be able to acknowledge, and glory in, the self-world I create, I find all of it to be good. Every so-called evidence of "death" which I live is as perfectly desirable as every so-called evidence of life which I live. I see all of my all as perfect, as wholly desirable, and none of it as imperfect or undesirable. With this *life* orientation death simply has nothing to do.

Patient. Then you see most, if not nearly all, of the connotations associated with the word "death" to have pejorative significance favoring repression; and the awful aura around the word "death" to represent the "return of the repressed" (that is, the rejected selfness, which continues to be expressed in terms of its unhappy bondage).

My interest is in what is good for *my* health. I do see truth in your statement: *All an individual can ever do is live.* Live himself, to be sure. He can live this truth in one of two ways: consciously or unconsciously. If he lives himself consciously, as seeing soul, all of himself enjoys maximal freedom, accountability, wholesomeness,—in short, the *summum bonum.* If he lives himself unconsciously, as blind soul, all of himself enjoys maximal signs and symptoms of his ignoring the health-giving practice of noticing his own existence as being the only truth of his every existent. Please say this in your words again.

Author. All I can do is to try to recognize that it is always myself before the observation lookout of my own life. My inattention to "the facts of life" as being the meanings of my very own life must lead me to indulge my illusion that I am empty of my true self. There is no safety for my proper sense of my human being except in that completeness of my observation which identifies it as self-observation; and, I hasten to add to this insight, there is no danger about my due appreciation of my human being except in its omission.

Patient. Since "consciousness" must mean *self-consciousness,* and since there is health benefit in having the selfness of consciousness conspicuous, why is this hygienic life orientation (my awareness of the healthfulness in my cultivation of my self-consciousness) kept an open secret? Even as I ask I see my answer to be in the fact that "communication" is an illusion. Each individual (all) must *grow* this, as every other, insight. You hold that there is no research except self-investigation, which may be conscious or unconscious.

Author. I find my every human virtue, including my full, free research ability, arises from my self-consciousness. My devotion to this truth of truths helps me to realize the greatness and glory of my human life. I strive to confine my attention to this life orientation, for it enables me to see ever green fields of novelty and truth.

Patient. I have noticed that you have chosen to participate in these conversations the finest representatives of their several walks of life. In my instance, for example, you have chosen a person who feels the need for a physician and who has worked hard to educate himself, particularly in the fields of education, psychology, and philosophy. Now, as an amateur philosopher I wish to challenge your postulatum, "mind."

A fundamental axiom of science holds: entities are not to be multiplied unnecessarily. By introducing your hypothesis, "mind," you violate this basic law of philosophical parsimony. The notion "matter" must be respected. You have not demonstrated that your substance "mind" cannot inhere in your substance "matter." You would give the name "mental" to what most people call "material," leaving the thing precisely as it was. That reasoning cannot be justified either by your *a priori* conception or by your *a posteriori* experience of "mind." Even as I word these views, I realize that you are renouncing the meanings "prior" and "post," and that your whole book concerns only your describing the comprehensiveness of your individuality. Whether your individuality is referred to in terms of "mind" or "matter" is really irrelevant to the purpose of upholding the truth of the (all, whole, united) individual. Anyway, please speak your mind, or matter, to this point.

Author. I have made myself rather familiar with the interesting winding of thought and by-passing of self-consciousness which can occur in the limiting meanings of logic.

Whether I use the generic term "matter" or "mind" to name the imaginings expressive of my human being *is* beside the point that it is my sole intention to attend to the *allness* meaning of my individual life.

However, I do find myself limiting my functioning by my restriction to the language of "objectivity" (for considering myself) as a materialist. Thus, even speaking of myself as "me" (object) rather than as "I" (subject), opens the door for all of my illusions of externality, plurality, and partiality. Speaking of myself as "I" (subject) facilitates my exercising my *consciousness* that I am individual (all), am doing all of the I-living. For me, "individual" is a synonym for all.

I-ness (individuality) is entirely *subjective,* incapable of being "objectified," or even conceived of as an "object." The intention of "objectification" is to try to provide "external" status for individuality, thus cancelling its *allness* meaning. I see *every* "objectification" of mine (including my mind's powers) as my effort to ignore my personal identity (subjective selfness) in my so-called "object." Hence my psychology busies itself with my living of (creating) my self-consciousness which is objectless. My I-ness living can also serve the purpose of reminding me that there is immeasurably more to me than just my apparent self-evidence observable in whatever self-view I momentarily create. Thus, self-conscious living may be described as the arousal of the real universal in the apparent particular.

The subjectivity meaning of "mind" favors the exercise of self-consciousness; the "objectivity" meaning of "matter" favors the exercise of self-unconsciousness.

The specific source of my self-helpfulness described in each conversation has been in my discovering how to appreciate the wholeness of my human being,—not in my discovering partial facts about the nature of the substance of that wholeness. The "who" I am necessarily precedes, for it gives all of the meaning to the "what" I am.

Patient. As far as I know, the general educator gives lip-service, if any, to this "I-don't-fence-me-in" foundation of mental health. Therefore, this meaning of learning must be the specific responsibility of the medical educator. Surely he is aware of the health importance of his medic's realizing that learning the facts of medicine is nothing but the student's directing his own self-growth into his medical way of living himself. It is good for every medic's health to perceive this drift in himself clearly; indeed, such seeing is the nature of all insight about health. Therefore, every medical educator must have this realization as the very life and keystone of his system of teaching. Is that not true?

Author. Every educator is an individual (all), and lives his meaning of education properly, according to whatever degree of insight he has worked up about it. Whenever I stop long enough in my fault-finding to review the facts (of the great effort I have had to put forth to create whatever insight I have), I invariably am grateful for the way my every educator is *always* doing the best he can do.

I have found that my *expecting* my fellowman to show more insight than he does is a costly displacement of a health demand upon myself which I sorely need as incentive for my own further growth of self-insight. The constant test of my own willingness to grow insightfully is my readiness to see my word "I" as convertible with my word "world."

Patient. This is important for me. You obviously regard your every living of "objectivity" as a brief but helpful insanity. You identify the act of negation as the act of division or mental dissociation, thus: I *and* not-I. You view self-ignoration as being the paradigm of mental disturbance. You see all of negation, or denial, as a process of repression (of self-ignoration). How does negation (mental dissociation) get started? How can I willingly disown powers of my own individuality by means of negation?

Author. The human mind seems to have a diremptive function which allows it to *appear* to divide itself into isolated parts. The so-called "parts of speech" of grammar reflect this illusional power. Thus, I can seem to divide my mind into meanings which I name "I" and meanings which I name "not-I."

The origin of my negation is in my effort to maintain an appreciation of myself which makes my life seem worth the trouble of living. In my earliest years I began classifying my dislikes (unpleasant experiences) as not-I, as life events not willed by me, as "involuntary" happenings. I separated my being into powers which I freely acknowledged as being mine and powers which I freely acknowledged as being not-mine. My life-powers which I segregated as being "not-I" live on in my being, and I often refer to each one by means of negative prefixes such as "unconscious," "involuntary," "undesirable," "impersonal," "unpleasant," "disunited," "dissociated," and so on.

Patient. I can see how I had to help myself as an infant and child by resorting to my mind's divisive force called "negation," and thus forfeit much of my appreciation of my life's actual unity, wholeness, and allness. I can also see how my world must appear as separable, or as seamless, as the rest of my mind does to me.

Please elucidate once more the *practical* benefit coming from seeing a horrible accident to an innocent child of your own as being a desirable event.

Author. My little daughter who has just lived having herself mangled by terrific crushing, cutting forces helps herself immensely by living a physician who sees her entirely as desirable quite as she is. She helps herself toward mobilizing her own constructive self-forces by living her physician's kind, cheerful, loving, tender, *practical* acceptance of what is, his readiness to work with whatever is, his appreciation of his privileged opportunity to be a fact-finder rather than a fault-finder, especially during such a necessary life adventure. Her presence of mind is of profound self-heal, and every experience of enduring humaneness which she can live prevents her demoralizing scatter of her self-interests. Most of all, she needs to grow an attending physician capable of caring for the truth of the vitalizing wholeness of his patient, particularly when the truth of that enlivening wholeness does not *seem* to be evident. Fortunate is the little one, who has serious need for a phyiscian, if she can live one devoted to the sane point of view about any and every health condition which enables him to renounce the time-honored name-calling which is the chief meaning of many quasi-medical expressions such as a "bad accident," "enemies to man," "fighting the microorganism," and so on. On the contrary, if this needy child must make herself live her physician who can only seem to be deploring and rejecting his little girl's presenting necessities (cut and bleeding flesh, bruised tissues, fractured bones, bewilderment, panic, and pain) then she must add this additional, disconcerting, burdensome experience to her already overwhelmed living of herself.

Patient. I love to skip and dance. How can I see that the loss of my legs is desirable, even after I have lost them; when I can no longer enjoy even walking?

Author. Hard as it may be to understand, the discipline of fact-finding leads to the renunciation of *all* fault-finding. It is only difficultly accomplished, this realization of the desirability of whatever is.

There is another insight which can be grown and which cannot be exercised too much. I refer to the fact that I *can* really skip and dance "after I have lived the loss of my lower extremities." Thus, it is essential for my health for me to discover that my running and jumping experiences have always been entirely psychological experiences. By the free use of my imagination I can always conceive myself as running and jumping and not have to frustrate myself *where the real thwarting takes place, namely, in my imagination.* As a blind artist I can paint in my imagination, as a deaf mute I can hear and speak in my imagination, on a strict dietary regimen I can eat and drink as I please in my imagination. Such efficacious use of imagination is of immense help, but there is extreme resistance even to soberly considering the wonderful benefit derivable from this health practice.

Patient. Why should there be such extreme resistance to the use of a sure form of helpfulness? Of course I now realize that "resistance" is therapeutic maintenance of my sense of personal identity, I help myself by realizing that all resistance is resistance to dangerous living.

Author. I find the best answer to that question of mine through observing my resistance to my trying to *extend* the use of my imagination. Immediately it becomes observable that this apparently highly modifiable power (self-conscious imagination) really functions with strictest limits. Extending the limits of self-conscious imagination extends the limits of my conscious self-tolerance, a self-growth which, although exceedingly healthful, is fraught with greatest danger to my prevailing sense of my personal identity.

Patient. "Resistance" I now appreciate always as a conspicuous expression of the one and only true humanity: human individuality. I am reminded of my Pestalozzi: "Man! in thyself, in the inward consciousness of thine own strength, is the instrument intended by nature for thy development."

You regard "externality" or "not-I" meaning of any kind, to be a "fixed idea," do you not?

Author. Yes. Max Stirner, who lived only fifty years (1806-1856) and who has been described as the most radical individual of all philosophers, recorded this precious insight (in *The Possessed*): "What is it then, that is called a 'fixed idea'? An idea that has subjected the man to itself."

Whatever meaning I live (be it a sensation, feeling, or idea) as if not mine, not all mine, creates my delusion and illusion of "objectivity." The fact is, when I am not noticing my living as being all my own, I do well if I can recognize that I am mentally disturbed.

Patient. Do you regard your Max Stirner as "the most radical individualist of all philosophers"?

Author. No; nor do I regard any philosopher necessarily as more or less philosophic than another, or than a poet, scientist, or possibly some "unknown" layman.

Patient. I realize that by "philosopher" you must mean (your) one who loves his own wisdom about his own allness, wholeness, oneness, and nowness.

Author. That is the general idea. Rare is my American fellowman who sees clearly and steadily that he cannot live in an "external" United States of America, that obviously all that he names his "country" or his "world" can be lived only in by, of, and for him.

Patient. I know of no leading American statesman who would agree that all of his democracy exists entirely in him; no leading American physician who would agree that his whole medical world lives only in him; no leading American author, editor, or literary critic who would agree that all of his literary world exists only in him; no leading American clergyman who would agree that all of his religious world exists only in him. And so on. The outstanding American educator-writers of today refer to the American citizen as: "a valuable member of society,"—is that not a vast oversimplification of the complex subject of human individuality (allness)?

Author. Only my fellowman can speak for, or listen to, himself in regard to his self-estimates, or anything else. Only he can know the extent to which he has developed his conscious imagination (conscious self-tolerance, self-insight) to see that he, and he only, lives all of his life. However, whatever is, is excellent,—and that clear, sweeping insight clears my mind for sane action. I strive always to be able to see that my fellowman is always right according to his viewpoint, as well as to see that he is also right in his refusal to give the same consideration to his author.

Patient. How can you renounce such satisfying superior-to-thou repressing forces as irony and satire? You will never be a popular author with your sobersides style. Aristotle advised to speak as the common people do, and to think as wise men do, you know.

Author. Only by seeing that my irony, or satire, must apply exclusively to myself can I achieve this renunciation. If I were to write anything "popular" I would first of all suspect such writing to be rich in self-deceptions of various kinds.

Patient. In his interesting book *Excellence,* John W. Gardner wrote in italics his ideal of heeding perpetual self-discovery in order to realize one's best self.[3]

Your devotion to cultivating as habitual your healing vision of selfness as your constant meaning of whatever you live is, first of all, difficult to understand; secondly, more difficult to try to see as my own; and thirdly, most difficult to practice. However, I do like your dogged persistence for it as well as your acknowledgment of your purely selfish interest in having your fellowman independently test its healing property upon himself. Many of your notions remind me of Rousseau's counsel, "Go directly contrary to custom, and you will nearly always be right," and, "He who has lived most is not he who has numbered the most years, but he who has been truly conscious of what life is," and "O men, be human! it is your highest duty." As far as your idea of your divinity is concerned, I am reminded most of Froebel, "By education, then, the divine essence of man should be unfolded, brought out, lifted into consciousness, and man himself raised into free, conscious obedience to the divine principle that lives in him, and to a free representation of this principle in his life."

As I stated at the start, I am interested in my philosophy, for it seems usually that my philosopher is interested in his own wisdom. However, had I not studied my philosophy as a life interest of mine, I doubt if I would have been able to enjoy these talks. Being a consciously self-educated individual has also helped me, for I have been able to appreciate my prescription of self-heal as being a form of learning health through living it. I regard my discovery of myself so that I can properly care for myself as being the cheering knowledge which is of most worth for my health and happiness. Montaigne noted, "The most manifest sign of wisdom is a continual cheerfulness."

What about your American patient who has not extended his self-tolerance through the growth of his conscious self-knowledge, as I have? How do you live his undisciplined individuality? How do you grow your patient who is *uninterested* in the fine ideal that he is his own physician, or that he must cure himself?

Author. I work with whatever sense of helpfulness my patient may have. I study (my) his way of helping himself, whatever way that may be, and fully respect it. I do all that I can do to try to live so that my patient may be able to find his living of his physician of some evident, as well as unrecognized, use to him.

I chose (my) you as my patient largely on account of your extraordinary ability to verbalize your health interests.

Patient. Is it your opinion that *any* patient can help himself specifically by his careful and regular accounting to himself for his life as being the creator of his world? Does this conscious self-orientation health regimen which your conversations uphold apply to a dull as well as to a bright patient?

Author. My experience has demonstrated that (my) *every* person who discovers his fundamental medical principle of self-help, who lives his health struggle in a consciously positive way, benefits greatly from this realized mobilization of his self-power. "I can help myself" is unitive effort; "I can be helped" is divisive effort.

The term "dull" can carry a pejorative force allowing its user to practice self-depreciation without consciously feeling it.

There is no medicine, or no physician, for any patient, except that which he experiences and feels in and by his own living. My history of health education has been one of profiting from advancing this solipsistic position and of consciously suffering the helpful signs and symptoms of disregarding it. The radical truth of individuality is hardly ever observed, much less practiced, however, a fact which, fully taken into account, explains each person's mental condition, that is, his interest in living peacefully his psychological and educational systems, and his concern about his health. Latest "scientific" references to complete individuality describe it in a few philosophical terms either implying, or clearly asserting, that it is fallacious, or impractical, or both.

Patient. By living "complete individuality" you mean: consciously living one's *allness* meaning. A vast amount of human nature comes to light in that view. Elizabeth Barrett Browning looked at her life somewhat as you do at yours,

> I walked on musing with myself
> On life and art and whether after all
> A larger metaphysics might not help
> Our physics—a completer poetry
> Adjust our daily life and vulgar wants
> More fully than the special outside plans
> Phalansteries, material institutes

The civil conscriptions and lay monasteries
Preferred by modern thinkers.

You seem to imply (with your *Whatever is, is right*) that La Rochefoucauld justly observed, "Narrow minds think nothing right that is above their own capacity." Now I must say that I have the greatest difficulty *considering soberly* (your "strong act" of the mind) your notions of sex,—particularly your view of masturbation as being adorable, necessary for full male and female development, essential for preventing early incidence of impotence, and the fundamental prototype of marital sexual intercourse. I suppose the very difficulty I have in soberly considering each of these views must itself offer me a clue as to the strength of my need to resist, deny, and even negate each one of them. I can understand also that the very strength of sexual passion is the factor which leads to my repressing it (denying its right to exist), as long as I must live it as if it can overwhelm me, instead of be consciously controlled by me. After all, you distinctly do not (and see you cannot) recommend your sexual (or any other) views to your fellowman. You have observed that only he can do that. You do not even ask your fellowman's sober *consideration* of your views, realizing that only he can ask himself to consider soberly his own views.

You must originate gratefully your David Riesman's human, hence individual, life appreciation: "I am insisting that no ideology, however noble, can justify the sacrifice of an individual to the needs of the group. Whenever this occurs, it is the starkest tragedy, hardly less so if the individual consents (because he accepts the ideology) to the instrumental use of himself."[4]

You know, Confucius replied to the question as to how he would first go about governing a nation: Correct the language.

Author. Yes. Never have I found a more fundamental definition of social justice than (my) Plato's: "Minding one's own business." Obviously one's idiolect can either facilitate or inhibit his study and practice of self-consciousness. Surely self-consciousness is my obvious essential for maintaining my mental equilibrium.

Patient. Please explain once more how you try to maintain your mental balance.

Author. I must ask my question and answer it.

I strive to keep my conscious mental balance by trying to realize that "on with the new" is not "off with the old" (The notion "on with the new and off with the old" supports the illusion called "change."); by heeding the truth that my personal identity, itself, is constantly growing itself and that, therefore, my conscious view of my personal identity must constantly grow itself with it, in order to be able to appreciate that development; by trying to understand and renounce my rigid face-saving tendencies; by *expecting* to throw myself off balance by my life's novel adventure.

Any one of my self-experiences which I may have to disown must *therefore* have the appearance of *making me* (my own self-experience, all mine!) feel less sure of myself, doubtful of my wonderful power, uncertain of my glorious sufficiency. Any day I may jolt myself from my truthful way of thinking (as seeing my every meaning as being entirely my mind's self-activity) and find myself frantically seeking security in seemingly foreign-made assurance associated with my alluring illusion about "otherness" (such as this one's or that one's "essential doctrine," "basic principle," "fool-proof nostrum," and so on). Every day by reminding myself of my ignorance I can cure myself of my indulgence of unconscious arrogance. Any moment I may unbalance my sense of personal identity enough to shake my confidence in my self-sovereignty. In an instant, I may see myself as a shifty back-slider deserting my difficultly attained theonomous position. I may require myself to think of myself any time as fitting Ambrose Bierce's definition of a hypocrite: "One who, professing virtues that he does not respect, secures the advantage of seeming to be what he despises."

Thus, I try to keep my balance by aiming to establish the broadest base for my footing as well as the most liberal interpretation and helpful appreciation of any so-called "imbalance" (as actually representing an unrecognized balance, if each prevailing force is duly considered). The term "imbalance" can really deny the basic meaning it is apparently supposed to describe fairly (a modification of balance). The view of truth which I wish to present throughout these conversations is visible in my recurring picture of negation as always involving concealed (unconscious) affirmation. Whatever is denied, must exist, or there would be nothing to deny. My mind's insightful use of "no" can provide it with a kind of dialectic for seeking truth, by seeing *that* truth's unity as the synthesis of elements contributed by each seperate angle of vision.

Often I remind myself of Shakespeare's wise description (*Henry VI,* Part 3, III. ii):

> And I—like one lost in a thorny *wood,*
> That rents the thorns, and is rent with thorns,
> Seeking a way, and straying from the way;
> Not knowing how to find the open air,
> But toiling desperately to find it out.

Patient. In *The Power of Reason,* a special report by Robert M. Hutchins, president of the Center for the Study of Democratic Institutions, Santa Barbara, California, I read a startling statement recently made by one of your colleagues, Herbert Ratner, M.D.:

> The modern medical school is really not much different from the veterinary school. It could, for the most part, just as well have the horse for its subject. There are only a few medical schools in the country that give a course in how to communicate with patients, for instance. I know of only one school that gives a course on the philosophy of medicine. Hardly any medical schools have a satisfactory course on medical ethics, and this is what every medical school should be doing with great advantage to the performance and to the public image of the physician.

Author. I appreciate Dr. Ratner's effort to be helpful. I am sure he realizes that a diagnosis is not an accusation, and that his chief intention is to practice his consciousness of medical education as he observes it.

16

American Chaplain

A man shall be as an hiding-place from the wind and a covert from the tempest, as rivers of water in a dry place, as the shadow of a great rock in a weary land.

ISAIAH

CHAPLAIN. THUS, IDEALIST Isaiah (740-701 B.C.), creator of the concept "Prince of Peace," described the individuality meaning of human being.

I have kept out of this "grand rounds" of the mind thus far, except to live with interest your apparent reliance upon the helpfulness of "the word" for citing society in solitude. I see that conscious or unconscious belief in one's self provides the only possible ground for any certitude; that conscious or unconscious self-appreciation is the only possible ground for affirmation of any kind (including divine omnipresence); that conscious or unconscious self-allness provides the only possible ground for reverence for any individuality; that conscious or unconscious self-reverence provides the only possible ground for every morality, mystic or "manifest"; and that self-consciousness provides the only possible ground for supervision of any description.

All I wish to voice is my view that spirituality is also the only constituent of *my* well-known walks of human and psychic life. Again, *it is only its consciousness which can be wanting.* Spirituality, as the soul of subjectivity, does not exist for publication. Unrecognized spirituality is only unconscious spirituality. The unlearned lesson of the work-a-day world of everyone is this desideratum of soul-consciousness. Taken-for-granted living cannot serve as the reality of the glory of life. May every man ask himself, "Are you afraid to soar with your soul?" and then answer himself. Life itself is lyrical, cannot be spoken, must be sung! I affirm that in the region of conscious spirituality lie all of the substantial truths of life. Self-reverence is the sanctuary of sanity. Man equals his destiny. He gives the name of impersonal destiny only to his living to which he has not yet attained *conscious* equality.

Author. I have wondered at your silence. And now I wonder at your song. Your *spiritual culture* consciousness evidently enables you to feel sure that *you* are living spirit, or spiriting life. Your elevated living contrasts with the timidity of my own conscious divinity, which timidity shames me again and again. As conscious man I can sustain my courage. As conscious god I am frightened, frightened by my need to "live up to" my self-appraisal.

Chaplain. The sure immediate cure for every complaint, which I first trace to too much divinity-consciousness, is to give myself another dose of God-consciousness. It is my God-consciousness which turns all apparent badness to goodness, all apparent time to eternity, all seeming space to infinity, all manifest war to peace, all evident impermanence to immortality, all pain to pleasure,—in short, all seeming devilry to divinity. Of whatever happens I observe, "Something divine has happened."

Author. What I name my "mind" I conceive to be my life interest and to enable my interest in my life. What you name your "soul," or "spirit," does not put quite the same value upon the meaning of life, does it?

Chaplain. Is that a question which only you can answer? For me, whatever is, is soul. True, I keep soul-conscious as much as possible, for I always find it all that can be relevant. My substantial meaningfulness is always accessible whenever I am mindful of the soul of me, or, if you wish, soulful of the mind of me. What is matter and, therefore, what matters is my spirituality. That consciousness marks the zenith, its absence the nadir, of my voluntary devotion to my existence. My wholeness value is made available for my appreciation if I recognize that my wholeness *is* the creator of my every act.

Author. Spiritual wealth, your soulful monopoly, is the product of the unconstrained activity of spirit, is it not? Your question.

Chaplain. I have tried to express my sense of freedom in those words, and can do so. If I wait until my spirituality is out of order before I can notice it, I lose track of the very goal of my devotion. It is when I am spirit-conscious that I feel most intensely my capacity for intensity of my every power. My spiritual hygiene (care) accords with my functional freedom to take care of my world. Love is the smoothened highway of spirituality. Morality is the policy of spirituality. Seeing my soul in whatever I live is my ever sure source of appreciation of my importance. It does not add to my divinity except insofar as addition means soul-affirming.

Author. You recognize no littleness of soul. Largeness is made up of itself disguised as littleness. Whoever cannot see goodness in badness cannot see goodness to begin with. Every word describing the unpleasant or undesirable simply describes my unreadiness to see the pleasant or desirable fully. Man's every misery is his lesson of love to be produced as his own. Peace of soul is to be found only in the appreciation of the subjectivity of the soul. No power can, so to speak, see that my soul *is* saved, except itself.

Chaplain. You are speaking as an undisguised religious worker, it seems. Is not the most commanding person the one who lives the most obedience? If I deny that I am my ever new self, if I must confound my very own feeling of "strangeness" or of "foreignness" with "not-self," it is a benefit that I cannot be aware of my peace of soul before I obey my own command to assume responsibly and authoritatively my novel existence.

Author. When to be awake, or when to be asleep, seems to be the most crucial problem of everyone's sphere of helpfulness. It is the uncertain adventurousness of experience which makes it seem desirable to prefer a familiar feeling of selfsameness to the strange feeling of constantly putting on the new man. As I have already observed, I fear nothing more than I do a loss of my sense of personal identity, so that the idea of "change" can be a serious threat to me.

Chaplain. I rate my appreciation of my spirituality by the amount of homesickness for it which I suffer when I must distract myself from its fulfilling meaning. I aim to awaken for it, and reckon sleep as a necessary unconscious living of it. I regard it as the very structure of perfection. I have had to cease busying myself unconsciously with illusion so that I might consciously get to work on it. To be consciously spiritual is the hardest, most exhilarating and comprehensive labor I have ever found. It has provided me with new meaning of "the thick of life," of "the essential," of "the dignity of the individual."

Author. Your bethinking yourself of the uncircumstanced nature of your self-helpfulness, and your expressing your views in the pacific language of love,—each is a wonder to behold. What I have had you say seems to describe greatly needed supplement to any dully conceived "bare walls of existence."

I can understand how it is that you feel that your work is God's work. I can see that it lies within the power of everyone to cultivate his spirituality, through consciously devoting interest to it, as you must have.

That is all that there is to it, as far as I can see. My true birth dated from the day I, for the first time, saw consciously my identity in my every experience. I knew then what Shakespeare meant by his words, "Before, I loved thee as a brother, John. But now I do respect thee as my soul." I said to myself, "*There* is god, and he is myself." No longer did it suffice for me to say that "god is great," and thus conceal my very own divine magnitude. Without this divine self-love I can conceive of neither sight nor insight for myself. It was only by my discovering my divinity that I was able to discover the divinity in everyone of my world. Conscious spiritual force is never wordish, ever word-dearthing, is it not? Only self-reverence *can* honor humanity. When man gains sight of his mind, all of his world is thrown in. Where there is no self-reverence, or "self-consciousness" there is always some reason or other to pass muster for self-certitude. Only self-reverence can be life-proof. All experience is self-devotion, every place a soul site. However, right now as I summon my self-reverence I note that conscious spirituality belongs only to the consciously spiritual-minded.

Only love can awaken consciousness to the truth of its selfness. The unification lust-love-reverence is most practical of all self-views, consciously integrating, as it does for me, my body-externality-divinity meanings.

Chaplain. The reverentially self-poised mind can support the burden of sanctity. *One's idiom of mind reveals his consciousness of his wonderfulness.* Self-reverence is the power that discloses all as perfect. The way in which I do my looking decides the meaning of what I see. Hunger and weariness signalize for me lack of conscious spirituality, when the former leads to starvation or overeating, and the latter leads to chronic overactivity or low-energy behavior. My soul view is my soul cure, as your mind view is your mind cure.

Author. All true. I bethink myself of Xenophon's report of the discussion of Socrates and Parrhasius, "Can the unseen be imitated?" whenever I fall into the abyss of conceiving learning as the product of anything but living. My hearer cannot listen to me—he can hear only his audible experience he grows through *his* hearing.

Chaplain. I wish to return to your idea that everyone is divinely perfect. One may be accustomed to think in terms of body, mind, and soul. Thus, I am comfortable conceiving my soul as spiritual. But now you would extend the meaning of soul, or spiritual to mind as well as body. Here is where I note soul sight.

Author. Excellent. Homecoming self-consciousness is the surest surveyor of bounds. Again awareness, or consciousness, has come to my rescue. I formerly had the confirmed habit of confounding spirituality with conscious spirituality, and, therefore, termed my unconscious spirituality by a special name, "corporeality." With the aid of my self-consciousness I have grown to see clearly that my soul *is* my all; that my psychological work is unrecognized soul stirrings; and that my anatomical work is unrecognized spiritual endeavor. *Realizing, however, the indispensable importance in not confounding any of my experience, or meaning, with that same experience, or meaning, lived consciously,—that realization has become the most effective ordering principle of my life.*

Chaplain. Just one moment, please. If everything is perfect, just as it is, or adorable, as you rightly observe,—I can see that therefore it is also perfect and adorable to work with whatever is painful or troublesome so that it will become pleasing or pacifying. However, this question comes to mind: Since whatever is, is divinely perfect or perfectly divine, why is earth unrecognized as heaven? Why in the best of all possible worlds, can there be so much discontent, so much "hell on earth"? Why is there written so much about utopia, when this is it? Why is the truth of "spirit" so repressed when the spirit of "truth" is its nature?

Author. Such questioning of myself led me to see the answer in my realization that, again, I was overlooking the all-important power of awareness. I was confusing unconscious perfection, or unconscious divinity, with conscious perfection, or conscious divinity. After that elucidation it was easy for me to see that whatever is, is perfect (or divine), whether I am perfectly aware or perfectly unaware of it.

Chaplain. As I have noticed all along, your notion of *conscious* inviolable individuality can appeal only to the elect. As you view and synthesize your meanings of life and try painstakingly to record them, are you not also taking pains to conceal from yourself the fact that the market for your idea of truth is culled from the passing years? You would have every man cultivate the strength of mind to see his precious independence, but rarely has a person trained his mind to perceptions which would make him more than faintly interested in your I-sovereignty remedy. You would be one of the first to see that you must first love and admire before understanding can develop itself. It is one thing for you to quote your Shakespeare about being of "such stuff as dreams are made on" and to say that imagination is your only possible mental action, but is it circumspect for you to expect your fellowman to have this studied apprehension of his mystic make-up?

Author. Everyone does all he can to exercise circumspection so that he will not overlook any pertinent facts. I presume you are referring to the scope of the organ of self-observation itself, rather than to the sweep of its view. By circumspection you must mean practicing the view that subjectivity (the soul of self) does all of the observing and all of the being observed.

Chaplain. Exactly. Not my life limitations but my own limiting opinion of myself would obstruct my recognizing my spirituality, would blind me to the meaning of my Emerson's spirit-sight:

> There is no great and no small
> To the Soul that maketh all;
> And where it cometh all things are;
> And it cometh everywhere.

Author. "It is all one to me," must be a favorite expression of yours. For you, all personal experience is conscious or unconscious spiritual creativity. Enthusiasm is natural to you. Your ecstatic living is expectable, not exceptional. Your life work consists of practicing the insight that omnipresent perfection, excellence, divinity, can be consciously meaningful only as you consciously exercise your subjectivity.

Chaplain. That last sentence says it, as I live it. Paraphrasing my former President John F. Kennedy's inspired self-observation, the creation and enjoyment of peace is always the achievement of individuality, always the easement of a soul. As every other meaning, peace is autocthonous. Soul sight provides *all* of the sanities of my life. The *practicality* of my conscious spirituality commends it most. It is an immense economy to be able to direct my devotion to my own helpfulness and to fear my own displeasure should I neglect this devotion. Self-command is desirable living which wisely extends to my every meaning. It is but natural to be able to sense my innateness in whatever I live. My conscious presence is my source of all of my "prestige," the basis for calculating my own rating. If I knew of a word more comprehensive, meaningful, and truly descriptive, than "divine" for naming my existence, I would use it.

You will appreciate Stephen Berrien Stanton's tribute to "insight," in his *Soul and Circumstance* (1910):

> Insight is the dulcet piper that charms out the children of the heart into a land of loveliness. With magic touch it rifts objectivity and opens vistas of inner meaning that fulfil our early dreams. Facts keep unfolding, curtains are constantly drawn aside and verities that transcend all expectation are unveiled. The enlargement of life is incredible.

Author. The "sacred integrity of the soul" is the basis of religious education, as I understand it. Please speak of this religious view.

Chaplain. Wherever I might begin in sacred history I would find allusions to evidence of every man's divinity. The Torah records that the Lord knew Moses "soul to soul." "I am That I am," is a tribute to the allness of individality, treating subjectivity as divinity.

Your idea of living your neighbor as yourself is possibly the oldest ethical proposition recorded. Every religion expresses appreciation for this inner equality. Confucius, Buddha, Zoroaster, and of course the Judeo-Christian teaching,—each indicates the practicality of self-consciousness for living one's fellowman with appreciation. Equality (sameness) is the divinity level.

Author. Do you foresee the unification of the work of religion and that of medicine?

Chaplain. I do not need to "foresee" it, for I see its actual existence now. I observe every interest called "secular" to be entirely, but usually unfamiliarly, *sacred.* Centuries ago a Hebrew poet wrote, "If I make my bed in hell, behold, Thou art there" (Psalm 139).

What you mean by the function of full, free imagination is what I mean by the conscious integrity of my soul. It occurs to me to point out that the risk in naming my mind's or soul's being is that I will fall into the trap of conceiving "naming" as a kind of "objectifying." Surely you renounce any illusional "objectification" of your mind's powers, do you not?

Author. With all of my might. I have had greatest difficulty, of the very kind you mention, with my wording of my individuality. Indeed it is my chief concern in my development of my idiolect, and every warning about it is helpful. The meaning of every name (or description of any kind) seems to stop short of conscious subjectivity. I cannot really "say" anything of myself without appearing to "objectify" that living of mine. The manifest mediacy of the word can slight insight, quite as the vision so-called "externality" can. The intrinsic meaning of "word," of "name," as being a counter, or tag, is kept conscious only with great difficulty. I presume that you encounter your most trying work where semantic subjectivity is overlooked. Reality can only be lived.

Chaplain. True enough. Subjectivity is totally intransitive. Said Whitman, "I announce a life that shall be copious, vehement, spiritual, bold," and, "What do you suppose will satisfy the soul, except to walk free and own no superior?" I study how to live consciously by my soul's law since I find my only alternative to be to live blindly by it. Any intolerance I show for so-called profane writing is but a seeming, for I find it always to be really sacred, however much its author disclaims its spirituality. In (my) Alexander Smith's choice word-painting,

> Some books are drenched sands
> On which a great soul's wealth lies all in heaps,
> Like a wrecked argosy.

Since every meaning is the work of the mind, is it not possible that all that passes for "reality" may well be described as one's spiritual abundance? Must one fear the outburst of his spirit throughout all of the years of his days? Is it not everyone's most important natural concern to find the purest, intensest, whole living of one's self? Seeing my answering for this kind of questioning has enabled me to view my spirituality with equanimity. I frequently make conscious (my) Plato's beautiful appreciation of his spirituality: "And this which you deem of no moment is the very highest of all: that is whether you have a right idea of the gods, whereby you may live your life well or ill."

Author. Dei plenus. I feel inspirited in this kind of living, certainly. Your spirituality consciousness reminds me of the insightful work of one of my psychiatric colleagues who refers to

> the tremendous mental energy one invests in the pursuit of a certain state of selfness, grace or sublime individuality. Concepts of godliness, heavenly bliss, Elysian plains, etc., are examples of this state but are considered actually attainable only through death or some other insurmountable barrier. Psychiatric "illness" may be regarded as a phenomenon of this very force, the symptoms representing manifestations of attempts to attain a godly feeling.[1]

Aristotle observed that "the soul is in a certain sense all things." This is understandable as meaning that the soul is its own "all things," which it must be. For purpose of reality orientation, it is necessary for me to find myself just where I lost myself, in my owndom. I wonder, and well I may, at the starry firmament I create, at the microscopic world I create, and so on and on. None of the power and glory is the less for my acknowledging that it is my own appreciation which I make possible for my own enjoyment of my own world. My study of the facts not only dispels my fault-finding but also my alienation of my perfection-finding. It is propitious to add (1) that the concept "spirit" is in no sense more a product of hypothesis than is the concept "matter," and (2) that evidence of "spirit" is of necessity based upon the idea of one's own immediate subjective experience, whereas evidence of "matter" is of necessity based upon the idea of one's mediated, impersonal "objective" world.

Chaplain. Your unconventional, warm acceptance of all of the cherished meanings of divinity as being appreciated powers of your own individuality contrasts with my poet's sane description of depersonalized deity:

> The unheeding and inexorable God
> Of "infinite eternal energy,"
> Spawn of a mechanistic century,—
> A god when found was scarcely worth the finding,—
> Indifferent, impersonal, alone.[2]

As I see it, spirituality cannot be kept out of any of one's living, only awareness of its presence can ever be wanting. It is insightless to identify spirituality with anything but individuality, for *individuality is all that exists.* Try as you will, you can conceive only an individual conception, perceive only an individual perception, sense only an individual sensation.

Author. I bow to my fact that all learning is esoteric, and that whatever I learn is a self-growth of mind. I am also aware that it will be the extremely rare hearer who will consciously find himself in his listening. It has been hard work for me to rescue my forgotten (repressed) spirituality-consciousness, and I expect my every fellowman to have similar work to do, if he has not already accomplished it.

However, I have included this particular section on the materiality of the ideal, for a work on elementary medical education would be incomplete without it. My mind is not an open book, and I have no intention to be "easily seen through." I know that I cannot be understood except by myself. I seek no understanding but self-understanding. If my reader understands himself less from his reading of his author's appreciation of spirituality, such a confession of adorable ignorance, or resistance, or whatever his un-understanding may represent, can also be life-affirming to him.

Ever since Anaxagoras first recognized his self-moving principle and grew the meaning "spirit," there seems to have been ever-ready resistance to conscious living of it. One's spiritual view of life has gained much support from the work of the modern physicist, which dispels the most coveted illusions of the materialist. However, even that issue is beside the point of this whole book, which has but one thesis: I am my own all. Said Wordsworth:

> Dust as we are, the immortal spirit grows
> Like harmony in music; there is a dark
> Inscrutable workmanship that reconciles
> Discordant elements, makes them cling together
> In one society. How strange that all
> The terrors, pains, and early miseries,
> Regrets, vexations, lassitudes interfused
> Within my mind should e'er have borne a part,
> And that a needful part, in making up
> The calm existence that is mine when I
> Am worthy of myself.

Chaplain. Jeláleddin tells of a heavenly voice saying to pilgrims who were moving the prescribed seven times around the holy temple of Kaaba: " 'Why stand ye here to worship stone? Go and adore in God's true house—the house of truth, home of the heart! Blessed is he who enters there!' "

Your ideal order of life, highlighting the efficacy of exercising the "ultimate in your life affirmation," and your specific illustration of the health benefit in the practice of life-consciousness in the form of self-insight,—each focuses human interest from the arid wastes of (mediate) formal education upon the green field of (immediate) individual living, where it belongs.

Kant considered monism to be necessity of the mind and allowed no "objective" validity to knowledge. Only the given mind's meanings, or interest, can be lived with any recognition or consciousness, whatsoever. Every mind conceives divinity in order to secure its own practical advantage (of "the ultimate in life affirmation," as you word it). However, unless the given mind increases its sense of self-possession (by self-conscious living), it cannot live its divinity meaning with a feeling of equality (with its sense of personal identity). Only as I grow able to acknowledge my own Godhood, can any meaning of divinity have the warranty of my mind,—thus "religious-consçiousness" can become, and be understood as being, a synomym for "self-consciousness." Indeed, it is no safer to base religious than mental health on any foundation other than that of human individuality. The nature of all reality is a mental problem, and the given mind's meaning for reality is the *only* solution of that problem. Reality's worth can be decided only by the adequacy of its meanings for the given individual, who is always the ground of all of his reality.

In his *Philosophy of Theism* (1887), Borden P. Bowne elucidates the necessary subjectivity of all knowledge:

> Nowadays only belated minds expect demonstration in any department of objective knowledge. It is evident, also, that all thinking, and hence all knowing, must be conditioned by our mental nature. In no way can the mind get outside of itself and grasp things otherwise than through the conceptions which its nature allows it to form.

Your mental seriousness about the limited advantage of endowing your own personifications ("Common Sense," "Society," "Romanticism," "Religion," "Medicine," "Law," "Humanity," "History," "Necessity") with mental attributes, is needed. This personifying tendency of the mind needs constant watching, e.g., "the facts of the external world." The absolute impossibility of imposing adventitious additions to the mind, by any so-called "external" authority, advances the *practicality* of looking for the source of each person's esthetics of life in that human individual's psychogenesis. One thing can be explained only by itself, and not by another thing. Any personification of mind, e.g., "external world," can be only my own abstraction from my own self-observations, for whose explanation I invented my personification. Full-measured appreciation of human individuality is the only possibility of full-measured appreciation of human life. And consciousness for complete importance of human life, above all, *must* not be beyond the power of the physician. That point is the whole one of this work of yours. Not mediate illusional "physical" but actual immediate mental, regeneration is your one theme. The soul's desert of "otherness" can be irrigated by the flow of self-consciousness. If anyone calls you a madman or a mystic, instead of a medic, you understand his need to resist sensing his personal identity in his "you," as well as his need to avoid the occasion for his conscious living of that resistance itself. In other words, you see *every* kind and degree of denial or negation as being nothing but therapeutic self-rejection (repression) which allows its creator to escape overwhelming himself with responsibility.

What I would need in order to understand my fellowman is, of course, exclusively necessary to my fellowman himself. Only he can have what it takes to understand himself. In other words, every scientist strengthens his mind by realizing that the "objects" of his science have no existence, except as creations of his own mind. The mind cannot abandon itself, regardless of the appearances of abdication it can produce. If I regard myself as *the* all of existence I must see all of my proof as my own. "External world" is a synomym for all that is purely blind in self-observation.

It would be helpful if every thesis would begin with avowed autobiographical data intended to be useful for recognizing and accounting for the largely unacknowledged autobiographical data then to follow. Said Keats, "We read fine things but we really do not understand them until we have gone the same steps as the author." Thus, the real origin of your conversations seems to have been your practical personal experience of maintaining a watch on yourself, of exercising your mind's eye. No doubt you recall indulging this proclivity in your childhood as being a way of distinctly enjoying the truth of your individuality. For instance, you may remember how you gave your imagination freedom, but found it helpful to be carefully selective of your expression for your living of each member of your family. You may have been described by your family members as a shy, self-centered one, often finding a book more wieldy than a "party," enjoying being "alone." Has it occurred to you that this writing may be largely an expression of your femininity? It reminds me of the eyes of Keat's *The Fall of Hyperion,* describing the vision of Moneta,

> Half-closed, and visionless entire they seemed
> Of all external things; they saw me not
> And in blank spendour beamed like the mild moon
> Who comforts those she sees not, who knows not
> What eyes are upward cast.

Some of your statements remind me of Meister Eckhart's *Eternal Rebirth of the Soul,* "The reborn soul is as the eye, which having gazed into the sun, thenceforward sees the sun in everything."

Author. I like the way I have had my you live views about your reading. Yes, I am in my hands, feet, eyes, otherness, externality, and so on. There is no frontier of my being. I do not end and, therefore, nothing else can begin. This kind of self-realization I recognize as being the pinnacle of my conscious personal being. I *belong* and, with a feeling of exhilaration, can assert of my all: I am I. With this quality of life vision I can indorse my life's creations. My lifelong task is that of dispelling my illusion of "external necessity" by seeing it as my living of my real internal or all-pervading *freedom.* I have had to drive myself sane enough to see: Be kind to everyone and everything; it is I. My humanity is held fast in my every sensation, perception, feeling, and consciousness.

Chaplain. You have just described what is generally named "mystical perception," the most difficult of all function of sensibility to grow. It is usually considered as being prophetic of a fuller development of human consciousness.

As you have observed, all education is individual living. My own unformulable mental growth is my only bridge uniting what I do not know to what I learn to know by living. Whether as Keats I describe the world as a vale of soul-making, or as Max Stirner describe the mind as a range of world-making, the abiding truth underlying either view is my own life's adventure.

By the way, it pleases me that you see no need to apologize for any certain evidence of exaltation your writing may express. I am pleased when I sense that my author has written with a feeling of excitement, particularly when I can feel sure that he knows that his great moments of illumination are not transferable. In your every human individual is "God's plenty," as (my) Dryden called (his) Chaucer. My discovery of my nature is my discovery of God.

What you describe as the arduous but vivifying exertion of *consciously* living yourself in all of your life's work *is* the mystic experience, the labor of "disintoxication" called by Santayana the true "note" of spirituality, the explication of the meaning of being from only "a dreaming thing, A fever of thyself" (Keats). What you describe as the unity, allness, completeness, wholeness, innocence, nowness, and justness of the individual *is* the subjective unity of the peace-abiding soul. Seeing yourself as life, rather than as only a vehicle of life, *is* awareness of divine presence. Acknowledging yourself as being your soul *is* religious consciousness.

According to your own notion of reality, denial of the truth of any of these views is tantamount to self-repudiation.

Author. My chaplain has made his point: god is all. Self allness conviction is "the divine look." However a person lives his life is divine.

Chaplain. A thief is a divine thief, a cheat is a divine cheat, a drunkard is a divine drunkard, a liar is a divine liar. Only the soul can attain *any* self-expression. Illusional knowledge of an external world can be only illusionally divisive. A man defends his illusional material goods as an unrecognized, unacknowledged but nonetheless pure and true defense of his own soul. It is for the seeing to see. Blasphemy can be no more than a prayer, or blessing, that has hidden itself. *Whatever* you cannot live consciously as excellent, perfect, most desirable, and in every respect divine, is already undergoing repression, according to you, is it not?

Author. Yes. It is divine also to be able to consider the fulfilment of life, the fruition of potential, the liberation of all of love.

Chaplain. Apparently you consider the extension of your self-conscious living to be your real coming of Messiah. I am pleased that you recognize no really disunited self,—only the appearance of it. A life shrinks from none of its living, only from extending itself to suicidal experience. Proper use is full use.

Please dilate upon your free-association therapy. It reminds me of religious soul-searching. How do you notice the results of your treatment of your mind? Do you not recognize in your self an unpopular order of human coherence?

Author. As I ask myself my question I am aware of the divisive connotation of "I am asking you," and of the unitive connotation of "I am asking myself." The unity of "I asking" and of "I answering" arises from the inward coherence of each as an individuation of one individual. When I discovered a new view of my unity, or creaturehood, which did not do violence to the very meaning of unity, to be possible,—at that moment I realized my necessity to wean myself from the insightless use of such not-I meanings as "popular," "unpopular," "fashionable" "unfashionable," and the like.

The facility of functioning of the body-center of the mind which follows achievement in free-association is wonderful to see. Furthermore, the whole consubstantial mind benefits from liberation of any of itself. My conscious mental freedom, as demonstrated by my ability to free-associate until I can find all of my mental functioning good, is characterized by the pure joy of heroic living. My gradual clarification of my proper (full) self-estimate is an ever sure source of life appreciation which I have never been able to find elsewhere.

As I find my self-intolerances, by attending diligently to my free flow of mental events, I can discover not only where I have bound up my mental energy by restraining it from occurring in my self-conscious living, but also how I can exert myself to extend my self-consciousness to include, and thereby resolve, such self-intolerant living. I sense my lifelong duty to myself to be my discovery and renunciation of my autohypnotic living, so that my self-conscious living may be unhampered.

Chaplain. I see where there is, and can be, no direct or indirect awareness of any external world or rich reality other than one's self. The thing-in-itself was to Kant only a working hypothesis. He saw the entire content of experience to be each one's mental product. I am able to hear your conversation as a fully healthy proclamation of emancipation from your illusions and delusions of "objectivity." Where your existence is concerned your every existent must be of your own creation. "Outward reality" is unrecognized internal meditation. There can be no identity other than that provided by unity.

Please discuss the view: My mind is my servant of my soul.

Author. Again I voice my question and listen to it. My "mind" is *all* about itself; my "soul," insofar as I may or may not distinguish it from my mind, is all about itself. Every such term as "lord," "king," "master" lends itself to delusional, divisive use. Every master lives his own servant; every king lives his every subject; and so on.

Chaplain. Please explicate your apotheosis. How and at what point in your self-growth did you recognize yourself as divine, I mean, as the *only* divinity? How and at what level of your self-learning did you realize that you, and only you, created your world?

How do you propose to your student or colleague that he, or she, is the *only* divinity and the only creator of his, or her, world?

Author. I have asked myself each question with keenest interest. My answer is always the same: When it became impossible for me not to do so; when I first realized the meaning of denial, or negation, as repression (my repudiation of elements of my own creation); when I could observe my word "god" to be my name for my conscious perfection, and my word "devil" to be my name for my unconscious perfection; when I saw clearly that my feeling of dislike protected my ignorance which, in turn, protected my sense of personal identity; when I recognized fault-finding as my necessary defense against fact-finding.

I *cannot* propose to my student or colleague that he, or she, is his or her only divinity and world creator. When I learned myself to be the all I am, I saw my fellowman as being the all he, or she, is. That insight helped me to renounce the illusion and delusion of traditional formal education.

Chaplain. I realize that your talking is not a form of (illusional) communication, but is a record of your self-discoveries.

You know the ancient materialist regarded the soul as real, but material. As a modern materialist you would see yourself displacing your appreciation of your soul's substantiality upon your unfounded, unaccounted for, body.

You use your language, not as an incarnation of your thinking and feeling, but as naming meanings. Aristotle tried to determine the essential categories of mental action by analyzing grammatical forms. You would try to develop a suitable grammar for respecting each mind's allness. Your systematic suscitation of the view of your conscious selfness is essential for maintaining the insight that the study of all meaning (psychology) is subjective. In your opinion every so-called "objective" datum has been first imagined as having no connection with what provides it with its only meaning; and then is mistaken for the ground of its own condition. You say: *All* mental life is not only unintelligible, but impossible, without the reality of the subjectivity of the given mind. Since you know your world only through your living it, the disappearance of your life would end all manifestation of your world.

You see clearly that your hearer must *create* what he hears, whether or not he is aware of this necessity. You observe that your hearer will *understand* what he hears (creates) if his self-experience to date calls for such growth of his conscious self-knowledge. You realize that neither hearing nor any other life activity of your hearer can violate the integrity of his own being, despite all "seeming" to the contrary. Your ideal hearer simply grows (as his self-knowledge) his appreciation of the way his author talks of, and listens to, himself.

In your conversations, consciousness recognized as selfness always supports your unshakable conviction of the allness of selfhood. Conversely, only consciousness which is imagined as containing "not-self" can support the illusion of "materialism." Your consciousness is your mental power which enables you to notice that your mind's activity is *organic* to you,—so that you can *sense* that a gain to it is a gain to you. Your consciousness enables you to extend your *recognized* field of existence so that you can see its security as being your personal responsibility. The wonderful use of your consciousness, therefore, is to enable you to localize your mental functioning entirely in your own human nature.

Author. May I be able to be as consciously self-full in my review of (my) your work.

Chaplain. You see man's effort to find order in "the universe" as being really (all it can be) his effort to find order in himself. His world order cannot be mechanistic or materialistic or hypostatized substantiality; but mental. Said Milton, he who would write a great poem must be one; said Emerson, he who would have a friend must be one; say you, he who would discover a new world must consciously create it. An administrator's effort to build up a strong organization of his external affairs is, after all, a displacement of his own need to feel his own oneness. According to your life ideal, the proper "organization" consists of imagining,—each "organization man" devoting himself steadily to the self-orientation that *his* organization *is* his own. How can you expect this degree of democratic appreciation of sovereignty of the individual citizen for his family, school, or business living, when he does not even clearly appreciate it as his loyal governmental insight?

Author. Right you are, as I live and breathe "you." Your great insight must prove most helpful for your living your physician and patient as heroically doing all that each can do while being all that he is. This ground insight is the foundation of educational wisdom, I find.

Chaplain. You name your talk "elementary medical education." Might it better be called "elementary health education," in view of its application to the whole of education? As you have indicated, health is everyone's chief concern,—not just the physician's. Besides, as you have also stated, the medical educator is always ideally doing the best he can; and, if that does not suffice, he himself would like to know it. He will quickly respond to his fellowman's demands for really self-respecting innovations of medical treatment. Too, if the medical educator would suddenly feel required to assume professional responsibility beyond his immediate ability, he, including his patient, would have to suffer the consequences of such disconcerting experience. As I see it, you are only, and I mean *only,* intending and trying to help yourself by your talking since you see and feel distinctly in yourself your great need for such help.

Author. I find each of these views to be worthy of my sober consideration. Each one helps to clarify the fact that everyone, layman or physician, can create and concern himself about his own health, through his medical education.

Chaplain. I am accustomed to attributing creation to God. Your notion that everyone creates his all can be based upon your acknowledging yourself as God. It is of spiritual force I would speak. I would discern with Elizabeth Barrett Browning,

> The spiritual significance burn through
> The hieroglyphic of material shows.

Or with Jacob Behmen,

> When and where is Paradise? . . . Do not let any sophistry teach that thy God is far aloft from thee as the stars are. God is in thee. Power, might, majesty, heaven, paradise, elements, stars, the whole earth—is thine.

Or with Emerson,

> Every spirit builds its house.
>
> He only is rich who owns the day.

(My) Epiphanius (315?-403 A.D.) read in (his) Philip's gnostic gospel: "The Lord revealed to me what the soul must say when ascending into heaven, and how she must answer each of the upper powers: 'I have come to know myself, and I have collected myself from everywhere. . . .' "[3]

My every detail of my whole world is a manifestation of my spirit, modifying itself in accordance with my mode of living myself. Spirit endeavors, achieves, accomplishes. My enthusiasm, as the word literally states, imbues me with my divine energy. Once I created my understanding of my spiritual philosophy, I felt reborn. That work of creation consisted of my painfully growing to see my greatness and credit myself with it. Emerson's lines took on new meaning for me,

> Wouldst thou sew up the avenues of ill?
> Pay every debt, as if God wrote the bill.

For the first time I understood and spiritually energized myself with that trite truth: Life is what we make it.

I have been posing myself a question. Since everything is all and only its own everything, why should it be necessary for an individual to create for himself his own consciousness for his unique selfhood? Why must he run the risk of creating an unrecognized illusion of a "not-I" by having to develop a definite appreciation of his I-hood?

The answer which came out of this questioning is: *In no other way than by comprehending his own discrete creaturehood can a person create his insightful meaning: individual* (*all*).

Author. Every hearer may study carefully this last question and its answer in the effort to see its profound and precious significance. It resolves a problem of the most troublesome kind for everyone who cannot see the practicality in attributing to the given life the things which are that life's. When I first grew this question and its answer my spirit enjoyed an uplift quite like that I frequently experienced in my very early living.

Chaplain. You see each person's parental *home and family living* as being that most likely to favor his fulfillment of his nature. Since he "comes from" each gender historically, he (or she) needs such private, intimate, intense parental family living in order to realize the potentiality of his (or her) male and female nature.

Furthermore, you see each parent's marital home and family living as providing essential developmental experience, so that each mother (or father) through the private, intimate, intense living of her (or his) growing male and female infant and child can experience consciously integrating recrudescences of her (or his) own life's possibilities.

What about "the fear of leaving home" which seems to be the chief obstacle to one's acknowledging the allness of his individuality?

Author. The "fear of leaving home" is the issue of indulgence of the appearance of "staying home." Its cure is the growth of the insight of *being home.* By denying that *I* live all that I call "home" and "family member," I create my every fear of my illusions of "coming" and "going."

Chaplain. To Lavater, Goethe wrote:

> We owe a great debt of gratitude to nature for having provided the existence of every living being with sufficient curative power to enable it to patch itself together after having got torn at one end or the other. And what are the thousand-odd religions other than a thousand manifestations of this curative power? You may find my plaster inefficacious; I yours. In my father's dramshop are many recipes.

What you describe as the localization of all mental functioning in the given individual mind is equally descriptive of religious living, e.g., "inward experience," "exalted spiritual feeling," "conscious inward knowledge," "inward life," "for we are members one of another," "He that loveth his own wife loveth himself," "individual liberty," "sacred integrity of the soul," "spiritual unity," "spiritual intuition" or "beholding," "love thy neighbor as thyself." The religious educator also regards it as his duty to learn what he can about his veritable self, to consult the facts of his own experience. For example, please consider this definition of the term "religion": "all those cultural manifestations, and they are indeed many, throughout all areas of the humanities and the social sciences, that result from the human feeling of cosmic awe."[4]

Would it not be more in keeping with your recognized self-allness to title your talks "My Allness"? The specific strength of this speaking lies in that unification (of yourself) which, by the way, may be seen as richly fulfilling Goethe's prerequisite, "No hypothesis can lay claim to any value unless it assembles many phenomena under one concept." I see your consciously pursuing and possessing new growths of your veritable self as enabling your activation of your faith in the divine power you see as yours,—"With faith all things are possible."

Author. It is most helpful to me to have (my) you keeping in good working order the fundamental truth that I *can* only talk about my own ideal elementary medical education.

Chaplain. Please list some practical ways how your self-help therapy works at your health education and rehabilitation center.

Author. In my every health struggle my mental attitude is of most practical importance. For instance, I can be regarding my health difficulty ("illness" or "accident") with either a partial view or a sane whole view, thus: as a failure, or as a success; as a punishment, or as a reward; as an unnecessary, stupid event, or as a desirable life lesson; as an unfortunate "break," or as a fortunate eye-opener; as an irreparable loss, or as an opportune gain; as the end of a cherished power, or as the beginning of an unused function; as a loss of money, or as the finding of a treasure; as a separation from home, or as my uniting myself; as the infliction of hateful pain, or as the loving guidance of my capacity to feel hurt; as a stopping of important work, or as a chance for some most valuable experience; as a temporary setback of independence, or as an occasion for activating my untapped resources; as a falling behind in essential responsibilities, or as a catching up with my life accounting; as a frightening reminder that I must die, or as a soothing meditation upon living; as an outburst of feelings of insecurity, or as a quieting reflection upon my mobilization of my health forces; as a giving up to whatever might happen, or as a taking firm hold of myself; as a demoralization, or as a challenge to show myself what I am made of; as another helpless brush with the mysteries of medical power, or as a privileged opportunity to grow some greatly needed medical education for myself; as a return to being "looked after," or as a test of my insight that only I can look after myself.

And so, on and on, my mental attitude during my every health turn is of largely unimagined therapeutic force. His use of his imagination, which can be disciplined as a power of life affirmation, is hardly guessed at by any patient I visit. The very word "imagination," for the most part, is apt to stand for "mental weakness" in his mind. He is particularly sensitive about considering himself a victim of "imaginary ailments." While undergoing his health ordeal his mind is naturally excited, which means his imagination is especially active. However, he is often even afraid to have his concern or curiosity or apprehensiveness "showing." It hardly occurs to him to try to imagine what might be "the matter" with him, beyond the reporting of his symptoms. His first effort to use his imagination (free his mind) beyond its familiar limitations (set up in his earliest years) always confronts him with his fear that he is "going out of his mind,"—out of his acknowledged mind, that is. Hence it is, he sorely needs to live a physician who sees his own imagination as his mind's consciously unifying health power.

Freedom of mind (unrestricted imagination) is necessary to the greatest trustworthiness of any use of mind (such as reasoning) including the mobilization of the health force of the individual. Every educational system which denies human freedom creates helpful symptoms of such self-deception. It is of inestimable value therefore to be able to appreciate every sign and symptom of so-called "impaired" health, every so-called "error" and "failure," as correctly and successfully announcing the consequences of efforts to curb mental freedom.

Chaplain. Most of this I already know. The idea that the amount of my mind's unrestricted imagination is all that can really represent my mind's free use, is indeed a fruitful one for my lifelong consideration. Also, the idea that every patient needs to grow an open-minded (freely imaginative) physician, capable of treating his "wild" fears and fancies with reverence rather than repression, seems to be one to stir a lagging imagination to create urgently needed medical educational opportunities. May every medical student create curricular and extracurricular opportunities for himself to learn how to use his imagination for his life affirmation, and thus learn to renounce having it seem to use him for his life ignoration. I see that a so-called "unimaginative," "matter-of-fact person" is not "matter-of-fact" at all about any meaning of his life which he cannot comfortably consider (imagine). I see how the degree of the free use of his mind (imagination) forms a person's character, disposition, and method of treating himself generally. A so-called "matter-of-fact" person seldom seems to show his potential spirit. All spirit is enlivening.

In what way can an "end of a cherished power" lead to a "beginning of an unused function"?

Author. You have selected perhaps the most practical of all ways in which one's self-insight can restore him to his appreciation of the largesse of his life.

From reading (your) my views on "depression," you probably realize that *I tend to mourn any so-called loss of my power for the sole purpose of making myself discover that I never did live that power consciously as my own mind's when I was exercising it.* For example, I would displace my power of seeing from my acknowledged mind to my optic apparatus without realizing that my "optic apparatus" is also entirely a functioning of my mind; or, I would displace my power of hearing from my acknowledged mind upon my auditory apparatus without noticing that my "auditory apparatus" is also entirely a functioning of my mind; or, I would displace my power of assimilation of my food from my acknowledged mind upon my digestive apparatus without heeding that my "digestive apparatus" is also entirely a functioning of my mind; and so on.

Perhaps you now see that by "unused function" I am referring to the fact that I may not use my imagination effectively enough to enable myself to recognize that all that I regard, or even term, "non-mental," or "physical," or "external," or "supernatural," or whatever, is, after all, constituted of meanings of my mind. Therefore, if I am addicted to the habit of imagining that I walk, run, jump, dance, etc., with limbs which are non-mental, then my (also imagined) loss of those "non-mental" limbs must mean to me that I can no longer use my mind for the purpose of walking, running, dancing, etc. It is this (*illusional*) loss of my mind's power which is all that can be mourned and which constitutes my (illusion of) "irreparable loss." *My discovery that all of this mental functioning is as much alive as ever, as reliable for exercise as ever, is essential for my recovering my sanative sense of being a whole human being, a whole person.* Imagine the importance to me of my being able for the first time to see (and thus dispel) my illusion that I cannot exercise my free-mindedness on account of my having once decided that much, if not most, of it was not mind at all. *Attention to the fact that all living which has any meaning at all takes place in the mind only, is the most practical insightful use of the medical educator's mind,* in my opinion.

Chaplain. In other words: all loss is illusional. Living is always additive and never subtractive. All meaning of "losing," such as the traditional obeisance to advanced senescence as "*sans* everything," is a *seeming.* "I am not the man, or woman, I used to be," or, "I'll never be the same," is simply a statement that one has had to help himself by curbing his potential mental freedom.

But, why should I deny the status of mind to the body center of it, or to my "externality" or "supernatural" meanings? The answer which comes to my question is: By my practice of autotomy upon parts of my mental living which threaten to disturb my sense of personal identity, I succeed in maintaining what sense of being a person I can,—otherwise, I would lose countenance, feel overwhelmed, and ultimately live as if I had "gone to pieces."

I appreciate that your mind consciousness does have most practical efficacy for your own health education. I also see that by "rehabilitation" you refer to your method of recovery of your "sanative sense of being a *whole* human being." I cannot see how you have your patient begin to let his light shine upon unimpaired wholeness of his being again.

Author. I work with the principle that *his self-conscious physician is a most therapeutic creation of each patient.* You are aware of the intensified living of his doctor which the consulting patient experiences. You are aware of the intensified living of his physician's self-consciousness which the mind-starved consulting patient maintains. You realize the spiritual comfort a consulting patient derives from sensing that his beloved physician must diagnose, treat, respect, and in every way live his patient as himself. You realize what it means to a consulting patient to cultivate a physician who understands all of his health trouble as wonderful therapeutic effort, who sees his "amputee" patient as entirely a whole human being, and who prescribes whatever he prescribes with the full insight that his patient is the only one who can, if he will, recover his health balance. Above all, you appreciate the practicality of a patient's growing a physician who can observe his every sign and symptom as good, and thereby conduct his medical work as an upright fact-finder rather than as a leaning fault-finder.

Chaplain. Let me try to describe my view of how my author works his mind. He is not one of the children of the dragon's teeth (Plato's expression for a "sense-bound" mind). First of all, you see yourself as being and doing absolutely nothing but living yourself. Your working your mind is nothing but your growing your mind. You find that you have cleared up many (phantom) problems of your mind by heeding the fact that it is always only expressing your living your individuality. Your ground of self-satisfaction is your joy of living. As far as your wants are concerned, you can content yourself basically with your observation that you are glad to be alive, or as alive as you are.

Your every meaning is your mental creation,—you see no extra-mental meaning and no meaningless experience. Only the evidence of self is found in every denial of it. For you *all* "objectivity" is unexplored and unrecognized subjectivity. You learned from your personal experience that every other kind of self-orientation *seems* easier to uphold, which accounts for every other one of your possible ways of appreciating your marvelous life. You see all of your validity as individuation of your self-certainty. "Is it I?" is your ultimate test of truth. Every "phenomenon" is an unconsciously lived *noumenon.* Selfness is your only value; conscious selfness is your only fully human estimate.

You uphold the radical individuality of the epistemological monist, the solipsist or absolute idealist. You consider "error" to be a pejorative word describing unrecognized accuracy, occurring with dislike. You equate individuality, subjectivity, reality, peace, freedom, universal, matter, and divinity. You observe no explanation but self-explanation, no existence but self-existence. You see all so-called "ontological otherness" as unconscious selfness and claim that your only evidence of any not-self is made up of your own non-evident selfness. In addition, you see all of your world's (phantom) problems as traceable to your fiercely maintained illusion that inviolable individuality is violable after all, that one need not be fully one, that What Is, really need not be What Is.

You claim that *you can live your "externality" sanely only as being your own living of special functioning of yours that is peculiarly distinguished by its unique differents, which only appear to be involuntarily and adventitiously lived by you.* In living such sensations and perceptions (conventionally referring to "an outer world") your mind, from habit, only tends to be unconscious of itself, thus favoring your creating your illusion of not-self. As did Plotinus, you renounce the theory of perception as seal impression and see sensory living as pure mental activity. The only respect in which you consider your sense world as a shadow land is with regard to its being a shadowy you. As did St. Augustine, and later Descartes, you put self-certainty above all, and see primacy in your self-consciousness:

> Without any delusive representation of images or phantasms, I am most certain that I am, and that I know and delight in this. In respect of these truths, I am not afraid of the Academicians, who say, "What if you are deceived?" For if I am deceived, I am. For he who is not, cannot be deceived; and if I am deceived, by this same token I am. And since I am if I am deceived, how am I deceived in believing that I am? For it is certain that I am if I am deceived. Since therefore, I, the person deceived, should be, even if I were deceived, certainly I am not deceived in this knowledge that I am. And, consequently, neither am I deceived in knowing that I know. For, as I know that I am, so I know this also, that I know.[5]

You note that the inability of (your) philosophers to "agree with each other" is based upon the unrecognized necessity of each one to *be,* not "agree" with, his disputant. And you observe that *any* so-called "agreement" must be nothing but an area of self-understanding. Thus, I feel that I "agree" with (my) you when I can say and understand what I have (my) you saying and understanding. "Agreement" you regard as an illustration of what Hume called "the mind's propensity to feign."

As Leibnitz conceived his monad to be free of composition and divisibility, so you conceive your human individuality as existing in absolute, homogeneous, and indivisible self-sufficiency, generating solely and wholly its every sensation and perception and every other sign of life. You dispense with Bowne's "fallacy of the universal" and Leibnitzian "pre-established harmony" by equating "individual" and "universal." You note that "interaction" is illusional, never a datum of experience, and no more actually possible than "interbeing."

Author. As I live it, your kind, earnest, and full account of your author's efforts to record his appreciation of his self-sight amounts to the finest kind of indorsement. Being is supreme and turns its gaze only upon itself. It is its own first and only activity, or movement. As St. Augustine saw, "To be true is the same as to be" (*De Trinitate*).

Chaplain. Redemption can mean to me what conscious living does to you: redeeming appreciation of all that is concrete and practical, the personal life. My imagination is not untutored in psychology, but I do wish to have you explicate further, if you will, the physical *vs.* mental, and individual *vs.* otherness, categories. *How can you feel certain that your view that you are all of your own externality is the only one which can really attest the existence of an external world?*

Author. Certainly all "experience" must be self-experience, so that whatever is held to be "impersonal" phenomenality cannot be a datum of experience. I am my only concrete existence, including my experience. Experience exists for me only as I live it. All of it is possible only through the growth of my self. The root meaning of "experience" derives from the Latin *experiri*: to test. The philosophic meaning of "experience" is: subjectivity. Therefore, empiricism can be only a term for learning (self) by living (self). All sensation, as all other living, is solely and wholly subjective, purely human in nature. Albert C. Knudson pointed out distinctly, "The universal fact is not the existence of thoughts and feelings, but, as Bowne said, the concrete experience that I think and I feel. The unitary and identical self is the presupposition of the entire mental life. The failure to see this has been one of the major shortcomings of empiricism."[6]

"Meaning" is the personal intrinsic unit of mind, so that whatever is held to be "physical" cannot be a datum of mind. This importance of meaning cannot be denied without being implied. To posit the "physical" as the ground of the "mental" is to deny the mind outright, as did the behavioristic psychologist. Mind is not motion, or action, or electricity, or waves, or corpuscles,—but mind. One either sees for himself that one thing is not another, or overlooks that helpful view. "Matter" is a word which can apply equally to spiritual, mental, and physical systems of knowledge. The really deepest essence of matter is the individual's being, existence, human nature,—his monism of life. Denial of one's divinity is the irreligion of the religious; of one's self-knowledge, the ignorance of the educated; of one's insight, the scotoma of the mind's eye; of one's spirit, the opacity of the soul-blind.

Insightful is the reader who wonders wisely with (his) Lotze

(*Microcosmus,* i, 263): "Among all the errors of the human mind, it has always seemed to me the strongest that it should come to doubt its own existence, of which alone it has direct experience, or to take it at second hand as the product of an external nature which we know only indirectly, only by means of the knowledge of the very mind to which we would fain deny existence." One's self is one's only "given," created, or otherwise experienced, reality. "Objective validity" is unrecognized *subjective certitude.*

Individual is other to nothing; nothing can be other to individual. As everything and everybody "else," otherness can be defined, or described, only in terms of the individual's selfness (which is all there is). There may be, however, innumerable combinations of words which would signify that nothing can be made of something, or something of nothing. So-called verbal habits of naïve realism ("common sense") are replete with such heterogeneous combinations of science and nescience. Obviously, the individual mind cannot establish anything but itself, its extramental positings being denied by its affirmations. The only realism of the epistemologist must be epistemology.

Now to pose myself the question: What is my ground for my certitude that my seeing my "external world" as all my own creation (and none of it "given") is the one true way for me to attest the existence of an "external world"?

I see the answer which comes is the same as that to my question: What is my ground for my certitude that my seeing that I am divine is the one true way for me to attest the existence of god? Answer: my bearing witness (to myself) of my own divinity is my only *possible* basis for my belief in god, for I am all of all I can conceive. Also, no description of god, other than that he is all of all that he is, can possibly satisfy the attributes of god. Therefore, if god is really all of all, I must be divine. So that, any way I look at it, I cannot escape the realization of all of all of my divinity.

Similarly, my "external world" subsumes all of itself. Every element of it is intrinsic to, and identical with, its (my external world's) particular "objective" makeup. Its existence is independent of all finite sensation and perception. Clearly, no description of my "external" world other than that it is all of all that it is can possibly satisfy the attributes of "external world." Therefore if my "external" world is *all* of the "objective" persons and places ascribed to it, *I* must be my "external world," too. Thus, if my "external world" exists (as such), I *must* subsume all of myself, and specifically all of all that I can mean by "externality." So that, any way I look at it, I cannot escape the realization that all of all of *my* "external world" is mine, as well as that all of *my* fellowman's "external world" is his. All certainty is self-certainty.

As the creator of my own creaturehood only, I create no "otherness," no separateness of being, and can thus spare myself the blind indulgence of my delusions of "plurality" and of "change." In positing my "self," I have my *self* subsume *its* otherness, and such "otherness" is constituted of the freedom, independence, and creativity inherent in my selfhood. Imagination is all that can be needed to clarify this view (that individual is made up of individuality only).

Chaplain. As I live each of these views as my own, (my) Hegel's great insight, "Whatever is real is rational," takes on deeper meaning for me. I find (my) you to be quite a systematizer of self-consciousness. I see myself considering that methodological working up of the practicality of my self-conscious living is my (spiritual world's) most urgent need.

I now realize that you do not regard yourself just as a personalist, any more than you classify yourself just as an individualist, or just as any other *type* of human being. Your life's self-activity cannot be subsumed by any so-called "philosophical movement." Your human individuality is all-comprehensive and cannot be swallowed up by any one of its posited wholes. My imagination is all that can be lacking, if that observation is not recognizably obvious to me. The unitary principle which integrates my world exists in me; the unitary principle which integrates my fellowman's world exists in my fellowman.

From living my you I have taught myself to see every pejorative word (e.g., "selfish," "egotistical," "heartless," "narrow-minded," and so on) as a sign of ignored (repressed) good. I thank myself for having my author painstakingly using lovingly each of these pejorative words for describing the necessary foundation of any self-respect, or self-reverence. Your conception of all knowledge as being esoteric must be resisted by anyone who would exalt his conventional use of language.

And now I reserve for my final observation the notable realization that (my) your individual-allness life orientation absolves itself from any trace of the fallacy successfully charged by the pluralist against anyone trying to uphold solipsistic insightfulness. The champion of a psychology of "externality," "otherness," "impersonal divinity," or "physical (non-mental) body," announces his satisfying proof of the untenability of solipsism in this accusation: the solipsist first denies the existence of his "others" and then tries to establish the truth of his solipsistic orientation by proving it to these same "others." Consistently I have found (my) you renouncing any and every claim that you can get at, or be-gotten at by, your "others." Your other one does his own speaking and is the only one who can listen to himself. He cannot speak to you, nor you to him. You may speak and hear yourself say what you have grown your fellowman saying and hearing of himself, or not, as you choose. Never before have I discovered this essential consistency in any philosophic discourse on the intense feeling and appreciation of human life, which is peculiar to solipsism.

Author. What the individual means can only be known in that individual's experience. Number is all, only, and purely a given mind's product. (My) your insight is properly attended by a proportionate exaltation of your self-feeling.

Chaplain. I find it most important to have your freedom from this so-called "fallacy of solipsism" completely cleared up in my mind, as follows.

Whether or not your colleague grows the insight that he lives his every meaning (solipsistic orientation), you are equally satisfied for you know he is helping himself ideally always. Whether or not he is *conscious* about his entire self-helpfulness, you are equally satisfied for you know that he would also be helping himself ideally by being unconscious of his entire self-helpfulness.

No matter how consciously or unconsciously you have your colleague entirely helping himself, you devote yourself to living your consciousness of your own entire self-helpfulness. Thus you renounce any plan of making yourself "feel better" through having your colleague grow self-insightfully. You accomplish this renunciation by your seeing (1) fault-finding instead of fact-finding in the illusion of betterment and (2) the truth of self-helpfulness instead of the illusion that your colleague can help you.

All of your motivation is self-motivation. Your work as a physician, and as author of these talks, is not to "alleviate suffering" but to cultivate your understanding of the indispensable helpfulness of the language of all suffering, so that it can count justly toward the sum of human happiness of your world. Whether or not your listener can find his listening of practical use to him, you are equally pleased. Although it may seem difficult for you to have your hearer turn from his hearing since he does not find it understandable, nevertheless in your heart you know that he helps himself by turning from, quite as another hearer helps himself by turning to, his hearing.

Since you aim at renouncing every view of "comparison" as being illusional, you also aim at renouncing such wish as "I hope all goes well," and aim at practicing the realism, "I wish for you whatever may happen." Whatever goes, goes well.

Your life orientation—Whatever is, is perfect—preserves your mental freedom and allows your self-helpfulness its full range. By seeing your painful suffering as your valuable therapy you economize on your investment in costly repressing energies and can apply this saving on further investment in full-measured, life-restoring self-helpfulness.

As I mind (my) you recounting the benefit of human individual idealism, I see my personal identity clearly in this living. I am pleased to note a practical application of the doctrine of self-helpfulness. In his helpful brochure, *Twenty-Five Years of Pastoral Training at University Hospital, Ann Arbor, Michigan, 1936-1961,* the Rev. Malcolm B. Ballenger, director of clinical pastoral training, records,

> This program operates under the philosophy that each student is his own teacher . . . . He learns that the only way he can really help "others" is to help himself. He discovers the importance of finding out who he himself really is, and learns

this is difficult to find out because he has not learned to live himself very consciously. He impresses himself with the truth that "every man must be his own physician, his own teacher, his own priest, his own everything." As best he can, he sets out on a program of self-discovery. Eventually he may realize the worth of himself and therefore the worth of what he has mistakenly called "others."

I would be interested to have (my) you define your term "spirit." How can you, a health educator, use it freely as you do?

Author. "Spirit" is a vocable of many meanings for me, ranging from experiences of ghostly depersonalization to my conscious identity as divinity. I may use the word with my "materialistic" (unconsciously idealistic) colleague who may limit his term comfortably to designate spirituous fluids.

In this writing I use "spirit" in a keenly conscious effort to designate my life as being consciously subjective (idealistic), in contrast with being unconsciously subjective ("objective" or "materialistic").

The incorporeality—meant by this word fits my need for a name (for my substantially vital existence) with which I can rescue myself from all that I *know* (from my experience) to be illusional (to wit, "object," "external," "physical," "non-mental," "extramental," "plurality," "composition," "divisibility," "there" and "then," "otherness," "dependence," "communication," "inequality," "inhumanity," "comparison," "coercion," "enemy," "you," "unfree," "time," "space," "motion," and so on and on). To the extent that my imagination is impoverished through maintaining and extending a delusional system of "externality," it must become increasingly impractical and uninventive for the purpose of my cultivating consciousness of the truth of my subjectivity-allness ("spirituality").

In this writing I equate "spirit," "soul," "self," "individuality," "life" "reality," "subjectivity," "divinity," "allness," "truth," "fact," "experience," "force," "peace," "imagination," "innateness," "ideality," "practicality." Thus, I am free to use my word "spirit" to name my being's *vis a tergo* or *vis vitae,* my life's intrinsic self-activity, my human nature's creativity, or my divinity's omnipotence.

Chaplain. Everyone has in mind helping himself to enjoy his life. The recognized purpose of altruism is that of personal ennoblement. Certainly you may consider your God to be all, since by taking all into account you know you help yourself most. Each one's idea of God is the idea which best suits his conscious needs. What I mean by a "power beyond myself" accords with your own concept of your self's constant renovation.

Since you mean the same thing by "selfish" that (your) everyone else means by "unselfish," why must you insist on that one word for naming human effort? You seem to be saying only what the scientist Lecomte du Noüy states in *Human Destiny,* that the next step in evolution is the individual's ruling himself according to his best interests, according to his spiritual needs. Man will either be a conscious God or a divine clod. Henry Drummond observed this truth about the conscious activation of one's spirituality, "If a man does not exercise his arm, he develops no biceps muscles; and if a man does not exercise his soul, he acquires no muscle in his soul, no strength of character, no vigor of moral fibre, no beauty of spiritual growth."

Author. My point, again, is that *everyone* is always exercising his soul when he exercises his muscle; that *everyone* is always of strong character, vigorous moral fibre, and beautiful spiritual growth; that a holier-than-thou life-orientation is always one's necessary effort to try to keep his mental, or spiritual, balance while feeling unequal to seeing and acknowledging divinity everywhere. Divinity is everywhere; *conscious* divinity nearly nowhere. One is not always ready to appreciate so-called craven conduct as another way of experiencing deity. To the extent that I insist upon leading an orderly life, without enjoying the insight that whatever happens is in perfect order, I may have to rely frequently upon the use of my negation "disorder." In my life nothing *can* happen but my perfectly ordered growth, usually called "experience." This conception of my growth has proved most practical, whenever my hurt pride has not prevented my creating it.

Chaplain. You would pray then only for what will happen? You claim, do you not, blasphemy is to be revered as hurt prayer? You would equate your self-tolerance with spiritual stamina? You would cure your unnerving "externality" with nerving self-consciousness? You consider self-pity, selfish demand, worry, narrow self-will, refusal to change (or "grow up"), cowardice, bitter resentment, revenge, sickness unto death, as sure signs of spiritual mettle, as indications of the soul's awakening and openness? You consider that your ability to see your identity in whatever happens, endows you with a new conscious dimension of health?

Author. When I am able to be absolutely, consciously honest, I answer each of these questions of mine in the affirmative. Each and every way I can behave myself is always and only my human nature's current and prevailing *ideal* way of trying to be (do) right, based solidly upon the perfect law of life. My mind cherishes (my) John Henry's idea: "Fear not that thy life shall come to an end, but rather fear that it shall never have a beginning."

Chaplain. It occurs to me to wonder if (my) you are aware that any use of the term "material" would appear to "objectify" what can only be a real subject. To illustrate, the expression "mental material" carries a connotation of "objective" substantiality quite as does "wooden material" or "iron material." The implication is that one's mental "material" can be accessible to another; that mental "material" consists of quantifiable, mechanistic data or phenomena. Thus, the illusion of segregation of one kind of mental "material" from another can be set up; the illusion of a part not consisting only of the nature of the whole can seem possible; the illusions of "passivity," "means," "plurality," "betweenness," "death," "imperfection," and all such compensations for ignored wholeness, can gain credence. The only helpful understanding I have ever been able to discover for the meaning "death" is its indispensable usefulness for making conscious the meaning of life, spirituality.

Still most grievously serious of all, this notion of "mental material" supports these widespread cherished illusions: (1) that the individual is not always helping himself in the only way possible, and (2) that one individual, therefore, is needed to help another individual. My religious meaning "spirit" helps me to avoid each of the illusional "externalities" introduced by the term "material." For me the expression "spiritual material" amounts to a contradiction in its term.

Author. As I have just lived (my) you affirming the wholeness, nowness, allness, justice, and unity of oneness I have appreciated the helpfulness in this conscious spiritual living.

Chaplain. The biblical account of Jehovah and Moses (*Exodus*) records Jehovah's words when Moses asked his name: *I am That I am.* This clear statement of religion of self-consciousness accords with the understanding of truth as being subjectivity. God is all. Whatever is, subjectively is. I can think, or speak, of the fundamental difficulty in knowing myself, and *thereby* deceive myself that it is possible for me to know what is not myself. I cannot deny the testimony of my selfhood in all that I live, without self-contradiction. Whatever I know I know intuitively, immediately,—and the seeming that I can know in any other way is a rationalization which spares my conscious self-limit but also makes such "impersonal" knowledge inaccessible for my conscious use. My full consciousness is always a clear seeing of myself as a seer of my irenic allness.

Author. How do you stand on the ever-recurring issue of introducing the study of one's religion in his public school?

Chaplain. I see that problem as a phantom one. I see nothing now except his religion in every pupil's or teacher's present living of his public school. Only (my) his immediate awareness for his own omnipresent divinity *can* be lacking. Of all of my human interests it is most ideal and practical that my every religious meaning be *seen* by me as entirely and only personal.

You find it helpful to be "for" whatever you live, not "against" any of your experience. My own voice plangently resounds my song of life, too. Your scripture reveals that your unerring way of "clearing up" anything in your mind consists specifically in your loving it. According to the degree of your love is the extent of your understanding. Your deity is not just a word, or definition, or dogma, or "elect" incarnation,—but is the only meaning of all of you. Your self-love has no possible "love of another" with which to oppose itself, since *it* subsumes every such grace. You find every "other" way of life, based upon selfness gone underground, without a great enough self-trust, without a large enough self-reverence, without anywhere near enough soul room. Only self-insight is *right thinking.* Everyone can claim to think rightly who is conscious that his thinking is self-contained, self-possessed, self-meaningful, self-emancipating, self-fulfilling, self-being. You see yourself as either a busy mind or a "busy-body."

You particularly renounce rebellion, or revolt, finding it to be the preserving negative of conformity,—quite as you see clearly in any supposed idealism which would exclude its opposite ("materialism") the very preservative of so-called materialism. According to you, *one who protests is thereby a preserver of that which he professes to repudiate.* You assert that it is still merely yourself *you* feel in *your* opposition. Rebellion, itself, is a negative conformity,—not a solution of it. *Only your (loving) renunciation of conformity (as being a valiant but illusional solution of the problem of one's own unrecognized authority) is its clear explication.*

In conceiving every negation as an (unconscious) affirmation, you also solve the problem of duality inherent in the theory of the mind as being made up of opposites. Thus, "wrong" is meaningful just insofar as it contains its opposite, "right"; "right" is meaningful just insofar as it contains its opposite, "wrong"; "true" is meaningful just insofar as it contains its opposite, "false"; "false" is meaningful just insofar as it contains its opposite, "true"; "ugliness" is meaningful just insofar as it contains its opposite, "beauty"; "beauty" is meaningful just insofar as it contains its opposite, "ugliness"; "cold" is meaningful just insofar as it contains its opposite, "hot"; "hot" is meaningful just insofar as it contains its opposite "cold"; and so on. In other words, every meaning subsumes its own opposite, which latter is only recognizable when the given meaning's own negation is featured. Every meaning derives its connotation thus from what it eliminates as well as illuminates. Whatever its connotation appears to negate (eliminate) supports (illusional) "objectivity," in that it provides the illusion of duality. Thus, I may tend to think in terms of "a given meaning *and* its opposite" (duality), instead of "a given meaning subsuming its opposite" (oneness-wholeness-allness). I am interested in your ideal definition of "No" as meaning only conscious (loving) renunciation.

Author. I have found wonderful helpfulness in making it a point first to try to say "Yes" to *whatever* I live. Without that first appreciation, my "No" can only mean repression (magic denial) instead of renunciation. Only by painstakingly cultivating that kind of sensibility can I depend upon it. I am a stream of life, and my consciousness of myself is most dependable for my steering all of my course. Thus I live (my) you as enjoying (consciously or unconsciously) only your own identity in any of your sensing "otherness" in your world's individualities. In 1910 Freud wrote on the theme of a word's subsuming its opposite meaning (*The Antithetical Meaning of Primal Words.*)

For my steering my life's course, love (including hate) is a mode of my guiding force of pleasure (including pain). Everyone of my world complains on some occasion of "being too sensitive to live,"—when the pain of immediate self-growth seems at first to exclude its pleasure. But pain really has meaning only insofar as it contains potential pleasure, quite as pleasure has meaning only insofar as it contains potential pain. Going from pleasure to pain only appears to "change the subject" (of pleasure). Going from love to hate only appears to "change the subject" (of love).

Love, itself, has meaning only insofar as it contains hate; hate, itself, has meaning only insofar as it contains love. I help myself to live my hate with love, by realizing that my hate *is* hurt love; I help myself to live my love as my potential source of hatred by realizing that my love is my joy of living which must often expose itself to, at first, hateful growing pains.

Chaplain. My spiritual oneness is the basis for my appreciation of my individuality, or *one life.* It is what I *believe,* which constitutes my very sense of reality. If I do not believe whatever I live, how can I regard it as real? I believe in my personal identity, and that faith endows it with its reality meaning for me. The freedom of my spirit (what you call your imagination) and my belief (what you call your reality) are my holiness (what you call your health) principles. I consider it my religious function to *notice* that I am filled with the fulness of divinity, that *whatever* I live is divine. It is not sufficient for me to observe one idea that God is all in all and then have that profound realization just give way to another idea, which so to speak, gives it the lie. For me there can be no evidence which is not a manifestation of my soul. Noticed Goethe, "If you wish to appreciate the whole, you must see the whole in the smallest." I need not even open my eyes to see the sovereignty of my soul.

Author. I can see that my meaning "reality" is based upon my feeling sure, or as you aptly describe it, feeling a certain belief or faith in my personal experience. Ideologist and political economist Destutt de Tracy, described feeling as the sole ground of evidence of human existence.

> The faculty of feeling is that which manifests to us all the others, without which none of them would exist for us, whilst it manifests itself that it is its own principle to itself; that it is that beyond which we are not able to remount, and which constitutes our existence; that it is everything for *us;* that it is the same thing as *ourselves.* I feel because I feel; I feel because I exist; and I do not exist but because I feel. Then my existence and my sensibility are one and the same thing.

Chaplain. Time was, you know, when the priest was the only physician, the temple the only place of healing, and spirituality the only *materia medica.* The course of man's development is, and always has been, steered largely by that wayward guide Reason, and rarely by the true compass: self-consciousness. Thus desperation, unrecognized inspiration, has charted the individual's life. It is to your credit that you recognize that there can be no adoration of an "external" God, no reliance upon an "external" physician, no fear of an "external" fate—that each such *appearance* of "external" power of any kind is pure illusion. Whether he is aware of it or not (your) everyone *is* his own God, including his every manifestation of power.

You see no possibility but self-consciousness in your fellowman. He always experiences nothing but his *self*-consciousness but *he* cannot always recognize that revelation. You see that only *self*-consciousness *can* exist, and thereby save yourself much trouble. The word "revelation" comes from "re" and "velo," meaning unveiling and uncovering. The Greek verb for "save," *sozo,* is usually defined as "healing," "making whole."

Author. Rabbinical, or Essene, curative procedures were revered of old. Living his early life among the Essenes, called "Therapeutae" in Egypt, could have been conducive to Jesus' discovering the sovereignty of his divinity.

I allow myself the fascinating appearances of historicity, even though (my) Emerson declared, "All history becomes subjective; in other words, there is properly no history; only biography. Every mind must know the whole lesson for itself."

For me, "Consciousness" is itself, its own cognition of its *immediate* activity only. It is a creating, organizing power in my life. With my Berkeley I affirm *esse* is *percipi.*

Schelling called spirit "invisible nature." Leibnitz asserted that all force is spirit. Solipsized Fichte, "In all perception thou perceivest only thine own condition." In 1799 Lichtenberg stated, "To perceive things *outside* ourselves is a contradiction; we perceive only within us; that which we perceive is merely a modification of ourselves, therefore *within* us." Also by summoning all of my insight I can appreciate Swedenborg's view: God creates the world through man.

It is your belief that all of the properties of your body are nothing but modifications of your mind, or soul, or spirit. Jonathan Edwards, perhaps the most insightful American metaphysician, created this view of his body. "When I say the material universe exists only in the mind, I mean that it is absolutely dependent on the conception of the mind for its existence. The human body and the brain itself exist only mentally, in the same sense that other things do."

Some of my observations at first may seem farfetched. Suppose I am incorrect? Epictetus wisely noticed: There is no mark for the misses. And as I have pointed out already, "nearness" and "remoteness" are only feelings of self-certitude and of self-incertitude respectively. Notions of "distance" are devices for maintaining imperturbability during the living of conditions incompatible with security feeling. My body's living of itself frequently has proved overwhelming to my sense of personal identity, so that I formerly felt safest in segregating it ("distancing" it) from appreciation as mental. Now I can see Berkeley was truth-oriented in regarding the human body, brain and all, as existing in the mind, or soul. Physical health and strength are mental forces, subjective powers. The greater the "distance" I put between my idea of myself and any of my other ideas which I associate with space and time, the less self-tolerance I have grown for that idea.

Interest in my every idea as being my own is my chief method of growing self-insight. You consider your body to be nothing but your inward thinking-feeling-wishing-sensing-perceiving-imagining being.

Chaplain. Yes. As did Liebnitz, I renounce the notion that sensation is in any respect a product of impression upon my body from without having the power to excite my mind. Every varying condition of my body tone has its only reality in my mind's disposition. Aristotle regarded the soul as an indivisible whole throughout the body. But it is rare for a human being to believe in the unique worth of his mind, so that he will not undervalue the importance of the specific *mental* nature of his health and its vicissitudes.

Author. The truth that my mind is carrying on all of the functions of my body is obscured by the fact that mind is entirely unconscious except for its one power, consciousness. Unconscious mental creation and organization account for all physiological action, and provide all of the so-called "wisdom of the body." Schelling realized "that all physical motion, activity, and life-effort are only an unconscious thinking." Every kind of mental position I assume expresses itself in *its* corresponding bodily condition.

Destutt de Tracy attempted an economic simplification of the idea of human being. He identified sensation as mental and even coined the term "ideology," but his contemporaries classified (disposed of) him as a materialist. Nevertheless, he claimed that "the principle of movement is the will, and that the will is the person, the man himself."

Chaplain. You know that the "modern" organized scientific (including medical) psychologist has continued to be largely materialistic in his mental orientation, what Hegel expressively termed "dirt philosopher." Your experience has taught you the fact of your own resistance to seeing the medical efficacy in idealism. It seems to me that the sustained insight that every body complaint (as all other meaningfulness) is mental, is nearly an unused and undeveloped health truth of greatest practical value for the medical educator. One who can at will use his mind to help his distressful mental condition can call to his aid the only possible power which can restore tissues and organs to harmonious functioning.

Author. Experience in believing in this inherent mental power called self-insightful self-helpfulness always reveals the sovereign remedy inherent in self-conscious self-reliance. My idealist of medicine believes in the power of his thought, beginning with his belief itself. Every discovery of his research is based upon his willingness to believe in the sensations he creates. His "sickness" is always his helpful realization that his self-deception (in not seeing his all as his own) is favoring his ending his life. Of the "invasion" of his every micro-organism (as of any other kind of tissue injury, atrophy, or proliferation) he observes his self-incurred danger and does what he can to save (heal) his life. He knows that he is always helping himself with his mind and that, as Kant believed, his mind is helpfully at work during sleep, else his life would become extinct.

I can see how "believing" is a term which means: voluntarily usable knowing. I consider my voluntary exercise of my faith and imagination to be my most trustworthy hygiene, and the most practical health discovery I have ever made. "Fiction" is a Latin-derived word for mental creation, as "poetry" is a Greek-derived name for similar meaning. By means of my fiction and poetry (which include all of my scientific terminology) I create my world of self-meaning. What I cannot believe to be my self-experience constitutes my "learned ignorance" and contributes helpfully to my painful realization that all is not apparently well (whole-willed) with me. Every "thing" is *thought,* only.

Chaplain. My saving and healing faith in my own power of self-help is my most cherished medical insight. I see that my mind does not "influence" my body, that it *is* my body as it is all else of my life's meaning, or belief. William Hamilton's expressive words point out: "The ultimate facts of consciousness are given less in the form of cognitions than of beliefs. Consciousness, in its last analysis, in other words, our primary experience, is a faith." And James Mill noticed: "To have a sensation and to believe that we have it are not distinguishable things. When I say 'I have a sensation,' and say 'I believe I have it,' I do not express two states of consciousness, but one and the same state. Sensation is a feeling; but a feeling and the belief of it are the same thing."

Author. I have been considering that revelation is a manifestation of intelligence, a mode of self-discovery, an intuitive, immediate self-knowing. I believe that godliness is allness and therefore cannot be exalted at the expense of manliness or anything else.

Chaplain. According to your faith be it unto you (*Matt. 9*: 29). Origen and Augustine regarded one's beliefs of Christianity as a fuller development of truths that man had made known to himself before. The believer of nearly every religion has considered his awareness of his divinity to be his indispensable source of appreciation of virtue. Said Seneca: "A god inhabits every virtuous man." Plato expressed a similar realization, having Socrates teach that actual virtue is innate, untaught (in *Menon*). Religious insight is not the product of dictation. Revelation is the issue of inspiration, a quickening of the activity of conscious realization. *Whenever* I voluntarily suspend my sense of the limits of my personal identity for the purpose of observing it grow more of itself, I operate my divine identity without imposing upon it the customary limits characterizing my habitual, personal frame of reference.

Author. I imagine that you consider prayer to be an unfailing specific for the spiritual turmoil which you consider "disease" to be. Intensity of the love of life may generate the spirit of prayer.

Chaplain. Also my spiritual "turmoil" is my hygiene agency. Many a medical scientist is willing to consider prayer to be a therapeutic device, as I certainly am. For me prayer is conscious recognition of my own spiritual potential for creating forces in myself both favorable and unfavorable to life. It is spiritual action of earnest self-helpfulness derived from my instinct to live. Prayer is the spirit of self-helpfulness out-pouring from the depths to the surface of my being.

Author. I would like to know how you define "chance" and "change."

Chaplain. "Chance" is only a name for my ignorance of necessary elements of my being. "Change" is only a name for my repression of the truth of my constant (unchanging) self-growth.

Most of all, I find it difficult to keep conscious the momentary nature of my personal identity.

Author. You believe, then, that every therapeutic device depends entirely upon the patient's voluntary and appropriate operation of his faith and imagination for its efficacy; that the contents of the entire *materia medica* are powerless except as aids to the imagination and faith of the physician and patient; that his every medical regimen functions solely and wholly as an excitant to each patient's very own self-helpfulness exercised through his aroused faith in, and stirred imagining of, his very own powers; that the "objective" scientist does well who reconsiders his hard and fast dichotomies of "voluntary" and "involuntary" functioning, of "blind" instinct and "seeing" intelligence, of "real" and "imaginary," "organic" and "functional," "physical" and "mental," "animate" and "inanimate," and similar vain efforts at undoing oneness.

Chaplain. Yes. I regard my instinctive living basically as my most reliable prescription for health troubles and most dependable counsel for my life in general. There is an instinct of worship which may be too rarely lived on impulse. Religiousness is constitutional or not at all, I believe. This divine instinct is always operating for my greatest good. I am not always aware of that fact, or I would appreciate it realistically. For me, my self-consciousness, whenever it functions, is analogous to my resurrection. All of my human trouble is traceable to my limited self-tolerance and its imposed limited use of my imagination which, in turn, limits the range of my happiness and is easily mistaken for and rejected as "disease," ("hypochondria," "melancholia," "hypobulia," "asthenia," and so on). My imagination's limits also save me trouble. In his mindful book, *Philosophical Ideas in the United States,* Harvey Gates Townsend wisely notes, "The realm of imagination is very real, but it is full of pitfalls for unwary feet and undisciplined minds."[7]

Author. Every patient enduring any health ordeal tends to lose track of the helpfulness of whatever practice of extending his self-consciousness he had formerly attained and enjoyed. He finds in his living of his self-conscious physician the specific he needs, spiriting *self*-appreciation and not dispiriting "disease"-consciousness. "Diseased" means uneasy and out of harmony with certain helpful but painful facts presently contributing to one's existence; only a seeming seceding from one's own natural efforts of self-help. To be able to think and feel in accord with my unconscious self-helpfulness is a great economy favoring my restoring my sense of wholeness. Prescribed consciously soul-longing Thomas Browne in his *Religio Medici*: "There is surely a piece of the Divinity in us. . . . He that understands not this much hath not his instruction or first lesson, and is yet to begin the alphabet of man." Loving *whatever* I experience, painful or not, is essential for the activation of my self-healing power. Self-preservation is only another word for omnipresent self-creation. Physiology, like theology, is living wisdom. Every "malady" is an unrecognized remedy, quite as every sin is strained sanctity. The real *inward* provides every semblance of "the outward."

Chaplain. I am happy that my diligent medical educators discovered that mind is the only real being. They are in accord with the pronouncement of their great American forebear Jonathan Edwards: "all existence is mental, and the existence of all exterior things (including of course the human body and its varying conditions) is ideal."

It is also gladdening relief to me to have (my) you awake to the specific hygienic force of poetry. My God, my divinity, is the perfect poet composing his own creation. How divinely (my) Browning is expressive of his belief, his spiritual system,

> There is an inmost center in us all,
> Where truth abides in fullness; and around,
> Wall upon wall, the gross flesh hems it in,
> This perfect, clear perception—which is truth.
> A baffling and perverting carnal mesh
> Binds it, and makes all error: and, to know,
> Rather consists in opening out a way
> Whence the imprisoned splendor may escape,
> Than in effecting entry for a light
> Supposed to be without.

17

Art of Medicine

One morning when I went downtown,
I felt such sunlight capsize down
That streets were glutted with more gold
I thought a glory much like this
Than all my heart could ever hold.
Must have been poured from Genesis.
I had not noticed until now
Such glittering of leaf and bough.
Not for a moment could I doubt
Telephone poles might start to sprout.
Brilliant gas stations, like bazaars,
Were jubilating with the cars.
The traffic in some triumph went
In pageant of astonishment.
And all the things in all the stores
Were like abundant metaphors.
More than the sun illuminated sight;
More than the sun and more than light
Seeped on the avenue a wonder
That everything grew porous under.
Houses and people, trees and I
Replied to each, as earth to sky.
I felt all objects linked and set
As in a vast, transparent net;
I felt that everything was part
Of rapture answering my heart;
Until I knew, until I knew
I was the world I wandered through.

LOUIS GINSBERG, "Morning in Spring"[1]

ARTIST. SINCE YOUR medical way of life is considered to be an art as well as a science, please outline your art of medicine. It seems to me that nearly all that you have so far observed bears mostly upon the sublime *art* of healing. "The sublime has been said to awake in us the consciousness of our own infinity."[2]

Author. All that I have said pertaining to the allness of individuality, to the subjectivity of reality, *is* specifically relevant to, and descriptive of, the art of medicine. The esthetic is wholly a subjective experience entirely free of the limitation I find in the illusional "objectivity" of the scientist's ideal. The esthetic is synonymous with the conscious human factor. A process of living, art is a creative event expressing the reality of the artist's meaning. The true subject of esthetic experience is the esthetician's own self. Melvin Rader describes esthetic living as uniquely resolving conflicts, combining variety and unity, familiarity and strangeness, repose and stimulation, order and spontaneity, the Apolline and the Dionysian moods.[3] The artist has the ability to introduce himself to his human nature broadly, thus attaining a conscious mental integration which would otherwise seem repugnant, or even alien, to him. It can be a conscious-self restorative experience to consult a work of art.

Artist. Do you mean that the viewer's seeing his selfness in his every kind of view, the auditor's hearing his selfness in his every kind of audition, and so on,—each is analogous to the physician's seeing his selfness in his every kind of patient? Do you mean that your definition of the learning process as being all and only a self-development, an ongoing glorification of one's self, is esthetic education?

Author. Again, I enjoy the way your questions clearly contain their own answers. Yes, only by means of my continuing esthetic education can my mind gradually develop its capacity for conscious self-contemplation, for appreciating all learning as integral to the given psyche (mine). The soul-mark of art is its profoundly private, personal, intuitive, satisfying nature. Thus, the so-called "value" of his art is its contribution to the artist's, or critic's, appreciation of his life itself. His work of art is always an expression of the artist's contemporary life value. The primary worth of each one's artistic production lies in its function of meaning to artist and critic alike: I am, all and only.[4]

Artist. Nietzsche contended that art is therapeutic through its balancing Dionysiac excitement and Apollonian tranquillity. This talk of yours, in that it exercises your unity of your design, operates not only as occupational therapy but also as a self-analysis. Throughout it, it is as if I can hear you say again and again, "Use your imagination, man." That sage German author Theodor Gottlieb von Hippel (1774-1796) wrote, "Everyone is mentally consumptive whose imagination walks on weak feet. Phantasy is the lung of the soul." He also asserted that what one ordinarily considers to be genius is really only persistent preoccupation with one's self. Lichtenberg reported his resort to hours of all sorts of phantasies, "Without this phantasy-cure which I made use of for the most part about the customary spa-season, I would not have lived so long."

Author. Whatever I live has life-affirming meaning for me.[5] A child, or senescent, who uproots himself from indulging his accustomed self-scenes, self-sounds, and other self-perceptions, feels the sense of loss with such force that he can become demoralized by the deprivation. Laboratory experiment can demonstrate the health significance of the general functional exercise of one's sensations and perceptions.

Emerson beautified his word-picture of a living man, "What a gallery of art have I here." And, "A beautiful behavior . . . is the finest of the fine arts." It does not require great imagination for me to see the connection with such a view of art and the science of medicine.

Artist. Baudelaire resolved the antinomy of art and science by these beautifully ordered words: "The imagination is the most scientific of the faculties because it alone understands the universal analogy." However, as you have repeatedly observed, education is easy only if it is not viewed entirely as conscious self-development.

Author. Élie Faure scored that salient point:

> Even Pascal did not feel life sufficiently to conquer the obstinate anguish to which he was condemned by the need of assigning to life an uncompromising moral finality, and thus rejoin Baudelaire on the summits of the imaginary world where plastic art, music, and poetry tend to associate themselves with mathematics in the intoxication of an objectless harmony.[6]

Artist. Are you aware you are implying that there can be no such dichotomy as Art *vs.* Nature? as original *vs.* imitation? Do you mean that all of his views of Nature can only be the artist's (conscious or unconscious) views of his own human nature?

Author. Quite. Whether I grow a perception of a sunset or of a painting of a sunset, each is equally my own artistic production. As is true of all of my efforts at "segregation," I find that such effort indicates my lack of my sanatizing insight: *everything is its own everything.* Whatever is, all and only is. This specific exercise of self-consciousness reveals my artistry in my natural as well as in my painted landscape. As my wife once described a natural scene, "Everywhere I looked I saw a beautiful picture."

Artist. Oscar Wilde wrote on nature's imitating art, pointing out that so-called "Nature" has not created man but that man has created "nature." Studying one's self in any painting educates one's mind to appreciate one's own view of one's self when it occurs in so-called "nature."[7] Thus, what one calls "nature" turns out to be an unconscious composite of his artistic self-experiences. My study of (my) art prepares me to see in (my) nature what I formerly ignored, and thus facilitates my conscious self-functioning.

Author. Quite. Whatever facilitates my exercise and extension of self-consciousness frees my appreciation of life itself. For me, therefore, the chief question of esthetics becomes, How can I cultivate my sense of the beautiful so that it can function for all of my living? Said Eugene Veron in his *Aesthetics* (1878), "Art consists essentially in the predominance of subjectivity over objectivity; it is the chief distinction between it and science." I can value and care for my life only to the extent that I can take pride in it.

Artist. You see every art lover, or beholder, as creating the work of art he studies. He "stays with" his living of a poem, or painting, or whatever, until he is finally able to say of it: It is I. He does not "make it his own," but rather observes it sufficiently to see that it *is* his own. In his book outlining aesthetic theory (*The Sense of Beauty*) Santayana asserted that beauty is pleasure objectified. What do you mean by "work of art," anyhow?

Author. Santayana also asserted beauty's subjectivity: "It is an emotion, an affection of our volitional and appreciative nature." He called esthetics "the theory of perception." Whatever is, is esthetic, a felt work of art. Whether I am conscious of that fact depends upon my developing my appreciation that "the ugly" is beautifully ugly. *Any other use of the word "ugly" has resistance and rejection (repression) in it.* I once asked several renowned artists—John S. Coppin, Marshall Fredericks, and Roy C. Gamble—how each would describe a student's earnest art makeshift,—for instance, a three-year-old child's painstaking scrawling. Each immediate reply was, "Beautiful." As all else, a work of art is where you find it. Beauty is the produce of the conscious self-love of the individual. As a child once observed, "Everything looks good on me." In his *Letters on the Aesthetic Education of Man,* Schiller wrote that art makes man whole and is needed by man for that purpose.

Artist. What do you mean by the expression "Art for Art's sake"?

Author. Probably it is usually meant to imply the dawning realization that one's art, as all else, is all and only about itself.

Artist. You struggle and strive to be able to contemplate yourself as your whole, healthful, holy, beautiful world, no less. Little wonder you describe education (your conscious self-cultivation) as regularly very difficult, steadily challenging the development and resourcefulness of a human being's utmost potential. Of whatever happens you try to work up your conscious self-orientation: That's the beauty of it. Seeing your every world experience as deriving fully from the activity of your own mind endows every event with the appearance of unity, balance, harmony, stability, pleasure, freedom, power, and so on, which constitutes the esthetic experience. Is not your seeing-your-selfness-in-all-of-your-world a kind of empathy?

Author. My empathy is a sensing of my identity. Wilhelm Worringer described empathy as esthetic enjoyment, which is "objectified" self-enjoyment.[8]

Freud greatly appreciated the insightful views of Theodor Lipps (1851-1941), who elaborated the theory of empathy thus: the ego's unconsciously supposing itself at one with the object. Said Lipps, "The esthetic enjoyment is not enjoyment of an object, but enjoyment of a self," "Empathy is the fact here established, that the object is myself and by the very same token this self of mine is the object," and "Empathy means, not a sensation in one's body, but feeling something, namely, oneself, into the esthetic object."

Artist. Freud saw art as a most helpful source of pleasure and comfort, did he not?

Author. Yes. Freud studied art as the successful expression of repressed wishes which operate powerfully as unconscious volition. The artist uses his mental device of "sublimation" to steer the psychic energy of his unfulfilled wishes into directions of esthetic production. Thus, instead of restricting his erotic, or aggressive, wishes to day-dreaming or sleep-dreaming he may build a tower, or sculpture a marble god, or contribute to literature, to release his mental tension. His fellowman with impunity may then easily put himself into a position of learning to live likewise, which relieves his own mind in a self-controlled way of the tensions of his unrenounced primitive wishes. To illustrate, Sophocles has Jocasta comfort Oedipus,

> For many a man hath seen himself in dreams
> His mother's mate, but he who gives no heed
> To suchlike matters bears the easier life.

Artist. In other words, my art permits me consciously (voluntarily) to liberate my erotic and aggressive meanings of my mind, which otherwise I would have to express in my unconscious (involuntary) behavior. Art spares me the necessity of the tail-wagging-the-dog living of my deep archaic impulses. Every art activity soothes as it seethes. It reinforces volition as it renounces compulsion. Every kind of artistic catharsis excites as it sedates. Conscious self-helpfulness must underlie the finest art.

Author. Conscious self-helpfulness underlies the art of quickest healing. However, Whatever is, is helpful,—despite every dislike which may be immediately associated with it. Whatever is, always affirms living, but does not always seem to affirm conscious living.

Artist. I wish to create for myself the finest appreciation of the art of mental healing. As I understand my mental formation, whatever of myself I can succeed in living with my feeling of love, thereby enjoys uninhibited development; but whatever of myself I succeed in living by withdrawing my feeling of love, thereby suffers arrested development, so-called "fixation." Each area of my mind which I live without my conscious feeling of *self-love* in it fails to excite my sense of personal identity. All of my living which I fail to recognize as being mine is lived by me unconsciously. I need to help myself carefully for each of these steps.[9] Please speak your mind freely here.

Author. I must acknowledge that I live consciously only when my attention is focused on the one fact that *I* am doing my living. Either I am exercising my specific sense of personal identity, or I am unconscious. To illustrate, as I consider that I am going "from one place to another," "speaking with this one or that," "seeing the sights," etc., I am living myself only, but without realizing that truth. In other words, I am living areas of *my* arrested mental development ("fixations").

Artist. So far so good. Now, my own mind's functioning which involves "fixation" living cannot be recognized as mine, and therefore I must posit some kind of existence other than my own. Thus I create in myself duality, and every other kind of plurality, delusions. Thus I invent my illusions of "not-I," which include my "impersonal" externality, god, time, space, motion, and every other kind of "otherness" meaning.

Author. I must acknowledge that my limiting of my self-consciousness saddles me with my delusion that I can be conscious of not-self.

Artist. Now then, my fixation-living decides the boundary of my self-conscious living. In other words, whatever new life experience I create which excites my fixation areas, also needs to be lived by me as not-I (not-self) living. I can allow myself to be aware of it as "it," but not as *my it.* Indeed, I must be aware of "it," for it consists of my own selfness, even though I live it without my conscious feeling of self-love and, hence, without arousing my sense of personal identity.

Author. I must acknowledge that I have just lived my you accounting for your illusion of every kind of so-called "material," as being your mental processes. You have also accounted for the necessity of the "return of the repressed," that is, for the absolute inability of ignored selfness to exist as non-existent. My so-called "not-self" existence must be lived by me without my functioning of my sense of personal identity. All of my sensory perceptual and ideational living which I conduct as not-I (such as "externality," "objectivity," "divinity," and so on) is really my own repressed selfness returning to me *incognito,* my own "alienated majesty" effectively remote beyond my ability to see my selfness in it.

Artist. True aesthetic living respects self-significance, the *autotelic* nature of whatever is.[10] I have just helped myself consciously to see that my self-love is the essential ingredient in my self-consciousness, that I must learn to live my most difficult experiences with conscious love or recognize that I am favoring my dying rather than my living. By recovering my self-love in its true expression of I-feeling, my sense of personal identity subsumes just that much more life appreciation. By restoring my conscious feeling of self-love to my life experience (from which I had formerly withdrawn it), I release my sense of my grandeur and care for myself accordingly. Little wonder I lost track of the true wonderfulness of my self-extent, when a chief method of my surviving at all depended upon my success in ignoring the truth of my oneness-wholeness-allness. I see now that I have been trying to unify my dissociated mind by my notions of grandeur, alien control, and persecution, directed toward my (illusional) "external world." Thus, it has seemed to me that "the scenery" was grand, not myself; "others" were interfering with me, not myself getting in my own way; "others" were picking on me, not my own chasing of myself; and so on. I now begin to see that it is of life-saving importance for me to notice that my every "like," or "dislike," is an indispensably valuable expression of myself which is needed to reveal to me my true measure and, hence, lead me to my true appreciation of (my) human life.

I see now that my supporting any illusional external world, by my so-called "external" perceptions, has been at the cost of my appreciating my true wonderfulness. This truth is obvious and yet rarely observed.

Author. My so-called "external" perceptions only *seem* to dislocate my mental functioning, for my every perception is a creation of my mind. In 1911, Freud pointed out that the illusional "external" projection of perception

> makes its appearance not only in paranoia but under other psychological conditions as well, and in fact it has a regular share assigned to it in our attitude toward the external world. For when we refer the causes of certain sensations to the external world, instead of looking for them (as we do in the case of others) inside ourselves, this normal proceeding, too, deserves to be called projection.[11]

Artist. Freud stated his intention to investigate further his insight that his sensation was his own creation, did he not?

Author. He did. This investigation may have been recorded in one of his missing metapsychological papers. However, throughout his writing are found statements indicating his use of duality (e.g. transference) to offset his appreciation of the oneness of individuality.

Artist. Rabindranath Tagore considered beauty the indispensable guide for insight's growth, and art the indispensable method for insightful (self-conscious) self-expression.

Author. Exactly. Again, it it noteworthy that self-conscious importance of art is responsible for its health significance. Every mental event becomes more distinct as conscious selfness, as my thoughts are deliberately and purposefully focused upon it. For example, overwhelming emotions (rapture, despair, fear, hate, jealousy) decrease in intensity when I find it possible to compel myself to consider the meanings associated with each such preempting fascination. My artistic living facilitates my free flow of life and thus enhances my enjoyment of my fuller self-use, of my "functional triumph."

Artist. Without realizing it, a person reveals his psychology, and his philosophy, in his artistic interests. Clinic "finger-painting" and other psychological tests take advantage of that fact. Only by increasing my conscious self-tolerance can I make beauty more accessible to me. It requires immense self-love to practice immense charity in my living of my world. My art appreciation varies directly with my growth of my self-insight. Emerson described the office of art to be the education of the perception of beauty which, itself, is everywhere, as if waiting to be appreciated.

"Art should exhilarate, and throw down the walls of circumstance on every side, awakening in the beholder the same sense of universal relation and power which the work evinced in the artist, and its highest effect is to make new artists."[12]

Author. (My) you would wish every educator, including every teacher of medical science, to devote his personal and professional living to his esthetic cultivation of his conscious self-knowledge.

Artist. If he will. Note a few remarks your Emerson made on the subject one hundred years ago:

> These geologies, chemistries, astronomies, seem to make wise, but they leave us where they found us.
>
> What manner of man does science make? The boy is not attracted. He says, I do not wish to be such a kind of man as my professor is. He has got all snakes and lizards in his phials, but science has done for him also, and has put the man into a bottle. Our reliance on the physician is a kind of despair of ourselves.
>
> No object really interests us but man.
>
> Beauty is the form under which the intellect prefers to study the world. Saadi described a schoolmaster "so ugly and crabbed that a sight of him would derange the ecstasies of the orthodox."
>
> The feat of the imagination is in showing the convertibility of every thing into every other thing.
>
> 'Tis curious that we only believe as deep as we live.

Author. (My) Emerson holds such great overall appeal that I favor the limited truth even in his rare self-deceptions. I am heeding the helpfulness in realizing that the essence of everyone's beauty is its appealing quality which arouses the mind to harmonious functioning of its own nature. Again, I find self-consciousness to be both the last resort and the first true ground of esthetics, as of all human endeavor.

Artist. Schelling's central thought of esthetics was that it elucidates the underlying identity of nature and self, and he regarded the consciousness of this unity as the solution of the riddle of the universe. He, Kant, and Schiller held similar views of beauty, namely, that the function of beauty is to see the real sameness of self underlying its apparent differences. Your contention that a *thorough* study of anything, or anybody, will reveal its perfection and thus disclose its desirability, restated, means only: By your creating each fact involved in your event, or condition, you succeed in growing "equal to it" so that you no longer feel compelled to repudiate it as though it were not made up entirely of your own selfness. Thus, as a consciously self-educated surgeon you are capable of sensing the inevitableness, perfection, and desirability in "the most horrible" injury and, thereby, not requiring your cut, fractured, and bleeding patient to force himself to add to his extreme agony the burden of his overwhelmed surgeon.

Author. The "greatness of man" consists in itself and is not the same as the *conscious greatness of man.* My conscious greatness consists in the fullness with which I realize my living, as such. The readiness with which my sense of personal identity in my living vanishes is a measure of the limitation of my self-tolerance. My power to live and feel (my very own personal private internal) "externality" in a most distinct and distinguishable way has life-saving importance. By means of recognizing which living of mine constitutes my so-called "externality" living I can regularly increase or decrease it at will, depending upon which serves my best interests. Otherwise I could and would destroy myself, by my unrecognized "externality" living. In my opinion this distinctifying kind of self-orientation deserves the most careful study,—all the more careful since it involves most difficult conscious self-development (education for conscious self-government).

Artist. I notice that a scientist devoted to the idea of "objectivity" depends upon his enjoyment of the feeling of accepting, and of being accepted by, his colleagues. I also notice that he cannot devote himself to the truth of the allness of his individuality without evoking the resistance of his colleagues. Unless he, so to speak, plays the game of "objectivity" he must be ready to live his colleague as if personally hostile to such "unscientific" living in himself. Once he commits himself to the cultivation of the comprehensive view of his individuality, he is judged as no longer of use for "power politics," or for "power psychology"; he seems no longer "a good organization man." He must then be willing to live all of the (helpfully) psychologically untenable, personally ungracious, and professionally unethical more-scientific-than-thou attitudinizing of his erstwhile "sociable" colleague.

Author. It is only natural that I feel threatened by any of my living which I cannot understand, particularly if that living seems to be powerful.

Walter Pater derived the word "mystic" from a Greek word which signifies "to shut," as if to shut one's lips in secrecy about what cannot be uttered. The Platonists themselves, however, derived it from shutting the eyes, to be able to see the more inwardly. Any and all individuality is mystic.

Artist. You are aware of the effort to account for the esthetic feeling by the loss of the sense of personal identity, are you not? Many people consider the loss of the sense of personality to be an integral part of the esthetic experience. How do you account for this view of esthetics as founded upon an anesthetic self?

Author. Autohypnotic trance can account for this theory very well. Esthetic experience can be of such intensity (ecstasy, transport, rapture) that a person must deny that the excitation belongs to his conscious self, or be entirely overwhelmed otherwise. *All irresponsibility is an effort to defend the limits of conscious self-tolerance of responsibility.* I can save my precious sense of selfhood which I *can* hold myself accountable for, by denying selfness status to all of my living which I *cannot* hold myself accountable for. The sense of individuality, however weakly or strongly developed, is everyone's only hold upon his sense of sanity, and whatever amount of conscious self-possession he has cultivated is appreciated by everyone as being his one indispensable possession. With the disappearance of his self-feeling a person feels "lost," a "goner," a "nobody," "empty," and "worthless." Aristotle observed that there can be no beauty without a certain magnitude. Of what meaning is it if I say, I experienced esthetic pleasure which *I* did not live?

Artist. Certainly, esthetic appreciation is founded upon feeling (including sensibility) and therefore can be understood only as subjective experience. Furthermore, esthetic feeling is intense only to the extent that it gives expression to the artist's, or beholder's, inner life. That is the ground for Plato's claim that only the mind is beautiful. Ideas occurring with esthetic feeling elaborate the thinking descriptive of the *life* meaning of the emotion. One's highest esthetic experience is produced by satisfaction which is appreciated by the most of one's nature. After all, my mind can delight only in its own meanings. Since all of my meaning is mental, my esthetic scale potentially extends to my every kind of meaningful living.

Author. My esthetic living is always recognizable as mine and, through that characteristic, is distinguishable from all of my painful emotional living; for I tend to associate my unhappy living with some object which I cannot see *is* my own creation. I am anxious to live self-consciously, for when I do so I am no longer needing to excite my anxiety so that it becomes overwhelming.

Artist. Please record views of your relieving your anxiety through your esthetic living. Kindly describe anxiety. I am beginning to see the good I too can find in that dreadful living.

Author. Gladly. First, it is noteworthy of anxiety and esthetic appreciation that each is a feeling and hence subjective.

Artist. Why do you make so much over an obvious view (that an emotion is subjective)?

Author. Since I began to realize that my understanding of my conscious self-integration is my primary life lesson, I have grown corresponding appreciation for my ability to recognize any and every undeniable evidence of my subjectivity. What is called "mental health" arises from the expression of human individuality noticed as *conscious* human individuality.

Artist. I see how my esthetic feeling is enhanced by my observation that I am exercising my power of noticing the beauty of my life's creativity. I presume that my thorough study of my anxiety must discover it to be beautifully designed to be helpful for my growing my self-world.

Author. My study of my anxiety discloses it to be of greatest use for my heeding that I can suffer a most disabling repression: my sense of my wholeness-unity-allness. As is every other human feeling, so anxiety is beneficial to me, even if seldom credited as being a life-saving human asset. Fear pertains to a known peril and is similarly indispensably useful. Anxiety occurs when the peril is not specifically known. The most economic and generally valuable exercise of each of these unpleasant emotional tensions is as a warning signal of impending danger to life.

Artist. You tend then to welcome all of your living which is compatible with your sense of personal identity as being esthetic, and anxiously reject all of your living which is incompatible with your sense of personal identity as being dangerous. Every experience you live with love you tend to regard as salutary and esthetic, and every experience you live without that joy of living (love) you tend to regard as a threat to your life. Your every feeling of unhappiness seems depreciatory as far as living, itself, is concerned. You consider your every word descriptive of unpleasantness to be a pejorative word favoring your disowning your living which occurs with unpleasantness, as seeming anything but adorable. You equate the esthetic and the divine look. Thus, you picture esthetic education as the specific life process through which each student purposefully experiences nothing but extended self-introduction, nothing but his conscious activation of his self creating its selfness. You describe esthetic living not only as practical but also as necessary for the cultivation of wisdom, as essential for the freeing and fulfilling of one's genius. You describe fact-finding as the discovery of beauty in truth which spares you fault-finding. You elucidate *all* fault-finding as being more or less hasty conclusion based upon insufficient study of the all-sufficing facts. You observe that it *seems* far easier to conclude, "Whatever is which appears undesirable should not be," than to learn from first-hand experience with all of the factors present, "Whatever is which appears undesirable reveals precious ignorance of mine and thus stirs my curiosity and arouses my interest."

Author. Yes, it can *seem* much easier for me to bemoan the "destructive" behavior of my fellowman as being something "he shouldn't have done," than to undertake the work of learning the plight and appreciating the necessities of my fellowman which reduce him to *constructive* efforts which may only give the appearance of being "destructive."

Artist. If I say, "I should have done whatever I did do," I become responsible for myself instead of feeling guilty about myself. Only by seeing first the sum of factors which made my act of violence (or whatever seemed undesirable) necessary, can I then see which factors to add, or subtract, which will render that behavior *unnecessary.*

Is there any danger that by learning to see everything as beautiful and desirable I will then have no incentive to aim my living at what I now regard as my highest ideal? I mean, if everything is perfect as it is, why should I exert myself to have it otherwise?

Author. Seeing all as perfect simply frees perfect incentive to function with perfect facility and with perfect economy,—my vital wishes and needs continue to function, my sense of pleasure operates, my recognition of safety and danger to my life is active, all of my powers of exercising myself in the interest of my whole self go on as usual. That is the beauty of seeing all as beautiful. As my Emerson noted, beauty is the form under which my intellect prefers to study its world.

However, I have understandably great resistance to this study-the-factors-involved technique for it requires me to (1) assume responsibility for being my own world, (2) apply myself to working upon the real problem, (3) renounce my easy pushing techniques, and (4) try to extend peacefully the established boundaries of my self-tolerance. No wonder responsibility for problem-solving of this kind is often shifted by me so that I cannot recognize that it is all mine.

Artist. I am willing to assume that you are not jesting at scars and that you have developed your sense of wholeness through feeling your wounds. However, how can a person, whose every loved one was exterminated in a gas chamber make himself see the benefit to himself in regarding that horrible experience as being desirable? How can he get himself to renounce his need to find fault with the ugly, not beautiful, behavior of his fellowman? How can you, yourself, not just condone, but extol, the terrible and terrifying so-called Nazi medical experiments upon human beings?

Author. Each such question is a painfully needed one. I cannot always see *my* Nazi fellowman as a consciously great-souled rabbi saw his, with loving mercy. When I am able to achieve this degree of self-tolerance, it is only *with the greatest of difficulty.* The difficulty is extremely trying, so that I find it possible to be kindly understanding of myself when I am loath to undertake it. My clear recognition of the truth that it is beneficial to me to keep trying to "grow equal" to living such horrible experiences with understanding which heals my wounded soul, rather than with bitterness which adds pain to my already overwhelming pain,—only that clear recognition enables me to keep at my extremely difficult task of trying to see the beautiful truth, the sorely needed lesson, in actual humanity which *seems* like inhumanity.

Artist. Perhaps I am seeing more clearly the immensely important health significance in "Don't cry over spilt milk" and "Grin and bear it, the worst is yet to come" views about my inexpressibly painful living, as well as about the minor everyday slights of my world. You mean that, as a victim, the necessary original painful experience I suffered is something for me to live as kindly as possible in myself since I am my own Nazi as well as my own "experimental" subject. You mean that my natural feelings of hatred and vengeance are best renounced as soon as possible since each applies to my own self only. You mean that my loathing and bitterness are understandable reflex sequences of tortured living, reverberating echoes of my initial torment, which must continue until I can regain my mental equilibrium. Please detail your views of your persecutor.

Author. As I create all of *my* world, so do I create my persecutor. Whether or not I am aware that my persecutor is entirely and only my own mind-child, decides the insightfulness with which I view my every delusion of persecuting, or of being persecuted by, my fellowman.

Artist. As the victim of so-called Nazi medical experiment, how can it matter to me if I realize that my persecutor is "out of his mind"? Why would not such an idea simply add to my terror?

Author. Such a thought might well add to my terror; but, again, it would be terror limited by its association with my real danger and not nightmare panic spread to all of my own unresolved illusions and delusions.

Artist. If I have myself castrated by the way I create my persecutor as fooling himself that he is not also his own persecuted one,—*I* am the one who is castrated, not my persecutor. I can see now that I am only making matters worse by not learning my soul-shaking life lesson that I am castrated and that, simply by my persisting in living rather than resorting to dying, I am responsible for being castrated, for living myself as castrated. It is true that, in the long run, I suffer less by making peace with the unalterable facts of my existence as quickly as possible. It is a help to take all of the comfort I can when I can. In the reality of my mind, I am also not castrated.

Author. That is another comfort which is most gratifying, and which can only be derived from my responsible endurance of suffering. I refer to the fact that every threat to my sense of personal identity, such as "loss" of the use of any of my functioning, has educated me to an ever further appreciation of the wonderfulness of my life, has opened surprisingly new and beautiful vistas of the meaning of my humanity, has taught me a joy of living I hardly guessed at before.

Artist. You mean that pain and suffering force otherwise unattainable self-growth, quite as conscious self-development always involves "growing pains." Some of my personal experience bears out that claim. You may well note as your greatest life lesson your insight that you do not "make the best" of your life's vicissitudes, but that you actually see them as being best. Please discuss *your* persecutor further, particularly as to why he should be as he is.

Author. By living my tormentor as if he does not need to be the way he is (as if he is not under the unconscious necessity of being all and only his own victim) I must forego the comforting insight that he suffers persecutory delusions. However, this lack of insight on my part originates in my own suffering of unrecognized delusions of persecution. My persecutor treats himself ideally, as best he can.

By my recognizing that my persecutor is my own necessary creation I can enjoy the benefit derivable from attending to that delimiting reality, and thereby relieve myself of the additional intense suffering derivable from unacknowledged, terrifying, infantile dreams and phantasies of "getting at," and of being "gotten at" by, the several violently wild members of my family.

It is ordeal enough for me to have to endure my living of my fellowman who deceives himself (that he can injure someone other than himself). I enjoy great benefit from not having to confound such living with any undispelled early life illusions I may have indulged of being "picked on" by a jealous father or mother.

If I have to undergo the hellish experience of my warring, it is a tremendous help if I can learn to renounce such agonies as soon as possible after my war is over. My continuing devotion to bitter delusions that what happened should not have happened may be necessary if I cannot recover my peace of mind, but I can lean on myself in this manner only at great cost, such as by my developing ulcers, high blood-pressure, or some other such saving sign that I am trying to help myself by the law of the talion, by the shortsighted principle that two 'wrongs' can make a right.

Artist. I am sure that you indulge your illusion daily that What is, should not be.

Author. I do. And I frequently have difficulty recognizing this truly pathetic wishfulness of mine as being only an understandable form of my crying out, "Ouch!" It helps me to say it again, I can live my loving appreciation of the goodness, truth, and beauty of pain and of all suffering only with the very greatest of effort.

Artist. You remind me of my difficulty in living up to (my) St. Augustine's insight, "Love and do as you please," and to my St. Thomas Aquinas' insight, "What pleases directly in perception is esthetically valuable."

Said Plotinus, "This, therefore, is the life of the Gods, and of divine and happy men, a liberation from all terrene concerns, and a flight of the alone to the Alone." And, as if to solve every (phantom) problem of loneliness, Jeláleddin oracled,

> All that is not One must ever
> Suffer with the wound of Absence.

Your psychology, which is the study of the pure unity of your individuality, commits you to the growth of your self-consciousness and frees you from any mystic devotion of yourself to a completely insensible, imperceptible, and every way inaccessible, so-called "external" world. Your own human-system of psychology reminds me of a statement of Plotinus:

> Now often I am roused from the body to my true self, and emerge from all else and enter myself, and behold a marvelous beauty and am particularly persuaded at the time that I belong to a better sphere and live a supremely good life and become identical with the Godhead, and fast fixed therein attain its divine activity, having reached a plane above the whole intelligible realm . . .
>
> Nor did he (who has had such a vision) concern himself with the beautiful, but had passed beyond beauty and had transcended the series of virtues as one might penetrate into the interior of the holy of holies, leaving behind in the temple the statues of the gods. These he would not see again until he came out after having had the vision of what lay within, and communion there with what was no statue or image but the divine itself—of which the statues were but secondary images. And perhaps his experience was not a vision but some other kind of seeing, ecstasy and simplification and self-surrender, . . . a thought centered upon being merged in the divine.

Author. "Looking within" is all there can be to seeing what there is to see. My "inner beholding" is not a directing of my mental vision, but is an accurate description of the localized functioning of my "mind's eye."

Artist. I define a "genius" as one who appreciates human being. Thus I see genius in each of my fellowmen. The greater my genius, the greater my appreciation of my human being. To be appreciated, human being must first be carefully and caringly recognized. To be recognized, human being must first be *present.* Only one's own human being *can* be present, *ever.* Therefore, the greatest genius is one who sees his own human being most extensively, that is, in his fellow creatures, and in his fellow existents of all kinds (stone, steel, or any "substance"). Let me illustrate what I mean:

The work of an architectural genius consists essentially of the disposition of his time and space meanings in the most humanely livable way. His structural theme which treats his illusions of "time" and "space" with the greatest insight, is the creation of his disciplined mind free to revere its own inviolable integrity, free to observe its "temporal" and "spatial" orientations as being only variations produced by modifications of its own elements. To illustrate, the architectural genius creates timeless (not "period") and spaceless (not "bound") works. He sees his building materials as means for furthering the truth of every individual's *allness* and *freedom.* He renounces the view "Man lives in his dwelling" as repugnantly belittling, and upholds the architecturally true view, "Every man's dwelling lives within him,—his home, his heaven, and his hell." It was a preciously humane Oscar Wilde who wrote in his *Letters from Reading Prison,* "Still I believe that at the beginning God made a world for each separate man, and in that world which is within us we should seek to live." Bernard Berenson described art as "ideated life."[13] And, as Beongcheon Yu speaks of Lafcadio Hearn, I can see man (myself) as "fundamentally an artist ever dreaming of completion of his only material—his life."[14] My appreciation of my life's worth is all and only what I am willing to strive to make it.

18

Love of Wisdom

If the glory of God is not also my glory and the salvation of society is not also my salvation, then God and society are necessarily strangers to me, and their good can be for me neither a moral obligation nor a psychologically conceivable motive.

WARNER FITE

Author. "God geometrizes," asserts Plato. "Number is the essence of reality," asserts Pythagoras. "The free and conscious self is the only unity of which we have any knowledge," and, "In no way can the mind get outside of itself and grasp things otherwise than through the conceptions which its nature allows it to form," asserts Borden P. Bowne. "I educate, not by lessons, but by going about my business," asserts Emerson. The love of wisdom is the love of peace. May my philosopher speak his mind.

Philosopher. I shall be brief. Possibly, only my rare hearer will make sense of his Philosopher. It has often occurred to me to rejoice at the regularity with which the physician has helped himself (treated his mind) by growing his insightful philosopher, —indeed by becoming his own philosopher. May such physicianary healing spread itself.

It was his careful self-conscious living that enabled Thomas Jefferson to incorporate in his Declaration of Independence the wisest philosophy of his experience bearing upon the dignity of the individual. Locke insisted upon examining his own mind in order to discover the nature and limits of his knowledge. His subjective certitude had to be the issue of his conscious devotion to his self-culture. Jefferson saw that any self-orientation based upon self-ignoration must carry in it the principle of its own refutation.

As you have noted, a negative position posits an impossibility,—

for example, if I say that I cannot be conscious of objects outside of myself. *Nothing can come to my consciousness which is not consciousness itself.* My mind is the one and only condition of my having any meaning ("object," "idea," "sensation," or whatever). Therefore, by my mentioning of "objects outside of myself," I use words entirely without their implied meaning. Such utterances are sounds disclosing my unconscious need to hide my limited self-tolerance even as I flaunt its boundaries.[1]

Author. I have been sorely missing (my) your trenchant observations, particularly in my effort to renounce my dependence upon every criterion in a given quiddity for which I assume any characteristic that *can* apply only to another. You have surely observed my strenuous efforts to see preserved the individuality of every individuation of my mind, and the difficulty I put in my own way due to my ("received") vocabulary of terms such as "cooperation," "coordination," "collaboration." To illustrate: How can I renounce implying that I can be conscious "of" or "for" anything but consciousness, or loving anything but or for love, or sensing anything but or for sense, and so on?

Philosopher. I have been passionately interested in following your idea of categorizing all consciousness as self-consciousness, all selfhood as only selfhood (e.g., all consciousness as only consciousness, every moment of living as all and only that living of that moment, love all about itself only, and so on), every particular its own universal (e.g., every meaning its own all, thus dispensing with the necessity for compensatory illusions and delusions such as "betweenness," "communication," "relatedness," "otherness," "opposites," "conflict"). Every colleague of mine considers his world to be an "intelligible whole," and many a one sees that it is his own whole being which is thus operative.[2]

I find all of my particular knowledge is based upon a general condition flowing from a specific nature of my sentience itself. By bringing this general condition to light I see it to be: the truth of the oneness-allness-wholeness-nowness which imbues my entire being. There can be no reporting of any power of me but self-reporting. Regular "appearance" to the contrary is of necessity always illusional. Whatever is reports only its is-ness. Only nothing exists "outside" of anything or everything. "Outside" is a term which, by definition, means ceasing to be. The mental activity that produces it is a process of elimination. Such is the insight upon which all of my clearly intelligible experience proceeds. On the contrary, my using my mind as if I can segregate one part of it from another involves me in no end of phantom "psychological problems." The no-solution reflects the impossibility inherent in the problem.

Author. I find myself reluctant to renounce certain presuppositions of mine, everyone of them based upon my wish to preserve my *status quo.* Thus, I find it most trying to live with liking the views that my present living is my only living; that my personal identity cannot be the same from one moment of presence to the next; that each of my notions of self-permanence is illusional; that no one, or nothing, of my world is capable of staying the same; that "change" of any kind supposes existence under my hypothetical conditions of time, space, force, and motion; that the only reality of my individuality is its foundation in the sameness of the subjectivity of my spirit, my life itself. In spite of arithmetic and logic the wholeness and sameness of my being is in its every different. Nevertheless, I would appreciate your explicating the category of quantity which beguiles everyone who would travel his "secure path of science" (Kant).

Philosopher. Kant himself indicated that only he whose self-consciousness functions with the freedom of freedom can sense that his appreciation of his own oneness is paradigmatic for his seeing the validity of the oneness in his every sensation, or perception, or notion, reporting so-called quantity. Analysis can be only about synthesis, quite as the truth of synthesis is evident only by way of analysis.

You observe that your every transition ("change") is your continuing *being.* This devotion to the functioning of your self-consciousness is your "categorical imperative of duty" (Kant). It gives distinctness of aim to your life, and has enabled your discoveries of your great nature. As (my) Edward Caird said of (his) Kant: "the reason why discoveries are made at a particular time lies, not merely in the increasing knowledge of facts . . . but in that ripening of the intelligence to self-consciousness which causes certain questions to be asked, a ripening which expresses itself above all in the progress of philosophy" (*The Critical Philosophy of Kant,* 1909). You would renounce all living "incapable of being brought into living relation with self-consciousness,—which is the distinguishing characteristic of the modern spirit."

Your own experience of your own life is the only possible sufficient basis for any of your truth-evidence. Whether you are aware of *that* or not is the only possible question about it. Your living is your only possible constitutive power. You assert that your self-consciousness and your (illusional) "otherness consciousness" must always seem to be turned against each other until you see your so-called "otherness consciousness" peacefully as illusional. For you, particular self-consciousness is the same as universe consciousness. From your diagrams of circles, it is evident that you view your concept of your own particular being quite as you view your concept of your fellowman, or of your anything of your universe. In other words, you see yourself as a universe of universals. You intend your conscious selfishness to subsume your world. You assert that you have, as you always have had, only yourself to go on, that an assertion of so-called "externality" has the human mind against it.

You work to renounce self-unconscious living since you sense from such apparent self-negation, an unpeaceful outcome for your spirit, which invariably resolves itself with your functioning of your self-consciousness.

I enjoy observing (my) you renounce temptation to relativize your life, in any particular. You distinctify in your own unique way (namely, by the manner in which you live it) whatever your fellowman asserts is "external" (to him). Your recognition that you live your sensation, or perception, or notion, or any other imagination, in a special way peculiar to each one provides you with your only source of appreciation of its particular meaning for your ongoing being.

By the way, I also take cognizance of the ease with which my fellowman comforts himself for his lack of insight about the allness of his individuality, by considering himself as a member of some psychological or philosophical sect, and therefore readily tagging his fellowman with some collectivist title of ignored self-allness ("individualist," "existentialist," "solipsist," "epistemologist," "idealist," "personalist," "humanist," "atomist," "cosmologist," and so on). Whoever cannot recognize that only he can initiate his own new philosophical, as well as every other, movement, must reveal the same lack of insight in his estimate of the allness of his fellowman. A man's study of his own mind's working is the only possible study of his philosophy. You focus your interest in your psychic activity for its meaning for your life's fulfilment, refusing to lose sight of the meaning of your self in its own functioning. I imagine you enjoy listening to your fellowman (speaking ever to himself, as you consistently assert) largely in order to observe how (your) he works his mind's powers. You see even the term "common sense" as a euphemism for authoritarianism, which you may use in an unconscious attempt to abdicate your spiritual independence, whenever you cannot see lovingly that your self-activity is the sole source and method of any kind of your sentience (including knowing and its refinement, consciousness). You recognize no possible conflict, contrast, or comparison—not even "between" religious authoritarianism and spiritual independence—since each position can only be a created all of the individual considering it. Consciousness for self, then, must be the principle presupposed in consciousness for any so-called "object," "thesis," or whatever.

Author. In (my) your philosophy you try to steer clear of mistaking partition for plurality. It is not sufficient that I satisfy myself with "the love of wisdom," except as I observe it to be *my* love occurring with *my* wisdom. I, too, consider true wisdom to consist of my striving for devotion to my freshly growing self as it experiences its world living. Furthermore, I see every element of my experience personally as an activity of my own. However, the reliable start for everyone is: what he is ready for. For the most part my fellow philosopher's conscious self-awakenings have been dateless.

Homer referred to the slave as half a man. Early in the fifth century B.C. Heraclitus plied his cultivation of his democratic orientation, sensing the worth in responsible individuality. Across the ages the responsible philosopher has refined this only possible organic conception of humanity. Confucius, known as the first political philosopher, asserted, "To fulfil the law of our being is what we call the moral law." He formalized the principle that an oath made under duress cannot be binding. The force of my oath (which only I can utter and sense) derives its only strength from my assuming personal responsibility for seeing its meaning, originating its expression, observing its delivery, and identifying all of its possible binding power as of any significance for myself only.

Philosopher. All any organ of sense can do is live, grow, be, act, or modify, itself.[3]

Even the modern philosopher of absolute idealism, subjectivism, epistemological idealism, individualism, personalism, or existentialism, tends to shy at conceiving his position as being that of pure solipsism. I see the heaviest weight the human mind can try to lift as being this idea: The whole truth is, I can conceive only the existent which I create.

John Dewey, student of the nature and law of real existence, did state that subject matter of a living experience develops most effectively and fruitfully "where there is no conscious distinction of personal attitudes and manner from material dealt with." Insightful indeed is Dewey's dictum: "So act as to increase the meaning of present experience." In that spirit I am aware that every logical method of investigation and verification must be only a variation of the Lockean ideal of looking within one's own breast.[4]

Consciously self-oriented Plato, in defining social justice as each person's *minding his own business,* was keenly aware of the necessity for every person's undergoing the conscious self-experience enabling him to see clearly his responsibility for minding his business of world proportions. (Everybody's responsibility *is* everybody's responsibility). He understood the role of the "conscious-human," for renouncing the "mob-member" kind of personal identity. It seems that he even saw "obedience" as an integral force in "command," and *vice versa* (cf., St. Thomas' basic belief that man is really responsible only to his own will). To date there has always been evident this humanistic trend in my philosopher's growing concern for his only humanity, his own.

Author. It would be helpful to experience (my) you speaking to yourself about your *summum bonum.*

Philosopher. When I have you express yourself in that way it seems almost like a waste of words, which I know it is not.

"What does man want of life?" is a question which excites another question, "What does human life want of man?" It is plainly best for me that my life orientation and mind orientation be viewed for the real oneness underlying them. My "greatest good" is inherent in my sensing my duty to observe my constant oneness, completeness, and sufficientness. Nothing is possible which implies either agreement or contradiction. If I ignore my duty to myself, I thereby have my spirit drain off its capacity for service into a compensatory interest, unrecognizable by me as a strictly personal concern of mine. An apparent limitation of human consciousness is that a complete view of all of life's inviolable oneness seems always impossible to it. The keynote of my speculation on my *summum bonum* is: conscious individuality growing itself. My appreciation of my independent and perfect reality is a necessity, if I would enjoy the truth in ascribing independent reality to any existent of my world, and perfection to my unalienated divinity. My *summum bonum* is my self-consciousness, itself,—its functioning power which is essential for my wishing to live.

Author. Please speak of your conception of thinking.

Philosopher. My present opinion is that thinking is a specific sensory experience of my mind. My life is my only possible basis for any evidence of any being. To illustrate, my conscious conception of God exists only in me, but only my ability to conceive all of myself as divine enables me to live that conscious conception as being my own life process. Being is always present subject, not object or predicate. As Kant indicated, existence must mean existence for a self. My thought is no exception to my being. *Position* refers only to itself, and cannot be negation of a so-called "whatever else." *Ex nihils nihil fit.* I must aim to see positively *my* living of *my* everything, if *I* would *see* my perfection. Quite as (my) Spinoza certified for himself, pure individuality is the nature of all real being. The individual's self-consciousness is needed to prevent his seeming to imprison himself in his own rejected selfness. I am always learning as freely as I live myself, and the source of all of my knowledge is my self's activity. My consciousness is its own subject, consisting of selfness. *Thus, a self cannot be the "object" even for its own consciousness.* The illusion "object" is always unconscious (as if alienated) subjectivity. Leibnitz taught that there was no such thing as passivity, even in matter. Whatever is, is individual,—the only material of its possibility. In vain man may try to experience that which is not his own identity, and call *that,* instead of himself, God. The operation of thought is merely a living process, an issue of mental growth, which may be associated with consciousness or not. *Indeed my conscious living of my sensory experience is an unrecognized form of my thinking process.* I say "unrecognized," on account of the difficulty in immediately seeing in my manifold of sensory being the continuing account of my living of my own biological interests. If I let my imagination go, around my sensory living (e.g., as I review my perceptual living of my dream), my free associations disclose its personal meanings. All of my experience is an exercise for the learning of my life lessons.

Author. I see that (my) you are a philosopher who has seen fit to study the mind with which you do your philosophizing, your attaining to your profound views of the question of your individuality. No doubt you find your self-analysis to be reminiscent of (your) Kant's *Critical Philosophy.*

Mentioning your views of space, time, motion, and force would be helpful. I cannot see how *my* sensation "witnesses to the presence of an object which produces it" (Kant).

Philosopher. My motion of "space" is that it seems to provide me with comfortable living room for my sense of personal identity. It enables me to enjoy my illusions of "external" perception, thereby saving myself from overwhelming my conscious self with my life experiences which I am unable to live cheerfully.

My notion of "time" also is that it seems to provide me with occasions for living comfortably my sense of personal identity. It enables me to enjoy my illusions of not-now, thereby saving myself from overwhelming my conscious self with my *presenting* life experiences which I am unable to live cheerfully.

My notion of "movement" is essential for supporting my illusions of time and space. My notion of "force" supports my illusions and delusions of my own impotence. I grow my sense world as if it consists of differents unless I cultivate my consciousness of being the one grower. I can grow my thought-world notion as a unit, for that can be done with one conception. My sensation is entirely innate; my every so-called "phenomenon" is a disguised noumenon occurring in my consciousness as if it could be not-self. A phenomenon is an impossible, implying immediate being and not being.

Kant stated that Hume interrupted his (Kant's) dogmatic slumbers when he called in question the traditional view of cause and effect (the illusion that one "all" can influence, or be influenced by, another "all"). This new look which Kant derived from (growing) his Hume enabled him to substitute conscious self for a self-alien God as the principle identifying sense data as self-experience. He thus developed the power to renounce every so-called "externality" as unknown and unknowable, enjoying the tremendous economy of being able to concentrate his study upon his real world. I am my only thing-in-itself.

I can certainly say of (my) you what Caird said of (his) Kant, namely, that to understand him, "is to detect a consistent stream of tendency which, through all obstruction, is steadily moving in one direction; to discern the unity of one mind which, through all changes of form and expression, is growing toward a more complete consciousness of itself." Caird indicated that "progress in speculative philosophy is a progress to self-consciousness."

I help myself greatly with my new-grown insight that I cannot speak directly or indirectly to or with anyone else; and that no one can speak directly or indirectly to or with me. I can now see how the illusion that one person can speak or listen to another is the most widespread fallacy in my educator's world, and that it provides a sure defense against everyone's sensing that only he *can* speak or listen to himself. Thus, I can defend myself against learning whatever I am unready to grow as my own self-knowledge, simply by deluding myself that I have already listened to someone tell it to me. I have always overlooked the truths that (1) my so-called "listening to my fellowman" can be nothing more than my growing *my* auditory experience of having him talk and listen to himself, and (2) my so-called "talking to my fellowman" can be nothing more than my growing his having his auditory experience of having his author talk and listen to himself. Those new views of "talking" and "listening" (as of "seeing" and "being seen," and so on) have thoroughly reintegrated my educational living. As long as I can delude myself that someone else can do my listening for me, why should I patiently develop the tolerance to listen to myself? As long as I can delude myself that someone else can do my talking (to me) for me, why should I take the great trouble to talk evidently to myself?

My philosophy, itself, is the study of the "why" as well as the "how" of any of my living. Its chief characteristics are its unity and comprehension of infinite multiplicity and diversity. Perhaps its most fundamental conception is that of *being.* Although it is usually considered to be the product of reason, certainly it is the product of the conscious self of each philosopher, and may be properly tested to see if it fulfils the criterion of the given philosopher's self-consciousness.

The stoicism of my philosophy enjoins me to love to *live* philosophically, rather than merely to love to consider ethics as just a branch of philosophy. Thus, I see my whole mind as being the true basis of my morality, and renounce every definition of my "conscience" which describes it as a separate power of my mind distinct from its other being. In the interest of my self-preservation I am duty-bound to affirm as worth living only that which I can recognize as my own life. My very meaning "duty" depends upon my sense of my personal identity and what seems beneficial to and for it.

The oriental individual grows his unique culture and philosophy, quite as does the occidental individual, and each must be subjective (intuitive, poetic, esthetic), but not necessarily self-conscious. If self-consciousness were made the common denominator of humanity, I can see how every kind of philosopher could enjoy his (including his fellowman's) philosophic uniqueness as his contribution to his world's peace.

I used to like to conceive thought as the soul of language and language as the body of thought, but I am beginning to see the extent to which language is not at all an adequate expression of thought. I can readily see any of my thinking, or feeling, as being mine; but once I start putting it to words I find it easy to overlook my personal identity in my words.

It is not difficult for me to understand why (my) you insist on such absolutely radical views of your allness-wholeness-oneness, particularly when I am willing to go as far as I can along that path.

Author. My theme is: my pleasure in locating accurately the point of my effective endeavor, the sacred allness-oneness-wholeness-nowness of each human life. Every negation points up a duty. I notice *with special helpfulness* that the very mental material ("opinion," "principle," "notion," or whatever) associated with radical oneness to which my colleague objects in himself is precisely the mental material which I need to live lovingly, in order to be able to appreciate fully my biocentric oneness. As my Kant did, I see my theory of learning as a kind of Copernican revolution in my education. Instead of my moving around all in my world, I maintain my one position and see all of my world occurring in me.

Philosopher. I have not experienced myself sufficiently in the direction of my meaning which I name "individuality." And by "experience" I mean: undergoing, enduring, and finally appreciating my all-important outgrowths of only my own actions; or what (my) you call "learning your life lessons" in order to educate your self-control and find out how to steer your self in the vital interest of your whole self. All that I call scientific foresight (the renunciation of magic, not of mystery) depends upon my free play of my imaginative insight.

Nearly all of my (individuality's) action consists of my unconscious self-use. I have begun to see all of my so-called "physical" activity as being mental, but I cannot yet achieve renunciation of the notion of "interaction," particularly where my idea of my "personal experience" is concerned. However, as William G. Sumner observed, "The most elaborate discussion only consists in revolving on one's own axis."

Author. Asserted Friederich Paulsen, "Philosophy is coextensive with mental life." My reality is grounded in my life, and it is a kindness to myself whenever I notice that fact. Only that which a subject cannot see is itself is called an "object." Being is dependent only and all upon itself. Little wonder that Martin Heidegger emphasized the necessity to study the meaning of being, and asserted that the term "Being" is the most universal and the emptiest of concepts.[5] John Ruskin asserted, "There is no wealth but life."

With my Plato, I "will not rest in the multiplicity of individuals which is an appearance only." A scientist cannot alienate any of his world from himself, despite his every claim that he can. Certainly, this writing is not a "philosophic generalization of science."[6] It may fit William James' description of philosophy: "more or less dumb sense of what life honestly and deeply means."

Philosopher. With Epicurus I regard philosophy as the study of the health of the soul, to be continued throughout life. I identify as my own John Dewey's meaning of truth, "that which guides us truly is true," "the true means the verified and means nothing else."

Despite the fact that my sociologist friend can see that every human tie must exist only in a human individual, my addiction to my view of "interpersonal relationships" ("exchange") remains strong. In his *Community* (1917), R. M. MacIver specifically states of everyone's social ties: "The ties exist *in* the personality of each, and there alone. . . . Society is in us, in each of us, in some degree in all, in the highest degree in the greatest of us," L. T. Hobhouse observes: "Society exists in individuals. When all the generations through which its unity subsists are counted in, its life is their life, and nothing outside their life" (*Social Evaluation and Political Theory,* 1911). Forty years ago St. John Ervine wrote that unless American individuality can grow and become vivid, it can hardly produce great art or literature. He said the American suffers from standardized thinking.

Author. Certainly my custom of overlooking the intactness of my whole being can be strong; but, as Dewey aptly asserted "All habits are demands for certain kinds of activity; and they constitute the self. In any intelligible sense of the word, they *are* will. They form our effective desires and they furnish us with our working capacities" (*Human Nature and Conduct,* 1922). Being is always novel; habit is a seeming.

Philosopher. The sociologist Albion W. Small recommended doing away entirely with the category *individual* on the basis that there is no separate, discrete, unrelated entity as implied by the term "individual." He recommended instead a term such as "socius." There is an old saying, "One man is no man." A well known abstraction of the sociologist claims, "The individual is an abstraction." Certainly your image of your ideal man, as a kind of personified self-consciousness enjoying whatever he lives, is an achievement. Many a philosopher has spurned the ideal of individuality on account of seeing it in an abstract form meaning eccentricity, or the opposite of "sociality."

Any philosopher could accept his own creation of an ideal of individuality which subsumes all that he means by "sociality," but it is difficult to create for oneself such a mental construct. Just observing (my) you create it for yourself serves me for considering it for my own philosophical orientation. John Caird (*Introduction to the Philosophy of Religion,* 1880) insists that "social morality reaches its ideal purity only then when the individual not merely loves others as himself, but can scarcely be said to have any other or exclusive self to love."

Author. Where Caird's statement says "not merely loves others," my statement must read, "not merely loves his others,"—otherwise I sense a begging of the question through an overlooking of the fact that the individual is the *end in himself* which he is. One's only possible means, or instruments, are the uses of his own ends. Even his hand has the wholeness (end) of his self in it.

Philosopher. Pope seemed to see the need to respect the allness of individuality,

> Men must be taught as if you taught them not,
> And things unknown propos'd as things forgot.

Spinoza asserted, "That thing is said to be free which exists from the sole necessity of its own nature and is determined to act by itself alone." Man cannot get along with or with out his fellowman, only *as* him. In his *Pendennis,* Thackeray declaimed, "Ah, sir, a distinct universe walks about under your hat and under mine. . . . you and I are but a pair of infinite isolations."

Author. Every element of my life, considered as "within" or "without," which I can succeed in evaluating as free self-assertion of my own will and as my integral self-growth and self-realization, constitutes that much of my attainment to the true life of my spirit. I conceive my life, including all of my individuality as well as my view of my personal identity, to be a process,—a process achieving the meaning of the worth of my living. Paulsen told himself tersely, "The goal at which the will of every living creature aims, is *the normal exercise of the vital functions which constitute its nature.*" Certainly it is my nature and a vital function of mine to be able to live *my* fellowman, as I live all of my world, exactly as he is, namely mine. The more primitive I am the more I fear whatever of my world I experience.

Philosopher. You keep pointing out that you unexceptionally consider any use of your mind as having no possible meaning for anyone but yourself. Thus, whatever you put into words you reiterate can have no value as a "conversation piece." Indeed, you trace all of your misunderstanding of your world to the regularly exercised and deeply cherished illusion that one person can converse with another. You describe your every so-called "conversation" as an enjoyable audile experience which includes (1) your speaking to and hearing yourself only, and (2) your fellow "conversationalist's" speaking to and hearing himself only. Instead of making something out of what your fellowman says and following it up, what meaning *do* you assign to it, I wonder.

Author. (My) Plato said that true education produces pleasure and pain at the right occasions. I love to live my fellowman speaking and hearing his mind's actions. I enjoy having him verbalize how he works his mind, how he helps himself, how he chooses to live his capacities, how he conceives his world, how he finds this or that easy or difficult to live with love, how he enjoys the use of his wonderful powers, how—, but I could never end the cataloguing of my pleasure in my living of my fellowman's voicing his views to himself. Everyone is the only observer of his own interest. What is "commended by the experience of mankind" may be least safe of all. In the *Guardian of Education,* London, 1802, appeared this notice about "France,"

> Horrid principles and practices of this Republic: That all men are *equal* by nature; that the free will or liberty of man is unrestrained by any law human or divine; that human nature possesses endless perfectibility.

Philosopher. You are a professor. You must believe in educational institutions.

Author. I most certainly do live my "educational institutions" lovingly. I have discovered that every so-called "institution" which I do not see clearly as my own is nevertheless lived by me as an unconscious personification of mine, and hence as a potential subject for my unfailing consideration. Unconscious personification promotes such illusions as, "Democracy recognizes nothing but 'common sense,'" "Democracy has no sympathy with personal devotion," and on and on. Each citizen is all of his own "democracy."

Philosopher. Your use of your categories of space, time, motion, and force, relieves you of the unbearable poignancies of your alert self-consciousness. Certainly, without such concepts as space and time you would be unable to image any kind of so-called "externality." I presume you have accounted for all of your "not-I" living as similarly helping you.

Author. That is as I see it clearly.

Philosopher. I am often tempted to allow my dislike occurring with what I hear to settle its worthwhileness for me,—but then I also realize that such is the most striking characteristic of my primitive fellowman, the so-called "savage." I try to be interested always in having my fellowman speak his mind thoroughly on any one of his viewpoints. This is the only way in which he can observe himself in any inaccuracy which may exist.

What do you consider "memory" to be? It is a normal psychical faculty, is it not?

Author. Memory is a supporting illusion, a function of the illusions of "then" (not now) and "there" (not here) which constitute "physics" (the so-called "knowledge" of "matter," "time" and "space"). *A priori* and *a posteriori* imaginings distract the philosopher from the overwhelming view of his present self as being ever a momentary existent. Thus, as a *rationalist* I can refuse to see clearly that my *reason* exists only in the form of my experience; or as an *empiricist* I can refuse to see clearly that my experience exists only in the form of my growing my (self-) knowledge. My every *existent* is, *ipse,* all and only a momentary self-existent.

Nothing of my being is permanent or durable except the flow of its every continuing self-activity. To speak of knowledge not solely derived from experience is a contradiction in term. The very wisdom of one's organs is based upon his constitution's experience. *A priori* and *a posteriori* thinking consist only of recognized and unrecognized present imagining, respectively. There is no possible "experience" for an individual other than his own present self's subjective activity. One's "experience" is a synonym for his own living, itself. Thus, mind *is* nothing but experience.

Philosopher. Herman Zanstra also offers a possible view of man as a solipsistic "I-conscious-present." He refers to Berkeley's view: "only minds and the experience within those minds (he calls them ideas) exist."[7] I suppose you object to his using "we," or "our," to signify his authorship, on the basis that it begs the question of "plurality" (hence "objectivity," including "communication") right from the start.

Author. One may really mean "we" when he says "I," or even "I" when he says "we,"—which reminds me of a whimsical poem of my Emily Dickinson's:

> I'm nobody! Who are you?
> Are you nobody, too?
> Then there's a pair of us—don't tell!
> They'd banish us, you know
>
> How dreary to be somebody!
> How public, like a frog
> To tell your name the livelong day
> To an admiring bog!

Philosopher. With his ideal "compactness of mathematical formulation," Zanstra describes the *essential point* of his chapter, "Hypothesis and Reality," as follows: "Only what is directly experienced, that is the 'I-conscious-present,' exists by itself and is absolutely certain, the rest can be attained only by means of hypotheses."[8] He can account for his knowledge beyond his present consciousness as the product of his logical thinking, memory, and induction. Thus he can cope with the popular objections posed by the solipsistic position.

Author. I have studied *The Construction of Reality* and found it extremely interesting. It is always gratifying to observe an eminent and distinguished scholar of my world attempting to record his self-data, as such, as pure thought in the very way that Aristotle conceives *nous.* Josiah Royce approximated that extent of self-consciousness, in his regarding the "social order" as simply his own "highest spiritual destiny in bodily form," and in his "absolute ideal" of living as though his and his neighbor's life were one to him. John Dewey localized democracy in his mind as a "belief in the ability of human experience to generate the aims and methods by which further experience will grow in ordered richness."

Philosopher. I may still think and speak of matter as external to me, as "extended," filling up "space" and "moving" part of the "time," but I know the true subjective nature (my personal experience) of these "ontological realities." However, according to your view, I cannot really know that all of my experience is subjective *unless* I prefer to think and speak and even sing accordingly. I can think and talk as if any of my living, any of my meaning, is outside of me only at corresponding expense to my self-appreciation.

Author. It is only in the true realm of conscious selfhood where symptom-free living is possible. My language and its corresponding habits of thought can grow so automatic that I hardly feel the truth that they are the issues of my own conscious choice. I pay an enormous price in peaceful understanding for deluding myself that I live a persistent and permanent personal identity consisting of but a small fraction of my true allness-wholeness-oneness. I call on my Pope's beautifully rhymed wisdom:

> All Nature is but art, unknown to thee;
> All chance, direction, which thou canst not see;

All discord, harmony not understood;
All partial evil, universal good;
And, spite of pride, in erring reason's spite,
One truth is clear, Whatever is, is right.

Philosopher. (My) James H. Snowden, in *The World a Spiritual System* (1910) mused, "Personality is not a limitation, but an added power. . . . The opposition of self and not-self is not a necessary relation. . . . The self is at once subject and object, and thus experiences this relation in itself." The American philosopher has nearly always been an idealist (individualist).[9]

The Thomistic philosopher observes a worthy distinction in his use of the term "one." Since you base your life orientation upon the meaning of "one" to you, you must be interested in every view about it, particularly in the insightful views of St. Thomas.

Author. I have studied my Thomistic ideas to my benefit.

Philosopher. St. Thomas noted: "The 'one' which is convertible with 'being' does not add a reality to being; but that 'one' which is the principle of number does add a reality to being, belonging to the genius quality." He considered "the one" to mean individual "being," and asserted that everything guards its indivision, since a thing *is* only in so far as it is one.

Author. I cannot deny: Whatever is, is one. For me, quantity is, for it is *one* view in the mind beholding it.

Philosopher. I would appreciate knowing what your term "relation" means to you. Aristotle records, "Those things are called relative which being either said to be of something else or related to something else are explained by reference to that other thing."

Author. In philosophical terms I can describe "relation" as an "accidental predicament." Aristotle shows due concern and care to relate relativeness to relativeness, to maintain the order of oneness, to secure awareness that the property of one subject cannot be that of another.

To be able to understand the total meaning of self-sovereignty (that is, the pure culture of individualism) for American democracy requires that one see his America as his own as does uncompromisingly self-devoted Walt Whitman in his "Song of

Myself," and not as a country foreign to him, as does gallantly self-sacrificing George Santayana in his *Character and Opinion in the United States* (1920). One cannot be at home with humanity except in his own conscious egoity. Human experience (one's own, of course) is the only possible stuff of any observation. All that *can* exist exists only for the individual mind which creates it, as (my) egotheistic Josiah Royce observed over and over again. What a human sacrifice, to conceive and promulgate an ethic the essence of which is located "between" human individuals, centered somewhere "in their relationships" (that is, nowhere!)

Philosopher. My majesty is interested in your view that love is the natural feeling of your life-instinct, and that hate, or every other disagreeable feeling, is a derivative of distressful or "hurt" love, thus: guilt being struggling or "hurt" responsibility (life affirmation); anxiety being struggling or "hurt" potency or functional triumph; anger or hate being distressful or "hurt" reposeful peace; jealousy, unappreciated self-possession; blame, repudiated praise; disgust, rejected hunger; suspicion, forbidden trust; doubt, denied faith; shame, prohibited pleasure of observation; intolerance, strained tolerance; pain, disowned pleasure; diffidence, resisted earnestness; boredom, averted overwhelming excitement; and every unpleasant mental occasion simply a kind of undeveloped negative of its corresponding joy of living.

It is hard to believe that unhappiness of every kind is, so to speak, prohibited happiness, e.g., that "hate" is inflamed "love." Maybe love regresses to its expression in one or another of its autoerotic components, e.g., hatred being its anal sadistic element.

Author. That view discloses valuable free-association for the subject. I too always accustomed myself to thinking of "opposites" as being furthest apart. I had to strive strenuously for insight before I could see that "hot" derives its meaning from "cold" (and *vice versa*), that "tolerance" derives its meaning from "intolerance" (and *vice versa*), and so on. I helped myself to see this truth by using an analogy. Thus, if I hurt my beloved hand, then it hurts me to use it, so that I help myself by hating its functioning (quite as, before its hurting, I lovingly enjoyed its functioning). My meaning of "resistance" is my reluctance to see my lovable personal identity in whatever I am unready to live consciously with loving peacefulness.

Philosopher. I see. If I just let all of myself function freely, then I enjoy the use of my power; but if, on any self-helpful account, I must block any zone of my functioning, then that particular zone maintains its blockade by evoking a specific unhappiness whenever its functioning is called upon. For example, if the one I live with love must suddenly spurn or jilt his (her) beloved, then it can become painful for me to live that one with love, so that my pained love constitutes my hate. Or, if as a child I am enjoying looking at my genitals, and suddenly I must turn to enjoy my mother's loving instead of my genital seeing, then my resulting pained seeing-pleasure constitutes my shame. My unwillingness to live my genital seeing with love is my resistance to it.

I am just now beginning to see that hate is specific resistance to the living of loving, blame is specific resistance to the living of praising, suspicion is specific resistance to trust, intolerance is specific resistance to tolerance, and each unhappiness or pain is a specific resistance to a particular happiness or pleasure. Please describe again how all feelings are derived from love. For example, you see hate as made up of love, do you not?

Author. Yes. I help myself with that view, as I do with my every view.

My self-love is my natural expression of my creature comfort, of my joy of living. While I am enjoying whatever experience I am living, I do not question the existence of that smoothly active self-love. It goes on quietly as the life-satisfying quality of my human nature. As long as I can please myself with this feeling of self-appreciation I can spare myself experience of discomfort, of life dissatisfaction. In this life of ease my sense of personal identity extends itself peacefully to my every actual personal experience.

However, if my difficult life experience is sufficiently excessive, my emotion of self-love is no longer evident in it. Instead, my self-love's stressful condition shows itself in one of its several forms of unpleasure, such as anxiety, pain, hate, guilt, shame, and the like. Each of these conscious pleasure-deprived modalities of self-love is conspicuous, "loud," attention-seeking, and unremitting, until the too-difficult-for-comfort life experience subsides. In other words, my every painful feeling is a symptom expressing my complaining self-love and, quite like every symptom, is a health ordeal constituted of struggling love. My each unpleasant kind of living is actually my love's exertion, my love's healing effort.[10]

I use my psychoanalytic experience for theorizing about this kind of love process. Under its own duress my love expresses a ready-made but unrecognizable version of itself, such as anxiety, anger, guilt, jealousy, or despair. Each such emotional "irruption" involves a suspension of conscious self-composure. It derives from phylogenetic fixation inherent in my native constitution. As Freud noted, its analogy may be seen in my "hysterical attack" traceable to a developmental fixation in my personal history. I consider love (or ecstasy) to be the natural feeling of human life. Every unhappy feeling is unrecognizable self-love stemming from overwhelming experience of my phylogenetic past.

Thus anger or fear or guilt may be understandable as a phylogenetic neurosis which, however helpful as a signal, otherwise, does not deal realistically with the presenting facts of my living. As true of all symptomatic living, no doubt the energy I have bound up in each such "neurosis" necessarily reduces the amount of energy I have freely available for my other life needs. Therefore it is imperative for me to learn how to use my every kind of unhappiness merely as a signal appropriately informing me of danger, so that I need not allow any such unhappiness to use me, as it were, by my throwing myself into a panic of it.

The psychoanalyst looks for traces of phylogenetic experience recapitulated in his own mental development. Indeed he is willing to view his own constitution as constituted of his living of phylogenetic and ontogenetic experience. He soberly considers the possibility that his disagreeable tension of fear is an instinctive repetition of violent living, a residue of his forbear's labored efforts while undergoing life-and-death struggle. The bodily signs of this painful emotion are prominently respiratory and cardio-vascular. In the history of the human individual's prehuman development some such experience as his ancestral transition from water to land and air may have initiated this unpleasantly stressful affective action-system (emotion). In the history of my human individual development my harrowing experience of birth (my leaving water for land and air) would naturally excite my dread pattern of fear inherently enabling my experience of pained self-love.

Philosopher. You consider yourself guilty of personal treason (however necessary and helpful) whenever you cannot love your living sufficiently to enjoy it with self-consciousness. Your solipsistic belief reminds me of observations made by Gabriel Marcel describing the central theme of his writings as "precisely the impossibility of thinking of being as object," and, "Truth is and can only be, mind." For you, whatever is, is all and only itself; none of it can be *attributed* "elsewhere" even, much less "communicated." You renounce all that you understand by your "beloved object" as being (illusional) self-repudiation which would make a means, not an end, of your love-life.

Author. A person arrives at the peak of sanity when he consciously comes only to himself, for only then does he cultivate the true meaning of life, his life. The only *possible* "authority," or sane theocratic conception, is the divine right of the individual being. The self-authority is a conscious master of the truth of his individuality. He proffers no advice, no "correction," no knowledge, no law, no treatment,—only profound reverence for his human individuality as ever divine.

Philosopher. I can live that all-important course only with the greatest of difficulty, and now I readily imagine your observing: "Certainly, it is most difficult, and correspondingly satisfying." Whenever I observe my fellowman perform a particularly difficult feat in any kind of human endeavor, other than this one of achieving expert living of self-insight, I appreciate his attainment and marvel at the hard work it represents. I presume I balk instinctively at the idea of my working to create further self-insight since that effort obviously stirs up my ancient fear of losing my prevailing cherished sense of my personal identity.

Do you regard as a waste of consciousness all of it which takes place in any of your thought (ideational affirmations) which ignores your spirit of subjectivity?

Author. As I pose this question, the idea occurs to me that the notion of "waste," itself, has a repressing force about it. The enlightenment provided by my self-consciousness enables a sensibility for my life meanings which are essential for my safely and sanely doing what I will with my own.

I find it very hard for me to keep imagining myself consistently as the subjective *stranger* I necessarily am, since my view of my personal identity *must* be ever a new one. I help myself greatly by realizing that my term "object" is a synomym for non-existent; that my refusal to see my subjectivity in what I call "object" makes my living of it completely anesthetic (and correspondingly irresponsible); that my feeling of love is conscious in direct proportion to my consciousness of my self; that my being is ideally open-lived only to the degree that my self-consciousness works. I cannot explain any of my being in any way except by seeing to it that the *subject* to be explained explicate itself. Thus, my love is all about itself; my consciousness is all about itself; my belief is all about itself; my body is all about itself; my "external world" is all about itself; my divinity is all about itself; and so on.

Philosopher. How can I account for my morality, or ethics? My etymologist tracks both the Latin and the Greek terms to their original meaning: custom. You, my "you" that is, trace all of your morality only to your personal sensibility for what benefits you.

Author. Yes. As (my) Warner Fite stated it succinctly:

> *Morality is the self-conscious living of life.* . . . The moral man is the man who, so far as he is moral, knows what he is about, and the immoral man is, thus far, he who does not know. . . . And to be thoughtful, intelligent, self-conscious—what is this but to be conscientious and responsible? . . . The moral life as I conceive it, is the examined life. Given the examined life, I say that nothing else is needed.[12]

It is necessary that all of my moral action clearly be freely chosen by me.

Philosopher. Fite observes: "I am inclined to say indeed that he who can explain just how I know my neighbor will have answered the last question in metaphysics."[13] According to you, you have settled that matter once and for all: there can never be any condition of this knowing so accurate and peaceful as your renunciation of knowing your neighbor. You can really appreciate that "your neighbor" is your own creation, and that he only can know his self.

Author. Yes. My neighbor "grows upon acquaintance," and by that I mean: I go on growing the meanings which I name "my neighbor" knowing his self.

Philosopher. That seems like an instance of "progress."

Author. For me, the notion "progress" *always* implies depreciation of is-ness (which constitutes all of existence) under the semblance of flattery, as if blame toward one's previous being could amount to praise for one's present living, as if a loss to one's so-called "past" could constitute a gain to one's present. My illusion called "progress" disregards the truth that my present subsumes all of my so-called "past" and so-called "future." I prefer to renounce all such views implying comparison (e.g., "I am better than I was," "smarter than I was," etc.) as containing exactly the same kind of disregard for the inviolability of individuality as does holier-than-thou or "healthier-than-thou" living.

Philosopher. This is the first time I have ever experienced anyone asserting to himself the real point in renouncing the illusion called "progress."[14] Please make a condensed statement of your idea of the meanings "self," "mind," and "consciousness" for life.

Author. In order to secure its existence, my self-allness, my "directing idea" (Claud Bernard), requires power of self-supervision based upon self-appreciation, or self-sensibility, the essence of mind, as of life. The very word "idea" derives from a verb meaning "the sensation of seeing." The only "seeing," or sensibility of any kind, is a knowing activity. The only "consciousness" is a knowing, supervising consciousness.

19

A Poet's Healing Force

"It is well for even those of us who lack the poet's fancy and the poetic faculty to, as Osler says, "recognize the true poetry of life, the poetry of the commonplace, of the ordinary man and the plain toil-torn woman, with their loves and their joys and their sorrow and their griefs."

DR. JAMES YOUNG

POET. EVER SINCE Hippocrates the physician has indicated his appreciation of the helpfulness of poetry.[1] Every individual mind may be likened to a poem. The making of a poet's mind may be defined as a kind of psychopoiesis, as the ideal expression of the ideal.

Author. A poet's esteem for his vivacity may seem somewhat irrelevant to concern for health, in the opinion of my "objective," "concrete," "materialistic," "impersonal" hearer. Nevertheless, I enjoy every confidence that you can thoroughly justify your idea that the data of anatomy, physiology, biophysics, and biochemistry, were, first of all, worked out along poetic lines.

Poet. I offer some considerations of the identity of conscious creativity and poetic genius, since you equate conscious creativity with specific psychotherapy.

Consider the rich store of psychoanalytic material in the following anonymous poem culled from the *Mother Goose* collection:

"There Was a Little Woman"

There was a little woman
As I have heard tell,
She went to market
Her eggs for to sell;

She went to market
  All on a market day
And she fell asleep
  On the king's highway.

There came by a peddler,
  His name was Stout,
He cut her petticoats
  All round about;
He cut her petticoats
  Up to her knees
Which made the little woman
  To shiver and sneeze.

When this little woman
  Began to awake,
She began to shiver,
  And she began to shake;
  She began to shake,
  And she began to cry,
"Lawk a mercy on me,
  This is none of I!"

"But if this be I,
  As I do hope it be,
I have a little dog at home
  And he knows me;
If it be I,
    He'll wag his little tail,
And if it be not I
  He'll loudly bark and wail."

Home went the little woman
  All in the dark,
Up starts the little dog,
  And he began to bark;
He began to bark
  And she began to cry,
"Lawk a mercy on me,
  This is none of I!"

Only when I am conscious of myself can I avoid affectation, a confused concept of myself. Conscious self-experience is the source and origin of the undisguised naturalness, earnestness, simplicity, economy, truth, and clarity constituting pure poetic production. The pure poet must have something to say which he knows *he* needs to hear. His poem is always his accepted soliloquy, which demonstration can win his own confidence only. His poem is a positive assertion of himself, to himself,—not half-conscious, but wholly conscious. Quite as Schopenhauer declared, "Style is the physiognomy of the mind, and a safer index to character than the face."

Author. It seems that you have discovered the healing and strengthening power in self-analysis.

Poet. Yes. I realize that you are undertaking a pioneering project in attempting to demonstrate that poetry is a most essential element to be duly honored in your elementary medical education. Therefore, it is my intention to show that every poet recognizes his poetic hygiene and dutifully devotes himself to his healthsome mind-consciousness.

Author. To point up this idea, a certain observation regarding the tendency to secure mind-help *via* mind-denial (repression) may be noteworthy. First of all, it is most practical to be able to see the true nature of that which is undergoing repression, namely, one's own human nature. Unhappy "mother" or "father" or "sibling" meaning is sometimes called the "repressed mental content." Only the meaning of an individual's very own personal living can exist for him. The fact is, and it needs to be said over and over, only one kind of living *can* be repressed, namely, *selfness,* the meaning constituting the personal mind of one's very own individuality.

Everyone is always alone, but seldom is one capable of the degree of mental sophistication consciously attesting the lone subjectivity of sanity. D. W. Winnicott aimed an interesting study at this insight.[2]

His poem "Silence" seems to be Edgar Lee Master's therapeutic resolution of some poignant puzzlement:

> And I ask: For the depths
> Of what use is language?
> A beast of the field moans a few times
> When death takes its young:
> And we are voiceless in the presence of realities—
> We cannot speak.[3]

The "talking cure" is also a sovereign remedy for the stunned self. It is life-affirming to be able to observe of one's released powers, "I didn't think it was in me." What one can just speak of is already undergoing some subjection to his self-control.

A working poet is a kind of practicing epistemologist. His is not a "received" vocabulary. He undertakes the work of originating his word and idiom. In his bright, likeable *Invitation to Poetry,* Lloyd Frankenberg notes, "Often the initial resistance to what has been called 'metaphysical' poetry is an uneasy recognition that there is more to it than first meets the ear."[4] Thus Bernard Goldman discovers his own location of his world,

> All the world I watch
> is void.
> How thankful they must be
> for me.[5]

Poet. The healing power of poetry has been experienced personally by poet Robert Graves, who had been wounded through the lung in World War I and was vulnerable to the killing influenza afterward. Of his desperate illness he said: "One thing kept me alive: the obstinate intention of getting my poem right. . . . By the thirty-fifth draft I had all but solved this, and was tottering about on a stick. The Troll's Nosegay saved my life."[6]

To modify Oscar Wilde's daring dictum on beauty ("One does not see anything until one sees its beauty") any linguistic expression, indeed any sound, is not really heard until it is recognized as poetic. In the numerous eulogies of the poet for his fellow singer his poem of praise is commonly devoted specifically to the great and glorious eloquence of his poesy. There is no such occurrence as a poet who does not revere his fine life process from which his esthetic creativity emerges. As Emerson mused,

> . . . Whom the Muses smile upon. . .
> In his every syllable,
> Lurketh nature veritable.

Author. My research on the identity of poetry with conscious self-creativity has served not only to strengthen and clarify my insight that everyone is his own creator of his all, but also has increased my appreciation of each one's individual way of exercising his creativity. Spenser called soul the form which makes the body, and Proclus called the universe the statue of the intellect. Amy Lowell also made this idea easier to see as true to life in her beautifully ironic "Epitaph of a Young Poet Who Died Before Achieving Success":

> Beneath this sod lie the remains
> Of one who died of growing pains.

Thus, it is not only the poet like Whitman who sings consciously of himself, but it is also the poet like Whittier who sings of *his* puritanism, or like Wordsworth singing of *his* common man, or each one who sings of *his* sea or seacoast or New England or Middle West or sky or whatever. Wilbert Snow, "Poet of the Maine Coast," realizes that his Maine Coast's local habitation is in his own living.

Van Wyck Brooks, in *America's Coming of Age* (1915), credits Whitman with having "precipitated the American character," as having "cast into a crucible" the meanings of apparent plurality—"action, theory, idealism, business"—whence they "emerged harmonious and molten, in a fresh, democratic ideal, which is based upon the whole personality." As Louis Untermeyer writes in his thoughtful, feelingful, insightful book, *The New Era in American Poetry* (1919) "It was Whitman's use of the rich verbal material that flowered in the street rather than in libraries that gave him such potency," enabling him to break "the fetters of the present day poet" so that he might free himself "for a clear look at himself."

Ludwig Lewisohn used his life-affirming self-insight to point out the life-loving, self-revering poetry of his Homer, Shakespeare, and Goethe. He illustrated the humane meaningfulness of a person's self-tolerance, of his ability to use a wide range of his mental materials artistically: how Homer could travel and experience in his mind, how Shakespeare could live his intense pleasure and pain esthetically, how Goethe could call his soul his own! Goethe declared, "You can't get rid of what is truly yours, even were you to throw it away," and, "Every being that is conscious of its oneness seeks to maintain its proper situation unfragmentized and unmoved," and, "Poetic content is the content of one's own life."

Although rarely conscious of the fact, every human *individual* personates all of his world. Being my own *all,* I have nothing outside of myself to "incorporate," "assimilate," "imitate," etc. I am always thinking for myself, always self-reliant, always self-helpful, etc, but not always self-insightful.

Poet. Yes. His profound realization that any wholeness of utterance, or unity of knowledge, or organization of meaning, *must* be the creation of a given mind, distinguishes the conscious poet. Note, please, the self-consciousness of William Byrd (1540-1623) in his "My Mind To Me,"

> My mind to me a kingdom is,
> Such perfect joy therein I find
> As far exceeds all earthly bliss
> That God or nature hath assigned;
> Though much I want that most would have,
> Yet still my mind forbids to crave.
>
> Content I live, this is my stay:
> I seek no more than may suffice:
> I press to bear no haughty sway:
> Look, what I lack, my mind supplies.
> Lo! thus I triumph like a king,
> Content with what my mind doth bring.

In a poem, as in a dream, the creator's sense of personal identity is located wherever he lives his feeling.

Author. Ever since he had his Freud spell them out for himself, every psychoanalyst has consciously created for himself these two insights: (1) existence does not necessarily mean *conscious* existence, and (2) non-existence does not necessarily mean *conscious* non-existence. However, quite as Seneca said, there is no man but prefers belief to the exercise of judgment. Similarly, there may be no man who does not prefer unconsciousness to consciousness for his hurt.

Poet. Self-consciousness is the power of living with which the poet renounces his posing and concentrates upon his poesy. Thus finely composed Emerson addressed the singer in his soul, relating the advantage he derives from extending his self-reverence (*The Poet*):

> And this is the reward: that the ideal shall be real to thee, and the impressions of the actual world shall fall like summer rain, copious, but not troublesome, to thy invulnerable essence. Thou shalt have the whole land for thy park and manor, the sea for thy bath and navigation, without tax and without envy; the woods and the rivers thou shalt own; and thou shalt possess that wherein others are only tenants and boarders. Thou true land-lord! sea-lord! air-lord! Wherever snow falls, or water flows, or birds fly, wherever day and night meet in twilight, wherever the blue heaven is hung by clouds, or sown with stars, wherever are forms with transparent boundaries, wherever are outlets into celestial space, wherever is danger, and awe, and love, there is Beauty, plenteous as rain, shed for thee, and though thou shouldst walk the world over, thou shalt not be able to find a condition inopportune or ignoble.

Seemingly from the very beginning of English literature the subject of poetic "science," the effort to objectify poetic living and subject it to "classic laws," has been "popular." However, first science must be a reality, before there can be a science of the real. Sang Emerson, "Dante's praise is that he dared to write his autobiography in colossal cipher, or into universality," and "The state of science is an index of our self-knowledge."

Author. That study and practice of medicine is right side up which concerns itself solely and wholly with keeping hale (whole) the life of the physician. Without my consciousness of the unity (intactness) of my own life, my concept of unity of anyone or of anything of my world lacks meaning.

Poet. La Bruyère rightly noted, however, "All the wit in the world is lost upon him who has none." Blind zeal to make poesy "popular," traceable to the laudable wish to provide "the vulgar" with all highly valued poetic experience, is of course always a displacement of one's own need for esthetic living. Can that zeal be true to life? It is of the very essence of poesy to be the original creation of each one who lives it, subject only to the nature of his being, just whatever that may happen to be. Indeed, it appears that the whim, or impulse, of the poet is his only motivation, and his individual taste is the only law of his word-artistry.

Author. The very growth of my sense of personal identity rests, at bottom, upon my seeing my likeness in each of my mind's productions, thus making way for my conscious birth of my next creation. The usefulness of similes and of metaphors, for explaining an unknown idea by a known one, is founded upon this intuitive power. Aristotle wisely considered a person's power of metaphor to be a mark of his genius. Even my mind's body only renews itself with that which is like it.

The most likely explanation of the belief that the heavenly muse is successfully courted by illness, or intoxicants, is the fact that an individual's health struggles of every kind summon curative accesses of his self-consciousness. Self-consciousness cannot be indulged without engendering a sense of life appreciation. Said Cervantes, in his *Journey up Parnassus,* "Everyone whose verse shows him to be a poet should have a high opinion of himself, relying on the proverb that he is a knave who thinks himself one." Goethe uttered it, "It is only knaves who are modest." And life-loving Lichtenberg quoted this sentence in his *Miscellaneous Writings,* "Modesty should be the virtue of those who possess no other."

Poet. As long as I lived unconsciously under the influence of my rejected selfness I also relied upon plurals and anonymity ("we," "they," "us," etc.). As I dared to assume responsibility for my being, I quickly sought to renounce these hiding places in myself. I am reminded of Schopenhauer's famous passage,

> It must not be forgotten that a true value attaches only to what a man has thought in the first instance *for his own case.* Thinkers may be classed according as they think chiefly for their own case or for that of others. The former are the genuine independent thinkers; they really think and are really independent; they are the true *philosophers;* they alone are in earnest. The pleasure and the happiness of their existence consist in thinking. The others are the sophists: they want to seem that which they are not, and seek their happiness in what they hope to get from the world.

Author. I would like to consider a poet's view of poetry.

Poet. Certainly. Conscious appreciation of the creative power of the "soul's immensity" (Wordsworth) can be furthered by noting its flashes of original integrations as they occur in poetry work, quite as in dream work. Coleridge's "Kubla Khan" is a beautiful illustration of the occurrence (1797) of an integration of poesy and dream work (conceivably furthered by an intoxication from his anodyne). How purely descriptive *his* homely definitions of prose and poetry: "prose,—words in their best order; poetry,—the best words in the best order"! Only that experience can be *insightful* instruction to a mind which is recognized as its own experience. John Ciardi thus epitomized insightfully the nature of the human individual, "For a man is finally defined by what he does with his attention." In order to be appreciated as worth living, the newness of a life, *per se,* must be *consciously* experienced. The "poetic effect" accomplishes just that. The product of a specific coming alive of the poet, poesy's meaning to its reader is likewise that of *his* novel action, of his fresh sensing, perceiving, feeling, noticing, realizing. Archibald MacLeish poetized this idea ("Ars Poetica"),

> A poem should not mean
> But be.[7]

The making of a man is the poetry of him. A poet knows how to take a fresh look; to enjoy "a beginning again" (Gertrude Stein); to wonder at what his fellowman misprizes as commonplace; to clothe his meanings in the language "of real life" (Wordsworth, "That which comes from the heart goes to the heart"); to discover in poetry, "a place for the genuine" (Marianne Moore, "Poets are literalists of the imagination"); to free "the fine delight that fathers thought" (Gerard Manley Hopkins); to live his mind consciously by observing the full range of his imagination; to live with his wholeness; to know with Shakespeare, "To hear with eyes belongs to love's fine wit"; to direct the sproutings of his imagery and reach out its shoots to its "Minute Particulars" (William Blake). In his sensitive, scholarly, self-conscious *William Shakespeare, a Critical Study* (1916), George Brandes succeeded in demonstrating how the growth of his poet's insight constituted the making of his mind's maturation and sophistication: "given the possession of forty-five important works by any man, it is entirely our own fault if we know nothing whatever about him. The poet has incorporated his whole individuality in these writings, and there, if we can read aright, we shall find him."

In his spirited *Autobiography of Mark Van Doren,* that kindly author records, "The completest existence of a poem is in that inner ear where no sound ever comes. The harmony is in the reader's brain, or better yet, his soul. And if he is a good reader he cannot bear anybody else's voice between him and the words."[8] In innumerable ways have poets identified such avowed conscious subjectivity with their insightful following of their own "bent." Wrote Byron (to his publisher, John Murray): "So far are principles of poetry from being invariable that they never were nor ever will be settled." A man reveals himself poetically whenever his language, as a part-act, is consonant with his whole movement. The pure poet is not the kind of actor who knows "about" his subject, but is the kind of being who *knows* his subject is his own living of it. Like Wordsworth's poet, he can live his past as present, his "emotion recollected in tranquillity."

C. Day Lewis states that while writing a poem the poet is in a creative phase of life and is not aware of a "need to communicate." His two conscious motives are: "to create an object in words, and to explore reality and make sense of his own experience." Of his own way of working, Lewis says, "Each new poem I begin is an attempt at making and exploring. Each finished one is, in effect, a way of praising life, a sacrifice in life's honor."[9]

Max Eastman has described modernism as "a tendency of poets to keep the values of their poems to themselves—or offer them to the reader incidentally to be enjoyed as a kind of colored puzzle." He sees the modernist as neglecting the function of communication, and in extreme cases as using language approaching "that of the insane or idiotic." According to him, perhaps "the best way to see what poetry is in its own nature is to imagine it originating in the incantations of medicine-men or magicians."

Author. According to Eastman, the ancient dispenser of incantations and spells devoted himself to "thinking up" names for experiences which would evoke their beings in his imagination.

Poet. Eastman describes pure poetry as speaking life without speaking about it, a pure poem being a unified moment of realization, "a realization of life through imagination and language." He sees the poet as having an increased awareness of life, as devoting himself "to the pure art of heightening or diversifying his consciousness." Of the modernists he says that it seems enough to them to offer a moment of life, an awakening of self.[10]

Joshua Whatmough points out that much of one's education is the transmission of verbal habit for which the study of language itself is the required corrective. He notices that *life fashions language,* not the converse.

Who is unafraid to make the effort to "live up" to his declaration of his divinity may simply define poesy as "the voice of god," divine diction which includes the sound of a sparrow's fall. In the sense that prayer is pursuit of one's own divinity, every art may seem to aspire to become prayer (Abbe Henri Bremond). Goethe wrote to Wilhelm von Humboldt (September 1, 1816),

> More than ever the web of this primeval tapestry the *Orestes* of Aeschylus makes me marvel. Past, present, and future are so felicitously interwoven that in beholding it you become a seer yourself—that is to say, one akin to God. And that, when all is said and done, is the ultimate triumph of poetry, covering its whole range.

Author. Please discuss the poet's concept of the wholeness of his being.

Poet. The ancient bard knew himself as a seer, seeing his life through his mind's makings. He knew the only power of a poem to be located in the mind happening to be living it (exciting the meanings of it).

The poet is literally the maker, the inventor. (Virgil gave the inventor a place beside the poet in Elysium.) He is distinguished by the extent of his realization that he makes only himself. He is unique insofar as he sees with more of himself concentrated in his seeing, and thus enjoys vivid, intensely felt self-expression.

Although the poet's expression of his love of his life is classically audible, and his acknowledged medium considered to be that of sound, probably no one would deny possession of essential poetic elements to the consciously self-contained mind of his evidently inspired and insightful, deaf and blind fellowman,—to his marvelous Helen Keller, for instance. As of all of a life's wonderful treasures, so too the soul of poetic effort is its specific power to activate the joy of living difficultly, to excite the pleasure of making and seeing life worth living. As one's every art comforts and relieves, even as it utters his interests, so also his poetic treatment of his profuse experience enables him to feel equal to it, thus furthering his sane equanimity. Every poet heals his mind by cultivating his awareness of the inwardness of all of his mental events, including his sensation and perception.

The appeal of the poet lies in the steadiness of his conscious self-appreciation, *the one and only source of mental freedom.* Every man, a hiding place from himself, is craving his own liberation into his demesne of personal identity,—hence his particular need for the balancing, centering power of poetry. A poem is always clearly and completely about its united self, using every device of prosody and poesy to distinctify its perfect individuality. Even a didactic poem is lived (created) unobjectionably, provided that the so-called teaching is clearly recognizable, from beginning to end, as being all and only self-activity, as heedfully learning *through the living of it* the knowledge of self. Indeed in this sense *all* poetry may be viewed as didactic, as furthering conscious self-knowledge.

A poet humanizes, in the only way possible, as he individualizes. All of one's prose which humanizes has the essence of poetry in it: *conscious subjectivity.* As a rule, the description of poetic being, such as a verse, includes its emotional significance which scores its *deep-felt* subjective meaning. Poetic living is a savoring of the beauty of one's life, and hence is as unhurried or hurried, as the living itself. Poetry is nearly always described as "awakening" something or other in the reader, indicating some realization that what occurs is the reader's living (creating) of his poem. As everyone perseveringly creates his perceptions which he calls *his* painting and, finally, is able to acknowledge that *his* thus perceived painting *is* his own; so reading poetry, one lives (creates) his poem over and over until his original sense of strangeness (really the novelty of his first reading of his poem) gives way to his sense of familiar personal identity, so that he can finally say of it, "It is mine." I make every experience mine in the first place, but I may only see it as mine after its initial seeming of strangeness is no longer overwhelming for my sanity-preserving sense of personal identity. *The ideal sense of personal identity features one's own never-ending novelty.*

It is not as though there were two choices: Subjective (Romantic) and Objective ("otherness"-centered) poetry. Whatever is, is purely itself (subjective). The only choices therefore are: whether or not to decide to be aware that all poetry is subjective. How beautifully Milton treated his blindness as a relief and adjuvant,

> . . . celestial Light,
> Shine inward, and the mind through all her powers
> Irradiate, there plant eyes, all mist from thence
> Purge and disperse, that I may see and tell
> Of things invisible to mortal sight.

Consciously subjective Swinburne described (his) Browning's plays as "monodramas, or soliloquies of the spirit."

Emerson noted, "Poetry is the perpetual endeavor to express the spirit of the thing." Pure poetry constantly vocalizes the equation: Truth equals subjectivity. Hence the bard is frequently described as "the revealer of the secret of things." It is the poetaster who confounds his poetry with his poetry's adornments. Shelley rightly localized the poet's throne "within the invisible nature of man." And Poe described his poetry as "the *Rhythmical* Creation of Beauty."

Wordsworth and Coleridge each considered individual liberty to be the mainspring of human action. Each regarded his poetry as "the antithesis to science," and thereby demonstrated profound self-consciousness as being the sure cure for any habit of living "the dull catalogue of common things" (Keats). The tuneful synthesis of classical artistic audition is readily distinguished from typical scientific analysis. To the poet the acquisition of empirical knowledge is nothing but the extension of his own self-heritage. This view accords with Schlegel's, "What we borrow from others, to assume a true poetical shape, must be born again within us." Understandably, Coleridge called Shakespeare "the myriad-minded." How else could my Stratford seer have his Ariel sing, "Where the bee sucks, there suck I"? Little wonder Carlyle's succumbing to (illusional) contrast, "We might say, in a short word, which means a long matter, that your Shakespeare fashions his characters from the heart outwards; your Scott fashions them from the skin inwards, never getting near the heart of them."

Wordsworth taught that poetry was the ideal of the individual and laid the foundations of poetry in the individual poet's perception and imagination. He held the function of poetry was "to awaken the mind from the lethargy of custom," and described the poet as "rejoicing more than other men in the spirit of life that is in him." What an awakening for everyone to discover that he has been talking poetry all his life! "There is no gap," says I. A. Richards, "between our everyday emotional life and the material of poetry. . . . If we do not live in consonance with good poetry, we must live in consonance with bad poetry."

Matthew Arnold sensed the pure subjectivity of the poem: "for poetry the idea is everything; the rest is a world of illusion, of divine illusion." But to attempt to restrict the boundaries of poetic liberty would be arbitrary. Even as I know mine to be true, I am ready to respect my fellowman's view of his.

Thoreau noted, "Good poetry seems so simply and natural a thing that when we meet it we wonder that all men are not always poets. Poetry is nothing but healthy speech."

Walter de la Mare appreciated the wholeness of his lyric being: "The first and greatest pleasure of the explorer (in poetry) is a kind of self-discovery." "That love is hand and glove with consciousness is indeed obvious; since it is a sovereign and unique condition of consciousness. . . ."

Alfred Noyes upheld the oneness of one ("The Two Worlds"):

> This outer world is but the pictured scroll
> Of Worlds within the soul. . . .
> O, well for him that knows and early knows

In his own soul the rose. . . .
Traversing to the sky's remotest ends
A world that he transcends. . . .[11]

Edwin Arlington Robinson's self-consciousness was dear to him (Peace on Earth"):

Your world is in yourself, my friend,
For your endurance to the end;
And all the Peace there is on Earth
Is faith in what your world is worth,
And saying, without any lies,
Your world could not be otherwise.[12]

In his deathless tribute to his poet friend, John Holmes, John Ciardi recorded,

Life is the act of being who you are.
Sentience is the state of registering that life.
Poetry is that way of making and saying
What that life is and how it feels.[13]

Lloyd Frankenburg wisely declared that poetry defines itself, but that its own definitions are not definitive. His sage version is applicable to all else as well:

> Perhaps its least and best description is to be found in Shakespeare's reeling conversation between Lepidus and Antony while they are wining aboard Pompey's galley "near Misenum":
>
> Lepidus: What manner of thing is your crocodile?
> Antony: It is shaped, sir, like itself; and it is as broad as it hath breadth; it is just so high as it is, and moves with its own organs; it lives by that which nourisheth it; and, the elements once out of it, it transmigrates.
> Lepidus: What color is it of?
> Antony: Of its own color too.
> Lepidus: 'Tis a strange serpent.
> Antony: 'Tis so. And the tears of it are wet.[14]

Author. I see your poetic orientation as identical with self-insight.

Poet. Yes. The pure poet's truth is consciously his truth, the real, presenting fact of his own making. The pure poet's language is comprised of words naming the stuff he makes himself of. Whoever of poetic bent needs to do so must identify his poetry with illusion, pretense, communication, suggestibility, two worlds, "common sense" credibility, representation, universal experience, natural law, and other such compensations for the overlooked allness, wholeness, fullness, unity, nowness, and completeness of his (including *his* poet's) personal individuality. The *nature* of any poem can never be anything but the nature of whoever experiences it,—in the first place, of the first poet who conceives (creates) it. And Richard Lovelace, in "The Grasshopper," scored the lot of the mind that forgets itself,

> Thus richer than untempted kings are we,
> That asking nothing, nothing need:
> Though lord of all what seas embrace, yet he
> That wants himself is poor indeed.

In the sense that science is a dead language (impersonal, dispassionate, matter-of-fact, bloodless, sensory, material, objective, concrete, consciously unimaginative, external), poetry is a live language (passionate, imaginative, inspired, creative, subjective, mental, internal, spirited, ideal, personal). Affirmed Keats, ". . . if Poetry comes not as naturally as the Leaves to a tree it had best not come at all." Once Gustave Flaubert was asked to identify the real life Madame Emma Bovary, and averred: "I am Madame Bovary!" Epicurus related, poetry has such charms that a lover might forsake his mistress to live it.

My study of great poetic lines helps me to discover the nature of poetry, for it exercises my appreciation of my living my Aonian world. That poetry belongs to the category of the truly excellent which is clearly recognized soliloquy. "Conscience is born of love" (Shakespeare), and consciousness is born of self-love. Note Robert Frost's description of bardic self-helpfulness, "A poem begins with a lump in the throat; a homesickness or lovesickness. It is a reaching out toward expression, and effort to find fulfillment. A complete poem is one where an emotion has found its thought and the thought has found the word."

My impoverished view of my living sees it as an "adjustment to my environment," rather than as my creation of my own environment, my living of my own world (the poetic view). "That is my life," is the only truth which I can live. What one loves most about a baby, or child, is the poetic living of each,—his undisguised self-consciousness. Frances Thompson described Shelley as a glorious child.

Author. Bliss Perry (*A Study of Poetry,* 1920) associated poesy with the consciousness of human being, with the perception of human nature: "Any inquiry into the nature and laws of poetry will surely lead into a deeper curiosity as to the nature and manisfestations of aesthetic feeling in general." He remarked the poet's vital creative power, referring to Thomas Lovell Beddoes' lines: "I have a bit of fiat in my soul, and can myself create my little world."

The poetaster tries to beautify signs of life he finds: Shakespeare finds beauty in his existence itself, and tends its health:

> Since brass, nor stone, nor earth, nor boundless sea
> But sad mortality o'ersways their power,
> How with this rage shall beauty hold a plea
> Whose action is no stronger than a flower?

With his amazing insight, Freud saw so-called "megalomaniac" ideas and feelings of grandeur as being natural to the mind. He felt "justified in assuming that megalomania is essentially of an infantile nature and that, as development proceeds, it is sacrificed to social considerations."[15] Describing the event of "falling in love" *via* repression (rather than rising to love *via* consciously living one's very own beloved) he quotes Rückert's translation of the verses of the insightful Persian poet Jeláleddin,

> For when the flames of love arise
> Then Self, the gloomy tyrant, dies.

Poet. Leonardo DaVinci pointed out that he who quotes authority hides in his memory instead of responsibly living consciously. You mean *your* Freud, no doubt.

Author. My Freud is my only one.

Poet. A. H. R. Fairchild, in *The Making of Poetry* (1912), insightfully observed that when the poet is poetical, he makes use of the activity called "personalizing." Fairchild provides several instances of a poet's observing his appreciation of his personal identity in his perceptions. He quotes Keats, "If a sparrow come before my window I take part in its existence and peck about the gravel." Goethe, describing the pictured sheep of the artist Roos, "I always feel uneasy when I look at these beasts. Their state, so limited, dull, gaping, and dreaming, excites in me such sympathy that I fear that I shall become a sheep, and almost think the artist must have been one."

Perry refers to this "identifying imagination" as being one of the oldest and surest indications of poetic faculty. The only poetic value or meaning of any word is constituted entirely of the vitality of the verbalist who is putting his life into that word. Perceptive Archibald MacLeish notes an urgent necessity for living poetically,

> Nothing is as close as poetry, as the poet's vision, to the tragic dilemma in which we live. If it is true, as it assuredly is true, that our dilemma is founded in those great events which have changed the human situation on this earth, and if it is true that the cleavage of the dilemma is that divorce of the feel of the fact from the knowledge of the fact which frustrates us in our efforts to know ourselves in the new world we live in, then only the poet's vision can right the world for us and right ourselves as actors in the world. . . . Only when poetry reclaims, in the consciousness of living men, the place it had always held in earlier civilizations, will triumphs of modern science promise us a world in which humanity can live alive.[16]

Hence it is that I include poetry as integral to my subject, elementary medical education. Who would deny the designation "poetic" to a baby's or a scientist's first use of any and every word? The fact is that every use of every word is a first use of it. Yet who is there who has not lived his word as a use-worn hackneyed expression without an appreciation of its poetic force? How unnoticed the figurative can thus take on the lifelessness of the literal. Two ways man may live himself: (1) enraptured and (2) asleep.

Author. It is a kindness to myself (life-preserving) to excite my lively appreciation of the poetry in my every exercise of language. Whatever is, is incommunicable. Human speech is always a form of *one* growing aloud. Every vocable is an instance of one's audible self-growth. Whenever I take my wonderful human being for granted, it is essential for my health and happiness that I awaken and, like Charles Lamb's true poet, learn to dream while being awake.

My life is all about my life, not about some other life, or about some other lifelessness such as "environment." As I see it, the worth of one's poetry lies in its function of singing for artist or critic: I am, all and only. The helplessness of the self-dissociated person to account for his likes and dislikes lies in his limitation in recognizing his every self-element as helpful. He is given particularly to such expressions as "external world," "force of circumstances," "unselfishness," "human relationships." For the most part his language tends to function as an unprized collection of forgotten life triumphs. (My) forgiveness itself is the love-borne appreciation of the helpfulness of guilt.

Please give a classic instance of a poet's own conception of his craft.

Poet. Thus Coleridge described his poetry as constituting consciously meaningful linguistic living:

> The poet, described in ideal perfection, brings the whole soul of man into activity, with the subordination of its faculties to each other according to their relative worth and dignity. He diffuses a tone and a spirit of unity, that blends, and as it were fuses, each into each, by that synthetic and magical power to which I would exclusively appropriate the name of Imagination.

I would appreciate an account of a psychoanalyst's view of his poetry. Only for an access of self-consciousness do you reserve, "one touch of nature makes the whole world kin."

Author. In 1908 Freud already considered the essential *ars poetica* to lie in the poet's "technique of overcoming the feeling of repulsion. . . undoubtedly connected with the barriers that rise between each single ego and the others." He compared the imaginative writer with the day-dreamer, and the poetical creation with the day-dream.

> No one has known, as a rule, what expectations to frame in approaching this problem; and often the connection has been

> thought of in much too simple terms. In the light of the insight we have gained from phantasies, we ought to expect the following state of affairs. A strong experience in the present awakens in the creative writer a memory of an earlier experience (usually belonging to his childhood) from which there now proceeds a wish which finds its fulfilment in the creative work. The work itself exhibits elements of the recent provoking occasion as well as of the old memory.[17]

Every psychoanalyst knows that the *specific* creation of his own psychoanalytic living is fresh insight. Psychoanalytic insight does not derive from functioning of an existing habit of mind, but is the product of a modification of that mind itself. It does not issue from looking at new living in the old way, but does issue from a new way of looking, itself.

Fresh insight is always associated with an access of conscious imagination. It requires the psychoanalyst's continuous growing of, and sensing, a new personal identity for himself, corresponding with the truth that his living is his growing *self*-experience. Thus, he sees his frame of personal reference undergoing constant alteration, in keeping with his extending the range of his life experience. His putting on the new man may be imperceptible but he knows that it is happening. Whenever his life experience runs counter to his habit of living, he feels the pain-principle (repulsion), the force of his resistance to acknowledging a personal identity which he is not yet ready to live as lovable.

Poet. Claimed Macaulay, "Perhaps no person can be a Poet, or even enjoy poetry without a certain unsoundness of mind." Apparently on account of his access to his unconscious mental events, a poet, as a genius, may sometimes seem to be irrational.[18] Shakespeare has his Theseus describe "The poet's eye, in a fine frenzy rolling," and voices this view:

> The lunatic, the lover and the poet
> Are of imagination all compact.[19]

Thus Plato quotes Socrates (*Phaedrus*):

> There are several kinds of divine madness. That which proceeds from the Muses, taking possession of a tender and unoccupied soul, awakening and bacchically inspiring it toward songs and

> other poetry, adorning myriads of ancient deeds, instructs succeeding generations. But he who, without this madness from the Muses, approaches the poetical gates, having persuaded himself that by art alone he may become sufficiently a poet, will find in the end his own imperfection, and see the poetry of his cold prudence vanish into nothingness before the light of that which has sprung from divine insanity.

And John Ciardi writes, "To be a poet is to vacillate between being a madman for ego and a desperate man for doubt."[20]

Author. Freud formulated his pleasure-pain principle as the ruling force guiding his conduct of living. *It also decides which life experience is to be lived as ego-syntonic, and which as ego-alien.* Whatever I live with the feeling of love (with pleasure) is life-affirming; whatever I live without the awareness of love (with pain) is life-threatening. My realization of the wholeness of my self is the measure of my so-called "mental health." My self-affirming experience contributes to my sense of personal identity, which includes my appreciation of the wholeness of my being. My self-threatening experiences restrict my sense of my personal identity, thus impairing my appreciation of the wholeness of my being.[21]

From my infancy on I live my every experience as either pleasurable (easily acknowledged as myself) or painful (easily acknowledged *as if* not-self). Whatever I can live *as* mine I can control voluntarily and thus renounce. All else I live must be repressed, thus relegated to my involuntary control. Control of masturbation, quite as sphincter control, is seldom achieved by way of renunciation. Yet, obviously the full appreciation of the allness of individuality cannot be achieved if masturbation, or sphincter, control has resulted from repression. Hence one's sane solipsistic position is, all but rarely, resisted as being "narrowly egoistic," "an untenable predicament," "primitively narcisstic," and so on,—without his insight regarding such propitious face-saving "manic denial." In other words, the full measure of the truth of the allness of one's subjectivity is possible only to the individual who does not blindly maintain (the illusions of) not-self meanings. My illusion that any of my mental growth is alien to me necessarily involves me in delusions of alien control.

The closest I can approximate a fear of loss of my life is my fear of the loss of my sense of my personal identity. Even my every craving for possession (including conscious self-possession) depends upon the functioning of my sense of my personal identity. Joan Riviere calls attention to the special difficulty most people have in accepting or understanding the psychoanalytic concept of the individual's phantasied "innerworld."[22] She points out that the fear of death largely relates to the fear of the loss of "one's present breath of life, and one's 'past life' out of which one's identity is constituted," and adds, "Each personality is a world in himself, a company of many." She cites attractive illustrations of "inward possession," such as that expressed by John Hoskins about his beloved,

"Absence"

Absence, hear thou my protestation
Against thy strength,
Distance and length;
. . .
. . .
To hearts that cannot vary
Absence is present;
Time doth tarry.

My senses want their outward motion
Which now within
Reason doth win,
Redoubled by her secret notion;
Like rich men that take pleasure
In hiding more than handling treasure.

By absence this good means I gain,
That I can catch her,
Where none can watch her
In some close corner of my brain:
There I embrace and kiss her,
And so enjoy her, and so miss her.

Or by Robert Louis Stevenson's word picture of his grandfather,

I cannot join myself on with the reverend doctor; yet all the while, no doubt, and even as I write the phrase, *he moves in my blood, and whispers words to me,* and sits efficient in the very knot and centre of my being.

Or by Samuel Rogers account of aloneness (in "Human Life"),

> . . . At moments which he calls his own,
> Then, never less alone than when alone,
> Those whom he loved so long and sees no
> more,
> Loved and still loves—not dead, but gone
> before—
> He gathers round him.

Or by Joseph Conrad's avowed insights (in *The Arrow of Gold*),

> "What are you thinking of?" she said.
>
> "Can I think of anything but you?" I murmured, taking a seat near the foot of the couch. "Or rather, it isn't thinking; it is more like a consciousness of you always being present in me, complete to the last hair, the faintest shade of expression, and that not only when we are apart but when we are together, alone, as close as this. I see you now lying on this couch, but it is only the insensible phantom of the real you; the real you is in me. How am I to know that the image is anything else but an enchanting mist?
>
> "I will tell you how it is. When I have you before my eyes there is such a projection of my whole being towards you that I fail to see you distinctly. I never saw you distinctly till after we had parted and I thought you had gone from my sight for ever. Then you took body in my imagination and my mind seized on a definite form of you for all its adorations—for its profanations too."

Or by Guillaume Apollinaire's poetic self-consciousness (in his *Alcools*),

> The stream of life went past me and I looked for
> my body there
> All those who followed on and on and who were
> not myself
> Were bringing one by one the pieces of myself
> There I was built up piece by piece as one erects a
> tower

The men and women piled up high and appeared
—myself
Who had been made of all the bodies, all the stuff
of man.

Perhaps the most convincing evidence of appreciation of the vitality of my theme, poetry is a process of making the self conscious, is the number of psychoanalysts who have chosen it as their own and worked it up, not without poetic power. For example, Marion Milner writes,

> Moments when the original "poet" in each of us created the outside world for us, by finding the familiar in the unfamiliar, are perhaps forgotten by most people; or else they are guarded in some secret place of memory because they were too much like visitations of the gods to be mixed with everyday thinking. But in autobiographies some do dare to tell, and often in poetry.
>
> Wordsworth says that as a child he was unable to think of external existence, he communed with all he saw as something not apart from but inherent in his own immaterial nature; when going to school he would often grasp at a wall to recall himself from the abyss of idealism. . . .[23]

In her mind-insightful study, "Psycho-Analysis and Art," she describes poetic genius as "the awakening of creative subjectivity itself."[24]

Whatever mental life I experience without the feeling of love nevertheless constitutes my own mental power, which I am trying to disown by means of any of my several feelings of rejection (hurt love). Study of the matter reveals that the psychoanalytic concept most difficult to live with is this one: Every one of my meanings of "external world" is nothing but my own mental being which is grown all and only by my own life process. Whatever I live without evident love is thereby already undergoing emotional rejection, rejection which spares my being conscious of the anxiety always associated with suspension of my awareness of love. The unknown is feared since it cannot be lived as surely lovable.

Pleasure is the debt of pain. Elation can be the successful wholesome issue of the work of depression, instead of just a successful escape from depression-consciousness. Poetry itself is the cherished property only of him who can see it as his own. Whoever appeals to his own consciousness for the evidence of his creativity is poesy-oriented. He acknowledges that he equates his originality to the originality of his everyone and everything. He recognizes his very vocabulary as an anthology of the language of his everyone.

Melanie Klein regarded mourning in the grown-up as a reliving of his earlier depressive anxieties.[25] She developed the concept of the "depressive position," conceived conscious integration to be activated by depression, and associated such reparative living of depression with the creative psychology of the artist. Claimed Coleridge, "What nature makes thee mourn, she bids thee heal!"

In 1930 Freud wrote to Viennese Richard Flatter, author and translator of Shakespeare into German:

Dear Mr. Flatter

I thank you for kindly sending me your translation of *King Lear,* which gave me the opportunity of rereading this powerful work.

As to your question whether one is justified in considering Lear a case of hysteria, I should like to say that one is hardly entitled to expect from a poet a clinically correct description of a mental illness. It should be enough that our feelings are at no point offended and that our so-called popular psychiatry enables us to follow the person described as abnormal in all his deviations. This is the case with Lear; we are not shocked when, in his sorrow, he abandons contact with reality, nor when, clinging to the trauma, he indulges in phantasies of revenge; nor when, in his excess of passion, he storms and rages, although the picture of a consistent psychosis is disrupted by such behavior. As a matter of fact I am not sure whether such hybrid formations of an affective clinging to a trauma and a psychotic turning away from it do not occur often enough in reality. The fact that he calms down and reacts normally when he realizes he is safely protected by Cordelia doesn't seem to me to justify a diagnosis of hysteria.

Sincerely yours

Freud[26]

Poet. Eminent high-minded Emerson, a parnassus of noble poesy, said of his "poet of humanity," Shakespeare, "he has no discoverable egotism," and, "he knew the laws of repression which make the police of nature." And of the poet in himself, Emerson observed, "He stands among partial men for the complete man." "The poet is the sayer, the namer, and represents a little beauty." "He is the true and only doctor." "The people fancy they hate poetry, and they were all poets and mystics!" "The poets made all the words." "The Ancient British Bards had for the title of their order, 'Those who are free throughout the world.' " "The religions of the world are the ejaculations of a few imaginative men."

Author. All language is poetry, waiting only to be named *self.* Everything is itself only,—and that is all that is true and all of the truth. To my recurring question, What *is* poetry?, my steady reply respects the allness of my existence, Poetry is *my* poetry. Honest, earnest, knowledgable Edmund Clarence Stedman ably contributed to his period poetry, as brilliant, self-educated Louis Untermeyer now ably contributes to his. It is enlightening to note the extent to which Stedman's literary criticism still applies. Of his concept of poetry he wrote, in *The Nature and Elements of Poetry* (1892), "Whether sung, spoken, or written, it is still the most vital form of human expression," and, "Poetry is rhythmical, imaginative language, expressing the invention, taste, thought, passion, and insight, of the human soul." And, of his ideal poet, "He utters, reveals, and interprets what he sees with that inward vision, that second sight, the prophetic gift of certain personages, —that which I mean by 'insight,' and through which the poet is thought to be inspired," . . . and, "his gain must come from self-development; otherwise his utterance will never be a force."

In my view Stedman was capable of excellent taste in idealized utterance,—epic, dramatic, lyric, or idyllic. And I know of no finer definition of taste than the one quoted by Stedman, himself: "the artistic ethics of the soul." *De gustibus non est disputandum.* Each of the works of that great psychoanalytic esthetician, Ernst Kris, attests the accuracy of Stedman's declaration of poetic independence.[27]

Throughout my talking I have intended to be spirited. By "spirit" I mean essentially: Consciousness of the greatness and glory, might and magnitude, of my existence. Irwin Edman worded the spirit idea in his wonderful way, "For it means nothing more than those moments in experience when we have some free glint of life for its own sake, some lovely unforced glimmer of laughter or reason or love."

Any and all of my observation which is not self-conscious is derived from my fixations, that is, from my amnesic mental material created by my having repressed my selfness in the interest of seeming lovable to myself (worth living). I did not know the full meaning of peace until I first saw the futility in trying to help my conscious self at the expense of my unconscious self (*my* fellowman). With that insight I was able to imagine the true meaning of peace as being understandable also only for my *consciously* self-responsible fellowman. Then my cherished war-cries of "the" world, "Respectability" and "Comfort," gave way to my peace-song, "Freedom of the soul."

The *only* real league of nations exists merely in the mind's self-world, individual-all, creating that beatific vision of heavenly earth.

The poet is the nourisher and healer of his imagination, the mind's hold of manpower. To be unimaginative is to be unmedicinal. It is the office of the physician, as of the poet, to remind himself of the first principle of self-consciousness by striving to see his beauty in immediate living, hard and easy alike.

Poet. I imagine that you realize clearly and fully the possible drastic consequences (for your popularity) of your daring to prescribe poetry for yourself, while earnestly purporting to set forth elementary medical education. You are certainly aware that it is the rare scientist who takes his poetry seriously, and the still rarer one who would expect to find in a poem any answer to the questions, any solution of the problems, of his working day. It is one thing to uphold the idea that imagination is all that can be practical, and quite another to extol the composition of poetry as an unfailing source of self-helpfulness, as a sure method of cultivating self-consciousness.

I accept that you define the imaginary as the only real, and the real as the only imaginary. I realize that you conceive yourself as more than a kind of divinely inspired psychic photographer. I can appreciate the view that conscious creativity is the poetry of poetry. But my "reason panders will." Somehow I cannot accustom myself to equating imagination and responsible mental work, or poetry and responsible medical discipline. I resist that just as I resist my other imaginings about solipsism. I shall try to apply George Moore's beautiful sentiment: "We must, if we would appreciate a writer, take into account his attitude towards life, we must discover if his version is mean or noble, spiritual or material, narrow or wide" (*Avowals*).

Author. I have found that my awareness of my resistance has been my indispensable bridge to my wholehearted acceptance, once I can love my resistance for its helpfulness (in sparing me overwhelming tensions incompatible with my conscious self-tolerance, i.e., my sense of personal identity) and, hence, renounce it at will.

Scientist. You rely upon your imagination more than I can on mine. For me poetry has never been a wonderland, or dose of bittersweet medicine which made my life's course run smoother or clearer. How can I learn to like poetry enough to try it?

Author. Only the hard work of devotion to poetry, the conscious exertion of effort to discover its practical helpfulness and the practice of invigorating myself with its vital originality have taught me to learn to like it. For example, I considered soberly the health claim in Marguerite Wilkinson's *New Voices* (1921): "Poetry is like the Pool of Bethesda. Until they have been plunged into eddies of rhythmical and imaginative beauty, many human intellects are, to a certain extent, sick and infirm."

Nearly every poet seems to attest the medicinal properties of song. Scientific writing can hardly be considered great literature with the scientist left out of it. Stated George Edward Woodberry: "Life-experience spiritualized is the formula of all great literature."

First, I had to recognize and carefully cultivate my *wish* to like poetry. Gradually this devotion led to my conscious effort to read it aloud as my own living and to enjoy its grace. Before long I began versifying a "good idea" into harmonious sound and metre.

Scientist. You regard your entire medical vocabulary as poetry. You say that every term is a poem, and wisely considered one. Is it possible that you have something of a poetic mind, and on that account identify poetic creativity with the conscious creation of your wholeness of being? What do you think of that? I presume you will say, "There is nothing to quarrel about but God."

Author. I have lived (my) Mark Van Doren making his self-observation, "Poetic thinking is wise thinking." I have lived my self-observation, "Poetic consciousness is self-consciousness."

Scientist. Do you disdain ordinary thinking? Your question.

Author. For me, all "ordinary" thinking is poetic thinking which may be unrecognized as such. The poetic process is a consciously forceful one. I equate life "force," "power," "energy," "vitality," "process," "activity," "course," "development." Each is a name for an existent, the ground of the ever new existence which is life itself. *New* man is always in the making.

Poet. Every person is a poet, is he not?

Author. A name such as "person," "individual," or even "one" tends to defeat its purpose, that of describing subjective allness, nowness, and wholeness. I am reminded of a beautiful passage from Herder:

> Theophron: But does not "the highest intelligence" demand the term "person," in that "unity of self-consciousness" would involve "personality"?
>
> Philolaus: I do not see why. On the contrary, "personality" always remains a strange and superficial term for this conception. Locke and Leibnitz also regarded it as such, and sought to explain it by means of more definite expressions. . . . The most intimate consciousness of self forgets the appearance of person."

Poet. Please word your working idea of "a poet."

Author. Whoever is able consciously to feel like a poet to that extent is one. Only the individual can see and appreciate the sublimity of the flowing stream ever making up his subjectivity. The universally acknowledged greatness of Shakespeare derives only from evidence of his conscious magnanimity. The Shakespeare critic who spells out that truth as ever new nominations will not be "vexing the dull ear of a drowsy man."

Poet. When do you think one feels like a poet?

Author. When he sees himself as a poem and is conscious of his creativity,—as when he considers the nature of his roots, the flowering and fruiting of his burgeoning being. Shakespeare must have felt it when he named the "wish father to the thought," or when he made Miranda cry out, "Oh, I have suffered with those that I saw suffer!"

That consciously self-knowing poet, Henrik Ibsen, was familiar with the past history of all the characters he created. For him love of self was the fundamental principle of all activity.

Poet. Then one can only know himself to be a poet.

Author. That is true. And the experience which is of the very greatest aid to my imagination is my consciously appreciated poetic experience.

Scientist. Your integration of poetry, religion, and medical education reminds me of a statement of my educator of educators, John Dewey, in *Reconstruction in Philosophy* (1920):

> When philosophy shall have cooperated with the course of events and made clear and coherent the meaning of the daily detail, science and emotion will interpenetrate, practice and imagination will embrace. Poetry and religious feeling will be the unforced flowers of life. To further this articulation and revelation of the meanings of the current course of events is the task and problem of philosophy in days of transition.

All science is already poetry. You are pulling against the firmly entrenched nostalgic music of myth and magic. I have done my looking with the eyes of the world, not with my mind's eye, and I acknowledge a prejudice against trying to mix potions and poems. Your emphasis on human individuality is like trying to start civilization all over again. According to you, mental hygiene consists in wearing as many hats as you grow new identities in your mind. Have you no desire for fame? A reply of sorts comes to me. When asked who was the wisest in the city, Dante replied, "He whom the fools hate worst."

Author. Once I could begin to localize my world where it really is (in my mind) I began to see devotion to one's own now-individuality as the only possible civilizing process, devotion to one's own now-humanity as the only possible humanizing process, devotion to one's own now-divinity as the only possible religious process, devotion to one's own now-mental growth as the only educative process,—and so on. As did Harriet Monroe, often I too found my "academic mind, the uncreative mind, trained upon the past and living upon formulae." I considered the notion of evolution itself to be suspect insofar as it confuses perfectibility with "uplift," and identifies being with evolving. As all else, becoming consists only of being.

Poet. In listening to all of this I have restrained myself from observing, If you must be poetic, must you always be lyrical? Shakespeare merely made Edgar observe, "The gods are just and of our pleasant vices make instruments to plague us."

I shall now state what I have been hearing, but in my own words:

Everything exists according to its own (inner) nature, and must undergo vicissitudes corresponding to what it can experience of itself. Its flux is characteristic of it, each fluctuation meaning a corresponding new identity. My being offers no exception to this account of self-dependence. Obviously, I cannot know anything about anyone or anything but myself. To claim that I can is to attempt to forswear the allness and nowness of my own subjectivity. For me conscious self-examination, or conscious self-ignoration, is all there can be. Whenever I ignore my self-living I involve myself in fictional "mechanistic" psychology and lose track of the actual subjectivity of my own organic nature. To the extent that I am not awake, I rest my I-feeling. My wide-awake being awesomely discloses my life as a thrilling adventure.

Author. My vigilant self-consciousness contains much of the nature of surprise and anxiety. Indeed one of my colleagues describes "anxiety" most interestingly as the essence of psychotherapy in that its force, and its force alone, empowers heightened concentrated self-consciousness.[28] Such appreciation of anxiety as the specific therapeutic (pathognomic of the practicing self-analyst, and indispensable for motivating conscious self-help) befits the recognition of one's living as: an ongoing process of one's giving birth to his ever new self. Freud observed the necessity to support ignorance and uncertainty for the sake of observing truth.

Poet. Freud said that sympton formation occurs in the interest of avoiding overwhelming anxiety.

Author. Yes. My conscious anxiety confronts me with realization of ready threats to my welfare, but it can upset my mental equilibrium. It can interrupt my sleep. By showing up the limited reliability of my self-intolerance, it can throw me into panic. It discovers the soporific nature of habit and confronts me with the discomforts of habit withdrawal. Therefore, I can denounce it as a disturber of the peace which I prefer to imagine would exist "if only I were not curious." Rather than attend to my anxiety's disciplining force, which would entail my "making my life over," rather than grow appreciation of its life-saving meaning, I may yield self-conscious ground in the interest of creating my symptom.

Poet. I can see how a work of art, including a poem, helps to relieve the overwhelming force of anxiety.

How do you distinguish the "manner" and "matter" of a poem? Are its structure and content one? How do you tell its style from its substance?

Author. I am all that can be substantive for me. I produce the substance of my every form and the form of my every substance,—creating each entirely out of my subjectivity.[29] Confusion always arises whenever I attempt to set up the meaning "my appearance" as being somehow separable from the meaning "my essence." Whatever is defines itself. The notion that everything is not all of its own meaning underlies my mistaking integration for aggregation and aggregation for integration.

Poet. It is your idea that everyone's world is really one requiring the free use of all of his powers; that everyone really has no choice other than to live dangerously; that everyone is wise to revere his anxiety since he needs it to alert his self-consciousness with respect to the innumerable sources of pain and pleasure in his living of his world; that there is no world responsibility, or world care, except that occuring in the one who is living *his* world.

You seem to think you can satisfy your soul's natural need for heroism by daring to aspire to be a *conscious hero of peace.* You mind your poetic living as being hygiene, for it consciously individualizes individuality and thereby provides the only trustworthy warranty for peace: no one to fight but one's self. What a fanciful imagination!

Please account concisely for your unconventional effort to integrate your poetic and physicianary powers. Briefly vindicate such daring if you can.

Author. First of all, it helps most for me to be able to recognize that each of the powers *is* mine. *That* is the central theme I try to live by, but the one which nearly every hearer, from his habits of authoritarianism, may overlook here.

A physician's ideal is that of preservation of *individual* life. He discovers that appreciation for life contributes most to its preservation, and that consciousness for living contributes most to its due appreciation.

A poet's ideal is that of expressing *individual* life in its natural beauty by breathing it into words which *immediately* mean beautiful living. A pure poet practices the healing art upon himself by his persevering devotion to *conscious* mindedness.

My every word itself is a biological fact as well as a name for a life meaning. Conscious responsibility for that *living* of life is insight, the unit of mental health which builds up my realization and appreciation of my unity. My every word makes meaning only of my selfness, and my heeding that truth is my linguistic source of appreciation of my wholeness (the very meaning of health itself).

Poet. Certainly you do not wish to renounce the concept of therapy. And yet how do you reconcile your view that your poetry heals with your view that your "popular" notion of so-called "therapy" consists largely of anachronistic magic (suggestion).

Author. The concept of therapy *is* a wonderful one. Implicit in it is devotion to human welfare. My therapy is a view which points the way to conscious wholesome living by beginning with appreciation for the wholesomeness of *whatever* kind of living obtains. Appreciation for life begets appreciation for life.

I see my poetry healing through revering whatever is. Whatever is, obviously is necessary. I see *all* of my living as helpful. Appreciation for my Whatever is, helps me to realize my wholeness. My Whatever which appears to injure (harm, hurt, traumatize, infect) is necessarily the only helpful event which can possibly occur when it does. My poetry upholds the truth of what is. Hence my poetry heals.

My so-called "therapy" is anachronistic magic to the extent that it presupposes melioration, overlooks the perfection in what is, denies helpfulness to any existing condition, assumes that one existent can influence another, ignores the allness of individuality, claims superiority for Whatever is not. Seeing all of my living as helpful (healing), I may nevertheless limit the term "therapy" to describe whatever aspect of my being I choose. "It belongs to me, not I to it" describes the psychic situation called peace and freedom.

Summary

The author kills himself in spinning out what
The reader kills himself in cutting short.
D'ALEMBERT

EDUCATION TO HEALTH resolves itself into a practical question of the peaceful conduct of one's meaningful life. How shall a person live so that the consequences of his living will necessitate free, not oppressed health? Discovery, not disregard? Self-evident, mental peace, not illusional mental "conflict"? The strong, healthy person of all time has observed the usefulness of pain as well as pleasure in his adventure of living, and has manned himself to use each.

A busy educator has urgent need of immediate practical utility. He must live emergencies. Every professional man in his regular work incurs danger deliberately and frequently. Efficiency is his necessity. Particularly, he must steer himself clear of all which unfits him for action. For instance, every medical practitioner must medicate, not meditate; operate, not orate. Weary with the severity of his daily toil, he must studiously examine every claim of medical helpfulness to see if it is truly workable as an instrument for improving his *practice.* With him, it is well to *do* well. In the interest of his life's pressing work he must spare himself vague speculations, however curious. Real existence commands his interest. If the imaginary is the only real, he wants to know it.

Self-insight, my appreciation of my own identity in all of my living, meets every test for practicality. It works as well for a minute as for an hour. It enters helpfully into every practical act, spoken word, touch of hand, look of eye, sign of regard. It requires no withdrawal into recesses of mind or dallying in the depths of thought. Its caring carefulness applies to kind restraint for my violent patient, as well as to sincere living of my valetudinarian, or to gentle handling of my "accident case." Its strengthening and healing force for every physician (or patient) is unfailing. Everyone has a store of practical insight already developed; everyone can grow more of it; any attempt to attempt to increase it never fails; it is never too late to start its growth; it is the source of all deep cheer and of all abiding peace.

The preceding "conversations" are based upon central views of mind:

1. The hard and fast, "time-honored" illusion called "communication," not the hard core truth of unification, supports my mind-unenlightened educator's conception of education as an interpersonal interchange. Renunciation of this educational fallacy is the number one prerequisite of health education. Peaceful respect for facts may well begin with this one. I must learn to renounce this powerful educational fallacy before I can realize that only I can speak or listen to myself; only my fellowman can speak or listen to himself. My most effective defense against learning self-consciously is to assume that "somebody else" can tell (teach) me anything, or that I can tell (teach) "somebody else" anything. Only I can hear myself talk to myself. I cannot listen to anyone else speak to me. (My) everyone else is my everyone else, who can only speak and listen to his self. This uniquely *peaceful* viewpoint needs to be reckoned with for my sober consideration of each traditional issue of psychology, philosophy, health, and education. My learning, thinking, perceiving, sensing, or every mental activity, really is my imagination, my creative intelligence,—always and only the natural biological process of and in my individuality, in precisely the same sense that my breathing is. The key to meaningful life is conscious self-growth, the insightful making of self-experience. My own mental growth provides me with my only meaning of change, innovation, process, experience, extension, or of every such modification of meaning itself. My resort to not-I living restricts my appreciation of the allness of my individuality. My renunciation of my not-I living restores my consciousness for my innocence.

2. I can know only about my own mental health and educa-

tion. Observation of the truth of truth, *subjectivity,* can never become repetition—its ever new shapes are innumerable, spirituality being one.

3. Conscious self-knowledge is the only knowledge essential for full and free sanity. Range of imagination, my mind's index of its exploratory freedom (conscious tolerance), depends on it.

4. Every pejorative word is verbal support of resistance, the force producing and maintaining repression (self-unconsciousness). My language can function as a help and as a hindrance for the cultivation of my cheerful appreciation of my life. To illustrate, temporal, spatial, personal (personification), and motor metaphors may obscure my realization that my mind is its own place, that my every one is a universal one. Smallness is unrecognized greatness. Every plurality (a single concept) is unrecognized singularity (a single concept).

5. My self-consciousness is the source of my acknowledged personal sensibility. Consciousness for self is totally local; it is always an act of inspiration. Conscious free imagination suffers no unrecognized illusion of loss, death, or negation.

6. Nothing is more practical for me than my power to steer my life through the functioning of my sensibility, that is, *consciously.*

7. My feeling of love is the joy of living, creating my zest for conscious self-possession. My every other feeling is a modification of my self's love.

8. There is no way to self-control except through self-consciousness. So-called "external" prohibition precludes renunciation. Only the unrenounceable can exert obsessive or compulsive force. Humaneness is the expression of self-interest only, not of unmanned man. Self-consciousness and renunciation derive from self-love.

9. The Oedipus, or Electra, complex would not be repressed, or would resolve itself, if the growing boy could see clearly that his mother could never be his father's wife, or if the growing girl could see clearly that her father could never be her mother's husband.

10. The growth of self-insight (self-consciousness) is entirely an epistemological (subjective) experience which is completely foreign to orthodox ("objective") scientific experience.

11. Freedom is subjective; the mind is the only free soil. Whatever is, can and must be equal to itself (the same as itself), only. Peace is the product of the evident, abundant self.

12. Individuality is absolute (unrelational and non-isolable).

13. Whatever is, is perfect—blame is perfect fault-finding based upon, and compensatory for, insufficient fact-finding. Precisely as far as that conscious self-knowledge extends, conscious self-knowledge *is* virtue.

14. Imagination subsumes all mental activity, voluntary and involuntary. For provident imagination *all things are possible.* Whatever I can learn of the resourceful unifying power of my imagination contributes to the hygiene of my mind.

15. All mental activity is innate (self-growth). Meaning is the birth of mentality and the basic unit of my mind.

16. Nothing is impossible to, or undesirable in, my own mind, where everything that is (of my world) really counts.

17. My every consideration is a product of, and indigenous to, my mind; and my realization of that truth provides a vast extension of my comprehension of my worth, enabling my caring for myself duly.

18. All of my life finds its realization in my imagination; all of my imagination finds its idealization in my practical behavior. Imagination is reality.

19. My interest, curiosity, inquisitiveness, are all and only about my own ever new living. My boredom is fear of my living.

20. My real (possible) science is always the science of my self. It can proceed from my attempt to use my language sanely, as self-wording. To record self-science it helps to word my views according to observable definitions. True science and true poetry are subjective creativity.

21. One's health is not the negation of disease but is the affirmation of his unity. Conscious wholesomeness is healthsomeness.

22. "Comparison" depends upon the illusion of plurality, quite as "plurality" depends upon the illusion of "objectivity."

23. Every distinction of virtue and vice is based upon limited self-conscious experience. Vicious living is ever a religious ordeal of a virtuous man. A disturbed mind is a constructively working mind.

24. In the very beginning of life there is self-development, and already then the truths of self-helpfulness and self-direction are most important. With ongoing self-knowledge, there is ongoing mental power; and making self-knowledge conscious, makes self-control conscious. Growing appreciation of the meaning of one's own life, and thus the life of meaning, is education which is health-centered.

25. My unrecognized bisexuality accounts for my not seeing myself only, in all of my living of my so-called "opposite sex."

26. All of my so-called personal power derives from my free use of my imagination; all of my so-called impotence derives from my limited use of my imagination.

27. Activation of my constitutional self-helpfulness is my only source of therapy of any kind whatsoever. All of my treatment is self-treatment, and must derive from my organic individuality.

28. Only my life experience sensed as self-experience can be well regulated by my pleasure-pain propensities. Throughout life, the greater the force of self-sentience, the lesser the "police force" (self-unconscious "coercion") required for preserving health. *With the introduction of "punitive measure," the child's spirited recognition of education as self-development ends.*

29. This truth of "allness of selfness" derives from direct self-observation, and the discernment of it marks the conscious mental integration. Like all veracity, it is accessible only to consciousness for self-perception. My immediate appreciation of the allness of my own living is essential for my true sense of self-esteem, for my true measure of the worth of living. Conscious selfness (health) is spirited selfness.

30. To strive toward the growth of medical living with self-insight is to lead a conscious physician's life. It is by means of my

self-consciousness that I can preserve my appreciation of my continuing identity and, as a person, can *present* my "past" experience for guidance ("profit from past experience"). My every art, religion, science, philosophy, or other meaning, is a self-meaning. My every term for my every meaning is a poetic creation.

31. The very deepest health insight, providing the most practical health measure, is the realization that all health is the issue of appreciable *wholesome* self-development, the product of conscious self-growth nourished by self-love. The nature of all education is entirely a matter of the nature of mind. Mind can only develop itself, what it actually *is,* by its own growth (psychic action, including "mental disturbance").

32. Devotion to this exalted human insight of conscious mindfulness is the efficacious living of human being. It is of limited wholesomeness to confound mind-conscious man with the indecisiveness and restricted self-development of the "impractical visionary." A mind-conscious one is a spirit-conscious one. It is divine to be human, and human to overlook it.

33. The very deepest health insight, all help is self-help, is the most difficult of all to attain and cherish. It is only natural to distrust the truth of self-helpfulness, if one has not grown and worked selfhood consciously.

34. Present health status is the natural condition of degrees of devotion to the fullest health insight. A lack of appreciation of what *is* practical is dangerous to life. Devotion to self-unconscious living ("in the external world," *"out of my mind"*) is practical dreaming which is helpful whenever it occurs. All living is unremitting self-helpfulness.

35. Once the individual senses the meaning of the growth of his rarely used powers, the health significance of his access to rarely reached truths, then it may be said of him that he knows enough not to misprize the benefits deriving from his further *conscious* development. Every great "practical" man is aware of his practical use of his mind.

36. There is no volitional control of anything, except to the extent that it is consciously loved. The awful illusion that self-

helpfulness can issue from "not-self" prescription is costliest of all. Who cannot conceive self-activity cannot conceive freedom. Who cannot conceive freedom cannot conceive health, appreciated wholeness of being.

All *conscious* use of the creative power of mental life derives its efficacy from being a healing method which excites the healthful wholesomeness of human nature to assert itself. The self-unconscious patient becomes the self-conscious healer by attaining to the knowledge of his wholeness and, thereby, the volitional control of the directing of his life. The traditional meaning of "illness" or "accident" is: I do not like the necessary facts and refuse to learn the life-saving lessons implicit in each one of them. Only by being a fact-finder can I renounce being a fault-finder. *Every* kind of threat to my health-giving happiness is sanely cherishable as a desirable event providing life-saving wisdom. In my all-giving imagination nothing ever ceases to be.

In his classic, *The Phantasies of a Realist,* insightful Popper-Lynkeus told of a king who, intrigued by his own great show of power, was awed by the independent individuality of one of his soldiers, only one, out of step with all of his marching troops and regardless of rhythmic marching band music. Upon being asked by the king about the source of this resolute individualism, the soldier replied that his reflection with his own thoughts "offered the strength" to him. He added that his inner strength was as nothing, however, compared with that of another man he knew. This man could observe nature in any of its modes with perfect equanimity. According to his wish, "the sun remains sun for him, the moon remains moon, the fog remains fog, the mountain is but a mountain. None of them have any language by means of which they can speak to him and alter his mood." The king wished dearly to see this man but was told that he had built a high wall around himself. The self-reliant soldier then added, there was even a stronger minded man whom he knew who was able "to have a truly equal interest in all people regardless of whether they are beautiful or ugly; and this, only one man could accomplish up to this day" without delusional help. Asked eagerly about this humanest man of all the soldier informed the king that this magnanimous one (Kung-fu-tse) tried "to improve the lot of man and to make him happier," but was accused of "just looking out for his own advantage." When the king learned that Kung-fu-tse died a lone, poverty-stricken old man, he threw himself down on his carpet and cried.

As I complete this tragic tale its strictly limited application to my self-centered life-helpfulness forcibly occurs to me. I specifically renounce any and all ambition to "improve the lot of man," for I see fault-finding hidden in the idea of "improvement." I also renounce any and all aspiration to make my fellowman "happier," for I realize that only he can live any of his life,—properly make himself happy or whatever. Too, I regard myself (including everyone of my world) as always being "lone." Furthermore, the term "poverty-stricken" can scarcely describe me since I claim sole ownership of my whole world.

I see everyone of *my* world, as myself, now-living *his* land of Prester John; now-creating all he now can of self-appreciation through self-insight, for its specific survival value; now-unconsciously healing his wounds, preserving his life generally, and intelligently exercising his mental powers of every kind (including consciousness itself); now-growing and imagining *his* own unique self-love life and its rationalizing ideational system; now-depending entirely upon his practice of self-consciousness for his sense of personal identity, for his acknowledged meaning of self; now-helping himself perfectly and ideally always; and ever under the health indication to function freely in his use of his imagination, or *seem* to be coerced by his very own perfect power, blinded by his very own glorious beauty, and similarly obstructed by his very own choice way of life.

Finally, I find the purpose of my mind to be that of enabling me to live all of my experience of any and every kind safely and sanely,—as being my own human experience. Functioning is being meaningful, and I enjoy living to the extent that I observe my meaningfulness. I comfort and cheer myself by realizing that I cannot call anyone names but myself, and such "name calling" is also helpful. I am sure that my own growing radical solipsistic position must be helpfully rejected by my every so-called "organization man," as being "antisocial" at least. He *must* presently help himself by unconsciousness for *his* solipsistic necessity, calling it "narcissim" or "autism" or "immaturity" or "atheism" or "unworldliness" or some name signifying his unconscious resistance. I help myself by understanding that any and all comparison, or generalization, is the expedient of one trying to make his grasp exceed his reach. I am grateful to myself that I can notice my protest against soberly considering any of my living merely indicates my defending the current limit of my soul-freeing conscious self-appreciation. Where I come from, all is I. Wherever I am, that I am.

Notes

Introduction

1. "The Field of Inattention—the Self," *Journal of Philosophy, Psychology and Scientific Method,* I (1904), 393.

2. "The Irresponsibles," *Nation,* May 18, 1940, reprinted in *The Intellectuals,* ed. George de B. Huszar (Glencoe, Ill.: Free Press, 1961), page 239.

Chapter 1

1. J. A. Curran, "Medical Education in Relation to General Education in the United States," *Pharos,* XXIII, No. 1 (January 1960), 15.

2. *The Heritage of Man* (New York: Charles Scribner's Sons, 1960).

3. See Owsei Temkin, "Scientific Medicine and Historical Research," *Perspectives in Biology and Medicine,* III (Autumn 1959), 70-85.

4. "The New Style of Science," *Yale Alumni Magazine,* February 1963, page 14.

5. Theodor Gomperz, *Greek Thinkers* (London: J. Murray, 1901-12), I, 3.

6. See Jürgen Thorwald, *Science and Secrets of Early Medicine* (New York: Harcourt, Brace & World, Inc., 1963); J. B. de C. M. Saunders, "The Transition from Ancient Egyptian to Greek Medicine," in Logan Clendening Lectures on the *History and Philosophy of Medicine* (Lawrence, Kansas: University of Kansas Press, 1963).

7. A Sumerian tablet containing the oldest medical handbook known (a pharmacopoeia including no mention of incantations, spells, or demons) has been recovered from the third millennium B. C.

8. William Hamilton, *Lectures on Metaphysics* (New York: Sheldon & Co., 1858) I, 37.

9. *The Discovery of the Mind* (Cambridge: Harvard University Press, 1953).

10. *A History of Philosophy* (New York: Harper & Bros., 1958), I, 23.

11. *History of Art,* Vol. II: *The Spirit of the Forms,* trans. Walter Pach (Garden City, N. Y.: Garden City Publishing Co., 1937), p. xviii.

12. "The Common Background of Hebrew and Greek Civilization," *Graduate Comment,* Wayne State University, VII, No. 1 (October 1963), 12.

13. Lectures on Metaphysics, I, 126.

14. *Ibid.*, I, 27.

15. *The Story of Civilization,* Pt. I: *Our Oriental Heritage* (New York: Simon and Schuster, 1954), p. 67.

16. Orpheus, or Arpha, derives from the Phoenician words *aour* (light) and *rophae* (healing)—he who heals by light.

17. Werner Jaeger, *Paideia: The Ideals of Greek Culture,* trans. Gilbert Highet (Oxford: B. Blackwell, 1939-44), I, xxvi.

18. Edouard Schure, *The Great Initiates, Sketch of the Secret History of*

Religions, trans. Fred Rothwell (Philadelphia: David McKay Co., 1925), I, 304 n.

19. *Paideia,* I, 67.

20. G. Lowes Dickenson, *The Greek View of Life* (New York: Doubleday Page & Co., 1922), p. 240.

21. Water is a well established symbol of birth.

22. Alfred H. Whittaker and Ralph E. Sloan, "The Roots of Medical Writing," *Journal of the Michigan State Medical Society,* LX (February 1961), 195.

23. Translated by Professor William Romanine Newbold.

24. See Edith Hamilton, *The Great Age of Greek Literature* (New York: W. W. Norton and Co., Inc., 1942), p. 35.

25. *The Fragments.* Horace Walpole's epigram, "Life is a comedy to one who thinks, a tragedy to one who feels," may be applied to Heraclitus and to Democritus, the "laughing Philosopher."

26. J. Oliaro, "The Cult of Minerva Medica," *Panminerva Medica,* Journal of the Italian Medical Association (English edition), May 1959, reprinted in *Pharos,* XXIII, No. 1 (January 1960).

27. Samuel X. Radbill, "The Symbolism of the Staff of Aesculapius as Illustrated by Medical Bookplates," *Journal of the Albert Einstein Medical Center,* X, No. 3 (July 1962), 108.

28. *The Grammar of Science,* (Everyman ed., London: J. M. Dent & Sons, 1951), p. 73.

29. See Ariel Bar-Sela and Hebbel E. Hoff, "Maimonides' Interpretation of the First Aphorism of Hippocrates," *Bulletin of the History of Medicine,* XXXVII, No. 4 (July-August 1963), 347-54.

30. For my source material here I lean most heavily upon Eliza Gregory Wilkins' delightfully instructive book *The Delphic Maxims in Literature* (Chicago: University of Chicago Press, 1929).

31. See his thoughtful work, "Basic Science, Medicine, and the Romantic Era," the Fielding H. Garrison Lecture, *Bulletin of the History of Medicine,* XXXVII (March-April 1963), 123.

Chapter 2

1. The uncritical view of "the man in the street" that he lives *in* an external world and has the evidence of his senses to prove it.

2. *The Logical Syntax of Language* (New York: Harcourt, Brace & Co., 1937), Foreword.

3. *The Claims of Psychoanalysis to Scientific Interest* (1913), *Standard Edition of the Complete Psychological Works of Sigmund Freud,* trans. James Strachey in collaboration with Anna Freud (London: Hogarth Press and Institute of Psycho-Analysis, 1953-63), XIII, 176-79. Cited hereafter as *Standard Edition.*

4. In this report Freud refers to Hans Sperber's *Über den Einfluss sexueller Momente auf Entstehung und Entwicklung der Sprache, Imago* I (1912), 405.

5. (Garden City, N. Y.: Doubleday & Co., 1953), p. 146. First published in 1944 by Yale University Press.

6. *The Miraculous Birth of Knowledge* (New York: Philosophical Library, 1948), pp. 240-41.

7. *The Orion Book of the Written Word,* trans. Rebecca Abramson (New York: Orion Press, 1961), pp. 23-24.

8. See Ella Freeman Sharpe, "Psycho-Physical Problems Revealed in Language: An Examination of Metaphor," *Collected Papers on Psycho-Analysis,* ed. Marjorie Brierley (London: Hogarth Press, Ltd., and Institute of Psycho-Analysis, 1950), pp. 155-69.

9. Lines from "Demos" and "The Burning Book" are quoted from Robinson's *Collected Poems* (New York: Macmillan Co., 1937), with the permission of the publishers.

10. The term "idiolect" was coined by Bernard Bloch. See Aaron Bar-Adon, "Analogy and Analogic Change as Reflected in Contemporary Hebrew," Ninth International Congress of Linguists, Cambridge, Mass., August 27-31, 1962.

11. See Wilhelm von Humboldt, *Humanist Without Portfolio* (Detroit: Wayne State University Press, 1961), p. 249f. Also see *Language: An Enquiry into Its Meaning and Function,* ed. Ruty Nanda Anshen (New York: Harper & Bros., 1957), p. 12.

12. See the meaningful study by Harold A. Basilius, "Neo-Humboldtian Ethnolinguistics," *Word,* VII, No. 2 (August 1952), 95-105, especially its reference to the word as being a construct of "the speaker's world."

13. See his *Prothrombin* (Cambridge, Mass.: Harvard University Press, 1962).

14. *Language and Myth,* (New York: Harper & Bros., 1946), p. 99.

15. For an excellent digest representing this viewpoint see *Handbook of Speech Pathology,* ed. Lee Edward Travis (New York: Appleton-Century-Crofts, Inc., 1957).

16. "The Concepts of Normality and Mental Health in Psychoanalysis," *International Journal of Psycho-Analysis,"* XLII (July-October 1961), 439-46. Also see Henry P. Laughlin, *The Neurosis in Clinical Practice* (Philadelphia: Saunders Co., 1956).

17. *Language: A Modern Synthesis* (New York: St. Martin's Press, 1956), pp. 227-28.

18. "Culture Studies," from *Latin and Greek in American Education, with Symposia on the Value of Humanistic Studies,* ed. Francis W. Kelsey (rev. ed.; New York: Macmillan Co., 1927) pp. 66-67.

19. "The Value of Greek and Latin to the Medical Student," *Ibid.,* p. 71.

20. Destutt de Tracy's view of political economy was greatly admired by Thomas Jefferson and John Adams.

Chapter 3

1. John M. Dorsey and Walter H. Seegers, *Living Consciously: The Science of Self* (Detroit: Wayne State University Press, 1959).

2. *The Growth of Self Insight,* ed. John M. Dorsey (Detroit: Wayne State University Press, 1962).

3. Quoted in Cassirer, *Language and Myth,* p. 51 n.

4. See my chapter, "The Excellence of Man," in *The World of Teilhard de Chardin,* ed. Robert T. Francoeur (Baltimore: Helicon Press, 1961).

5. *Principles of Literary Criticism* (New York: Harcourt, Brace & Co., Inc., 1955), pp. 52n., and 244 respectively. First published in 1925.

6. *From Shakespeare to Existentialism* (Garden City, N. Y.: Doubleday

& Co., 1960). In the Preface Kaufmann states: "In this book 'nobility' means being hard with oneself, making demands of oneself, devotion."

7. Cf. Marjorie Brierley, *Trends in Psychoanalysis* (London: Hogarth Press, Ltd., and Institute of Psycho-Analysis, 1951).

8. *A History of Western Philosophy* (New York: Simon and Schuster, Inc., 1945), pp. 703, 656, respectively.

9. *Cure of Mind and Cure of Love* (South Bend, Ind.: University of Notre Dame Press, 1962), p. 19.

Chapter 4

1. Ernest D. Gardner, M. D., professor and chairman of the Department of Anatomy and dean of Wayne State University College of Medicine, provides the valuable services of anthropologist Dr. Gabriel W. Lasker for his students.

2. Dr. Walworth Slenger, editor of "The Newsletter," Michigan Society of Neurology and Psychiatry, practices editorial self-insightfulness.

3. Dr. William O. Stapleton, Jr., associate dean, emeritus, Wayne State University College of Medicine, is a medical educator of great self-responsibility.

4. (New York: Columbia University Press, 1961), p. 123.

5. See J. M. Dorsey, "A Psychoanalytical Appreciation of American Government," *American Imago,* XVIII, No. 3 (Fall 1961), 207-33.

6. J. M. Dorsey, "Living Education," *Michigan Educational Journal,* April and May 1957, pp. 397-98; 404-5.

7. Dr. Thomas J. Heldt, for decades the able director of the Division of Neuropsychiatry of Henry Ford Hospital, created a splendid record of unifying psychiatric with general hospital living. Every general hospital has a wonderful development as it adds a psychiatric service. Dr. Raymond W. Waggoner, professor and chairman of the Department of Psychiatry at the University of Michigan, is outstanding for the way in which he identifies psychiatry with medicine.

Chapter 5

1. See his clarifying article, "Explaining to the Patient, a Therapeutic Tool and a Professional Obligation," *Journal of the American Medical Association,* November 2, 1957, from which the chapter epigraph is taken.

2. *From Shakespeare to Existentialism,* p. 375.

3. According to Albert D. Ruedemann, professor and chairman of Ophthalmology at Wayne State University College of Medicine, and director of the Kresge Eye Institute, vision is a process of the mind's *learning* to see. Said Dr. Ruedemann, "One must learn how to use his eyes. One's degree of visual acuity is also an index of his achievement in learning to see."

Mindful Ross Stagner, Chairman of Wayne's Department of Psychology, has set up a center for the study of the cognitive process, under Dr. Eli Saltz.

4. J. D. Salinger, "Teddy," *Nine Stories* (New York: New American Library, 1962), p. 144.

5. *Yale Review,* XLIII (Summer 1953), 575.

6. Randolph G. Adams, "Thomas Jefferson," in *Three Americanists* (Philadelphia: University of Pennsylvania Press, 1939), p. 95.

7. Ernst Cassirer, *The Myth of the State* (Garden City, N. Y.: Doubleday & Co., 1955), p. 67. First published in 1946 by the Yale University Press.

8. *Standard Edition,* XIII, 190. Also see Grete L. Bibring, "Some Considerations of the Psychological Processes in Pregnancy," *Psychoanalytic Study of the Child,* XIV (1959), 113-21.
9. Louis I. Bredvold, *The Natural History of Sensibility* (Detroit: Wayne State University Press, 1962).
10. Cf. *ibid.,* pp. 11-26.
11. See *Adventures of Ideas* (New York: Macmillan Co., 1933), p. 197.
12. (Chicago: University of Chicago Press, 1958), p. 17.
13. *On Beginning the Treatment, Standard Edition,* XIII, 140.

Chapter 6

1. *The Meaning of Love* (London: Geoffrey Chapman, Ltd., 1954), p. 5.
2. "Who hates vice hates mankind."

Chapter 7

1. *On Narcissism: An Introduction* (1914), *Standard Edition,* XIV (1958), 85.
2. Trans. M. D. Herter Norton (New York: W. W. Norton, Inc., 1949), pp. 17-18.
3. Cf. J. M. Dorsey, "Morale," *American Imago,* X, No. 4 (Winter 1953), 345-73.
4. Rilke, *op. cit.,* p. 18.
5. "If an ape looks in the mirror, no apostle will look out."
6. *Observations by Henri Peyre on Life, Literature, and Learning in America* (Carbondale: Southern Illinois University Press, 1961), p. 248.
7. See Dickenson W. Richards, "Homeostasis," *Perspectives in Biology and Medicine,* III (Autumn 1959), 244.

Chapter 8

1. *The Logic of the Sciences and the Humanities* (New York: Meridian Books, Inc., 1959), Preface, p. ix.
2. Cf. Anna Freud, Some Remarks on Infant Observation," *Psycho-Analytic Study of the Child,* VIII (1952), 9-19; also Hermann Nunberg, *Allgemeine Neurosenlehre auf psychoanalytischer Grandlage* (Bern: Huber, 1932).
3. I first termed the definition of "research" as *me-search* when one of my medical students, now Dr. Bernard H. Wittenberg, created this insightful expression.
4. My friend and colleague, Dr. Jacques S. Gottlieb, professor and chairman of Wayne State University Department of Psychiatry, and director of Lafayette Clinic, supervises and conducts research insightfully on several levels.
5. Lincoln Barnett, *The Universe and Dr. Einstein* (New York: Harper & Bros., 1948), p. 19.
6. *The Unconscious Origin of Berkeley's Philosophy* (London: Hogarth Press, Ltd., and Institute of Psycho-Analysis, 1953), p. 56.
7. Quoted in Dr. Bean's "A Testament of Duty," *Journal of Laboratory and Clinical Medicine,* XXXIX, No. 1 (January 1952), 4.
8. *What Is the Mind?* (New York: Macmillan Co., 1929), p. 68.
9. Henry B. Selleck and Alfred H. Whittaker, *Occupational Health in America* (Detroit: Wayne State University Press, 1962), p. 5.

10. *The Meaning of Psychology* (New York: Harper & Bros., 1926), p. 217.

11. *An Introduction to the Philosophy of Science* (New York: Macmillan Co., 1937), pp. 261-63.

12. *Ibid.*, p. 452.

Chapter 9

1. There is practical application of this view in Ruben Meyer, Morton Levitt, Mordacai L. Falick, Ben. O. Rubenstein, *Essentials of Pediatric Psychiatry* (New York: Appleton-Century-Crofts, 1962). Also see Ian Stevenson, *Medical History-Taking* (New York: Harper and Row, Hoeber Medical Division, 1961).

2. See author's "Vis Medicatrix Naturae," *Journal* of the Michigan State Medical Society, LX (January 1961) 43-48, 51; also Jules H. Masserman, "The Problem of Homeostasis," *Journal of the American Medical Association, Archives of Neurology and Psychiatry,* LXV (1951), 93; and Karl Menninger, with Martin Mayman and Paul Pruyser, *The Vital Balance* (New York: Viking Press, 1963).

3. *The Destiny of Western Man* (New York: Reynal and Hitchcock, 1942), pp. 3, 140, respectively.

4. See *Types of Onset of Neurosis* (1912), *Standard Edition,* XII (1958), 229.

5. *Critique of Religion and Philosophy* (New York: Harper & Bros., 1948), p. 77.

6. *Negation* (1925), *Standard Edition,* XIX (1961), 237, 239.

7. *The Examined Life: An Adventure in Moral Philosophy* (Bloomington: Indiana University Press, 1958), p. 247. First published as *Moral Philosophy* (1925).

8. *Shakespeare* (New York: Henry Holt & Co., Inc., 1939), Introduction, p. xiv.

9. *Human Values in Psychological Medicine* (London: Oxford University Press, 1933), p. 105.

10. Cf. *Ideas, General Introduction to Pure Phenomenology,* trans. W. R. Boyce Gibson (New York: Macmillan Co., 1952), p. 456.

11. See *The Dynamics of Transference* (1912), *Standard Edition,* XII, 108.

12. *The Claims of Psycho-Analysis to Scientific Interest, Standard Edition,* XIII, 175.

Chapter 10

1. Cf. Anna Freud, "Some Remarks on Infant Observation," *op cit.* (above ch. 8, note 2).

2. *Standard Edition,* XI (1957), 33, 34.

3. See Franz Alexander and Helen Ross, *The Impact of Freudian Psychiatry* (Chicago: University of Chicago Press, 1961).

4. See Otto Fenichel, *The Psychoanalytic Theory of Neurosis* (New York: W. W. Norton and Co., 1945), pp. 237-67.

Chapter 11

1. See Heinz Hartmann, *Psychoanalysis and Moral Values* (New York: International Universities Press, 1960).

2. See Editha Sterba, "Analysis of Psychogenic Constipation in a Two-Year-Old Child," *Psychoanalytic Study of the Child* III-IV (1949), 227-52.

3. Also a spoken view of my Professor Freud.

4. See Alexander Grinstein and Editha Sterba, *Understanding Your Family* (New York: Random House, 1957).

5. See the brilliant account of orthothanasia in K. R. Eissler, *The Psychiatrist and the Dying Patient* (New York: International Universities Press, Inc., 1955).

6. See Heinz Hartmann, "Notes on the Reality Principle," *Psychoanalytic Study of the Child,* XI (1956), 31-53.

7. Joseph J. Michaels, *Disorders of Character* (Springfield, Ill.: Charles C Thomas, 1955); also Fritz Redl and David Wineman, *Children Who Hate* (Glencoe, Ill.: Free Press, 1951).

8. *Bemerkungen über die Übertragungsliebe, Gesammelte Werke, Zehnter Band* (1913-17) (London: Imago Publishing Co., 1946).

9. *The Myth of the State,* pp. 343-44.

10. *Ibid.,* p. 219.

11. "Some Remarks on Infant Observation," *op. cit.,* p. 13.

12. *Ibid.,* p. 9.

13. The latter through the excellent cooperation of Pauline Park Wilson Knapp, president, Merrill-Palmer Institute; Dr. Walter H. Seegers, professor and chairman of the Department of Physiology and Pharmacology; and Dr. H. Harrison Sadler. Dr. Sadler trained at the justly famed Menninger Clinic in Topeka. Assistant Dean Alexander Walt now provides the program of curricular integration with his skilled attention and extensive medical experience.

Growing out of Mrs. Samuel Hamburger's loving observation of the need has come a generous gift from the Samuel and Louis Hamburger Foundation enabling the establishing of the Chair of Psychiatry in Pediatrics, in the Children's Hospital of Michigan, where Dr. Paul V. Woolley, Jr., professor and chairman of Wayne's Department of Pediatrics, is pediatrician-in-chief.

14. Cf. *The Jefferson-Dunglison Letters,* ed. John M. Dorsey (Charlottesville, Va.: University of Virginia Press, 1960).

15. See J. M. Dorsey, "A Psychotherapeutic Approach to the Problem of Hostility," *Social Forces,* XXIX, No. 2 (1950), 197-206.

Chapter 12

1. Cited by George M. Acklom in the new Introduction to Richard Maurice Bucke, *Cosmic Consciousness* (New York: E. P. Dutton & Co., 1951).

2. Cf. Principles of Medical Ethics, the American Medical Association.

3. Dr. Lindsay E. Beaton, during the proceedings of the Eighth Annual Conference of Mental Health Representatives of State Medical Associations, Chicago, Illinois, 1962.

Chapter 14

1. *The New Man* (New York: Harper & Bros., 1956), p. 60.

2. *Democracy: A Man-Search* (Detroit: Wayne State University Press, 1960).

3. *Genius and the Mobocracy* (New York: Duell, Sloan, and Pearce, 1949), p. 64.

4. See J. M. Dorsey, "A Psychoanalytic Appreciation of American Government," *American Imago,* XVIII, No. 3 (Fall, 1961), 207-33.

Dr. Leo H. Bartemeier, medical director, Seton Institute, Baltimore, Maryland, has liberally contributed his valuable helpfulness to this important aspect of the cause of medicine. (In Michigan Dr. Peter A. Martin is the able psychiatric consultant for Governor George W. Romney.)

5. See *Language, Thought, and Reality,* ed. John B. Carroll (Cambridge: Technology Press of M. I. T., 1956).

6. See his "Some Effects of a Course in General Semantics," *Etc.,* Review of General Semantics, XVIII, No. 3 (1961), 315-46.

7. Trans. J. H. Oliver, in "Two Athenian Poets," *Hesperia:* Suppl. VIII (1949), 246; quoted in the *Journal of the American Medical Association,* July 21, 1962, by its editor, John H. Talbott, M. D.

Chapter 15

1. *When Doctors Are Patients* (New York: W. W. Norton & Co., Inc., 1952).

2. In his chapter, "A Psychoanalyst Passes a Small Stone," *ibid.* Dr. Grotjahn's father, Dr. Alfred Grotjahn, published the book as *Aerzte als Patienten* (Leipzig: George Thieme, 1929).

3. He describes individual fulfilment as being the ideal purpose that will lift all American education to a new level of meaning. I feel sure that Gardner has in mind here a new level of meaning of "health." (New York: Harper & Bros., 1961).

4. *Selected Essays from Individualism Reconsidered* (Garden City, N. Y.: Doubleday & Co., 1955), p. 27.

Chapter 16

1. Edward C. Dorsey, "An Essay on Psychotherapy," unpublished MS., (1961).

2. Wilbert Snow, "Whistling Buoy," *Collected Poems of Wilbert Snow* (Middletown: Wesleyan University Press, 1960). Quoted with the permission of the publisher.

3. Quoted in Hans Jonas, *The Gnostic Religion* (2nd ed.; Boston: Beacon Press, 1963), p. 168.

4. Harold A. Basilius, "Religion and Theology in a Theory of the Cultural Sciences," *Contemporary Problems in Religion,* ed. Harold A. Basilius (Detroit: Wayne State University Press, 1956), p. 95.

5. *The City of God,* xi, 26.

6. *The Philosophy of Personalism* (New York: Abingdon Press, 1927), pp. 390-91.

7. (New York: American Book Co., 1934), p. 20.

Chapter 17

1. First published in the *Atlantic Monthly,* April 1955. Quoted with the author's permission.

2. A. C. Bradley, "The Sublime," *Oxford Lectures on Poetry* (Bloomington: Indiana University Press, 1961), p. 58. First published in 1909.

3. *A Modern Book of Esthetics* (3rd. ed.; New York: Holt, Rinehart & Winston, Inc., 1960).

4. See K. R. Eissler, *Leonardo da Vinci, Psychoanalytic Notes on the Enigma* (New York: International Universities Press, 1961).

5. J. M. Dorsey and E. P. Richardson, *A Tour for War Nerves: A Guide to an Hour in the Galleries,* printed for the Detroit Institute of Arts, 1945.

G. Alden Smith, Chairman of Wayne's Art Department, provides opportunity for student development of this kind of art experience.

6. Élie Faure, *History of Art,* II, 240.

7. K. R. Eissler, *Goethe: A Psychoanalytic Study* (Detroit: Wayne State University Press, 1963), I, 566.

8. *Abstraction and Empathy,* trans. Michael Bullock (New York: International Universities Press, 1953). Originally published as *Abstraktion und Einfühling* (Munich, 1921).

9. See Freud, *Psycho-Analytic Notes on an Autobiographical Account of a Case of Paranoia (Dementia Paranoides) (1911), Standard Edition,* XII, 67-71.

10. See Friedrich Kainz, *Aesthetics the Science,* trans. Herbert M. Schueller (Detroit: Wayne State University Press, 1962), pp. 53-59.

11. *Standard Edition,* XII, 66.

12. For the art-beholder's living of his artist's product, see E. Kris, *Psychoanalytic Explorations in Art* (New York: International Universities Press, 1952), pp. 52-63.

13. *Aesthetics and History* (Garden City, N. Y.: Doubleday & Co., Inc., 1948), p. 36.

14. *An Ape of Gods: The Art and Thought of Lafcadio Hearn* (Detroit: Wayne State University Press, 1964), p. 275.

Chapter 18

1. See Stephen C. Pepper, "Metaphysical Method," in *American Philosophers at Work,* ed. Sidney Hook (New York: Criterion Books, 1956), pp. 259-76.

2. Ledger Woods, "Recent Epistemological Schools," in *A History of Philosophical Systems,* ed. Vergilius Ferm (New York: Philosophical Library, 1950), pp. 516-40.

3. See C. E. M. Joad, *Guide to Philosophy* (New York: Dover Publications, 1936), pp. 56 and 70-73.

4. See Harvey Gates Townsend, *Philosophical Ideas in the United States* (New York: American Book Co., 1934), pp. 116-30, and 253-65.

5. *Being and Time* (New York and Evanston: Harper & Row, 1962).

6. Ralph Barton Perry's definition of "Naturalism."

7. *The Construction of Reality* (New York: Macmillan Co., 1962), pp. 33, 11, respectively.

8. *Ibid.* p. 31.

9. Each an ardent devotee of the great idealist George W. F. Hegel and Goethe, the young German Henry Brokmeyer, William Torrey Harris, and Denton J. Snider contributed greatly to American philosophic individualism, and (1867-93) published their own insightful *Journal of Speculative Philosophy.* The Philosophical Society of St. Louis also edited *The Western,* a "Review of Education, Science, Literature and Art." See Herbert W. Schneider, *A History of American Philosophy* (New York: Columbia University Press, 1946), pp. 177-93.

Also see, *Morality and the Language of Conduct,* edited by Hector-Neri Castaneda and George Nakhñikian, Wayne State University Press, Detroit, 1963.

10. Freud, *Notes on a Case of Paranoia, Standard Edition,* XII, 71.
11. *Metaphysical Journal* (London: Rockliff Publishing Corp., Ltd., 1952), Preface, pp. viii, xi.
12. *The Examined Life,* pp. 2-3.
13. *Ibid.,* p. 17.
14. Also see Chapter 9, "Psychotherapy."

Chapter 19

1. I mention only a few poet physicians:
Empedocles (500 B. C.)
Hippocrates (400 B. C.)
Lucretius (98-55 B. C.)
Wei Wang (699-759)
Avicenna (980?-1037)
Rabelais (1490-1553)
Ambrose Pare (1510-1590)
Thomas Campion (1567?-1620)
Thomas Browne (1605-1682)
Thomas Sydenham (1624-1689)
John Locke (1632-1704)
Samuel Garth (1661-1719)
Tobias Smollett (1721-1771)
Oliver Goldsmith (1728-1774)
George Crabbe (1754-1832)
John Keats (1795-1821)
Joseph Rodman Drake (1795-1820)
Oliver Wendell Holmes (1809-1894)
William Osler (1849-1919)
Arthur Conan Doyle (1859-1930)
Francis Thompson (1859-1930)
Arthur Schnitzler (1862-1931)
John McCrae (1872-1918)
William Carlos Williams (1883-1963)
Merrill Moore (1903-1957)
Jean Braxton Rosenbaum (1927-)

For a list of over 400 names, consult Mary Lou McDonough's *Poet Physicians* (Springfield, Ill.: Charles C Thomas, 1945).

2. "The Capacity To Be Alone," *International Journal of Psycho-Analysis,* XXXIX, Part VI (1958), 416-20.
3. *Songs and Satires* (New York: Macmillan Co., 1944). Quoted with the permission of the publishers.
4. (Garden City, N. Y.: Doubleday and Co., Inc., 1956), p. 212.
5. *9 Poems* (Detroit: Gaylord Press, 1947). Quoted with the author's permission.
6. Paul Engle and Joseph Langland, 'The Poet on His Poem," *Saturday Review,* August 11, 1962, p. 12.
7. Also see this great American's *Poetry and Experience* (Boston: Houghton Mifflin Co., 1961).
8. (New York: Harcourt, Brace & Co., 1958), p. 290.
9. "The Making of a Poem," in *Adventures of the Mind,* 2nd ser., from

8. (New York: Harcourt, Brace & Co., 1958), p. 290.

9. "The Making of a Poem," in *Adventures of the Mind,* 2nd ser., from the *Saturday Evening Post* (New York: Alfred A. Knopf, 1961), pp. 459, 472.

10. See *The Literary Mind* (New York: Charles Scribner's Sons, 1931), Ch. 3, particularly pp. 79-84.

11. *Collected Poems* (Philadelphia: J. P. Lippincott & Co., 1947). Quoted with the permission of the publishers.

12. *Collected Poems* (New York: Macmillan Co., 1937). Quoted with the permission of the publishers.

13. "Manner of Speaking," *Saturday Review,* August 11, 1962, p. 13.

14. *Invitation to Poetry,* p. 401.

15. *Notes on a Case of Paranoia, Standard Edition,* XII, 65.

16. *New York Times Magazine,* December 25, 1960.

17. *Creative Writers and Day-Dreaming* (1908), *Standard Edition,* IX (1959), 151.

18. Cf. the excellent psychological study, Richard and Editha Sterba, *Beethoven and His Nephew,* trans. Willard R. Trask (New York: Pantheon Books, 1954).

19. *A Midsummer Night's Dream,* V, i. Thomas Warton wrote: "Shakespeare wandered in pursuit of universal nature. The glancings of his eye are from heaven to earth, from earth to heaven. We behold him breaking the barriers of imaginary method" (*The History of English Poetry*).

20. *Saturday Review,* August 11, 1962, p. 13.

21. "The ego needs the Thou in order to become a Self" is a theme which Otto Rank developed in several aspects, including the artistic. See *Das Inzest Motiv in Dichtung und Sage* (Leipzig-Vienna, 1912).

22. Joan Riviere, "The Unconscious Phantasy of an Inner World Reflected in Examples from English Literature," *International Journal of Psychoanalysis,* XXXIII, Part II (1952), 160-72.

23. Marion Milner, "Aspects of Symbolism in Comprehension of Not-Self," *International Journal of Psycho-Analysis,* XXXIII, Part II (1952), 181-95, at 184, 189, 194, respectively.

24. In *Psycho-Analysis and Contemporary Thought,* ed. John D. Sutherland (New York: Grove Press, Inc., 1959).

25. Melanie Klein, "Mourning and Its Relation to Manic-Depressive States," *Contributions to Psycho-Analysis,* 1921-45 (London: Hogarth Press, 1948).

26. *Letters of Sigmund Freud,* ed. Ernst L. Freud (New York: Basic Books, Inc., 1960), p. 395.

27. See Ernst Kris, "Probleme der Aesthetik," *Internat. Zeitschrift für Psychoanalyse und Imago,* XXVI (1941), 142.

28. Edward C. Dorsey, M. D., "Anxiety and Psychotherapy," unpublished MS. (1963).

29. Cf. A. C. Bradley's "poetic experience" (*Oxford Lectures on Poetry*).

30. Wayne State University is represented by a university-wide poetry center, The Miles Modern Poetry Committee. Poet Finvola Dewey is its present chairman. Pulitzer prize winner William D. Snodgrass and Hopwood Major Literary Award winner Jay McCormick are members.

Index

The manuscript was edited by Barbara Woodward and the book was designed by Richard Kinney. The text typeface is Linotype Garamond adapted by Joseph Hill in 1925 and based on designs originally made by Aldus Manutius around 1532. The display face is Craw Clarendon designed by Freeman Craw in 1956 for the American Typefounders.

The book is printed on S. D. Warren's Olde Style Antique and bound in Columbia Mills' Bayside Linen. Manufactured in the United States of America.